Applied Mechanics

J. D. Walker
BSC(ENG), CENG, FIMECHE

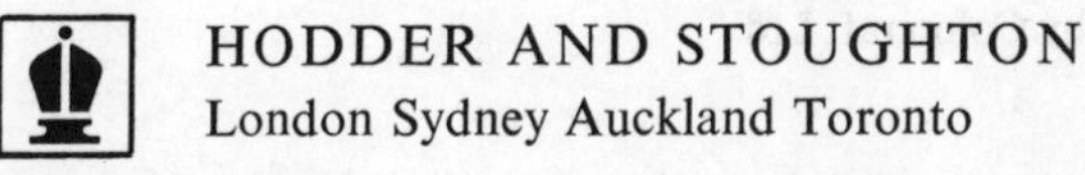
HODDER AND STOUGHTON
London Sydney Auckland Toronto

ISBN 0 340 11539 4

First published (as *Applied Mechanics for National Certificate*)
1957
Second edition 1958
Reprinted 1959, 1961
Third edition 1965
Reprinted 1968
Fourth edition 1972
Reprinted 1975, 1976, 1978, 1981, 1982

Printed in Hong Kong
for Hodder and Stoughton Educational,
a division of Hodder and Stoughton Ltd,
Mill Road, Dunton Green, Sevenoaks, Kent,
by Colorcraft Ltd.

To N. L. without whose generous help some time ago this book could never have been written

Preface

This book is intended to cover the requirements of students reading Applied Mechanics in the Technician Education Council (TEC) courses in Mechanical and Production Engineering, Ordinary National Certificate or Diploma courses in Engineering or Technology, or in the first year of the Higher National Diploma or Degree courses in Engineering.

To present the basic principles of applied mechanics in a manner acceptable to the student; to furnish the student with a liberal quantity of worked examples, including graphical solutions; to supply the student with a number of exercises for his own practice—these are the aims which the author has had predominantly in mind during the preparation of this work.

The introduction of SI units has helped to resolve many of the difficulties which arose from the different systems of units previously in use, particularly in the dynamics section of the subject. Perhaps there is a tinge of regret in realising that the controversies surrounding slugs and poundals will now become a thing of the past. Undoubtedly the student will benefit by the rational system now being accepted, and particularly by the fact that it will become standard practice.

Presumably all students taking a course of this type will have made a reasonable study of mathematics along lines suited to the requirements of this book. It would seem purposeless to claim that this presentation of applied mechanics has been made without recourse to mathematics. Any student who is not sufficiently at home with mathematics to be able to appreciate the development of formulae, and the solution of examples herein set down cannot claim to have reached the standard demanded by National Certificate requirements. Mathematics is one of the tools of the engineer: he is encouraged to use it in these pages.

It is likely that some students will come to a study of applied mechanics without being previously in a Mechanical Engineering Science class. For these students, matter is presented in this volume which has appeared previously in the author's book *Certificate Mechanical Engineering Science*. Topics such as vectors, relative velocity, force, and mass are among the examples of the need for this repetition. In other cases, a summary is provided of work with which the student should be familiar before proceeding with the more advanced work about to be presented.

Typical questions have been taken from examination papers set by the following organisations: the Union of Lancashire and Cheshire Institutes, the East Midlands Educational Institution, the Union of Educational Institutions, the Northern Counties Technical Examinations Council, the Yorkshire Council for Further Education, the Welsh Joint Education Committee, and the Institution of Mechanical Engineers. These have been acknowledged in the text and the author expresses his appreciation for the cooperation of these examining Boards.

The author would like to place on record his grateful acknowledgement of the valuable help given by the publishers and the general editor, and his indebtedness to many of his colleagues, particularly Mr A. R. Field for the considerable help with the revision, and to his wife for her patience and encouragement during a preparation period which only the wife of an author can appreciate.

J. D. WALKER

Contents

Units

The Système International d'Unités, abbreviated to SI, has been accepted by the International Organisation for Standardisation as the most rational system of measurement. It is being introduced all over the world and will ultimately be the only system of units in use not only in technical and business areas of work, but also in everyday life.

The system is based on six units, which are arbitrarily defined.

Quantity	Unit	Symbol
length	metre	m
mass	kilogram	kg
time	second	s
electric current	ampere	A
temperature	kelvin	K
luminous intensity	candela	cd

Other units and combinations of units are, with limited exceptions, made up from the above.

Multiples of these units are expressed, again with limited exceptions, in powers of 1000, i.e. 10^3 10^6 10^{-3} 10^{-6}, and are given characteristic prefixes, of which the following are the more usual.

Prefix	Symbol	Multiply by
mega	M	$1\,000\,000 = 10^6$
kilo	k	$1\,000 = 10^3$
milli	m	$0{\cdot}001 = 10^{-3}$
micro	μ	$0{\cdot}000001 = 10^{-6}$

The following units are used in this book.

Length	m	metre
	km	kilometre
	mm	millimetre
	cm	centimetre
Area	m^2	square metre
	mm^2	square millimetre
Volume	m^3	cubic metre
	l	litre (1000 cm^3)
Mass	kg	kilogram
	g	gram
	t	tonne (1000 kg)
Density	kg/m^3	kilogram per cubic metre
Time	s	second
	min	minute
	h	hour
Velocity	km/h	kilometres per hour
	m/s	metres per second
Acceleration	m/s^2	metres per second per second
Temperature	K	kelvin
	°C	degree Celsius
Force	N	newton
	kN	kilonewton
Torque and moment	N m	newton metre
	kN m	kilonewton metre
Work and energy	J	joule
	kJ	kilojoule
Power	W	watt
	kW	kilowatt
Stress	N/m^2	newton per square metre
	N/mm^2	newton per square millimetre
Pressure	N/m^2	newton per square metre
		bar (10^5 N/m^2)
Frequency	Hz	hertz

Chapter 1

Velocity and Acceleration

It is usual to start a study of applied mechanics with the section dealing with motion, which is often called *dynamics*. Alternatively, a start could be made with the other main division of the subject, relating to stresses and strains, and forces and frameworks, generally referred to as *statics*, although the more specialised title 'strength of materials' is sometimes used to describe this section.

Whichever section is chosen as the starting-point, a knowledge of vectors is essential, since both velocities and forces are vector quantities. In general, there are two types of quantities: *scalar* and *vector*. A *scalar* quantity is one which can be defined purely by a number. For example, the number of nuts and bolts in a tray is a scalar quantity, since a number such as 50 would describe the quantity. Similarly, the length and diameter of the bolts are also scalar quantities, since again numbers such as 75 mm and 10 mm are sufficient to describe the length and the diameter. A *vector* quantity is one which is completely defined only when a direction is added to the number. The value of a force is completely given only when the direction 'downwards' is added to the magnitude '10 N'. The value of a velocity is completely given only when the direction, 'north-east', is added to the magnitude, '50 kilometres per hour'. Hence both forces and velocities are vector quantities.

A vector quantity can be represented by a line drawn to scale and in the stated direction, with an arrow indicating the sense of the line. This line is usually called a vector.

Addition and Subtraction of Vectors

Scalar quantities can be added together by the normal arithmetical rules of addition, and similarly one can be subtracted from another in the normal arithmetical manner. Addition and subtraction of vector quantities must, of course, take into account the direction of the vectors concerned. In fig. 1.1 (i), lines A and B represent two vector quantities, such as two forces. We require to know their sum and their difference.

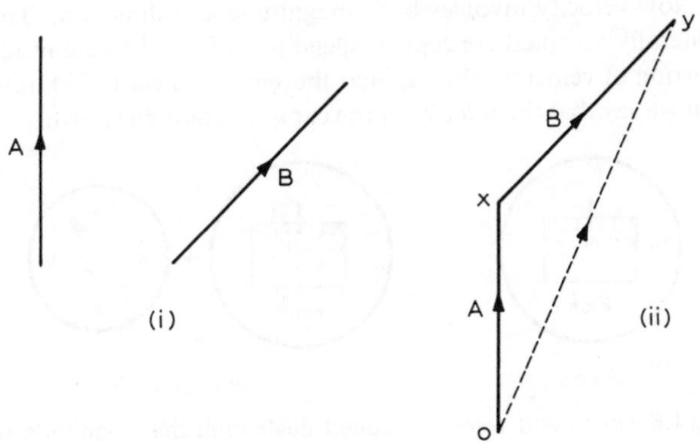

Fig. 1.1 Sum of vector quantities

Sum of Two Vectors

1 Draw $\boldsymbol{ox}$ to represent in magnitude and direction the quantity A. Note that the bold italic type for the letters $\boldsymbol{ox}$ indicates that a vector is being represented, and therefore direction and sense from o to x is being taken into account.

2 From the point x at the end of $\boldsymbol{ox}$, draw the line $\boldsymbol{xy}$ to represent in magnitude and direction the quantity B.

3 Join oy. Then $\boldsymbol{oy}$ represents in magnitude and direction the sum of the vectors A and B.

Important. Note that the direction of the final vector is always from the start, o, to the finish, y.

Example 1.1 Find the sum of the two vector quantities (i) 30 units due east, (ii) 4 units due north (fig. 1.2).

$\boldsymbol{oa}$ represents the 30 units due east quantity. From a we draw $\boldsymbol{ab}$ to represent 40 units due north. The vector $\boldsymbol{ob}$ (from start to finish) is the sum of the other two vectors, and by measurement is 50 units in the direction 53° 8′ north of east.

Had there been more than two vector quantities to add together, the extra ones would have been added on, in turn, to the end of the previous vector.

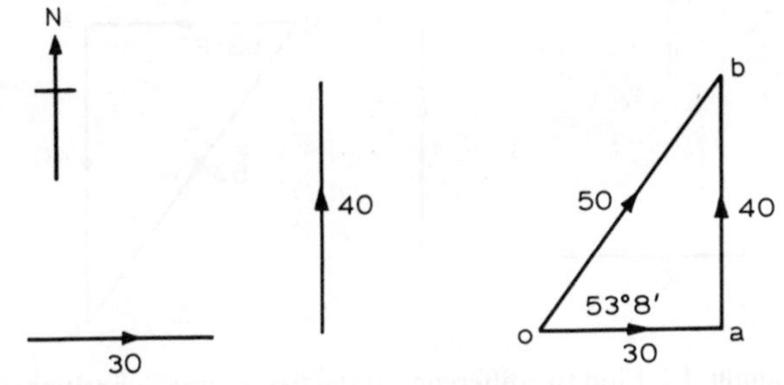

Fig. 1.2

Subtraction of Two Vectors

The difference of two quantities (scalar or vector) can be written in the form of the addition of one of the quantities to the negative of the other.

Hence $\qquad A - B = A + (-B)$

Now if the line $\boldsymbol{oa}$ in fig. 1.3 (i) represents a vector quantity A, then the line $\boldsymbol{ao}$ in fig. 1.3 (ii) represents the vector $(-A)$. Making use of this fact, let us determine the difference of the two vector quantities represented by A and B in fig. 1.1 (i), reproduced again in fig. 1.4 (i).

Fig. 1.3 Representation of negative vector

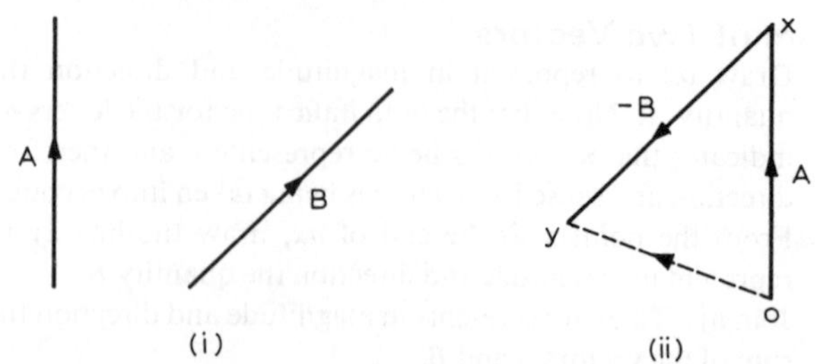

Fig.1.4 Subtraction of vector quantities

1 Draw *ox* to represent in magnitude and direction the quantity A.

2 From the point x at the end of *ox*, draw the line *xy* to represent in magnitude and direction the quantity $-B$. This will mean that the direction of *xy* will be opposite to that of the given quantity B, but the magnitude represented by *xy* will be equal to that of B.

3 Join *oy*. Then *oy* represents in magnitude and direction the sum of A and $(-B)$; that is, *oy* represents the difference of the two vectors.

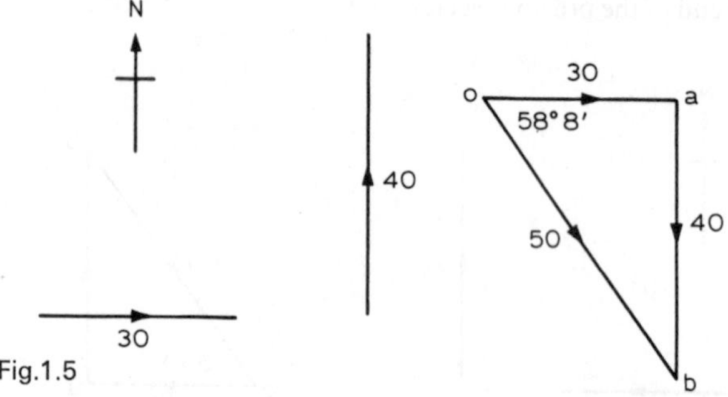

Fig.1.5

Example 1.2 Find the difference of the two vector quantities (i) 30 units due east, (ii) 40 units due north.

oa represents the 30 units due east quantity (fig.1.5). From *a* we draw *ab* in the southerly direction, opposite to the direction stated for the second vector. The length of *ab* represents the magnitude of 40 units. The vector *ob* (still from start to finish) is the difference of the other two vectors, and, by measurement, is 50 units in the direction 53° 8′ south of east.

Hence (30 units east) − (40 units north) = 50 units 53° 8′ south of east.

Vector Notation

As an alternative to defining a vector quantity by means of 'compass points', such as north and north-east, it is quite usual to indicate the quantity in the following manner:

$$10_{90^\circ}$$

This means that the magnitude of the vector is 10 units, and that its direction is 90° to the horizontal, measured in an anti-clockwise direction.

Thus 10_{90° and 10 units due north are the same,

5_{0° and 5 units due east are the same,

6_{200° and 6 units 20° south of west are the same.

Displacement

If a point moves from one position to another position, we say that it has been displaced. To indicate the amount of the displacement, we must state both the *magnitude*, sometimes called the distance, and the *direction* of the displacement. Thus displacement is a vector quantity. If the quantities mentioned in example 1.1 were displacements, suggesting that a point was displaced 30 m due east and then 40 m due north, its final displacement, being the sum of these two, would be 50 m 53° 8′ north of east. This would indicate the resultant displacement of the point relative to the starting position. You will notice that the distance moved by the point is 30 + 40 = 70 m. This is another illustration of the difference between a scalar quantity, such as distance, and a vector quantity, such as displacement.

The unit of displacement is the *metre*.

Velocity

The *velocity* of a point is the rate of change of its displacement. If the velocity is uniform, that is if the point has equal displacements during equal intervals of time, then we can say that its velocity is equal to the displacement in unit time, or the displacement per second, since the second is the normal unit of time. Having uniform velocity, we should expect the point to have the same displacement in successive intervals of time.

If the velocity is varying, we can state its value at a given instant. We can say, for example, that the magnitude of the velocity of a point at a particular instant is 10 m/s, by which we mean that, if it maintained that velocity without change, then the point would move 10 m in the next second. In fact, the point may move 100 m or 2 m in the next second, if its varying velocity is increasing or decreasing.

Now velocity involves both magnitude and direction. The generally accepted concept of speed is, in fact, the magnitude portion of velocity. We say that the *speed* of a car is 60 km/h, but we say that the *velocity* of the car is 60 km/h due north.

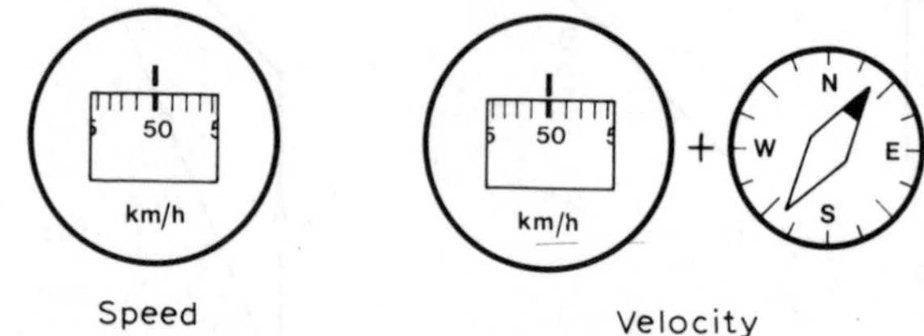

Fig.1.6 Speed and velocity. Speed deals with the magnitude or number part. Velocity has to do with both the magnitude and the direction of the motion.

Velocities are vector quantities, and their addition and subtraction, which play an important part in applied mechanics, are carried out as previously indicated.

Acceleration

Any change in the velocity of a moving point involves an *acceleration* (or a *retardation*, which is simply a negative acceleration).

Acceleration is the rate of change of velocity. If the velocity of a point is 10 m/s at one instant, and this velocity is increasing at the rate of 2 m/s each second, then at the end of 1 second the velocity will be 12 m/s, and at the end of the next second it will be 14 m/s. The rate of increase of 2 m/s each second (written 2 m/s^2) is the acceleration of the point. If the velocity were decreasing by 2 m/s each second, then we should refer to a retardation of 2 m/s^2.

In practice, accelerations change as much as velocities, but for the purpose of our work in applied mechanics we shall be concerned only with uniform acceleration, and with a rather special type of motion in which the varying acceleration follows a clearly defined mathematical pattern.

Accelerations, since they involve velocities, are also vector quantities.

Now because a change in velocity is produced if either the magnitude or the direction of the velocity is changed, it follows that two types of accelerations are involved in these changes. Figure 1.7 indicates the magnitude of the velocity of a car moving along a straight road; thus the direction of the velocity remains constant. The magnitude is increasing and the car is accelerating. The acceleration is in the direction of the velocity of the car, and is known as *linear tangential acceleration*, although at this stage it may not be very apparent as to why this name 'tangential' is used.

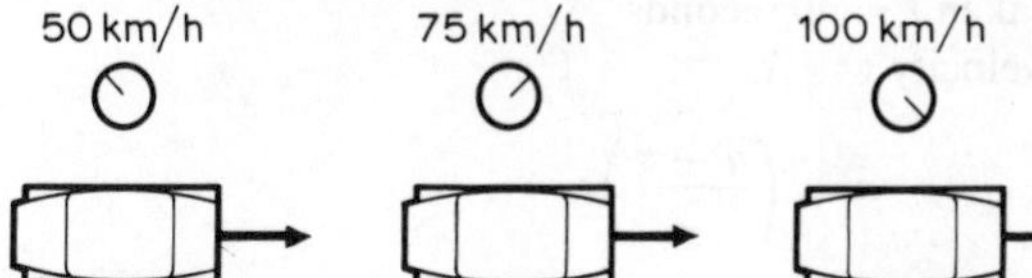

Fig.1.7 Acceleration due to change of magnitude of velocity. The direction of this car is constant. The magnitude of its velocity is changing from 50 to 100 km/h. Hence the car is accelerating.

Figure 1.8 indicates a car moving in a circular path whilst the speedometer remains constant, i.e. the speed of the car is constant. The direction of the velocity is constantly changing. It is always taken as tangential to the path of motion. The arrows are therefore vectors, indicating the velocity of the car at successive intervals. These velocities are 45 km/h NE, 45 km/h E, and 45 km/h SE. The velocities are changing, and hence acceleration is involved. This acceleration is known as *centripetal* or *radial acceleration*, and is perpendicular to the direction of motion, although we must wait until we come to study motion in a circular path before we fully appreciate this.

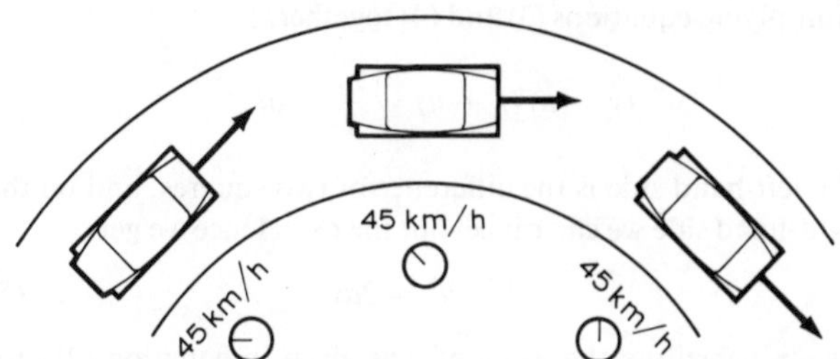

Fig.1.8 Acceleration due to change of direction of velocity. The magnitude of this car's velocity is constant at 45 km/h, its direction is, however, changing, as it moves in a curved path. There is, therefore, a change in the velocity of the car. In other words, the car is accelerating.

Relationship between Displacement, Velocity, Acceleration, and Time

Now let us establish some expressions which connect these four important quantities. The following symbols are usually adopted:

s = distance travelled in m
t = time in seconds
u = initial velocity in m
v = final velocity in m/s after t seconds
a = acceleration in m/s^2

Whilst the velocity increases uniformly from u m/s to v m/s, in time t seconds, the average velocity will be $\frac{u+v}{2}$ m/s.

Distance travelled = average velocity × time

i.e.
$$s = \frac{(u+v)t}{2} \quad . \quad . \quad . \quad . \quad . \quad . \quad . \quad (1)$$

The initial velocity, u, will be changed to

$u + a$ at the end of 1 second
$u + 2a$ at the end of 2 seconds
$u + 3a$ at the end of 3 seconds
$u + at$ at the end of t seconds

Representing this by v, the final velocity, we have

$$v = u + at \quad . \quad . \quad . \quad . \quad . \quad . \quad . \quad (2)$$

Taking u across to the other side, we have

$$v - u = at \quad . \quad . \quad . \quad . \quad . \quad . \quad . \quad (3)$$

Now we have seen that

$$s = \frac{(u+v)t}{2}$$

which can easily be converted into

$$u + v = \frac{2s}{t}$$

or

$$v + u = \frac{2s}{t} \quad . \quad . \quad . \quad . \quad . \quad . \quad (4)$$

Multiplying equations (3) and (4) together,

$$(v - u)(v + u) = \frac{2s}{t} \times at$$

The left-hand side is the difference of two squares, and on the right-hand side we can cancel out the t's. Hence we get

$$v^2 - u^2 = 2as \quad . \quad . \quad . \quad . \quad . \quad . \quad (5)$$

Again, substitute the value of v as given in equation (2) into equation (1):

$$s = \frac{[u + (u + at)]t}{2}$$

$$s = \frac{(2u + at)t}{2}$$

$$s = ut + \tfrac{1}{2}at^2 \quad . \quad . \quad . \quad . \quad . \quad . \quad . \quad (6)$$

These formulæ are extremely important. For convenience they are collected together here.

Uniform velocity ($a = 0$)

$$s = vt$$

Uniform acceleration $v = u + at$

$$s = \frac{(u + v)t}{2}$$

$$v^2 - u^2 = 2as$$

$$s = ut + \tfrac{1}{2}at^2$$

If the body is accelerating, a is positive.
If the body is retarding, a is negative.

Example 1.3 A car passes a certain point with a velocity of 10 m/s, and a point 1 km away with a velocity of 30 m/s, the acceleration being uniform. What is the average velocity of the car? How long did it take the car to travel the distance between the two points? What was the acceleration of the car?

Average velocity (since acceleration is uniform)

$$= \frac{u + v}{2}$$

$$= \frac{10 + 30}{2} \text{ m/s}$$

$$= 20 \text{ m/s}$$

$$\text{Time taken} = \frac{\text{distance (m)}}{\text{average velocity (m/s)}}$$

$$= \frac{1000}{20} \text{ s}$$

$$= 50 \text{ s}$$

Increase in velocity $= (30 - 10)$ m/s $= 20$ m/s

This occurs uniformly in 50 seconds

$$\therefore \text{Acceleration} = \frac{\text{change in velocity}}{\text{time}}$$

$$= \frac{20}{50} \text{ m/s}^2$$

$$= 0{\cdot}4 \text{ m/s}^2$$

i.e. Average velocity is 20 m/s, the car takes 50 seconds to travel between the two points with an acceleration of 0·4 m/s².

Example 1.4 With what initial velocity must a body be travelling in order to come to rest in 100 m as a result of a uniform retardation of 8 m/s²?

Acceleration $a = -8 \text{ m/s}^2$
Distance travelled $s = 100 \text{ m}$
Final velocity $v = 0 \text{ m/s}$
Initial velocity $u = ?$
Now $v^2 - u^2 = 2as$

$$0^2 - u^2 = 2 \times (-8) \times 100$$

$$u^2 = 1600$$

i.e. Initial velocity, u, is 40 m/s.

Example 1.5 Two signals are 1 km apart. A train passes the first with a speed of 108 km/h and passes the second signal 40 seconds later. During this period, the brakes are applied to give a uniform retardation. Determine the velocity of the train passing the second signal, and also the magnitude of the retardation.

$$\text{Initial velocity } u = \frac{108 \times 1000}{60 \times 60} = 30 \text{ m/s}$$

Distance travelled $s = 1000$ m
Time taken $t = 40$ seconds
Final velocity $v = ?$

$$s = \left(\frac{u + v}{2}\right)t$$

$$1000 = \left(\frac{30 + v}{2}\right)40$$

$$v = 20 \text{ m/s}$$

Retardation $s = ut + \tfrac{1}{2}at^2$

$$1000 = 30 \times 40 + \tfrac{1}{2} \times 40^2 a$$

$$a = -0{\cdot}25 \text{ m/s}^2$$

i.e. Retardation of train is 0·25 m/s², and the train passes the second signal at 20 m/s.

Velocity-time Diagrams

The velocity-time diagram is a graph in which the velocity of a point is plotted against a time base. Figure 1.9 illustrates three such diagrams. On the left-hand side is a velocity-time diagram for a point moving with uniform velocity; in the centre

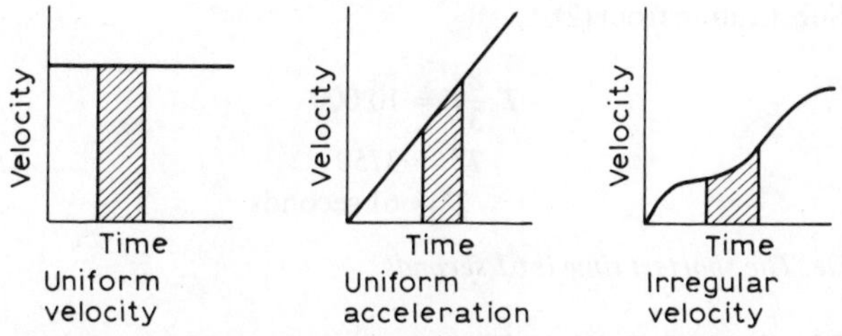

Fig.1.9 Velocity-time graph. The area under such a graph represents the distance travelled.

we have a diagram for a point moving with uniformly increasing velocity, i.e. with uniform acceleration; whilst the diagram on the right is for a point whose velocity is varying in an irregular manner.

In each case, the distance travelled by the point is numerically equal to the area under the corresponding portion of the graph. This important relationship applies to all forms of motion, however complicated they may be. Many problems dealing with varying velocities can be solved very neatly by using the velocity-time diagram. In the case of irregular variation of velocity, the area under the diagram can be found by one of the methods indicated in Appendix 2.

Example 1.6 A train travelling between two stations 3 km apart completes the journey in 5 minutes. During the first 30 seconds the train is moving with a constant acceleration; whilst a uniform retardation brings the train to rest in the last 20 seconds. For the remaining portion of the journey the train is moving with uniform speed. Calculate the value of (a) the uniform speed, (*b*) the acceleration, and (c) the retardation, both in units of m/s².

Illustrate your answer with a speed-time graph, and use this graph to obtain the distance travelled in the first and last minutes of the train's motion. NCTEC

Let a = acceleration, m/s²
f = retardation, m/s²
v = uniform velocity, m/s

then during first 30 seconds $v = at$ (since $u = 0$)

$$v = 30a \quad \ldots\ldots (1)$$

During last 20 seconds $u = v - ft$

$$0 = v - 20f$$
$$v = 20f \quad \ldots\ldots (2)$$

Equating (1) and (2), $30a = 20f$

$$\therefore f = \frac{3}{2}a \quad \ldots\ldots (3)$$

Distance travelled whilst accelerating

$$s = ut + \tfrac{1}{2}at^2$$
$$= 0 + \tfrac{1}{2}a \times 30^2$$
$$s = 450a \text{ m}$$
$$= 15v \text{ m from (1)}$$

Distance travelled at uniform speed

$$s = vt$$
$$= [(5 \times 60) - (30 + 20)]v$$
$$= 250v \text{ m}$$

Distance travelled during retardation

$$s = vt - \tfrac{1}{2}ft^2 \text{ (negative due to retardation)}$$
$$= 20v - \tfrac{1}{2}f \times 20^2$$
$$= 20v - 200f$$
$$= 20v - 10v \text{ from (2)}$$
$$= 10v \text{ m}$$

Total distance travelled $= 15v + 250v + 10v$

$$= 275v$$
$$= 3000 \text{ m}$$
$$\therefore v = \frac{3000}{275}$$
$$= 10{\cdot}9 \text{ m/s}$$

a) Uniform velocity $= 10{\cdot}9$ m/s

b) Acceleration $a = \frac{v}{30}$ from (1)

$$= \frac{10{\cdot}9}{30}$$
$$= 0{\cdot}363 \text{ m/s}^2$$

c) Retardation $f = \frac{v}{20}$ from (2)

$$= \frac{10{\cdot}9}{20}$$
$$= 0{\cdot}545 \text{ m/s}^2. \text{ (Check with equation (3).)}$$

Figure 1.10 shows the velocity-time diagram with the shaded portions representing distances travelled during the first and last minutes.

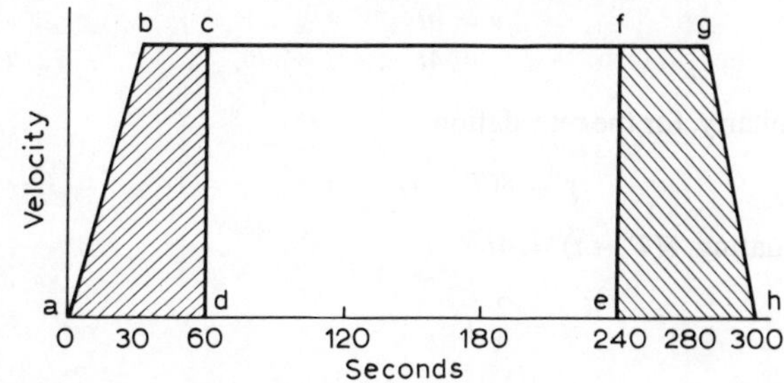

Fig.1.10

Distance travelled during the first minute

$$= \text{area of trapezium } abcd$$
$$= \tfrac{1}{2}(bc + ad) \times cd$$
$$= \tfrac{1}{2}(30 + 60) \times 10{\cdot}9$$
$$= 490 \text{m}$$

Distance travelled during last minute

$$= \text{area of trapezium } efgh$$
$$= \tfrac{1}{2}(fg + eh) \times fe$$
$$= \tfrac{1}{2}(40 + 60) \times 10{\cdot}9$$
$$= 545\,\text{m}$$

i.e. The uniform velocity is 10·9 m/s, the acceleration is 0·363 m/s², and the retardation is 0·545 m/s². During the first minute the train travels 490 m, and during the last minute 545 m.

Example 1.7 The maximum acceleration of a body is 4 m/s², and the maximum retardation is 8 m/s². What is the shortest time in which the body can move through a distance of 5 km from rest to rest?

The shortest time occurs when the body accelerates to its maximum speed and immediately retards. The velocity-time diagram is then a triangle, similar to fig.1.11.

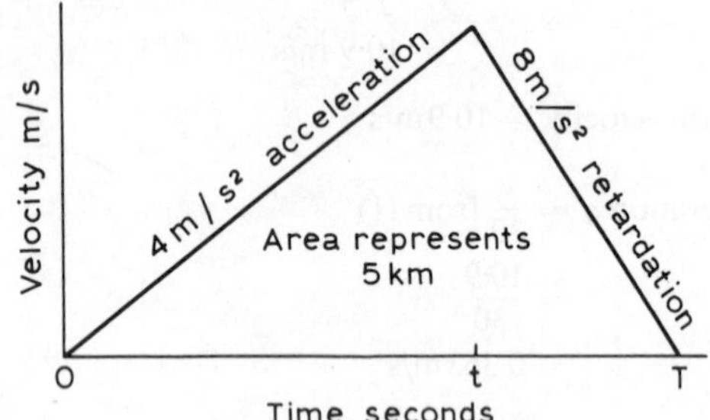

Fig.1.11

Let
$$T = \text{total time in seconds}$$
$$t = \text{time to accelerate}$$
$$T - t = \text{time to retard}$$
$$v = \text{maximum velocity, m/s}$$

Initial velocity is zero and acceleration is uniform, hence maximum velocity is given by

$$v = at$$
$$= 4t \qquad \ldots \ldots \qquad (1)$$

Similarly, for the retardation

$$v = 8(T - t)$$

Equating, $8(T - t) = 4t$

$$t = \frac{2}{3}T$$

Hence from (1) $v = 4 \times \frac{2}{3}T$

$$v = \frac{8}{3}T \qquad \ldots \ldots \qquad (2)$$

Area of triangle represents distance travelled:

$$\tfrac{1}{2}T.v = 5000$$
$$Tv = 10\,000$$

Substituting from (2),

$$T.\frac{8}{3}T = 10\,000$$
$$T^2 = 3750$$
$$T = 61 \text{ seconds}$$

i.e. The shortest time is 61 seconds.

Motion of Falling Bodies

When a body is allowed to fall freely to the ground, it moves with a uniform acceleration produced by the gravitational attraction of the earth. This acceleration varies from place to place on the earth's surface. Its value is approximately 9·81 m/s² at London, and this is the value which we shall normally use in our calculations. The small letter g is the symbol associated with the acceleration due to gravity.

The important fact in connection with falling bodies is that, since they are all subject to the same gravitational acceleration at the same place on the earth's surface, it follows that they will all travel through the same distance in the same interval of time. Whilst we may feel that a heavy body would fall quicker than a light body, and that it would travel faster, this is not, in fact, the case. Neglecting any wind resistance, the two bodies would move with the same velocity, and take the same time to fall through the same vertical height.

The equations for motion due to gravity follow the same pattern as those for linear motion, with the slight modification of introducing g as the acceleration, instead of a. We shall also have to be rather careful in connection with the sign of the various quantities involved. For example, a body thrown upwards will reach a certain height and then begin to fall. The direction, as well as the magnitude, of the velocity will change. To allow for this we consider all upward directions to be positive, both for displacements and velocities. Downward directions will be negative. This will include the gravitational acceleration, which is always down, and will therefore always be negative. Hence the motion equations applied to falling bodies become:

$$v = u - gt$$
$$v^2 - u^2 = -2gs$$
$$s = ut - \tfrac{1}{2}gt^2$$

Upward displacements and velocities are *positive*.
Downward displacements and velocities are *negative*.

Note that in all cases the value of s is the displacement of the body from the starting-point, and not necessarily the distance travelled from the starting-point. For example, the body may have travelled 50 m upwards and at the instant under consideration may have fallen 40 m from the highest point reached. The value of s will be + 10 m, indicating that the body is 10 m above the starting-point, although the body has actually travelled 50 + 40 = 90 m.

Example 1.8 A stone is allowed to fall from the edge of a cliff 122·5 m high. What will be its velocity after 3 seconds? How far will it have travelled at the end of 3 seconds? How long will it take the stone to reach the base of the cliff? What will be its striking velocity on reaching the base of the cliff?

Since the stone is just allowed to fall, its initial velocity is zero, i.e. $u = 0$.

Velocity after 3 seconds:

$$v = u - gt$$
$$= 0 - 9{\cdot}81 \times 3$$
$$= -29{\cdot}43\,\text{m/s}$$

i.e. Its velocity is 29·43 m/s downwards.

Distance after 3 seconds:

$$s = ut - \tfrac{1}{2}gt^2$$
$$= (0 \times 3) - (\tfrac{1}{2} \times 9{\cdot}81 \times 3^2)$$
$$= -44{\cdot}15\,\text{m}$$

i.e. The stone has travelled 44·15 m downwards from the point at which it was released.

Time taken to reach base:

In this case $u = 0$ m/s

$s = -122{\cdot}5$ m, i.e. 122·5 m down from the point of projection

$$s = ut - \tfrac{1}{2}gt^2$$
$$-122{\cdot}5 = 0 - \tfrac{1}{2} \times 9{\cdot}81 \times t^2$$
$$t^2 = 25$$
$$t = 5 \text{ seconds}$$

Striking velocity:

$$u = 0\,\text{m/s}$$
$$s = -122{\cdot}5\,\text{m}$$
$$v^2 - u^2 = -2gs$$
$$v^2 - 0 = -2 \times 9{\cdot}81 \times (-122{\cdot}5)$$
$$v^2 = 2400$$
$$v = 49\,\text{m/s}$$

i.e. After 3 seconds the velocity of the stone will be 29·43 m/s. It will have travelled 44·15 m in the first 3 seconds. It will reach the base of the cliff in 5 seconds, when its striking velocity will be 49 m/s.

Example 1.9 A body is projected upwards with a velocity of 50 m/s from the top of a tower 100 m high. How long will it take to reach the ground? What will be the velocity with which the body strikes the ground?

$u = +50$ m/s (upwards)

$s = -100$ m (ground is 100 m below top of tower)

$t = ?$

$$s = ut - \tfrac{1}{2}gt^2$$
$$-100 = 50t - \tfrac{1}{2} \times 9{\cdot}81 \times t^2$$
$$t^2 - 10{\cdot}2t - 20{\cdot}4 = 0$$

which gives $t = 11{\cdot}9$ seconds

Striking velocity:

$$u = +50\,\text{m/s}$$
$$s = -100\,\text{m}$$
$$v = ?$$
$$v^2 - u^2 = -2gs$$
$$v^2 - 50^2 = -2 \times 9{\cdot}81 \times (-100)$$
$$v^2 = 2500 + 1962$$
$$= 4462$$
$$v = 66{\cdot}9\,\text{m/s}$$

i.e. Body strikes the ground after 11·9 seconds, with a velocity of 66·9 m/s.

Example 1.10 State Newton's Laws of Motion. An object is dropped from an helicopter and strikes the ground 12 seconds later. Determine the height of the helicopter and the velocity with which the body strikes the ground.

If a second object had been projected upwards from the ground with a velocity of 200 m/s at the same instant as the first object was dropped from the helicopter, determine where and when they would meet. UEI

Reference is made to Newton's Laws of Motion in Appendix 3.

Height of helicopter:

$u = 0$ m/s (released from rest)

$t = 12$ seconds

$s = ?$

$$s = ut - \tfrac{1}{2}gt^2$$
$$= 0 \times 12 - \tfrac{1}{2} \times 9{\cdot}81 \times 12^2$$

$= -706$ m (negative sign indicating downward displacement from starting-point)

Striking velocity:

$$v = u - gt$$
$$= 0 - 9{\cdot}81 \times 12$$

$= -118$ m/s (velocity is downwards)

Considerable care is required with the last part of this question, particularly with regard to the signs.

s_1 = distance travelled by first object

s_2 = distance travelled by second object

Equation of motion of first object:

$$s_1 = ut - \tfrac{1}{2}gt^2$$

$s_1 = \tfrac{1}{2}gt^2$, since $u = 0$

Equation of second object:

$s_2 = 200t - \tfrac{1}{2}gt^2$ ($u = +200$ m/s)

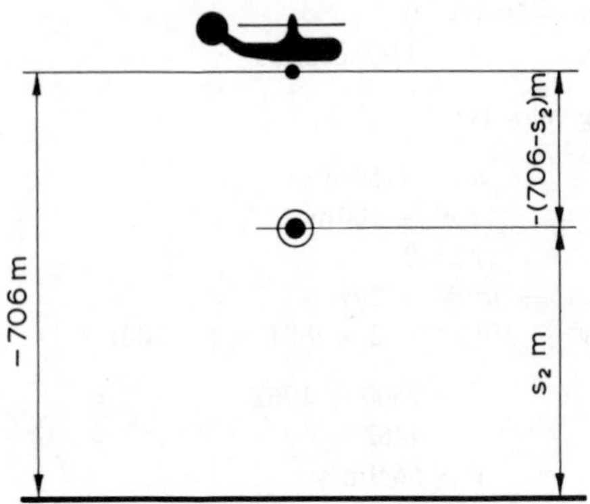

Fig.1.12

Now, referring to fig.1.12, we see that the ground is −706 m from the helicopter, so that the second object, having travelled s_2 from the ground, is $-(706 - s_2)$ from the helicopter. When this distance is equal to s_1, the two objects will meet.

$$-(706 - s_2) = s_1$$
$$-706 + s_2 = s_1$$
$$-706 + 200t - \tfrac{1}{2}gt^2 = -\tfrac{1}{2}gt^2$$
$$200t = 706$$
$$t = 3{\cdot}53 \text{ seconds}$$

Distance from ground to point of meeting:

$$s_2 = 200t - \tfrac{1}{2}gt^2$$
$$= 200 \times 3{\cdot}53 - \tfrac{1}{2} \times 9{\cdot}81 \times 3{\cdot}53^2$$
$$= 645 \text{ m from the ground}$$

i.e. The helicopter is 706 m high, and the object strikes the ground with a velocity of 118 m/s. A second object projected upwards from the ground with a velocity of 200 m/s would meet the first at a height of 645 m, 3·53 seconds after the instant of projection.

Angular Displacement, θ (theta)

So far, we have been thinking about motion in a straight line, such as the motion of a piston in a cylinder. The other important form of motion is *angular motion*, such as the motion of the crank around the crankshaft.

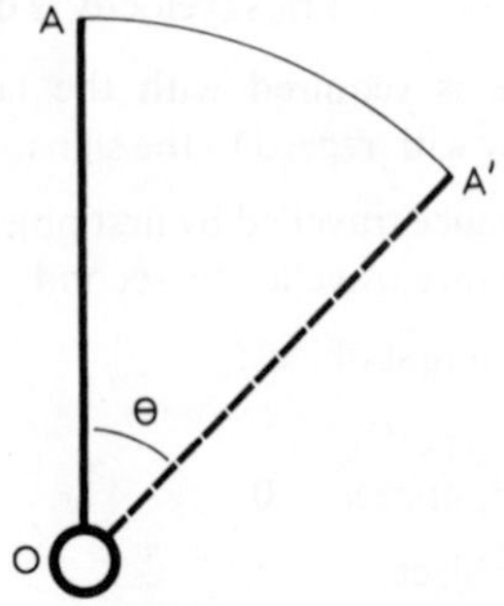

Fig.1.13 Angular displacement

The rod OA in fig.1.13 is moving in a clockwise direction about the fixed axis passing through O. The displacement of the rod can be expressed as an angle. Thus, when the rod has moved from the position OA to the position OA′, the displacement is θ radians.

The unit of angular displacement is the radian.

Angular Velocity, ω (omega)

Angular velocity is the rate of change of angular displacement. It is properly expressed in terms of radians per second, although for practical purposes the number of revolutions per second, or revolutions per minute, is often quoted.

Since 1 revolution is equal to 2π radians, it follows that

$$N \text{ rev/min} = \frac{2\pi N}{60} \text{ rad/s}$$
$$= \frac{\pi N}{30} \text{ rad/s}$$

$$\text{Conversely, } \omega \text{ rad/s} = \frac{30\omega}{\pi} \text{ rev/min}$$

As in the case of linear motion, the angular velocity either may be uniform or may vary.

Angular Acceleration, α (alpha)

Angular acceleration is the rate of change of angular velocity. For our purposes, we shall be concerned only with motion involving a constant angular acceleration or retardation. Angular retardation is a negative angular acceleration.

Relationship between Angular Displacement, Velocity, Acceleration, and Time

ω_1 = initial velocity in rad/s
ω_2 = final velocity in rad/s after t seconds
α = angular acceleration in rad/s²
θ = angle turned through in radians
t = time in seconds

The initial angular velocity, ω_1, will be increased by α rad/s at the end of each second. At the end of t seconds, its velocity will be $\omega_1 + \alpha t$.

This gives

$$\omega_2 = \omega_1 + \alpha t \quad \ldots \quad (1)$$

or

$$\omega_2 - \omega_1 = \alpha t \quad \ldots \quad (2)$$

Since the velocity is increasing uniformly,

$$\text{average velocity} = \frac{\omega_1 + \omega_2}{2}$$

and since displacement = average velocity × time

$$\theta = \frac{\omega_1 + \omega_2}{2}t \quad \ldots \quad (3)$$

Rearranging, we have

$$(\omega_1 + \omega_2) = \frac{2\theta}{t}$$

or

$$(\omega_2 + \omega_1) = \frac{2\theta}{t} \quad . \quad . \quad . \quad . \quad . \quad (4)$$

Multiplying (2) and (4) together,

$$(\omega_2 + \omega_1)(\omega_2 - \omega_1) = \frac{2\theta}{t} \times \alpha t$$

The left-hand side is the difference of two squares, and on the right-hand side we can cancel out the t's. Hence we get

$$\omega_2^2 - \omega_1^2 = 2\theta\alpha \quad . \quad . \quad . \quad . \quad . \quad (5)$$

Again, substituting the value of ω_2 as given in equation (1) into equation (3):

$$\theta = \frac{[\omega_1 + (\omega_1 + \alpha t)]t}{2}$$

$$\theta = \frac{[2\omega_1 + \alpha t]t}{2}$$

$$\theta = \omega_1 t + \tfrac{1}{2}\alpha t^2 \quad . \quad . \quad . \quad . \quad . \quad (6)$$

We can tabulate these formulæ together, and notice the similarity with those obtained for linear motion.

Uniform angular velocity ($\alpha = 0$)

$$\theta = \omega t$$

Uniform angular acceleration

$$\omega_2 - \omega_1 = \alpha t$$

$$\theta = \frac{(\omega_1 + \omega_2)t}{2}$$

$$\omega_2^2 - \omega_1^2 = 2\alpha\theta$$

$$\theta = \omega_1 t + \tfrac{1}{2}\alpha t^2$$

If the body is *accelerating*, α will be *positive*.
If the body is *retarding*, α will be *negative*.

Example 1.11 An electric motor is rotating at 3000 rev/min when it is brought to rest with uniform retardation in 15 seconds. Calculate (a) the value of this uniform retardation, and (b) the number of revolutions made by the motor in coming to rest.

$$3000 \text{ rev/min} = \frac{3000}{60} \times 2\pi \text{ rad/s}$$

a)

$$\omega_1 = 314{\cdot}2 \text{ rad/s}$$
$$\omega_2 = 0 \text{ (at rest)}$$
$$t = 15 \text{ seconds}$$
$$\alpha = ?$$
$$\omega_2 - \omega_1 = \alpha t$$
$$0 - 314{\cdot}2 = 15\alpha$$
$$\alpha = -\ 21 \text{ rad/s}^2$$

The negative sign implies a retardation.

b)

$$\omega_1 = 314{\cdot}6 \text{ rad/s}$$
$$\omega_2 = 0$$
$$t = 15 \text{ seconds}$$
$$\theta = ?$$
$$\theta = \frac{\omega_1 + \omega_2}{2} t$$
$$= \frac{314{\cdot}2 + 0}{2} \times 15$$
$$\theta = 2356 \text{ radians}$$
$$= \frac{2356}{2\pi} \text{ revolutions}$$
$$= 375 \text{ revolutions}$$

i.e. The motor has a retardation of 21 rad/s², and makes 375 revolutions in coming to rest.

Example 1.12 A large gear-wheel rotating at 40 rev/min has an angular retardation of 1 radian per minute per second. Calculate its angular velocity after 30 seconds, and the number of revolutions it makes (a) in 40 seconds, and (b) in coming to rest. UEI

$$40 \text{ rev/min} = \frac{40}{60} \times 2\pi$$
$$= 4{\cdot}19 \text{ rad/s}$$
$$\omega_1 = 4{\cdot}19 \text{ rad/s}$$
$$t = 30 \text{ seconds}$$
$$\alpha = -\ 1 \text{ rad/min (retardation)}$$
$$= -\frac{1}{60} \text{ rad/s}^2$$
$$\omega_2 = ?$$
$$\omega_2 = \omega_1 + \alpha t$$
$$= 4{\cdot}19 - \frac{1}{60} \times 30$$
$$= 3{\cdot}69 \text{ rad/s}$$
$$= 3{\cdot}69 \times \frac{60}{2\pi} = 35{\cdot}2 \text{ rev/min}$$

a) Revolutions made in 40 seconds:

$$\omega_1 = 4{\cdot}19 \text{ rad/s}$$
$$t = 40 \text{ seconds}$$
$$\alpha = -\frac{1}{60} \text{ rad/s}^2$$
$$\theta = ?$$
$$\theta = \omega_1 t + \tfrac{1}{2}\alpha t^2$$
$$= 4{\cdot}19 \times 40 - \tfrac{1}{2} \times \frac{1}{60} \times 40^2$$
$$= 154{\cdot}3 \text{ radians}$$
$$= \frac{154{\cdot}3}{2\pi} = 24{\cdot}6 \text{ revolutions}$$

b) Revolutions in coming to rest:

$$\omega_1 = 4{\cdot}19 \text{ rad/s}$$
$$\omega_2 = 0 \text{ rad/s (at rest)}$$
$$\alpha = -\frac{1}{60} \text{ rad/s}^2$$
$$\theta = ?$$
$$\omega_2{}^2 - \omega_1{}^2 = 2\alpha\theta$$
$$-4{\cdot}19^2 = -2 \times \frac{1}{60}\theta$$
$$\theta = 527 \text{ radians, or 84 revolutions}$$

i.e. The velocity after 30 seconds is 35·2 rev/min. In 30 seconds the wheel makes 24·6 revolutions; and in coming to rest, 84 revolutions.

Conversion from Angular to Linear Velocity

We often want to know the linear velocity of a point such as A on a rod OA when we are told the angular velocity of rotation of the rod. The same relationship exists between linear and angular velocity as between length of arc and angle in radians.

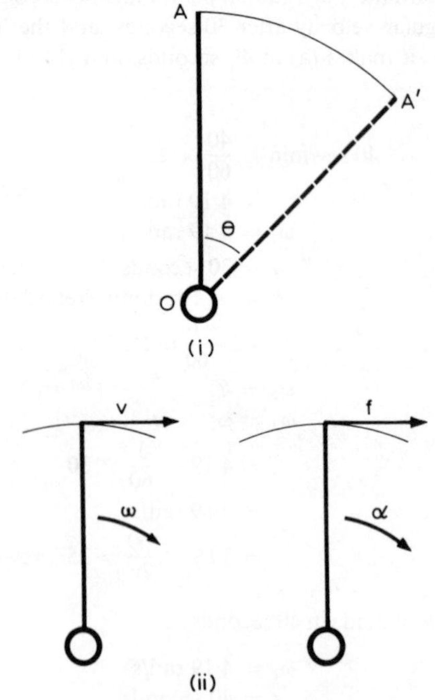

Fig.1.14 Angular velocity and acceleration

Referring to fig.1.14(i), we can say

$$\text{length of arc} \quad AA' = \text{angle in radians} \times \text{radius}$$
$$s = \theta \times OA$$

But if the rod is rotating with uniform velocity ω, the angle θ is given by $\theta = \omega t$.

Hence $s = \omega t \times OA$

so that point A travels distance $\omega t \times OA$ in time t seconds, which gives the linear velocity of point A as $\frac{\omega t . OA}{t}$ or $\omega . OA$.

Hence linear velocity = angular velocity × radius

and $$\text{angular velocity} = \frac{\text{linear velocity}}{\text{radius}}$$

Similarly linear acceleration = angular acceleration × radius

and $$\text{angular acceleration} = \frac{\text{linear acceleration}}{\text{radius}}$$

These relationships can be expressed in terms of symbols, thus:

	Linear	*Angular*
Velocity	$v = \omega r$	$\omega = v/r$
Acceleration	$a = \omega r$	$\alpha = a/r$

where r is the radius

General Relationship between Displacement, Velocity, and Acceleration for Motion in a Straight Line

Consider the following equation, which indicates the displacement, s, of a body in time t seconds:

$$s = 5t + 10t^2$$

At the end of 1 second ($t = 1$) the body has travelled 15 m. At the end of 2 seconds ($t = 2$) the body has travelled 50 m. Hence, during the 2nd second, the body travels $50 - 15 = 35$ m, and its average velocity is therefore 35 m/s.

At the end of $1\frac{1}{2}$ seconds ($t = 1{\cdot}5$) the body has travelled 30 m; so that, during the interval $t = 1$ to $t = 1{\cdot}5$, the body travels 15 m, and its average velocity is therefore $15/0{\cdot}5 = 30$ m/s.

Let us tabulate these values, and add more to them.

t seconds	2	1·5	1·2	1·1	1·05
s m	50	30	20·4	17·6	16·27
Increase in s m . . .	35	15	5·4	2·6	1·27
Increase in t seconds . .	1	0·5	0·2	0·1	0·05
Average velocity m/s . .	35	30	27	26	25·4

Notice that we have gradually reduced the time interval. In the last column we are considering the distance travelled between 1 and 1·05 seconds. You will see that the value of the average velocity is getting smaller. In fact, the time interval 0·05 seconds has become so small that we can practically consider the velocity of the body at the end of the 1st second as being equal to the average velocity during the time interval

1 − 1·05 seconds (and the smaller we make this interval, the more nearly accurate does this statement become).

Now let δt represent a small change in the value of t, and δs represent a corresponding change in the value of s.

Try not to let this expression δt worry you. It is purely a shorthand method of indicating a small change in the value of the quantity for which the symbol stands. Whenever you see the Greek letter *delta*—δ, or the corresponding capital, Δ—associated with any symbol you will know that you are to think of a small quantity. For example, δt may imply 1 second, or 0·05 second, or 0·00001 second; and δs may imply 0·001 m, or 0·000001 m. As small as you can imagine! But the important thing about these small quantities is this: although δt and δs may be very small, yet when one is divided by the other the quotient may be very large. For example, if δs is 0·0001 m and δt is 0·000001 second, the quotient $\frac{\delta s}{\delta t}$ is $\frac{0{\cdot}0001}{0{\cdot}000001} = 100\,\text{m/s}$, which is certainly not small.

So, then, t increases to $t + \delta t$, and this value can be substituted in the equation $s = 5t + 10t^2$, so that we can obtain the new distance, $s + \delta s$.

$$s + \delta s = 5(t + \delta t) + 10(t + \delta t)^2$$
$$= 5(t + \delta t) + 10(t^2 + 2t\delta t + (\delta t)^2)$$
$$= 5t + 5\delta t + 10t^2 + 20t\delta t + 10(\delta t)^2 \quad . \; . \quad (1)$$

But $\qquad s = 5t + 10t^2 \quad . \; . \; . \; . \; . \; . \; . \; . \; . \quad (2)$

Subtracting (2) from (1)

$$\delta s = 5\delta t + 20t\delta t + 10(\delta t)^2$$

$$\text{Average velocity} = \frac{\text{small distance travelled}}{\text{small time interval}} = \frac{\delta s}{\delta t}$$

$$\frac{\delta s}{\delta t} = \frac{5\delta t + 20t\delta t + 10(\delta t)^2}{\delta t}$$

$$= 5 + 20t + 10(\delta t)$$

Just as a test, work out the average velocity for the case where $t = 1$ and increases to $t = 1{\cdot}1$, i.e. $\delta t = 0{\cdot}1$ second.

$$\frac{\delta s}{\delta t} = 5 + (20 \times 1) + (10 \times 0{\cdot}1) = 26\,\text{m/s}$$

which is the same result as we obtained in column 4 of the previous table. Try the same test for other values.

Now, the smaller we make the time interval δt, the less important becomes the value of $10\delta t$. In fact, if we make δt equal to one-millionth of a second, or smaller if you like, we can completely neglect $10\delta t$, and we can say that the average value of the velocity during the millionth, or less, of a second is equal to the velocity of the body at the beginning of that small interval.

Let $\frac{ds}{dt}$ be the special value of $\frac{\delta s}{\delta t}$ when δt has become so small that we have neglected it on the right-hand side of the above equation. Then

$$\frac{ds}{dt} = 5 + 20t$$

which gives us the velocity of the body at any instant t. The velocity when $t = 1$ is 25 m/s, which was the value to which all the values were gradually tending in the last row of the previous table.

Well, you will probably have realised that the work which we have just done is known as 'differentiation', and you will no doubt have done some of this in mathematics. It has a very important application in mechanics. If we differentiate with respect to time an expression for displacement or distance, we obtain an expression for velocity. If we differentiate with respect to time the expression for velocity, we obtain an expression for the acceleration.

Displacement $\quad = s$

Velocity $\quad v = \frac{ds}{dt}$

Acceleration $\quad a = \frac{dv}{dt} = \frac{d^2s}{dt^2}$

Similarly, if we integrate an expression for acceleration, we obtain the velocity expression; and this, when integrated, will give the displacement equation.

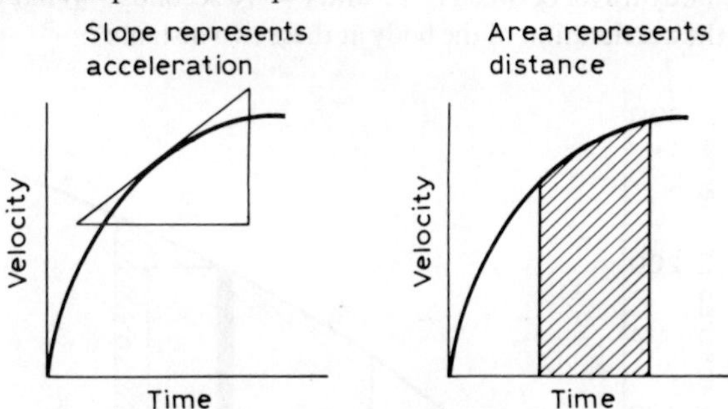

Fig.1.15 Importance of velocity-time graphs

As an example of this let us take the equation

$$s = ut + \tfrac{1}{2}at^2$$

where u and a are constants.

Velocity $\quad v = \frac{ds}{dt} = u + 2 \times \tfrac{1}{2}at$

$$= u + at$$

Acceleration $\quad a = \frac{dv}{dt} = 0 + a$

$$= a$$

both equations which we have previously obtained.

Example 1.13 The motion of a point P on a straight line is given by $s = 2t^2 - 3t + 4$, where s gives the distance in metres from a fixed point O on the line, t seconds after a given instant. Determine the velocity and acceleration of P, and its distance from O after 2 seconds.

Displacement equation $s = 2t^2 - 3t + 4$

After 2 seconds ($t = 2$) $s = 2 \times (2)^2 - 3 \times 2 + 4$

$= 6\text{m}$

Velocity equation $v = \dfrac{ds}{dt} = 4t - 3$

After 2 seconds ($t = 2$) $v = 4 \times 2 - 3$

$= 5\text{m/s}$

Acceleration equation $a = \dfrac{dv}{dt} = 4$

The acceleration is constant and equals 4/ms.

i.e. After 2 seconds the point has travelled 6 m, has an instantaneous velocity of 5 m/s, and a constant acceleration of 4 m/s².

Example 1.14 The equation $v = 10\left(3t - \dfrac{t^2}{20}\right)$ gives the velocity in m/s of a body t seconds after a given instant. How far will the body travel between $t = 5$ and $t = 10$ seconds? What will be the acceleration of the body at these two instants?

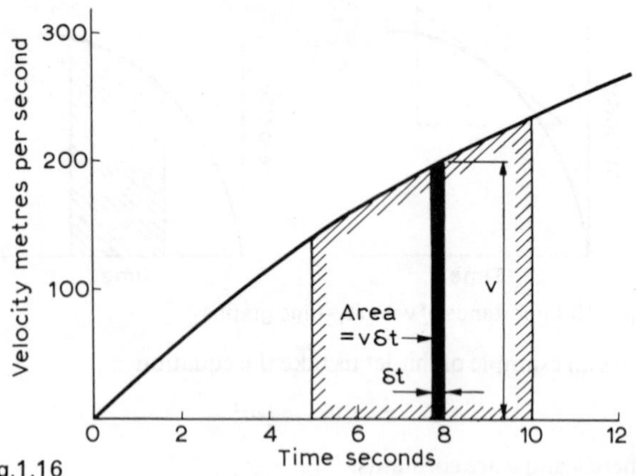

Fig.1.16

A velocity-time graph of the motion will be similar to that shown in fig.1.16. The required distance is represented by the area between the ordinates at $t = 5$ and $t = 10$.

Area of shaded strip, width δt, $= v\delta t$

$$= 10\left(3t - \frac{t^2}{20}\right)\delta t$$

Total area required $= \displaystyle\int_5^{10} 10\left(3t - \frac{t^2}{20}\right)dt$

$$= \int_5^{10} \left(30t - \frac{t^2}{2}\right)dt$$

$$= \left[\frac{30t^2}{2} - \frac{t^3}{6}\right]_5^{10}$$

$$= \left[15 \times 10^2 - \frac{10^3}{6}\right] - \left[15 \times 5^2 - \frac{5^3}{6}\right]$$

$$= 1500 - 166{\cdot}66 - 375 + 20{\cdot}83$$

$$= 979{\cdot}17\text{ m}$$

Distance travelled in 5 seconds from $t = 5$ to $t = 10$ seconds $= 979{\cdot}17\text{m}$.

The acceleration a of the body is given by $\dfrac{dv}{dt}$

$$v = 10\left(3t - \frac{t^2}{20}\right) = 30t - \frac{t^2}{2}$$

$$\frac{dv}{dt} = 30 - t$$

Acceleration at the end of 5 seconds $= 30 - 5 = 25\text{m/s}^2$.

Acceleration at the end of 10 seconds $= 30 - 10 = 20\text{m/s}^2$.

i.e. Between t = 5 and t = 10 seconds, the body will travel 979·17 m, and its acceleration at these times will be 25 m/s² and 20 m/s² respectively.

Exercise 1

1 Determine the sum of two vectors: 10 units due north and 20 units north-east.

2 Determine the sum of two vectors: 15 units south-east and 15 units south-west.

3 What is the value of $30_{45°} + 20_{180°}$?

4 What is the value of $40_{10°} + 30_{200°}$?

5 What is the value of the vector quantity which when added to 100 units due south will give 100 units north-west?

6 What is the value of $40_{20°} - 50_{340°}$?

7 What is the value of $5_{90°} - 4_{180°}$?

8 A body is projected upwards with a velocity of 120m/s from the top of a tower 30m high. Determine (a) the maximum height reached relative to the ground, (b) the time taken to reach the ground from the instant of projection, (c) the velocity with which the body strikes the ground, and (d) the time from the instant of projection to that when the speed is 60m/s.

9 A train travelling at 30m/s is at a certain instant 1500m behind another train travelling at 15m/s in the same direction. What is the least value of the retardation of the fast train if a collision is to be avoided, assuming that the slow train moves at constant speed?

10 A pit cage travels through a vertical distance of 500 m. Its maximum acceleration is $3\,m/s^2$ and its maximum retardation is $6\,m/s^2$. What is the shortest time of descent?

11 The speed of a body at a certain times is given in the accompanying table. Draw the speed-time graph, and find the distance travelled during the first 20 seconds of its motion.

Time, seconds . . .	0	4	8	12	16	20	24
Speed, m/s	0	8	10	16	20	20	16

12 The motion of a point P on a straight line is given by $s = 4t^2 - 2t + 6$, where s gives the distance in metres from a fixed point O on the line, t seconds after a given instant. Determine the velocity and acceleration of P and its distance from O after 2 seconds.

13 The motion of a point on a straight line is given by the equation $s = 3 \sin 10t$, where s is the distance from a point in the line of motion after t seconds from a fixed instant. Determine the velocity and acceleration of the point after 2, 4, and 6 seconds. Note: $10t$ is the value, in radians, of an angle.

14 The displacement in metres of a piston from the end of the cylinder is given by the expression $s = 10(1 - \cos 0{\cdot}5t + 0{\cdot}1 \sin^2 0{\cdot}5t)$.
Determine the displacement, velocity, and acceleration of the piston when t is 2 seconds.

15 State what the slope of a velocity-time curve at any point represents, and also what is indicated by the area between the velocity-time curve, the time axis, and the ordinates at the two given times?

A stopping strain travels between two stations 8 km apart, and takes 10 minutes. It can be uniformly accelerated to the maximum speed at $1{\cdot}5\,m/s^2$ and uniformly retarded from the maximum speed at $4{\cdot}5\,m/s^2$. What are the maximum speed and the distance travelled at this speed? How far has the train travelled in the first and last minutes of its motion?

16 Find the minimum time for a train to travel between stopping-places 2 km apart if the acceleration is $1\,m/s^2$, the deceleration $1{\cdot}5\,m/s^2$, and the speed is constant at 72 km/h during the intervening period. NCTEC

17 A motor car passes points A and B, 1500 m apart, at speeds of 18 km/h and 90 km/h respectively. If the acceleration is constant, calculate its value in m/s^2, and the position of the car when the speed is 72 km/h. NCTEC

18 The driver of an express train travelling at 90 km/h sees a local train 100 m ahead on the same line travelling at 30 km/h in the same direction. He immediately applies his brakes and stops just in time to avoid a collision. Calculate the retardation of the express, assuming the local train maintains its speed. NCTEC

19 A boy on a bicycle moving at a constant speed of 24 km/h overtakes a train which is just about to start off from a station with a uniform acceleration of $0{\cdot}5\,m/s^2$. How far will the train go before it overtakes the cyclist if the tracks are parallel? NCTEC

20 Two ships start together for a trial on the same course. One works up to full speed 40 km/h in 20 minutes, and the other works up to full speed 42 km/h in 25 minutes, both with uniform acceleration. How far are the ships apart after 1 hour from the start? NCTEC

21 A tower is 100 m high. One body is dropped from the top of the tower, and at the same instant another body is projected vertically upwards from the bottom, and they meet half-way up. Find the initial velocity of the projected body, and its velocity when it meets the descending body. UEI

Chapter 2

Projectiles

If a shell were fired with a horizontal velocity from the top of a cliff, its subsequent motion would be made up of two parts.
1 Immediately it left the barrel of the gun, it would come under the influence of gravity, and would be attracted to the ground with an acceleration of g m/s^2.
2 It would continue to move forward with the same horizontal velocity with which it left the gun. (We are neglecting any effects due to air resistance.)
Hence its time of flight, i.e. the time elapsing before it strikes the ground, is dependent upon the gravitational attraction of the earth, and is independent of the initial horizontal velocity of the shell. In fact, the time taken for the shell to strike the ground would be the same as that taken for a body falling from rest through the same vertical height.

The horizontal distance from the cliff to the point where the shell strikes the ground is dependent upon the time of flight and the horizontal velocity of projection. In fact, it is equal to the same distance through which a body would move in the same time with a uniform horizontal velocity equal to that of the velocity of projection.

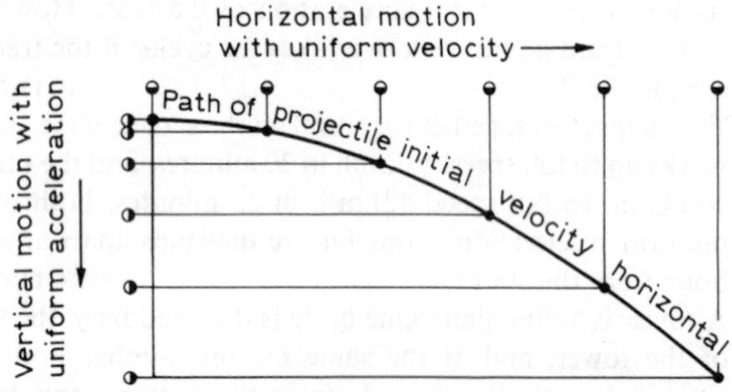

Fig.2.1 Motion of projectile. The horizontal velocity remains constant. The vertical velocity increases in a similar way to that of a body falling freely, with uniform acceleration of gm/s^2. The resulting motion carries the projectile on a parabolic path.

Figure 2.1 shows the motion of three bodies. On the left-hand side of the diagram is the motion of a body falling freely with uniform gravitational acceleration. Positions of the body at the end of equal intervals of time are shown. It will be seen that the distance travelled in equal time intervals is gradually increasing.

Along the top portion of the diagram, the motion of a body moving with uniform velocity in a horizontal straight line is shown. In this case, the distances travelled in equal intervals of time are constant.

In the centre portion of the diagram, the path of motion is given of a body projected with a horizontal velocity from a given height. It will be seen that the motion of this projectile is the combined motion of the two other bodies: the vertical displacement of the projectile is equal to the corresponding displacement of the falling body; the horizontal displacement of the projectile is equal to the corresponding displacement of the body moving with uniform horizontal velocity.

This is the important principle behind our work on projectiles.

Let us consider in more detail the motion of a body projected from the top of a cliff, height h, with a horizontal velocity u.

Horizontal displacement after t seconds, $x = ut$ m . . (1)

Vertical displacement after t seconds, $y = -\frac{1}{2}gt^2$ m . (2)

(from $s = ut - \frac{1}{2}gt^2$)

From (1) $\quad t = \dfrac{x}{u}$

which, substituted in (2), gives

$$y = -\tfrac{1}{2}g\left(\frac{x}{u}\right)^2$$

$$y = \left(\frac{-g}{2u^2}\right)x^2$$

This is of the form y = constant $\times\ x^2$, which is the equation of a parabola. The path of the projectile is therefore parabolic.

Let T be the time taken to strike the ground, in seconds. The value of y at this instant will be $-h$. If these values are substituted into equation (2), we have

$$-h = -\tfrac{1}{2}gT^2$$

$$T = \sqrt{\frac{2h}{g}}$$

During this time, the body will have travelled a horizontal distance given by

$$x = uT$$

$$= u\sqrt{\frac{2h}{g}}$$

It is not intended that these formulæ should be remembered, but rather the method of derivation should be understood. It is far more satisfactory to be able to deal with each problem by working from first principles.

Example 2.1 Determine the distance from the base of a cliff 44 m high to the point in the sea where a shell will strike, if the shell is projected horizontally from the top of the cliff with a velocity of 100 m/s.

Time of flight = time for body to fall from rest through 44 m

$$s = -44\text{ m}$$
$$u = 0$$
$$t = ?$$
$$s = ut - \tfrac{1}{2}gt^2$$
$$-44 = 0 - \tfrac{1}{2} \times 9{\cdot}81 \times t^2$$
$$t = 3\text{ seconds}$$

During this time, the shell will have travelled through a horizontal distance given by

$$\begin{aligned} \delta &= ut \\ &= 100 \times 3 \\ &= 300\,\text{m} \end{aligned}$$

i.e. The shell strikes the sea 3 seconds later, and at a distance of 300 m from the base of the cliff.

Example 2.2 An aeroplane releases a bomb from a height of 3 km when flying horizontally at 360 km/h and rising vertically at 25 m/s. Assuming no air resistance, calculate the horizontal distance travelled by the bomb before reaching the ground, and the time taken. NCTEC

The bomb has a velocity equal to that of the aeroplane at the time of release. In this case, the bomb has an initial upward velocity. The time of flight is therefore the time taken for the bomb to fall to a point 3 km below the starting-point if its initial velocity is 25 m/s upwards.

$$\begin{aligned} s &= -\,3000\,\text{m} \\ u &= +\,25\,\text{m/s} \\ t &= ? \\ s &= ut - \tfrac{1}{2}gt^2 \\ -\,3000 &= 25t - \tfrac{1}{2} \times 9{\cdot}81t^2 \\ t^2 - 5{\cdot}1t - 612 &= 0 \end{aligned}$$

from which $t = 27{\cdot}48$ seconds

Horizontal distance travelled $= ut$

$$\begin{aligned} u &= 360\,\text{km/h} \\ &= 100\,\text{m/s} \end{aligned}$$

$$\begin{aligned} \text{Horizontal distance} &= 100 \times 27{\cdot}48 \\ &= 2748\,\text{m} \end{aligned}$$

i.e. The bomb strikes the ground 27·48 seconds after release, at a horizontal distance of 2748 m from release point.

Oblique Projection

Consider now the case in which a body is projected from the ground with a velocity of u m/s, inclined upwards at an angle of θ degrees to the horizontal.

Horizontal component of velocity $= u\cos\theta$.
Vertical component of velocity $= u\sin\theta$.

The time of flight of the projectile is equal to the time taken for a body to return to the ground if the upward velocity of projection were $u\sin\theta$.

Since $s = 0$ in the fundamental equation,

this is given by $0 = (u\sin\theta)t - \tfrac{1}{2}gt^2$

Hence $t = \dfrac{2u\sin\theta}{g}$

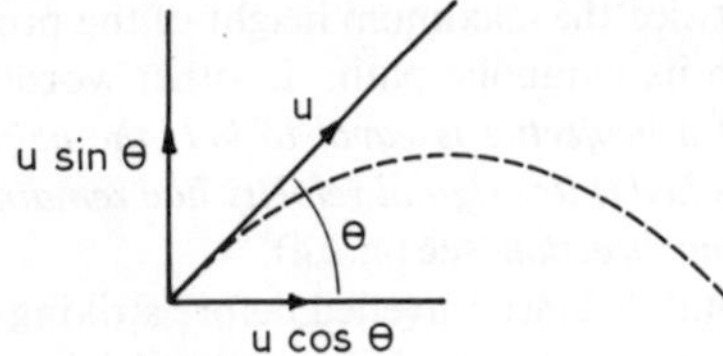

Fig.2.2 Components of initial velocity

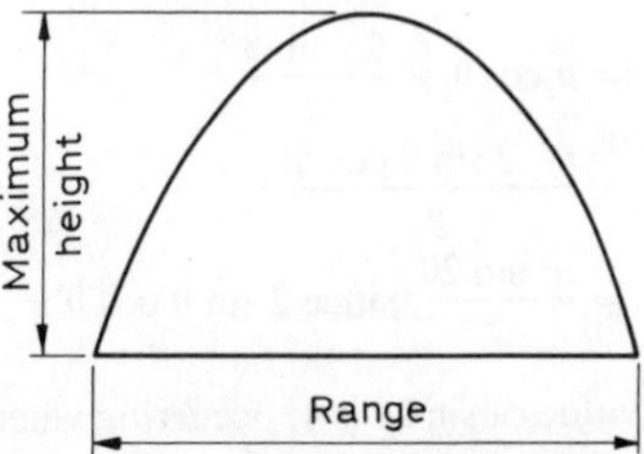

Fig.2.3 The vertical component determines the flight time, and incidentally the maximum height reached. The horizontal component and the time of flight determine the range.

The body reaches the maximum height in a time equal to half the time of flight, i.e. in $\dfrac{u\sin\theta}{g}$ seconds. The value of the maximum height is obtained if we substitute this time and the vertical component of the projection velocity into the fundamental equation ($s = ut - \tfrac{1}{2}gt^2$).

Maximum height reached

$$\begin{aligned} &= (u\sin\theta)\left(\frac{u\sin\theta}{g}\right) - \tfrac{1}{2}g\left(\frac{u\sin\theta}{g}\right)^2 \\ &= \frac{u^2\sin^2\theta}{2g} \end{aligned}$$

It is interesting to note that, if the projectile had continued in a straight line with its original velocity, it would have covered an inclined distance of $u \times \dfrac{u\sin\theta}{g} = \dfrac{u^2\sin\theta}{g}$ in time $\dfrac{u\sin\theta}{g}$ seconds, which is equal to half the time of flight.

The vertical height reached by the projectile would then be

$$\frac{u^2\sin\theta}{g} \times \sin\theta = \frac{u^2\sin^2\theta}{g}$$

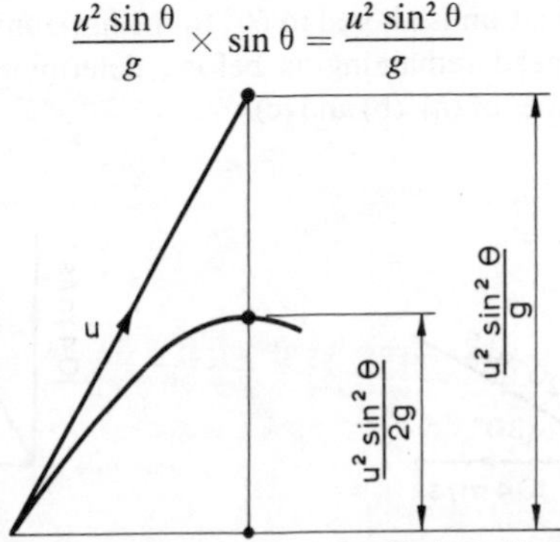

Fig.2.4 Maximum height of the projectile is half that of a body moving in a straight line with constant initial velocity.

This is just twice the maximum height of the projectile as it moves through its parabolic path. In other words, *the maximum height of a projectile is equal to half the height which it would have reached if its original velocity had remained constant in magnitude and direction* (see fig.2.4).

The horizontal distance travelled before striking the ground (this is known as the range of the projectile) is given by the horizontal component of velocity × time of flight.

$$\text{Range} = u\cos\theta \times \frac{2u\sin\theta}{g}$$

$$= \frac{u^2.2\sin\theta\cos\theta}{g}$$

$$= \frac{u^2\sin 2\theta}{g}, \text{ since } 2\sin\theta\cos\theta = \sin 2\theta$$

The maximum value of sin 2θ is 1, occurring when 2θ is 90°, or when θ is 45°. It follows, therefore, that the maximum range is u^2/g, occurring when the angle of projection is 45° to the horizontal.

If you refer to example 6.3, you will find an alternative method of solution to these problems.

Summary of Formulæ

Velocity of projection = u m/s from the ground
Angle of projection = θ to the horizontal

$$\text{Time of flight} = \frac{2u\sin\theta}{g} \text{ seconds}$$

$$\text{Maximum height reached} = \frac{u^2\sin^2\theta}{2g} \text{ m}$$

$$\text{Range} = \frac{u^2\sin 2\theta}{g} \text{ m}$$

$$\text{Maximum range for given velocity} = \frac{u^2}{g} \text{ m when } \theta \text{ is } 45°.$$

Example 2.3 A projectile is fired from the ground with a velocity of 120m/s at 30° to the horizontal. Determine (a) the time of flight, (b) the range, and (c) the maximum height reached.

If the inclination is altered to 60° to the horizontal, with the projection speed remaining as before, determine the corresponding values of (a), (b) and (c).

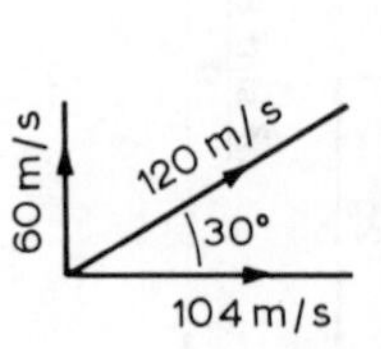

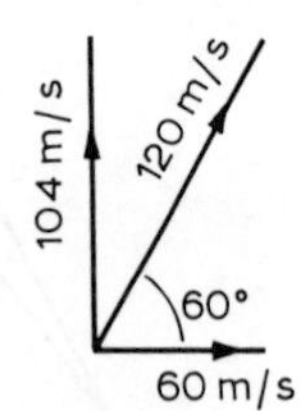

Fig.2.5

30° inclination	*60° inclination*
Vertical component of velocity (fig.2.5):	
120 sin 30° = 60m/s	120 sin 60° = 104m/s
Time of flight is given by $0 = ut - \frac{1}{2}gt^2$ (firing from ground to ground $s = 0$):	
$0 = 60t - 4{\cdot}9t^2$	$0 = 104t - 4{\cdot}9t^2$
$t = \frac{60}{4{\cdot}9} = 12{\cdot}2$ seconds	$t = \frac{104}{4{\cdot}9} = 21{\cdot}2$ seconds
Horizontal component of velocity:	
120 cos 30° = 104m/s	120 cos 60° = 60m/s
Range is given by $R = ut$, where u is horizontal component.	
$R = 104 \times 12{\cdot}2 = 1270$m	$R = 60 \times 21{\cdot}2 = 1270$m
Maximum height is given by $v^2 - u^2 = -2gs$.	
But $v = 0$ at maximum height; u is the vertical component in this case.	
$0 - 60^2 = -2 \times 9{\cdot}81s$	$0 - 104^2 = -2 \times 9{\cdot}81\,s$
$s = \frac{3600}{2 \times 9{\cdot}81}$	$= \frac{104^2}{2 \times 9{\cdot}81}$
= 184m	= 550m

It will be noticed that the range is the same for the two angles of projection. On the other hand, the projectile climbed to a much greater height in the one case than in the other. Striking velocities will be equal to firing velocities, except that directions will slope down instead of up. The second projectile will strike the ground much nearer vertically than the first; it is therefore likely to have much more penetrating power than the first.

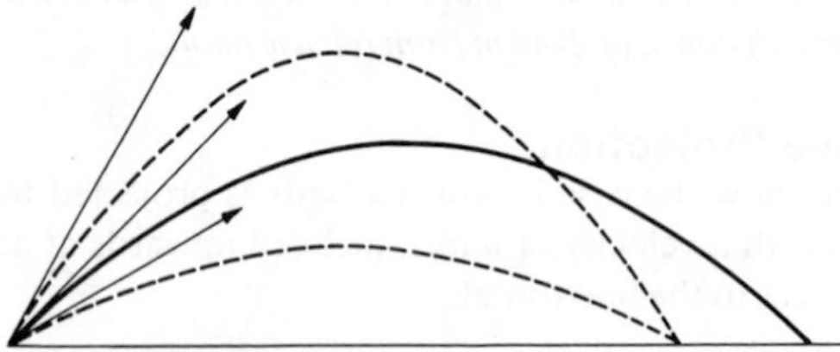

Fig.2.6 Effect of inclination on range. How equal range can be obtained with different inclination of projection.

Example 2.4 A body is projected from the top of a tower 30m high, and strikes the ground 10 seconds later at a point 600 m from the base of the tower. Determine (a) the velocity of projection, and (b) the velocity with which the body strikes the ground. In each case, state both the magnitude and the direction which the velocity makes with the horizontal. NCTEC

Let u = velocity of projection, and θ = inclination of velocity (fig.2.7).

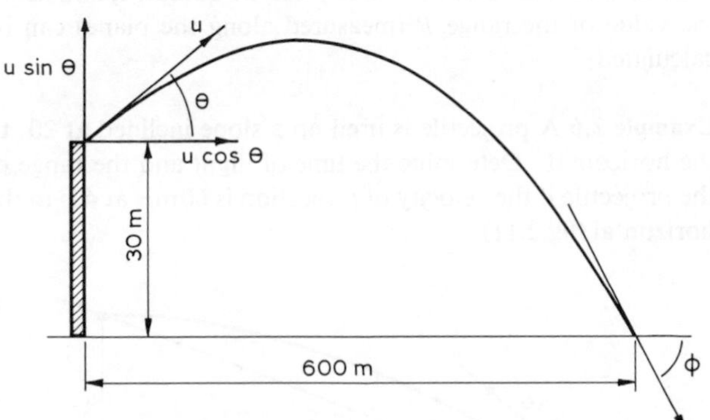

Fig.2.7

a) Velocity of projection.

Horizontal component of velocity $= u \cos \theta$

Horizontal distance travelled $= u \cos \theta \times t$

$$600 = u \cos \theta \times 10$$

$$u \cos \theta = 60 \quad . \quad . \quad . \quad . \quad . \quad (1)$$

Vertical component of velocity $= u \sin \theta$

Vertical distance travelled $= u \sin \theta \times t - \frac{1}{2}gt^2$

$$(s = ut - \tfrac{1}{2}gt^2)$$

$$-30 = 10u \sin \theta - 4{\cdot}9 \times 10^2$$

$$u \sin \theta = 46 \quad . \quad . \quad . \quad . \quad . \quad . \quad . \quad (2)$$

Velocity of projection $= \sqrt{\text{horiz. comp.}^2 + \text{vert. comp.}^2}$

$$= \sqrt{60^2 + 46^2}$$

$$= 75{\cdot}8\,\text{m/s}$$

Inclination. $\tan \theta = \dfrac{\text{vertical component}}{\text{horizontal component}}$

$$= \frac{46}{60} = 0{\cdot}7667$$

$$\theta = 37^\circ\, 28'$$

b) Velocity on striking the ground (fig.2.8).
Horizontal component $=$ 60 m/s (This remains constant throughout the flight.)

Vertical component is given by $v = u - gt$

$$= 46 - 10\text{g}$$

$$= -\ 52{\cdot}1\,\text{m/s}$$

Striking velocity $= \sqrt{60^2 + 52{\cdot}1^2}$

$$= 79{\cdot}5\,\text{m/s}$$

Inclination. $\tan\phi = \dfrac{\text{vertical component}}{\text{horizontal component}}$

$$= \frac{52{\cdot}1}{60}$$

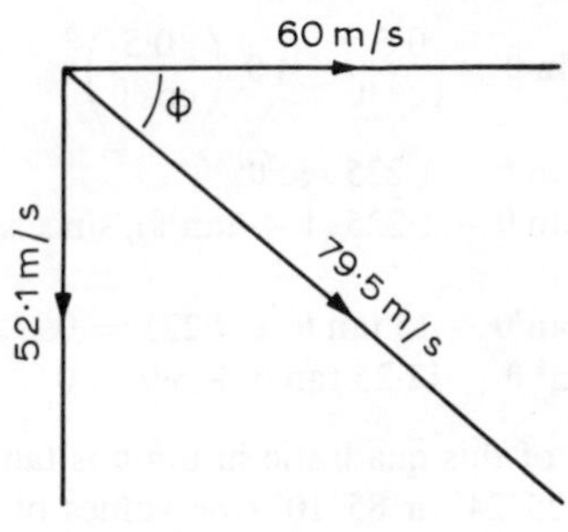

Fig.2.8

$$= 0{\cdot}8683$$

$$\phi = 40^\circ\, 58'$$

i.e. The velocity of projection was 75·8 m/s, at 37°28′ upwards to the horizontal; and the body strikes the ground with a velocity of 79·5 m/s, at 40°58′ to the horizontal.

Example 2.5 A body is projected with a velocity of 30 m/s from a point 15 m in front of a vertical wall 6 m high. Determine the inclination of the projection to the horizontal necessary to enable the body just to clear the top of the wall (fig.2.9).

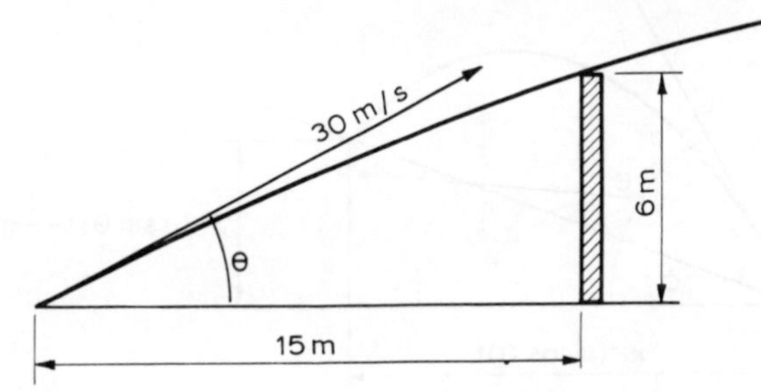

Fig.2.9

Let t seconds $=$ time to reach top of wall, and $\theta =$ angle of projection.

Horizontal component of projection $= 30 \cos \theta$ m/s

Horizontal component $\times$ time $= 15$ m

$$30 \cos \theta \times t = 15$$

$$t \cos \theta = 0{\cdot}5$$

$$t = \frac{0{\cdot}5}{\cos \theta} \quad . \quad . \quad . \quad . \quad (1)$$

Vertical component $= 30 \sin \theta$ m/s
Considering the vertical motion, we have

$$s = ut - \tfrac{1}{2}gt^2$$

$$6 = (30 \sin \theta)t - \tfrac{1}{2}gt^2$$

Substituting for t from (1),

$$6 = 30 \sin\theta \times \frac{0{\cdot}5}{\cos\theta} - 4{\cdot}9\left(\frac{0{\cdot}5}{\cos\theta}\right)^2$$

$$6 = 15\tan\theta - 1{\cdot}225\sec^2\theta$$

$$6 = 15\tan\theta - 1{\cdot}225\,(1 + \tan^2\theta),\ \text{since}\ \sec^2\theta = 1 + \tan^2\theta$$

$$\therefore 1{\cdot}225\tan^2\theta - 15\tan\theta + 7{\cdot}225 = 0$$

$$\tan^2\theta - 12{\cdot}25\tan\theta + 5{\cdot}9 = 0$$

The solution of this quadratic in $\tan\theta$ is $\tan\theta = 0{\cdot}475$ or $11{\cdot}77$, i.e. θ is $25°24'$ or $85°10'$ (the values of θ in the third quadrant not being considered).
i.e. The inclination of projection is either 25°24′ or 85°10′.

Projection on to an Inclined Plane

A more complicated problem involves the projection of an object onto an inclined plane, as in fig.2.10.
Angle of projection $= \theta$ to horizontal
Inclination of plane $= \phi$ to horizontal
Velocity of projection $= u$
Vertical component of velocity $= u\sin\theta$
Vertical displacement in t seconds $y = (u\sin\theta)t - \frac{1}{2}gt^2$
Horizontal component of velocity $= u\cos\theta$
Horizontal displacement in t seconds $x = (u\cos\theta)t$

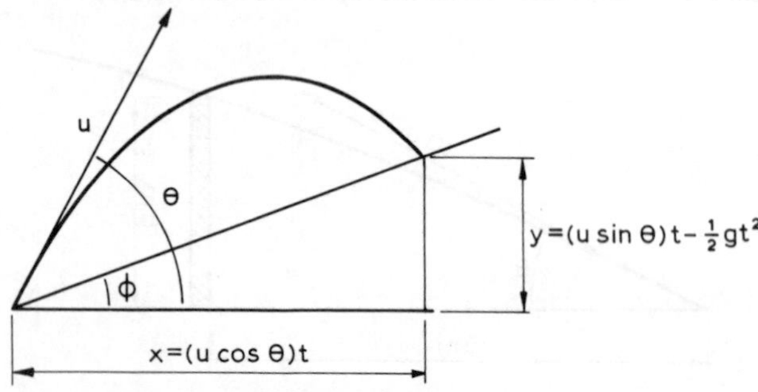

Fig.2.10 Projection on inclined plane

When the projectile strikes the plane, the relationship between x and y will be

$$\frac{y}{x} = \tan\phi$$

$$\therefore \frac{ut\sin\theta - \frac{1}{2}gt^2}{ut\cos\theta} = \tan\phi$$

$$\therefore \tan\theta - \frac{gt}{2u\cos\theta} = \tan\phi$$

$$\tan\theta - \tan\phi = \frac{gt}{2u\cos\theta}$$

$$\text{Time of flight } t = \frac{2u\cos\theta\,(\tan\theta - \tan\phi)}{g}$$

From this, the values of x and y can be obtained, and hence the value of the range R (measured along the plane) can be calculated.

Example 2.6 A projectile is fired up a slope inclined at 20° to the horizontal. Determine the time of flight and the range of the projectile if the velocity of projection is 60 m/s at 40° to the horizontal (fig.2.11).

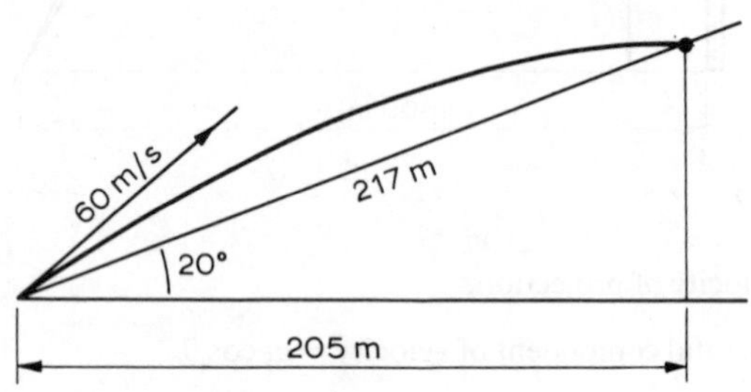

Fig.2.11

Horizontal component of velocity $= 60\cos 40° = 45{\cdot}96$ m/s

Horizontal distance travelled in t seconds $x = 45{\cdot}96t$ m

Vertical component of velocity $= 60\sin 40° = 38{\cdot}58$ m/s

Vertical distance travelled in t seconds $y = 38{\cdot}58 - \frac{1}{2}gt^2$

When the projectile strikes the plane $\frac{y}{x} = \tan 20° = 0{\cdot}364$

$$\frac{38{\cdot}58t - 4{\cdot}9t^2}{45{\cdot}96t} = 0{\cdot}364$$

$$38{\cdot}58 - 4{\cdot}9t = 45{\cdot}96 \times 0{\cdot}364 = 16{\cdot}7$$

$$4{\cdot}9t = 21{\cdot}88$$

$$t = 4{\cdot}45 \text{ seconds}$$

Horizontal distance travelled $= 45{\cdot}96 \times 4{\cdot}45 = 205$ m

$$\text{Range of projectile measured along slope} = \frac{205}{\cos 20°} = 217\,\text{m}$$

i.e. The time of flight is 4·45 seconds, and the range 217 m.

Exercise 2

1 Determine the distance from the base of a cliff 75 m high to a point in the sea where the shell will strike, if the shell is projected horizontally from the top of the cliff with a velocity of 1500 m/s.

2 A jet of water issues from an opening in the side of a tank of water with a horizontal velocity of 18 m/s. How far below the opening will the jet of water be at a horizontal distance of 3 m?

3 An object is dropped from an aeroplane travelling with a horizontal speed of 480 km/h at a height of 3000 m. Assuming no air resistance, calculate the horizontal distance travelled by the object before reaching the ground, and time taken.

4 A body is projected from the ground with a velocity of 18 m/s at an upward angle of 30° to the horizontal. Determine (a) the time of flight, (b) the distance from the point of projection to the point where the body strikes the ground, and (c) the maximum height reached.

5 A projectile is fired with a velocity of 30 m/s at an upward angle of 60° to the horizontal. Determine its velocity in magnitude and direction after 2 and 5 seconds.

6 A shell is fired with a velocity of 300 m/s at 20° to the horizontal from a point at the foot of a slope inclined at 10° to the horizontal. Determine the range of the shell measured along the slope.

7 The path of a jet of water coming from the opening in a side of a water tank is such that the jet falls through a distance of 120 mm in a horizontal distance of 1·2 m. What is the velocity (assumed horizontal) with which the jet leaves the tank?

8 A projectile has a horizontal range of 180 m, and the time of flight is 4 seconds. Find the velocity of projection in magnitude and direction, assuming no air resistance.

What further information is required to enable the kinetic energy of the projectile when it leaves the gun to be calculated? NCTEC

9 A ball hits a point 6 m vertically above and 45 m horizontally from the point of projection. Calculate the initial speed and angle of projection if the time of flight is 4·5 seconds. NCTEC

10 A body is projected upwards from a point on level ground with a velocity of 30 m/s at an angle of 30° to the horizontal. Working from the expressions for uniformly accelerated motion in a straight line, determine (a) the time of flight, (b) the distance from the point of projection to the point where the body strikes the ground, and (c) the maximum height reached. NCTEC

Chapter 3

Relative Velocity

Let us consider three of the ways in which we can observe the motion of a train B travelling at 100km/h. In each case we will make our observations as we are seated in the coach of a second train, A.

1 Our train A is at rest in the station. Then, on a parallel track, comes train B speeding past the windows, and we have the experience of seeing a train moving at 100km/h.

2 Our train is moving at 100km/h, and train B, on a parallel track, is coming towards us at 100km/h. As it flashes past the window, we have the experience of watching a train moving at apparently 200km/h. It is a remarkable fact that trains which meet us always appear to be travelling faster than we do.

3 Our train is still moving at 100km/h, and train B, still on the parallel track, is now travelling in the same direction as we are. For quite a while now the door of a compartment on the second train has remained opposite to the door in our compartment. In fact, the second train does not appear to be moving at all. It seems that it would be so easy to step from one train to the other.

The velocity of the train B, although being the same in each case, does in fact appear to vary, and we only see the real velocity when we make our observation from a stationary position. The velocity which the train appears to have is always dependent upon the velocity of the observation point. We say that a body has a certain velocity *relative to* another body, and by that we mean that the first body appears to have such a velocity when observed from the second body.

Or, if we think of two bodies A and B each having independent motion, then the velocity of B relative to A is the velocity which B *appears* to have to an observer travelling on A.

Let A and B be two bodies whose velocities v_A and v_B are in the directions shown in fig.3.1. We require to find the velocity of B relative to A, i.e. the velocity with which B appears to be moving when observed from the moving point A. Notice that the required velocity is to be relative to A. We must consider a method of bringing A to rest.

Imagine that A and B are moving over a sheet of paper. If the paper is moved with a velocity equal and opposite to that of A (i.e. with a velocity of $-v_A$), the effect will be that A is brought to rest. As fast as A moves forward, the paper moves backward with the same velocity, and consequently A makes no progress, at any rate as far as the earth is concerned. You will see, however, that A would ultimately reach the end of the paper. The same effect would be produced if you were running forward on an endless belt moving with a velocity equal but opposite to that of your velocity. As far as the surrounding structure was concerned, you would be stationary, moving neither forwards nor backwards. The effect as far as the belt was concerned would be that you were running forward with a certain velocity.

Now consider what is happening to B in fig.3.1. Not only is it moving with its original velocity v_B, but it has also had added to it the velocity of the paper, which is $-v_A$. The resultant velocity of B can be obtained from the velocity triangle.

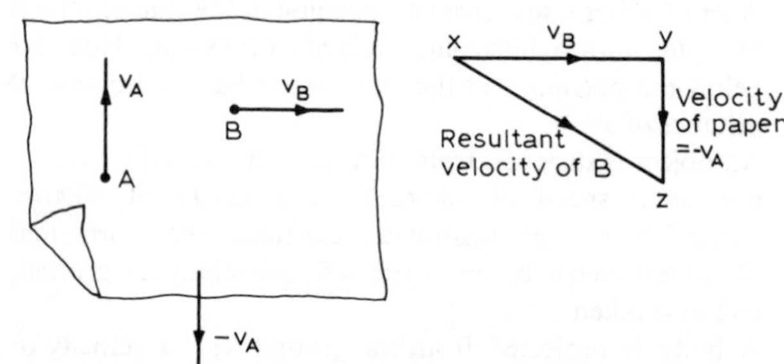

Fig.3.1 Relative velocity. The paper is moved so that A is brought to rest. This requires that the paper moves with a velocity equal and opposite to that of A. This effects the velocity of B.

xy represents the velocity of B, v_B.
yz represents the velocity of the paper, which is equal and opposite to that of A, so that $yz = -v_A$.
xz represents the resultant velocity of B.

We now have A brought to rest, and B moving with a velocity represented by ***xz***; so that if you were situated on A, then the velocity which B would appear to have would be ***xz***. Hence ***xz*** is the velocity of B relative to A.

Referring again to the velocity triangle, we have

$$xz = xy + yz, \text{ or}$$

velocity of B relative to A = velocity of B + velocity of the paper
= velocity of B + (– velocity of A)
= velocity of B – velocity of A
= difference of the velocities

Definition. The velocity of B relative to A is the vectorial difference of the two velocities.

This can be written in symbols as follows, provided that by v_{BA} we understand the velocity of B relative to A:

$$v_{BA} = v_B - v_A$$

It may be useful to note at this point that:
the resultant of two velocities is the vectorial sum of the velocities; whilst
the relative velocity is the vectorial difference of the velocities.

The basic method of drawing the velocity triangles is shown in fig.3.2.

oa represents the velocity of A.
ob represents the velocity of B.
ba represents the velocity of A relative to B, i.e. v_{AB}.
ab represents the velocity of B relative to A, i.e. v_{BA}.

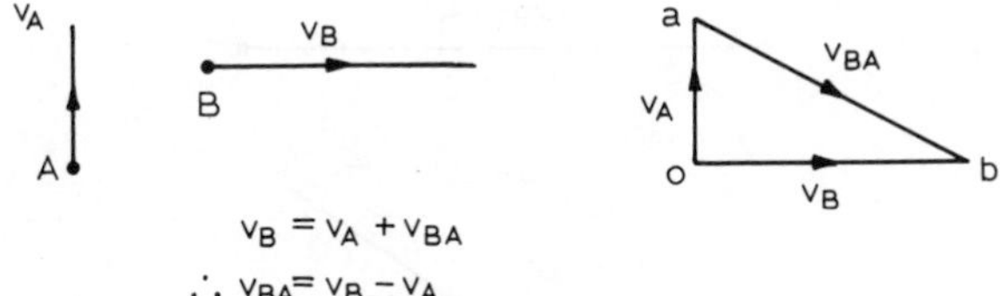

Fig.3.2 Relative velocity. The velocity of B relative to A is the velocity of B minus the velocity of A.

Note that the letter to which the arrow points indicates the velocity under consideration. In the vector ***ab***, the arrow points to *b*, hence the vector represents the velocity of B relative to A.

All velocities drawn from *o* are absolute velocities (their definition is given in the next section), whilst all vectors drawn from points other than *o* are relative velocities.

Now let us apply this general rule to the matter of the two trains, which began this discussion.

Case 1. Velocity of our train A = 0 km/h.
Velocity of train B = 100 km/h.
Velocity of train B relative to A = 100 − 0 = 100 km/h.

Case 2. Velocity of our train A = +100 km/h.
Velocity of train B = −100 km/h (opposite direction).
Velocity of train B relative to us = −100 − (+100) = −200 km/h
(the negative sign implies that the direction is opposite to that of our train).

Case 3. Velocity of our train A = +100 km/h.
Velocity of train B = +100 km/h (same direction).
Velocity of train B relative to A = +100 − (+100) = 0 km/h.

Note. You will have to make sure that you subtract A from B: velocity of B relative to A = velocity of B − velocity of A
The order of the letters B . . . A is the same on both sides of the equation.

Absolute Velocity

By absolute velocity we mean the real or true velocity of the body as observed from the earth. Fundamentally, it is true to say that, due to the compound nature of the earth's movement, even a body at rest on the earth is actually moving in space. But for our considerations we shall assume that the earth is a fixed datum, and that the velocity which a body has when observed from the earth is the true or absolute velocity. It is in fact a velocity relative to the earth.

When we say that a train is travelling at 100 km/h, we mean that when observed from the fixed station platform the train is moving at 100 km/h, and this is its absolute velocity. If you walk along the corridor at 5 km/h, which is really your velocity relative to the train, then your absolute velocity, or your velocity with respect to a fixed point on the earth, is either 100 + 5 = 105 km/h or 100 − 5 = 95 km/h, depending on whether you are moving to the front or the back of the train. You would certainly be more conscious of your real, absolute velocity if you were to walk along the roof of the carriage, rather than inside the corridor.

Example 3.1 Determine the velocity of a ship B relative to a ship A if B is travelling at 20 km/h in direction 30° east of north, and A is travelling at 30 km/h 60° east of south.

Method 1

Figure 3.3 (i) shows the velocities of the two ships. Since we require to know B's velocity relative to A, we must imagine A brought to rest by thinking of the sea moving with the same velocity as A but in the opposite direction (i.e. 30 km/h in direction west of north). The effect of this is to give B two velocities:

a) 20 km/h 30° east of north, and
b) 30 km/h 60° west of north.

These velocities are represented respectively by ***xy*** and ***yz*** in fig.3.3 (ii).

The resultant, ***xz***, representing 36·06 km/h 26° 18′ west of north is the velocity with which B appears to be moving when viewed from the now stationary ship A, i.e. the velocity of B relative to A.

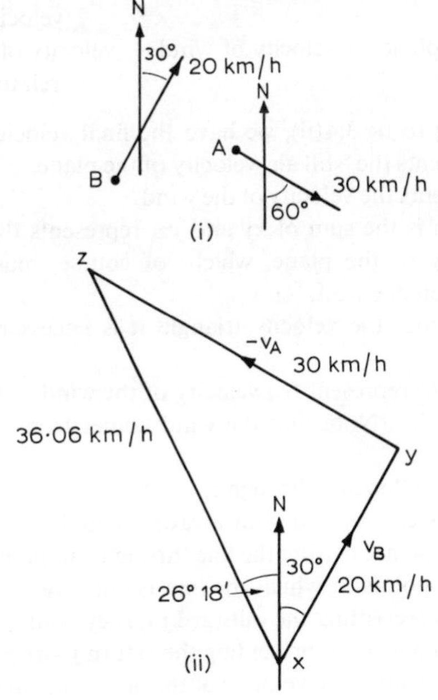

Fig.3.3

Method 2—Use of basic equation

Velocity of B relative to A = velocity of B − velocity of A (note the order of the letters: B, A)

= velocity of B + (−velocity of A)

= velocity of B + reverse velocity of A

1 Draw xy to represent the velocity of B to scale, 20 km/h 30° east of north.

2 Draw yz to represent reverse velocity of A to scale, 30 km/h 60° west of north.

3 The velocity of B relative to A = xz

= 36·06 km/h at 26° 18′ east of north.

Notice particularly the direction of the vector xz; xz is the sum of xy and yz, and is drawn from the start, x, to the finish, z.

Example 3.2 A light aeroplane having a speed of 600 km/h in still air travels 1000 km due east when the wind is blowing from 60° east of north at 120 km/h, and then returns to base. Determine the time taken on the outward and return journeys, and the directions steered.

When we speak of the velocity of a plane in still air, or the velocity of a boat in still water, we really mean the velocity of the plane relative to the air, or the velocity of the boat relative to the water. In order to obtain the absolute velocity of the plane, i.e. the velocity which would be observed by someone on the ground, we must apply the relationship:

velocity of plane relative to wind = velocity of plane − velocity of wind

velocity of plane = velocity of wind + velocity of plane relative to wind

Referring to fig.3.4 (ii), we have the final velocity triangle.

xy represents the 'still air' velocity of the plane.

yz represents the velocity of the wind.

xz, which is the sum of xy and yz, represents the absolute velocity of the plane, which, of course, must be in a direction due west.

To construct the velocity triangle it is necessary to commence at y.

Draw yz to represent the velocity of the wind, 120 km/h 60° west of south. (Note that the wind comes from 60° east of north.)

Draw a line due east through z.

With y as centre, and with a radius equal in scale to 600 km/h, draw an arc cutting the line through z in point x. There will be two points in which the line is cut; one, as shown in fig.3.4 (ii), representing the outward journey, and the other, as shown in fig.3.4 (iii), representing the return journey. Then xz represents the absolute velocity of the aeroplane in magnitude and direction.

For the outward journey xz represents 490·8 km/h, so that the time taken would be 1000/490·8 = 2·04 hours. The plane must be steered in the direction of xy, i.e. in a direction 84° 16′ east of north.

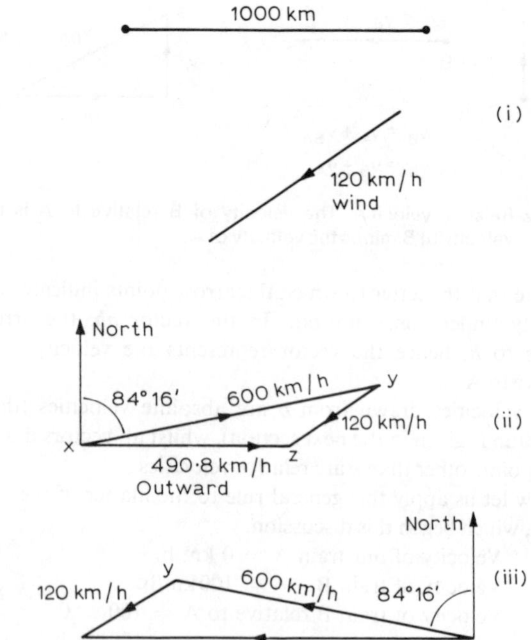

Fig.3.4

For the return journey, xz represents 698·4 km/h, so that the time taken would be 1000/698·4 = 1·43 hours. The plane must be steered in the direction 84° 16′ west of north.

The above values have been calculated using the cosine and sine rules. Note that the total time taken is 3·47 hours, compared with 2000/600 = 3·33 hours with no wind.

Example 3.3 Two ships A and B are 15 km apart at a given instant, B being south-east of A. A is travelling at 30 km/h due east, and B is travelling at 50 km/h due north.

Determine (a) the velocity of B relative to A, (b) the shortest distance between the two ships, and (c) the time elapsing from the above instant to that when the ships are nearest.

Fig.3.5 (i) indicates the position of the two ships when 15 km apart. The velocities of the ships are also shown.

Since we are concerned with the velocity relative to A, we must bring A to rest. This is done by imagining that a sea current is at work with a velocity equal and opposite to that of A. Thus, if the current is 30 km/h in direction due west, A will be brought to rest. At the same time, the resultant velocity of B will be the vector sum of:

By representing the velocity of B, 50 km/h due north, fig.3.5 (ii); yz representing the velocity of the current, 30 km/h due west. The resultant velocity is Bz, equal to 58·3 km/h in direction

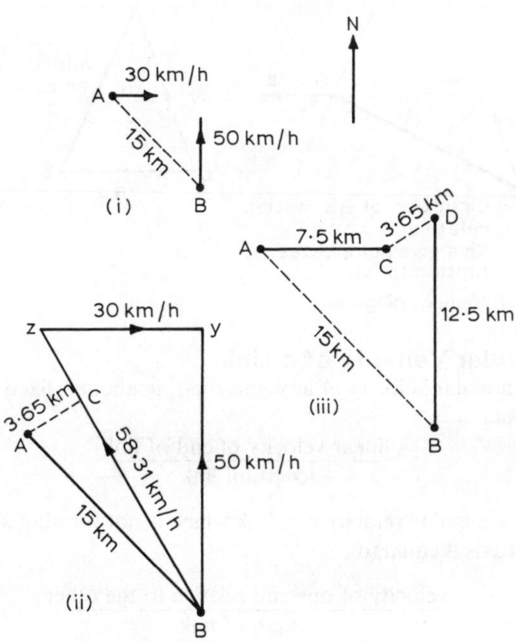

Fig.3.5

30° 58′ west of north. Hence the velocity of B relative to A is 58·3 km/h in direction 30° 58′ west of north.

Now in fig.3.5 (ii), the positions of A and B have been drawn to scale. (Note that this is quite a different scale from the one we used in connection with the velocities.) In this diagram, one ship is considered to be at rest at the point A, whilst ship B is travelling along the line ***Bz***. If C is the foot of the perpendicular from A on to ***Bz***, then C is the point at which B is nearest to A, and the distance AC is the shortest distance between the ships. AC measures 3·65 km. As B proceeds beyond C, the distance between the ships increases.

Hence the shortest distance between the ships is 3·65 km. When this occurs, the position of B is 59° 2′ east of north with respect to A.

The distance from B to the point C is equal to 14·55 km, and since the velocity of B along Bz is 58·31 km/h, B will take 14·55/58·31 = 0·25 hour, or 15 minutes, to reach the point where the distance between the ships is the shortest. Hence the time taken for the ships to come nearest together is 15 minutes.

But we must not forget that fig.3.5 (ii) gives a rather artificial picture of the actual movements of the ships. A and B have both been moving in their respective directions with their own velocities, e.g. B has been travelling due north all the time at 50 km/h. In the 15 minutes, A has travelled 7·5 km due east at 30 km/h, and B has travelled 12·5 km due north. The ships will have arrived at the points C and D, as shown in fig.3.5 (iii).

You will see that the distance between C and D is 3·65 km and that the position of D with respect to C is 59° 2′ east of north, which are the values given in the answers above. If you were to plot the positions of the ships at other time intervals, you would find that the distance between them is always greater than 3·65 km.

Special Case of Relative Velocity

The basic equation for work on relative velocity is

velocity of A relative to B = velocity of A − velocity of B

This can be rewritten in the form

velocity of B = velocity of A + velocity of B relative to A

We can use this form if we require to know the velocity of any point B, if we are given the velocity of another point A and we know the velocity of B relative to A.

In the case of ships moving in the water, and aeroplanes moving in the air, the magnitude and direction of the velocity of one relative to another can be any value, since there is no restriction on the movement of these vessels. If, however, we consider the motion of two points on a rigid link, such as a crank, or a connecting-rod of an engine, then we shall find that the velocity of these two points is very restricted, at least as far as direction is concerned.

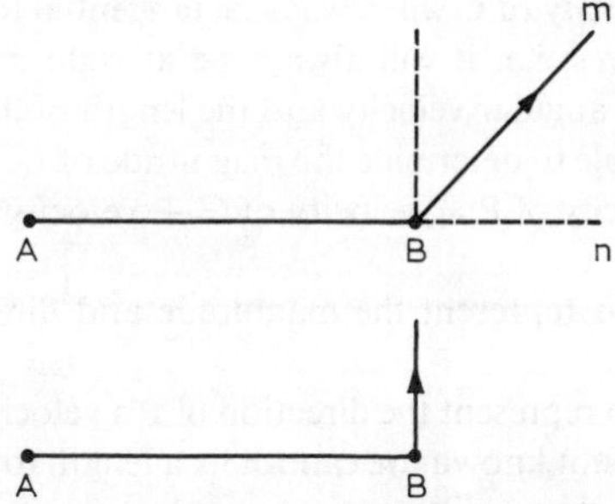

Fig.3.6 Motion of rigid rod. Any motion which B has relative to A must be in a direction perpendicular to the length of the rod; otherwise the rod will either stretch or collapse.

AB is a rigid rod, fig.3.6. This means that the distance AB is fixed. It cannot be increased as though it were made of elastic, neither can it be decreased as if it were a telescope. Now suppose that the velocity of B relative to A is along the line ***Bm***, the direction of which was made at random. The component of this velocity along the length of the rod is ***Bn***, which means that B is moving away from A with a velocity ***Bn***, i.e. the length of AB is increasing. But since the rod is rigid, AB cannot increase. Therefore there cannot be a ***Bn*** component. You can apply the same argument if the direction of ***Bm*** were such as to make the ***Bn*** component be directed towards A. If there is no ***Bn*** component, then the direction of the relative velocity ***Bm*** must be perpendicular to AB. This leads to a very important rule.

In any rigid body, the velocity of one point in the body relative to another point in the body is always in a direction perpendicular to the line joining the points.

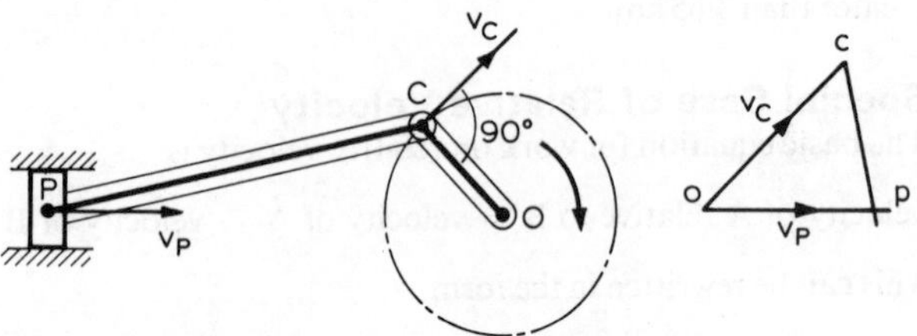

Fig.3.7 Velocity diagram for engine mechanism

This rule will apply in all cases, irrespective of the type of motion which the body may be making. For example, consider the crank and piston mechanism of an engine (fig.3.7). The crank OC rotates with a uniform velocity about O. The piston slides backwards and forwards along the horizontal line PO, being driven by the connecting-rod CP. One end, C, of the connecting-rod moves in a circular path, and the other end, P, moves on a straight line. You may have carried out an exercise in your drawing class to show that the motion of any other point on the connecting-rod is on an elliptical path. Well, the velocity of C will always be tangential to the path on which it moves, i.e. it will always be at right angles to OC. Knowing the angular velocity and the length of the crank OC, we shall be able to determine the magnitude of v_C.

Now, velocity of P = velocity of C + velocity of P relative to C.

Draw ***oc*** to represent the magnitude and direction of C's velocity.

Draw ***op*** to represent the direction of P's velocity. Since the magnitude is not known, we cannot fix a length to ***op***.

Through *c*, draw a line to represent the velocity of P relative to C, its direction being perpendicular to PC. Again the length of ***pc*** cannot be fixed.

The intersection of these lines gives the point *p* such that ***op*** is equal to the velocity of the piston P.

Rotation of Link

Figure 3.8 shows a link AB moving in one plane such that A has a velocity v_A and B has a velocity v_B. Then the velocity of B relative to A is ***ab***. If we can imagine that we are standing on point A and looking towards B, we should see that B moved in the direction of ***ab***; a direction which has been shown dotted on the end of the link. The direction is down and to the right. This means that the rod AB is turning in a clockwise direction. If you were to be standing at B, the point A would appear to be moving in direction ***ba***, which is in a directly opposite sense to the one just mentioned. But you will see that the direction of rotation is still the same—clockwise.

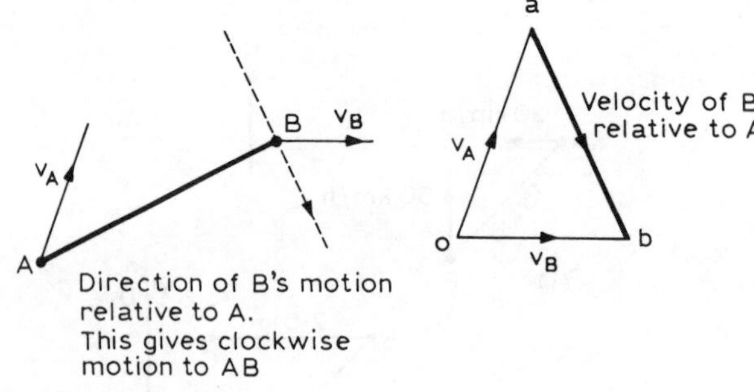

Fig.3.8 Velocity diagram

Angular Velocity of a Link

The angular velocity of any link rotating about a fixed centre is equal to

$$\frac{\text{linear velocity of end of link}}{\text{length of link}}$$

The angular velocity of a link which is not rotating about a fixed axis is equal to

$$\frac{\text{velocity of one end relative to the other}}{\text{length of link}}$$

In the case of the link AB in fig.3.8,

$$\text{angular velocity of AB} = \frac{v_{BA}}{AB} = \frac{ab}{AB}$$

In addition to the angular velocity of the link, it also has a linear velocity. It is usual to indicate this linear velocity by stating the linear velocity of the centre of gravity of the link.

Velocity of Point on Link

Sometimes we require to know the velocity of a point other than the two end points on a link. This can easily be obtained from the velocity diagram. In fig.3.9, *aob* is the velocity triangle for the link AB, with ***oa*** and ***ob*** representing the velocities of A and B respectively, and ***ab***, having been drawn perpendicular to AB, representing the velocity of B relative to A. We require to know the velocity of a given point C on the link.

On the line ***ab***, determine the point *c* such that $\frac{ac}{ab} = \frac{AC}{AB}$. Join *oc*, then ***oc*** represents in magnitude and direction the velocity of C.

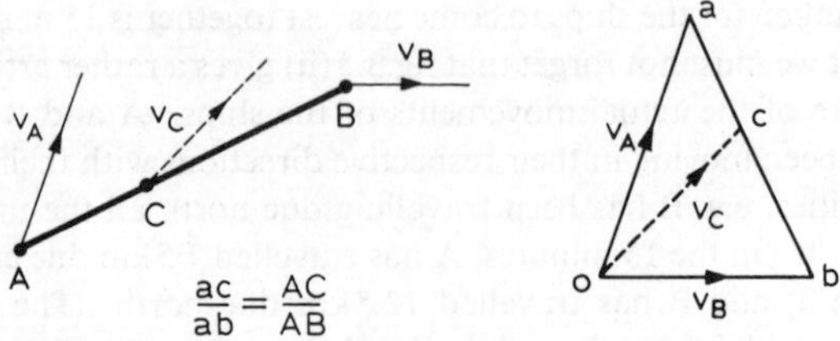

Fig.3.9 Velocity of point on link

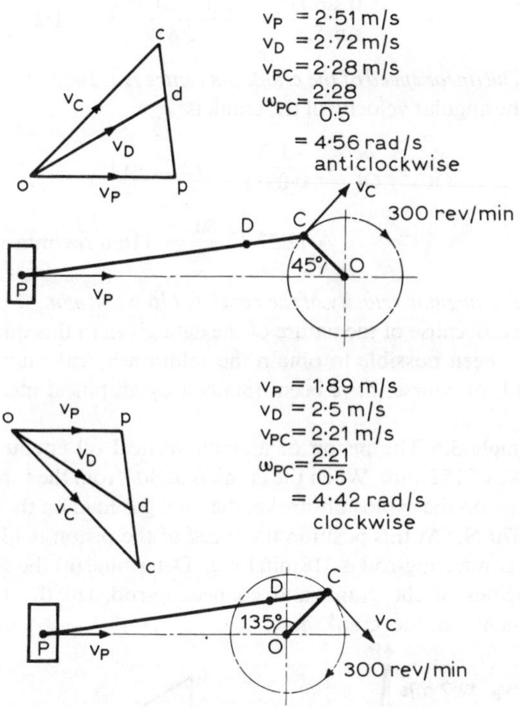

Fig.3.10

We know that $v_C = v_A + v_{CA}$. The velocity of C relative to A will be perpendicular to CA, and will be proportional to the distance from C to A. Thus, if C were half-way between A and B, then the velocity of C relative to A would be half that of B relative to A. Hence by obtaining the point c such that $\frac{ac}{ab} = \frac{AC}{AB}$, the vector $\boldsymbol{ac}$ satisfies both conditions of direction and magnitude, and thus represents the velocity of C relative to A. Therefore $\boldsymbol{oc}$, which is the vector sum of $\boldsymbol{oa}$ and $\boldsymbol{ac}$, will represent the velocity of C.

Example 3.4 The crank and connecting-rod of an engine are 100 mm and 500 mm long respectively. The crank rotates at 300 rev/min. Determine the velocity of the piston, the velocity of a point on the centre line of the connecting-rod and 100 mm from the crank-pin centre, and the angular velocity of the connecting-rod for the positions in which the crank has turned through 45° and 135° from inner dead-centre, i.e. from the position when the piston is farthest from the crankshaft.

The solution applies to both diagrams, the upper one showing the angle of 45° and the lower one showing an angle of 135°.

$$\text{Angular velocity of crank} = \omega = \frac{300}{60} \times 2\pi$$

$$= 31 \cdot 42 \text{ rad/s}$$

$$\text{Velocity of C} = \omega \times \text{OC}$$
$$= 31 \cdot 42 \times 0 \cdot 1 \qquad \text{(since 100 mm} = 0 \cdot 1 \text{ m)}$$
$$= 3 \cdot 142 \text{ m/s}$$

1 Velocity of C: magnitude, 3·142 m/s; direction, perpendicular to OC. Draw vector $\boldsymbol{oc}$ to represent this.
2 Velocity of P relative to C: magnitude, not known; direction, perpendicular to link CP. This is a relative velocity, therefore the vector is drawn through a point other than o. Draw a line through c perpendicular to CP to represent the direction of this velocity.
3 Velocity of P: magnitude, not known; direction, since P moves in a straight line, the direction of its velocity is in the direction of its displacement. This is an absolute velocity, therefore the vector is drawn through the point o. Through o draw a vector parallel to P's motion. This vector will intersect the vector drawn in (2), in the point p. Then $\boldsymbol{op}$ represents in magnitude and direction the velocity of the point P.
4 Velocity of D, distance 0·1 m from C. Obtain the point d on the line cp so that $\frac{cd}{cp} = \frac{CD}{CP}$. Join od. Then $\boldsymbol{od}$ represents in magnitude and direction the velocity of the point D.
5 Angular velocity of the connecting rod. This is equal to $\frac{v_{PC}}{CP} = \frac{cp}{CP}$.

In the case of the 45° angle

$$v_{PC} = 2 \cdot 28 \text{ m/s}$$

Hence
$$\omega = \frac{v_{PC}}{CP} = \frac{2 \cdot 28}{0 \cdot 5} = 4 \cdot 56 \text{ rad/s}$$

Note that the direction of P's velocity relative to C is given by the vector $\boldsymbol{cp}$, which is down and slightly to the right. If you imagine P moving in this direction when viewed from C, you will see that the direction of rotation is anticlockwise.

In the case of the 135° angle

$$v_{PC} = 2 \cdot 21 \text{ m/s}$$

Hence
$$\omega = \frac{v_{PC}}{CP} = \frac{2 \cdot 21}{0 \cdot 5} = 4 \cdot 42 \text{ rad/s}$$

In this case, the direction of P's velocity relative to C is given by the vector $\boldsymbol{cp}$, which is up and slightly to the left. If you imagine P moving in this direction when viewed from C, you will see that the direction of rotation is clockwise.

Example 3.5 In a simple reciprocating-engine mechanism, the connecting-rod, 400 mm long, is inclined at 10° to the direction of motion of the piston when the crank makes an angle of 125° with the rod. If in this position the speed of the crosshead is 1 m/s, find the linear speed of the crank-pin centre and the rev/min of the crank. IMECHE

The mechanism is drawn to scale, as in fig.3.11 (i). It will be seen that the crank angle POC is equal to 180° − (10 + 125)° = 45°.

Applying the sine rule, we have

$$\frac{\text{OC}}{\sin 10^\circ} = \frac{0{\cdot}4}{\sin 45^\circ}$$

$$\text{OC} = \frac{0{\cdot}4 \sin 10^\circ}{\sin 45^\circ} = \frac{0{\cdot}4 \times 0{\cdot}1736}{0{\cdot}7071} = 0{\cdot}0981\,\text{m}$$

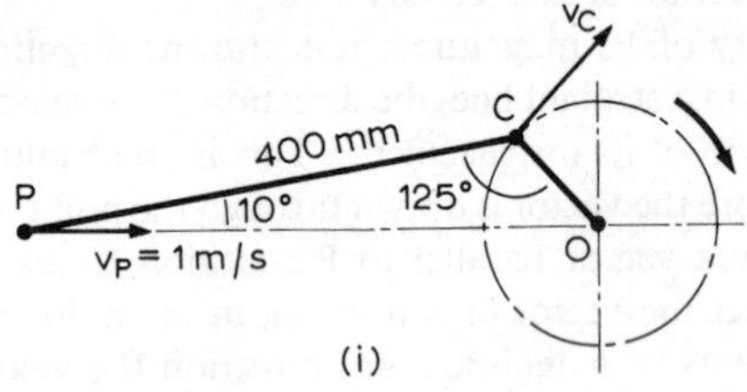

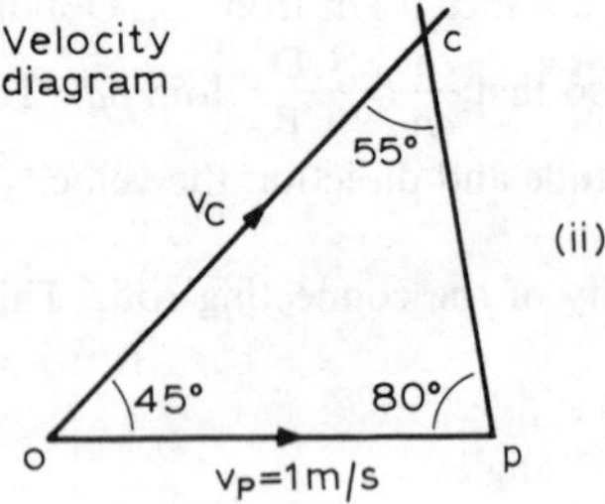

Fig.3.11

The velocity diagram *ocp*, fig.3.11 (ii), can now be drawn.

For this example we begin with the velocity of the piston or crosshead P. Incidentally, the direction of P's motion will not affect the working of the question. We shall assume that it is travelling towards the crankshaft at O.

op is drawn to a scale to represent 1 m/s.

Since C moves about centre O, its instantaneous absolute velocity is in the direction perpendicular to OC, as shown by the arrow.

Through *o*, draw a line parallel to this direction to represent the direction of C's velocity.

The velocity of C relative to P is perpendicular to PC.

Through *p* draw a line perpendicular to PC to represent the direction of C's velocity relative to P.

These two lines intersect at *c*, such that:

oc represents the velocity of C,

pc represents the velocity of C relative to P.

It will be seen that ∠*poc* is 45°, ∠*opc* is 80°, and ∠*pco* is 55°.

Hence

$$\frac{oc}{\sin 80^\circ} = \frac{1{\cdot}0}{\sin 55^\circ}$$

$$oc = \frac{1{\cdot}0 \sin 80^\circ}{\sin 55^\circ} = \frac{1{\cdot}0 \times 0{\cdot}9848}{0{\cdot}819} = 1{\cdot}2$$

i.e. The linear speed of the crank-pin centre is 1·2 *m/s.*

The angular velocity of the crank is

$$\frac{v_C}{\text{OC}} = \frac{oc}{\text{OC}} = \frac{1{\cdot}2}{0{\cdot}0981} = 12{\cdot}22 \text{ rad/s}$$

$$= 12{\cdot}22 \times \frac{60}{2\pi} = 116{\cdot}6 \text{ rev/min}$$

i.e. The angular velocity of the crank is 116·6 rev/min.

Note. Because of the nature of the data given in this question, it has been possible to obtain the solution by calculation. It could, of course, have been obtained by graphical means.

Example 3.6 The piston of a small vertical oil engine has a stroke of 152 mm. When the crank is at 30° from the top dead-centre, on the explosion stroke, the total gas load on the piston is 6670 N. At this position the speed of the piston is 13·7 m/s. The connecting-rod is 318 mm long. Determine (a) the angular velocities of the crank and connecting-rod, (b) the turning moment on the crankshaft. IMECHE

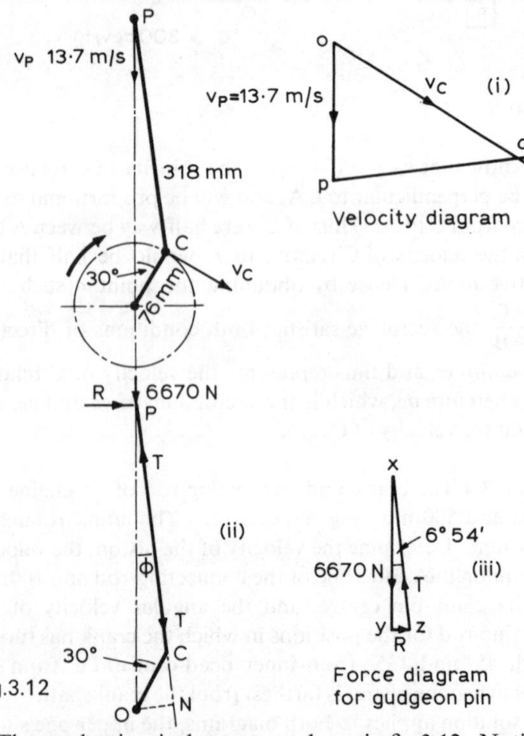

Fig.3.12

The mechanism is drawn to scale, as in fig.3.12. Notice that the crank length is 76 mm, i.e. half the length of the stroke. The crank is at top dead-centre position when the crank-pin C is at the highest point.

Choose a suitable scale for the velocity diagram, and proceed as follows.

1 From o, draw op to represent the velocity of the piston P, 13·7 m/s.
2 Through o, draw a line parallel to the direction of C's velocity, i.e. perpendicular to OC. Since the magnitude of this velocity is unknown, we cannot fix the length of this line.
3 Through p draw a line to represent the velocity of C relative to P. The direction of this line will be perpendicular to PC. Again, the magnitude of this velocity is unknown, so that we cannot fix a length to this line.
4 The intersection of these lines gives the point c, such that **oc** represents the velocity of C and scales 22·7 m/s, **pc** represents the velocity of C relative to P and scales 19·7 m/s.

The angular velocity of the crank is given by

$$\frac{oc}{OC} = \frac{22{\cdot}7}{0{\cdot}076} = 298 \text{ rad/s or } 2846 \text{ rev/min}$$

The angular velocity of the connecting-rod is given by

$$\frac{pc}{PC} = \frac{19{\cdot}7}{0{\cdot}318} = 62 \text{ rad/s or } 592 \text{ rev/min (anticlockwise)}$$

Figure 3.12(ii) indicates the three forces acting on the gudgeon-pin which fastens the connecting-rod on to the piston:
a) the force due to the gas pressure, 6670 N;
b) the thrust, T, taken by the connecting-rod, and transferred by it to the crank; and
c) the side thrust, R, between the piston and the walls of the cylinder.

In the triangle of forces for the gudgeon-pin, fig.3.12(iii):
xy represents the gas force, 6670 N;
zx represents thrust T, drawn parallel to the connecting-rod; and
yz represents the reaction R, drawn horizontally.

The value of T can be calculated. Applying the sine rule to triangle OCP, we have

$$\frac{76}{\sin\phi} = \frac{318}{\sin 30^\circ} \quad \text{from which } \phi = 6^\circ 54'$$

Hence $$T = \frac{6670}{\cos 6^\circ 54'} = 6700 \text{ N}.$$

The perpendicular distance from O to the line of action of this thrust is given by ON.

$$\angle PON = 90^\circ - 6^\circ 54' = 83^\circ 6'$$
$$\angle CON = 83^\circ 6' - 30^\circ = 53^\circ 6'$$
$$ON = 76 \cos 53^\circ 6'$$
$$= 46 \text{ mm}$$

Hence the turning moment on the crankshaft, produced by T, is equal to

$$T \times ON = 6700 \times 0{\cdot}046 = 309 \text{ Nm}$$

For an alternative solution, the student should refer to example 3.8.

Instantaneous Centre

If we mark a line on a disc which is rotating about its axis I, then we can indicate the directions in which the two ends A and B are travelling at a given instant, fig.3.13(i). In each case, the direction will be perpendicular to the radial line from the centre I to the point concerned. Also, if we are given the value of the velocity of A, we could calculate the angular velocity of the wheel, and therefore, since the velocity of B is given by ω.IB, we could obtain the velocity of B in terms of the velocity of A and the distances of A and B from the centre of rotation, I.

$$\omega = \frac{\text{velocity of A}}{\text{IA}}$$

$$\text{velocity of B} = \text{velocity of A} \times \frac{\text{IB}}{\text{IA}}$$

Now consider the case of a part of a machine represented by the line AB in fig.3.13(ii). Let us assume that we know the magnitude and the direction of the velocity of one end, A, and also the direction of the velocity of the other end, B. We require to know the magnitude of the velocity of B. If the end A of the link were rigidly fastened to any point on a line drawn perpendicular to the direction of A's velocity, then A would be forced to move in the direction originally stated. Similarly, if the end B were rigidly connected to any point on a line drawn perpendicular to the velocity of B, then B would be forced to move in the direction originally stated. Now if the link AB were rigidly attached to the point of intersection of the above two perpendicular lines, then both A and B would move in the directions originally stated. This is because a point must move in a direction perpendicular to the line joining that point to the centre of rotation. So we can consider the point of intersection, I, as the centre about which AB is rotating. But we must think of it as a centre for only an instant, since the original directions of A and B's velocities may be true for only an instant. For this reason, we define I as the instantaneous centre of rotation for the link.

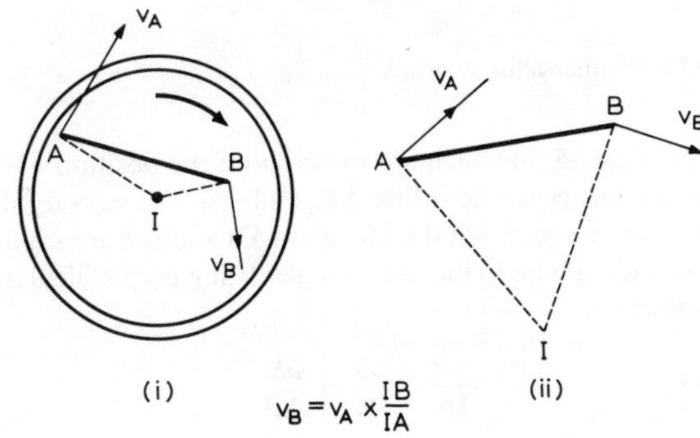

Fig.3.13 Instantaneous centre

Definition. The instantaneous centre of a link is that point about which the link may be considered to be rotating at a given instant. It lies at the intersection of the lines drawn from any two points in the link perpendicular to the directions of the velocities of these points.

It follows from what we have said above that the magnitude of B's velocity can be obtained as follows:

$$\text{velocity of B} = \text{velocity of A} \times \frac{\text{IB}}{\text{IA}}$$

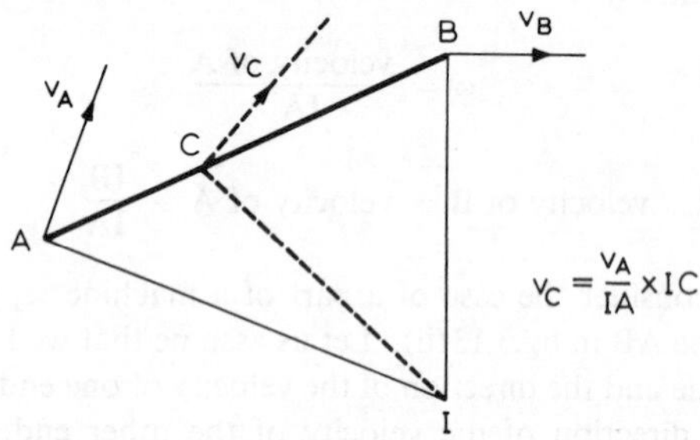

Fig.3.14 Velocity on point of link

The velocity of any other point on the link can also be obtained from the instantaneous centre. For example, the point C (fig.3.14) must be moving in a direction perpendicular to the line IC, and the magnitude of its velocity will be given by

$$\text{velocity of C} = \text{velocity of A} \times \frac{\text{IC}}{\text{IA}}$$

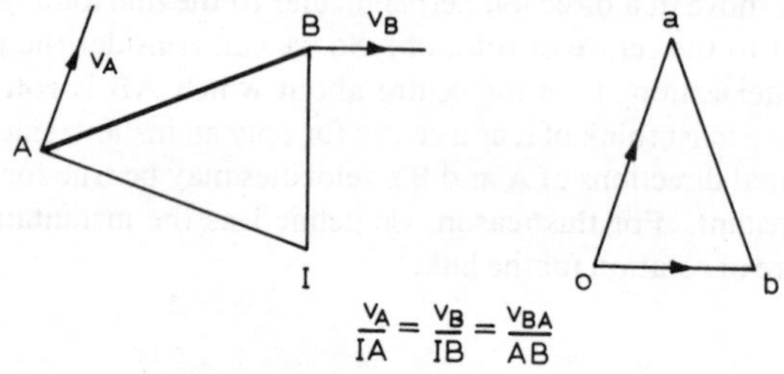

Fig.3.15 Angular velocity of link

From fig.3.15, in which are shown both the position of the instantaneous centre of a link AB, and also the velocity diagram, it will be seen that the triangles IAB and *oab* are similar, corresponding lines in the two triangles being perpendicular to each other.

$$\frac{oa}{\text{IA}} = \frac{ob}{\text{IB}} = \frac{ab}{\text{AB}}$$

or

$$\frac{v_A}{\text{IA}} = \frac{v_B}{\text{IB}} = \frac{v_{BA}}{\text{AB}}$$

We have already established the first portion of this relationship. It is now possible to obtain the velocity of one end of the link relative to the other, i.e. v_{BA}.

$$v_{BA} = v_A \frac{\text{AB}}{\text{IA}}$$

$$\text{Angular velocity of link} = \frac{v_{BA}}{\text{AB}} = v_A \frac{\text{AB}}{\text{IA}} \times \frac{1}{\text{AB}} = \frac{v_A}{\text{IA}}$$

$\frac{v_A}{\text{IA}} = \frac{v_B}{\text{IB}} = \frac{v_{BA}}{\text{AB}} = \omega$, the angular velocity of the link AB about the instantaneous centre I.

The direction of this rotation will be obvious from the direction of v_A and the position of I.

Example 3.7 In a simple reciprocating-engine mechanism, the connecting-rod, 400 mm long, is inclined at 10° to the direction of motion of the piston when the crank makes an angle of 125° with the rod. If in this position the speed of the crosshead is 1 m/s, find the linear speed of the crank-pin centre, and the rev/min of the crank. IMECHE

Example 3.8 The piston of a small vertical oil engine has a stroke of 152 mm. When the crank is at 30° from the top dead-centre, on the explosion stroke, the total gas load on the piston is 6670 N. At this position the speed of the piston is 13·7 m/s. The connecting-rod is 318 mm long. Determine:

a) the angular velocities of the crank and connecting-rod,
b) the turning moment on the crankshaft. IMECHE

Both these examples have already been worked out using the relative-velocity method; see examples 3.5 and 3.6. The solution by the instantaneous-centre method will now be indicated. The following method will apply to both examples.

1 Draw the mechanism to a suitable scale, and indicate the direction of the velocity of the crank-pin and of the piston.
2 Draw a line CI perpendicular to the direction of v_C. This line will be a continuation of OC. If C is connected to any point on the line CI, then C would have to move in the same direction that has been indicated on the diagram.
3 Draw a line PI perpendicular to the direction of v_P. If P is connected to any point on the line PI, then P would have to move in the same direction that has been indicated on the diagram.
4 The intersection gives the point I, which is the instantaneous centre for the connecting-rod PC. Imagine the rod rotating about I, and you will see that the instantaneous velocities of P and C are in the directions originally stated.

Then $\frac{v_C}{\text{IC}} = \frac{v_P}{\text{IP}} = \frac{v_{PC}}{\text{CP}}$

Incidentally this quotient gives the angular velocity of the connecting-rod.

In the first example [fig.3.16(i)] IC = 555 mm, IP = 460 mm.

$$v_C = v_P \times \frac{IC}{IP} = \frac{1 \times 555}{460} = 1{\cdot}2\,\text{m/s}$$

$$\text{Angular velocity of crank} = \frac{1{\cdot}2}{0{\cdot}0981} = 12{\cdot}22\,\text{rad/s, or } 116{\cdot}6\,\text{rev/min}$$

In the second example [fig.3.16(ii)] IC = 365 mm, IP = 220 mm.

$$v_C = v_P \times \frac{IC}{IP} = \frac{13{\cdot}7 \times 0{\cdot}365}{0{\cdot}22} = 22{\cdot}7\,\text{m/s}$$

$$\text{Angular velocity of crank} = \frac{22{\cdot}7}{0{\cdot}076} = 298\,\text{rad/s, or } 2846\,\text{rev/min}$$

Angular velocity of connecting-rod

$$= \frac{v_C}{IC} \text{ or } \frac{v_P}{IP}$$

$$= 22{\cdot}7 = 62\,\text{rad/s, or } 592\,\text{rev/min}$$

Part (b) of this question is identical to that indicated in the relative-velocity method in example 3.6.

Example 3.9 An engine is travelling with a velocity of 20 m/s along a horizontal track. Determine the velocity of a point on the rim of one of the wheels at each of the four instants when the point is at the end of either the vertical or horizontal diameters.

The point under consideration is shown in each of the positions (i)–(iv) in fig.3.17.

Velocity of point = velocity of engine − velocity of point relative to engine

Every part of the engine is moving along the track with a velocity of 20 m/s.

Relative to the engine, a point on the rim of the wheel has a velocity of magnitude 20 m/s, but of constantly changing direction. (Note. The rim speed of the wheel must always be equal to the linear velocity of the engine, assuming no slip.)

Case (i). The velocity of the point relative to the engine is 20 m/s in the direction of the engine's motion.

oa = velocity of engine = 20 m/s.
ab = velocity of point relative to engine = 20 m/s.
ob = ***oa*** + ***ab*** = 40 m/s

which is the absolute velocity of the point.

Case (ii). The velocity of the point relative to the engine is 20 m/s vertically down. In this case, ***ob*** is the vector sum of ***oa*** and ***ab***, and is equal to 28·28 m/s, inclined down at 45° to the horizontal.

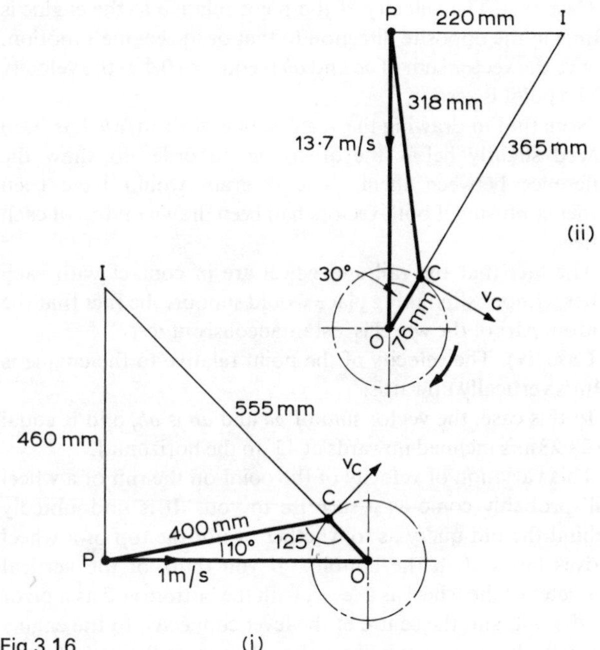

Fig.3.16

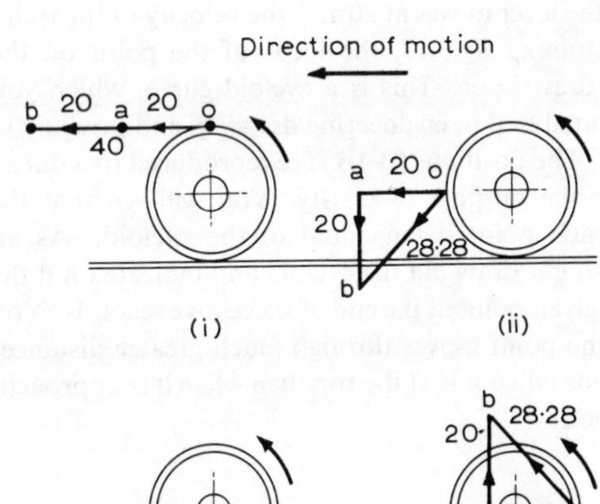

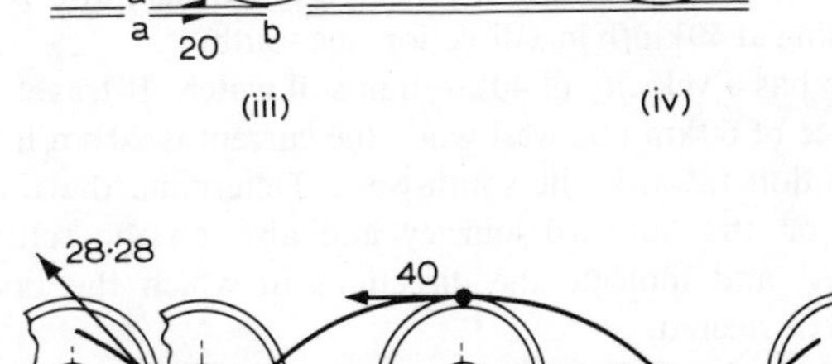

Fig.3.17

Case (iii). The velocity of the point relative to the engine is 20 m/s in the opposite direction to that of the engine's motion. Hence the vector sum of ***oa*** and ***ob*** is equal to 0, i.e. the velocity of the point is zero.

Note that in drawing the vectors, one of them, ***ab***, has been placed slightly below the other, ***oa***, in order to show the difference between them. The diagram would have been rather confusing if both vectors had been drawn on top of each other.

The fact that the rail and wheel are in contact with each other without slip taking place would support the fact that the bottom part of the wheel is instantaneously at rest.

Case (iv). The velocity of the point relative to the engine is 20 m/s vertically upwards.

In this case, the vector sum of ***oa*** and ***ab*** is ***ob***, and is equal to 28·28 m/s inclined upwards at 45° to the horizontal.

This variation of velocity of the point on the rim of a wheel will probably come as a surprise to you. It is undoubtedly behind the old query as to whether or not the top of a wheel moves faster than the bottom. If you think of the vertical diameter of the wheel as a lever, with the bottom end as a pivot on the rail, and the centre of the lever connected to the engine through the axle, you will see that the top of the lever (really the top of the wheel) moves with a velocity of 40 m/s, whilst the centre of the lever moves at 20 m/s, the velocity of the train.

At the bottom of fig.3.17, the locus of the point on the wheel rim is drawn out. This is a cycloid curve, which you have already analysed in engineering drawing, and possibly in mathematics. The positions (i)–(iv) are reproduced in a different order for the purpose of clarity. You will see that the velocity of each point is tangential to the cycloid. As an exercise you might draw out the cycloid and indicate on it the position of a given point at the end of successive seconds. You will see how the point moves through much greater distances in the same time when it is at the top than when it is approaching the bottom.

Exercise 3

1 Determine the velocity of a ship A relative to a ship B if A is travelling at 30 km/h in a direction north-east, and B is travelling at 40 km/h in a direction due south.

2 A ship has a velocity of 40 km/h in still water. It travels a distance of 60 km due west when the current is 20 km/h in a direction towards the south-west. Determine the time taken on the outward journey and also on the return journey, and indicate the directions in which the boat would be steered.

3 Two ships A and B are 10 km apart at a given instant, B being north-west of A. A is travelling at 20 km/h north-east, and B is travelling at 30 km/h due east. Determine (a) the velocity of B relative to A, (b) the shortest distance between the two ships, and (c) the time elapsing from the above instant to that when the ships are nearest.

4 Two straight railway lines intersect at right angles. Train A, on the line running south to north, approaches the crossing at 80 km/h, whilst train B, on the line running east to west, approaches the crossing at 40 km/h. When A passes a bridge 6 km south of the crossing, B is 8 km east of the crossing. Determine the shortest distance between the trains, and the time at which this occurs, measured from the instance when the train B was under the bridge.

5 Figure 3.18 (i) indicates a rigid link, AB, 3 m long, in which end A is travelling at 3 m/s due north, whilst B is moving on a line in the east–west direction. Determine the velocity of B, and also the angular velocity of the rod AB.

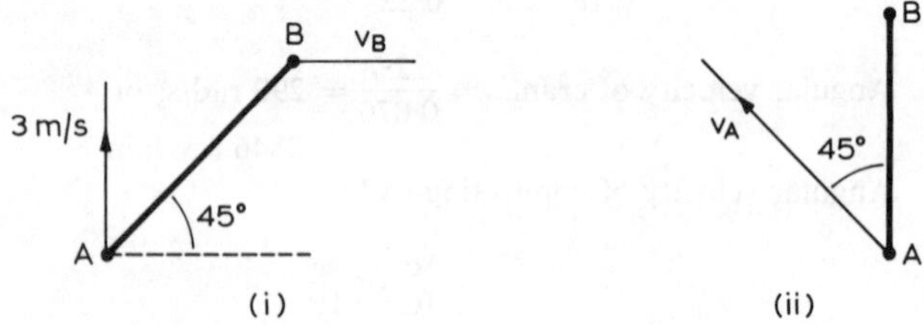

Fig.3.18

6 The link AB in fig.3.18 (ii) has an angular velocity of 10 rad/s clockwise. If the link is 5 m long, and the velocity of A is 4 m/s in the direction shown, determine the magnitude and direction of the velocity of B.

7 The velocity of the point B (fig.3.19) on the rigid link ABC is 5 m/s in the direction shown. If AB is 4 m and BC is 3 m, determine the velocity of A, whose direction is indicated, and of C, and also the angular velocity of the rod.

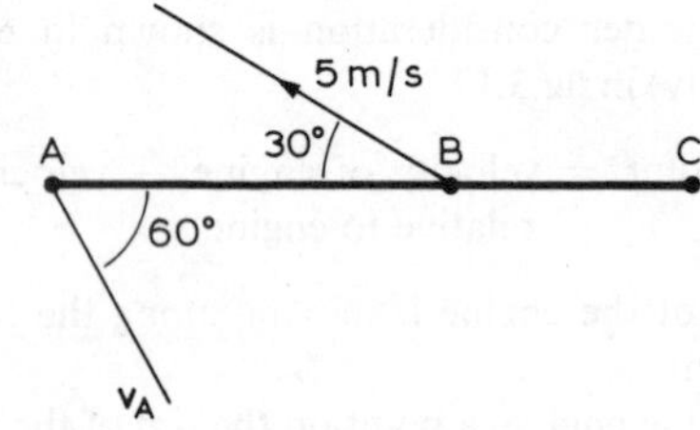

Fig.3.19

8 An aeroplane having a speed of 240 km/h in still air travels 270 km due north in a wind blowing from 30° east of north at 60 km/h and returns to its starting-point over the same line. Find the time taken on the outward and return journeys, and the directions steered. NCTEC

9 Find the velocity of a ship A relative to a ship B if A is travelling 20° east of south at 24 km/h, and B is travelling 60° east of north at 40 km/h. NCTEC

10 Explain what is meant by 'relative velocity.' A ship A is travelling due south at 30 km/h, and another, B, due south-west at 48 km/h. Find the velocity of B relative to A in magnitude and direction. NCTEC

11 A motor-boat having a speed of 16 km/h in still water travels to a point 20 km due north-east. If there is a current of 6 km/h running due west, find the time taken on the journey, and the direction in which the boat is steered. NCTEC

12 The crank and connecting-rod of an internal-combustion engine are 60 mm and 270 mm long respectively. The crank rotates clockwise at 2250 rev/min. When the crank has turned through 45° from the inner dead-centre, determine (a) the velocity of the piston, (b) the magnitude and direction of the velocity of a point on the centre-line of the connecting-rod and 120 mm from the crank-pin centre, and (c) the angular velocity of the connecting-rod. ULCI

13 A ship A is sailing due west at 40 km/h. Another ship, B, travelling at 50 km/h, is first sighted 24 km due north of A. From A the ship B appears to be moving south-east. Find (a) the direction in which B is actually moving, (b) the nearest distance that the ships approach one another, and (c) the time that elapses, after first sighting, before the ships are nearest one another. ULCI

14 The crank and connecting-rod of an internal-combustion engine are 50 mm and 200 mm long respectively. The crank rotates at 1200 rev/min. When the crank has turned through 40° from the inner dead-centre determine (a) the velocity of the piston, (b) the velocity of a point on the centre-line of the connecting-rod and 75 mm from the crank-pin centre, and (c) the angular velocity of the connecting-rod. ULCI

15 The connecting-rod of a reciprocating engine is 1·2 m and the crank 300 mm long. When the crank is in the position 150° past the inner dead-centre the piston speed is 4·5 m/s. By the instantaneous-centre method, or otherwise, determine (a) the speed of the crankshaft in revolutions per minute, (b) for the crank position stated, (i) the angular velocity of the connecting-rod, and (ii) the velocity, in magnitude and direction of the mid-point along the axis of the connecting-rod. ULCI

16 Explain what is meant by 'instantaneous centre' and show how linear and angular velocities can be determined when it is known.

In a reciprocating engine, the crank is 200 mm long, and it rotates at 200 rev/min. The connecting-rod is 875 mm long, and its centre of gravity is 375 mm from the crank-pin. The mass of the rod is 68 kg and its radius of gyration about the centre of gravity is 250 mm. When the crank is at 30° to the inner dead-centre, determine (a) the linear velocity of the reciprocating parts and of the centre of gravity of the rod, (b) the angular velocity of the rod and its angular velocity relative to the crank, and (c) the kinetic energy of the rod. IMECHE

17 The lengths of the crank and connecting-rod of a marine diesel engine are 250 mm and 1·5 m respectively, and the crank rotates at 150 rev/min. The centre of gravity of the connecting-rod is 625 mm from the crank-pin end.

(a) Determine (i) the velocity of the piston, (ii) the velocity of the centre of gravity of the connecting-rod, and (iii) the angular velocity of the connecting-rod, when the crank is 45° and 120° respectively from the inner dead-centre position.

(b) If the mass of the connecting-rod is 114 kg, and its radius of gyration about an axis through the centre of gravity at right angles to the plane of motion is 500mm, calculate the total kinetic energy of the rod in the first position.

18 At midnight, a vessel A was 80 km due north of a vessel B. Vessel A is steaming 40 km/h on a south-west course, and vessel B 24 km/h due west. (a) Determine the velocity of B relative to A. (b) If A and B can exchange signals when they are not more than 20 km apart, determine when they can begin to exchange signals, and for how long they can continue to exchange signals. ULCI

Chapter 4

Mass and Motion

The following is a summary of the work relating to the above subject which will normally have been covered at this stage.

1) When a force is applied to a solid body, an acceleration is produced. This resulting acceleration is dependent upon the magnitude of the force, and upon the quantity of matter which is contained in the solid body. We define the quantity of matter which the body contains as the *mass* of the body. It is a fixed quantity and can be changed only by adding matter to, or taking matter from, the original body.

2) Between all bodies there is a force of attraction, defined as the *gravitational force*. The magnitude of the force depends upon the distance between the bodies. Sir Isaac Newton discovered the law relating the force to the masses and the distance between them, and expressed it as follows:

$$\text{force} = \text{constant} \times \frac{\text{product of the two masses}}{(\text{distance between them})^2}$$

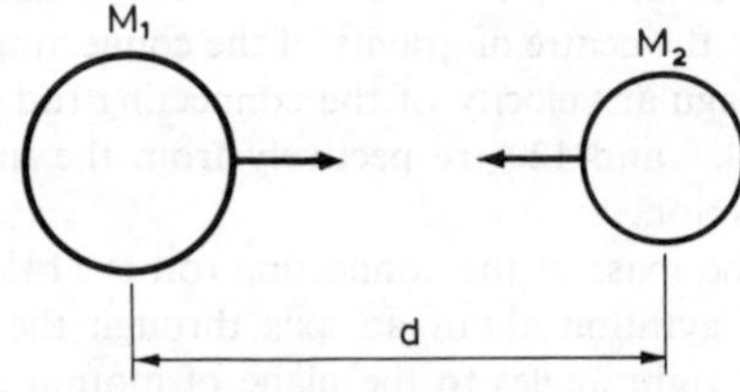

Fig.4.1 Attraction between two bodies. There is a force of attraction between all bodies. This force, which is normally very small, depends upon the mass of each body and the distance between them. When one of the bodies is the earth, then the force can be very considerable. If the other body is free to move, it will be drawn towards the earth; in other words it will fall. The force between the earth and the body is known as the *weight* of the body.

If one of the bodies which we are considering is the earth itself, and the other is an object which we may be holding, then the force of attraction, or gravitational force, between the two bodies is sufficient to try to move the object which we are holding. Consequently we have to apply an upward force to prevent the object falling. This force acting upon the object, or gravitational force, being a force, is measured in newtons. It has been usual to refer to this force as the 'weight' of the object and this expression will find a limited use in these pages. The time may come when expressions such as 'weight' and 'weighing' may drop out of our technical and even our commercial vocabulary; until that time, we should be aware of their implications. In view of the fact that the gravitational force is dependent upon the distance between the body and the earth (and we usually consider the distance between the centres of gravity of the bodies concerned), it follows that this force will vary as the distance between the body and the earth varies. The force of gravitation will be smaller as the body moves farther away from the centre of the earth, and it will be greater the nearer the body approaches the centre of the earth. It follows, therefore, that although the mass of a body will remain constant, the gravitational force acting on the body (or the weight of the body) will vary.

3) It is important that we should understand correctly the principle behind the two generally accepted methods of 'weighing' a body. One method is by means of the beam balance, in which certain 'weights' of known magnitude are put into one scale pan to try to balance the body whose 'weight' is required, which is in the other scale pan. By this means we are simply comparing the two masses. We say, in effect, that the quantity of matter in the one scale pan is equal to the quantity of the matter in the other scale pan, and we should get an identical reading wherever we may have the balance. We should find the same reading, for example, in London as on any other part of the earths' surface. We should get the same reading at the top of Everest as at the bottom of one of the deep mines.

On the other hand, we may 'weigh' the body by means of a spring balance, in which either the extension or the compression of a spring to which the body is attached indicates the 'weight' of the body. By this means we are measuring the force exerted by the body on the spring, which is the same as the gravitational force exerted by the earth on the body, or the 'weight' of the body. The extension of the spring will be dependent upon the force exerted on the body. If the force is increased, as it would be at the bottom of a deep mine, the extension of the spring will increase, and the 'weight' of the body will appear to increase. In the same way, it will appear to decrease if the measurement is made at the top of Mount Everest. In fact, you will find a great variation in the 'weight' if the measurement is taken in a lift. As the lift begins to ascend, the 'weight' will appear to increase, then return to its normal value as the lift moves with uniform motion, and finally will appear to decrease as the lift comes to rest.

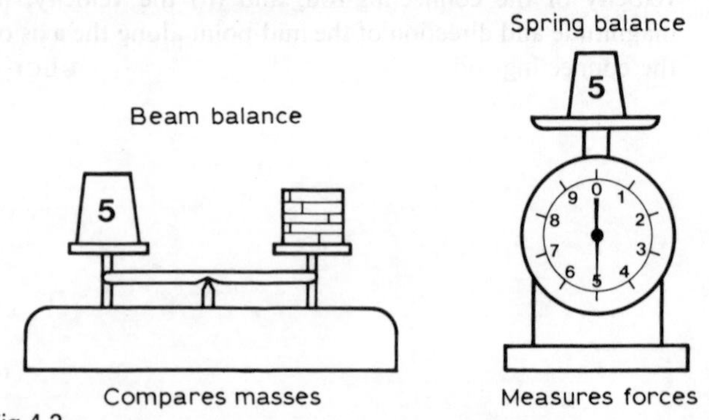

Fig.4.2

In this way we see that the beam balance really compares two masses; whilst the spring balance measures the gravitational force acting on the body, or the 'weight' of the body.

4) When we think about a body in motion, we introduce the idea of *momentum*. The momentum of a body is defined as the

product of its mass and its velocity. Since velocity is involved, it follows that momentum will be a vector quantity; that is to say, direction is involved. It will be possible to represent the momentum of a body by means of a vector, and it will be possible to resolve momentum into two components, or to compound momentum together, in the same way as we have been able to in dealing with forces and velocities.

The momentum of a body can be changed if we change either the mass or the velocity, and since velocity is changed if there is a modification of either its magnitude or its direction, it follows that there are three methods in which the momentum of a body can be changed.

The momentum of a rocket in flight is decreasing as the fuel burns away, since the mass of the rocket is decreasing.

The momentum of a truck on the 'Big Dipper' increases as it speeds down the straight track, since the magnitude of the velocity of the truck is increasing.

The momentum of a jet of water changes as it strikes against a wall, since the direction of the velocity of the water changes when it strikes the wall.

Whenever there is any kind of change of momentum taking place, there is always a force either causing the change or being caused by the change. The second of the laws which Sir Isaac Newton expounded in consideration of motion states that change of momentum per unit time is proportional to the applied force, and takes place in the direction of the applied force.

Force $\propto$ rate of change of momentum ($\propto$ means 'is proportional to')
$\propto$ rate of change of mv
$\propto m \times$ rate of change of v, if m is constant
$\propto$ mass $\times$ acceleration, since rate of change of velocity is equal to acceleration. Writing this in the form of an equation, we have

$$\text{force} = k \times \text{mass} \times \text{acceleration}$$

where k is a constant.

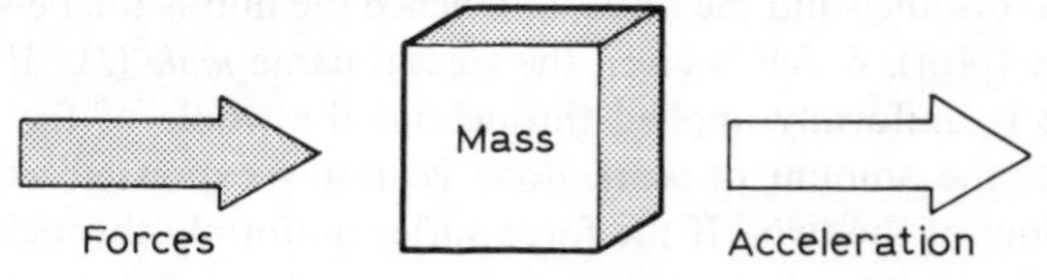

Fig.4.3

We can make the constant equal to 1 if we choose a force which will give a unit mass a unit acceleration.

The force chosen is the *newton*, N, which is defined as the force which will give a mass of one kilogram an acceleration of one metre per second per second.

Now we know that if a body is allowed to fall freely due to gravitational forces, it will have an acceleration of $g\,\text{m/s}^2$, where g has slightly different values, depending on the point at which the body is on the earth's surface. Variation due to latitude can be as much as $\frac{1}{2}\%$, to which must be added variations due to height above sea level and local land masses such as mountains. For the purpose of calculations in which bodies at the earth's surface are involved, an average value of $9{\cdot}81\,\text{m/s}^2$ is used.

If an acceleration of $1\,\text{m/s}^2$ is produced by a force of 1 newton acting on a mass of 1 kilogram, it follows that an acceleration of $9{\cdot}81\,\text{m/s}^2$ is produced by a force of 9·81 newtons acting on the same mass. Hence the gravitation force acting on a mass of 1 kg is 9·81 newtons.

Similarly, the gravitational force acting on a mass of M kg is $9{\cdot}81\,M$ newtons. Accepting the usage of the word 'weight' already mentioned, we can, for the time being, say that the weight of a mass of M kg is $9{\cdot}81\,M$ newtons.

In these days of space travel, we must be careful to use $9{\cdot}81M$ newtons as the weight of a mass of M kg only for problems at the earth's surface. The 'weight' of an object, such as a satellite or space vehicle, progressively decreases as the object moves further from the earth, until eventually the earth's gravitational attraction is negligible, and the vehicle and its contents become 'weightless', until they enter the different gravitational field of another body, such as the moon, where they will 'weigh' less than they did on earth.

Example 4.1 A body travelling at 50 m/s is acted on by a force, constant in magnitude and direction, for 0·5 seconds, and then moves at 100 m/s in a direction at 60° to the original direction. If the mass of the body is 4 kg, find the magnitude and direction of the force.

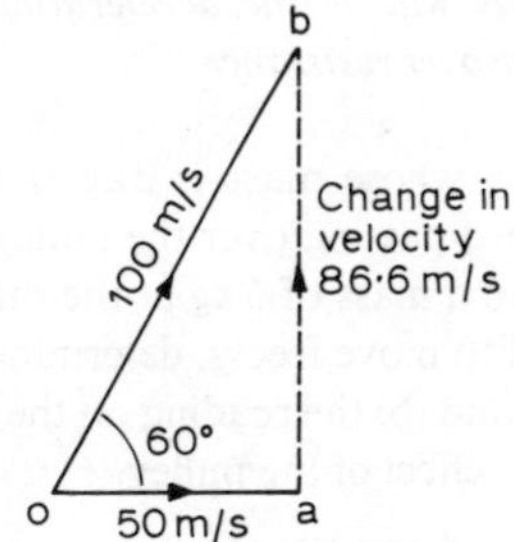

Fig.4.4

Referring to the velocity diagram, fig.4.4, we have:

Change in velocity = final velocity − original velocity
= ***ob*** − ***oa***
= ***ab*** (note: ***ob*** = ***oa*** + ***ab***)
= 86·6 m/s at 90° to the original direction

$$\text{Acceleration} = \frac{\text{change of velocity}}{\text{time}}$$

$$= \frac{86{\cdot}6}{0{\cdot}5}\,\text{m/s}^2$$

$= 173{\cdot}2\,\text{m/s}^2$ at 90° to the original velocity

$$\text{Force} = \text{mass} \times \text{acceleration}$$
$$= 4 \times 173{\cdot}2\,\text{N}$$
$$= 692{\cdot}8\,\text{N}$$

i.e. The applied force was 692·8 N, acting at 90° to the direction of the original velocity.

Example 4.2 Distinguish between mass and weight. A train of mass 330 tonnes attains a speed of 30 km/h from rest in $1\frac{1}{2}$ km. Find the excess of tractive force over resistance, both assumed constant. NCTEC

The mass of a body is the quantity of substance which it contains, and is constant. The 'weight' of a body is the force exerted on the body by the earth—the gravitational pull of the earth on the body. This force varies slightly, and is dependent upon the distance of the body from the centre of the earth.

Acceleration of the train: $v^2 - u^2 = 2as$

$$v = 30\,\text{km/h} = 8{\cdot}33\,\text{m/s}$$
$$s = 1500\,\text{m}$$
$$8{\cdot}33^2 - 0^2 = 2a \times 1500$$
$$a = \frac{69{\cdot}5}{3000}\,\text{m/s}^2$$

Mass of train = 330 × 1000 kg

Force producing the acceleration = mass × acceleration

$$= \frac{330 \times 1000 \times 69{\cdot}5}{3000}$$
$$= 7623\,\text{N}$$

This force of 7623 N will be the accelerating force, i.e. the excess of tractive force over resistance.

Example 4.3 A pulley whose mass is 2 kg is supported by a spring balance. A cord passing over the pulley carries a mass of 7 kg at one end and a mass of 5 kg at the other end. When the system is allowed to move freely, determine (a) the acceleration of the system, and (b) the reading on the spring balance. Neglect the rotational effect of the pulley.

Let T = tension in cord (newtons),
a = acceleration of the system. (See fig.4.5.)

Gravitational force on 7 kg mass = 7 × 9·81 newtons
Gravitational force on 5 kg mass = 5 × 9·81 newtons

Equation of motion for 7 kg mass:

$$\text{force} = \text{mass} \times \text{acceleration}$$
$$7 \times 9{\cdot}81 - T = 7 \times a$$
$$T = 7 \times 9{\cdot}81 - 7a \quad . \quad . \quad . \quad . \quad . \quad (1)$$

Equation of motion for 5 kg mass:

$$T - 5 \times 9{\cdot}81 = 5 \times a$$
$$T = 5 \times 9{\cdot}81 + 5a \quad . \quad . \quad . \quad . \quad . \quad (2)$$

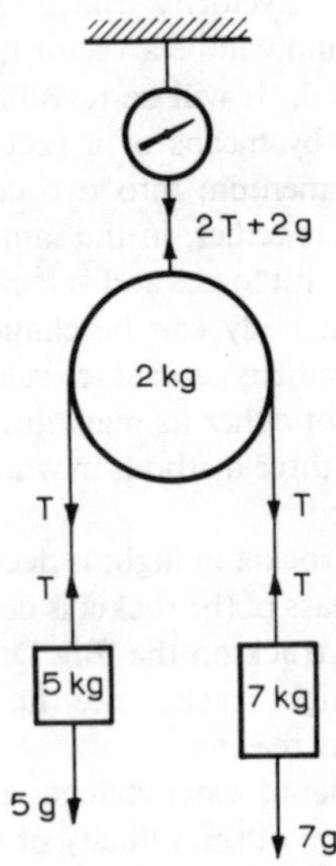

Fig.4.5

Equating (1) and (2),

$$7 \times 9{\cdot}81 - 7a = 5 \times 9{\cdot}81 + 5a$$
$$a = 1{\cdot}64\,\text{m/s}^2$$

From (1)

$$T = 7(9{\cdot}81 - 1{\cdot}64)$$
$$= 57{\cdot}19\,\text{N}$$

Downward pull on spring balance $= 2T + 2 \times 9{\cdot}81$
$= 134\,\text{N}$

i.e. The acceleration of the system is 1·64 m/s², and the spring balance reading is 134 N.

Work

The association of force and motion leads to the idea of work and power.

Work is said to be done when a force, overcoming a resistance, moves through a distance. It is expressed as the product of the distance and the force, and hence the unit is the newton metre (N m), which is given the special name *joule* (J). If the force is uniformly applied throughout the whole of the distance, the amount of work done is simply expressed as the product of the two. If the force varies uniformly throughout

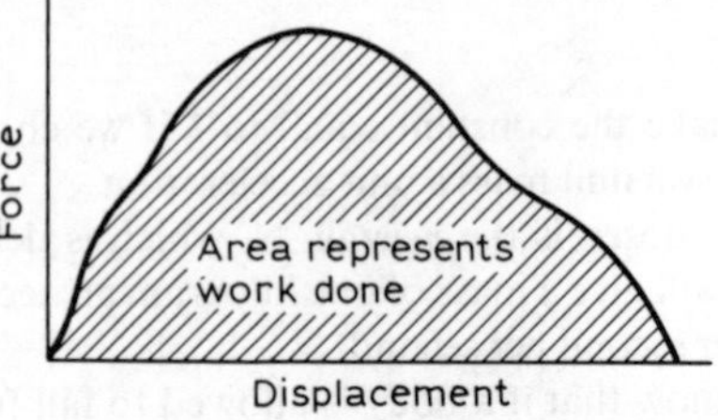

Fig.4.6 Force-displacement diagram

the distance, it is necessary to take the average force and multiply this by the distance traversed. If the force varies in a non-uniform manner, then the amount of work done is obtained either mathematically or by means of a force-distance graph. If a graph is drawn with distance plotted horizontally and force vertically, then the area under the graph is numerically equal to the work done by the force. Methods of determining the area under a curve are indicated in Appendix 2.

Power

Power is the rate of doing work. The more work a machine is required to do per second, the more powerful it is said to be. The unit of power is the *watt* (W).

1 watt = 1 joule per second
1 kilowatt = 1000 joules per second

An engine is said to develop 1 kW if it can do work at the rate of 1000 joules every second.

Now, work done per second is given by the product force × distance per second, which is equal to force × velocity. Hence a very useful expression for power is:

power (watts) = force (newtons) × velocity (metres per second)

Normally the power of a machine is used in overcoming:
a) external resistances or loads,
b) gravitational effects,
c) frictional effects within the machine itself, and
d) in accelerating the load.

At the conclusion of the section dealing with energy, a rather different analysis is given of the way in which power can be distributed.

Example 4.4 A mass of 10 tonnes is being hauled along a level track, and at a certain instant the velocity is 9 km/h and the acceleration $0{\cdot}2\,\text{m/s}^2$. If the total frictional resistance is 1200 N find the pull in the rope, and the power exerted at the instant. NCTEC

Mass of load = 10 × 1000 = 10 000 kg
Force to accelerate = mass × acceleration
= 10 000 × 0·2
= 2000 newtons

Total force required to move = force to overcome resistance + force to accelerate
= 1200 + 2000
= 3200 N

i.e. Pull in rope at the instant is 3200 N.

Power = force × velocity
9 km/h = 2·5 m/s
∴ Power = 3200 × 2·5
= 8000 watts

i.e. Power exerted at the instant is 8 kW.

Motion up a Slope

By 'slope' we mean the distance measured along the incline to give unit vertical rise. Thus a slope of 1 in 100 means that by moving 100 m along the incline we also move through 1 m vertically. Hence the slope, expressed as a fraction, is the sine of the angle. It will be seen that a body of mass M, weight Mg, is held in equilibrium on the plane by a force F equal to $Mg \sin \theta$ and represented by the component ***bc***.

Therefore the force required to move a mass M with uniform velocity up an inclined plane is always:

$$F = Mg.\sin\theta$$

or

$$F = Mg \times \text{slope}$$

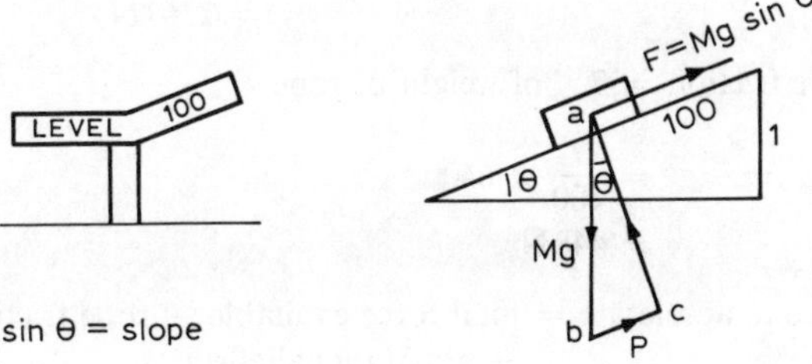

Fig.4.7 Motion up slope

Example 4.5 A mass of 2000 kg is being hauled up an incline of 1 in 100. The frictional resistances are constant at 200 N. Calculate, for the instant when the velocity of the load is 36 km/h and its acceleration is $1\,\text{m/s}^2$, (a) the pull in the rope, and (b) the power exerted.

A mass of 2000 kg is a load of 2000 × 9·81 N = 19 620 N.

Force in rope to move load with constant velocity
= load × slope

$$= 19\,620 \times \frac{1}{100}\,\text{N}$$

= 196·2 N

Force in rope to overcome friction = 200 N

Force in rope to accelerate load = mass × acceleration
= 2000 × 1
= 2000 N

Total pull in rope = 196·2 + 200 + 2000
= 2396·2 N

Power exerted = force × velocity

$$36\,\text{km/h} = \frac{36 \times 1000}{60 \times 60} = 10\,\text{m/s}$$

∴ Power = 2396·2 × 10 = 23 962 W
= 23·962 kW

i.e. The pull in rope is 2400 N and the power is 24 kW.

Example 4.6 The roadway of a haulage system is on an incline of 1 in 40. The load consists of 9 trucks each of mass 1 tonne. The rope passes parallel to the rails from the drum at the top of the incline. It weighs 16 N/m, and rope friction may be taken as equivalent to 7% of the weight of rope out. Determine (a) the acceleration possible when the pull in the rope at the drum end is 10 000 N and the length of rope out is 400 m, (b) the power expended at a steady speed of 3·6 m/s with 200 m of rope out. IMECHE

Weight of mass of 1 tonne = 1000 × 9·81 = 9810 N

a) Total load to be moved = (9 × 9810) + (400 × 16) = 94 690 N

Pull parallel to plane to hold this load = load × slope

$$= 94\,690 \times \frac{1}{40}$$

$$= 2367\text{ N}$$

Rope friction = 7% of weight of rope

$$= \frac{7}{100} \times 6400$$

$$= 448\text{ N}$$

Force to accelerate = total force available − rope friction − gravitational effect

= 10 000 − 448 − 2367

= 7185 N

Mass to be accelerated = 9 tonnes = 9000 kg

$$\text{Acceleration} = \frac{\text{force}}{\text{mass}} = \frac{7185}{9000}$$

$$= 0{\cdot}798\text{ m/s}^2$$

i.e. The acceleration is 0·798 m/s².

b) In this case there is no acceleration.

Total load to be moved = (9 × 9810) + (200 × 16)

= 88 290 + 3200

= 91 490

Pull parallel to the plane to hold this load (or to move it with uniform velocity) $= 91\,490 \times \frac{1}{40}$

= 2287 N

$$\text{Rope friction} = \frac{7}{100} \times 3200$$

= 224 N

Force required in rope = force to overcome friction + force to overcome gravitational effect

= 224 + 2287

= 2511

Power expended = work done per second

= force × velocity

= 2511 × 3·6

= 9039 W

i.e. Power expended is 9·04 kW.

Exercise 4

The weight of a mass of M kg may be taken as 9·81 M newtons.

1 If the maximum force available for moving or stopping a truck of mass 2 tonnes is 200 N, determine the shortest time in which the truck can be moved a distance of 16 m, starting from rest and being brought to rest at the end of the distance. Rail resistance is 40 N/tonne.

2 A hoist of mass 4 tonnes is hauled vertically upwards by a cable, and covers a distance of 3·2 m in 4 seconds from rest, with uniform acceleration. Determine the tension in the cable.

3 Determine the power required to move a train of mass 200 tonnes at 72 km/h along a level track in 5 minutes, starting from rest, assuming that the resistance to motion is constant and equal to 80 N/tonne.

4 A body travelling at 32 m/s in a direction due north is acted on for 0·25 seconds by a constant force of 200 N acting in a direction due east. If the mass of the body is 1 kg, determine its final velocity.

5 Calculate the power exerted by an engine at the instant when its velocity is 36 km/h and its acceleration is 0·16 m/s² if the total mass of the train is 300 tonnes and the resistance to motion is 100 N/tonne.

6 A motor car of mass 800 kg is working at 20 kW when travelling at 72 km/h on the level. Find the power necessary to drive it at 30 km/h up an incline of 1 in 100, assuming the frictional resistances in each case to be equal.

7 A constant force acts on a body in the direction of motion; state the relation connecting the increase of momentum and the time during which the force has acted.

A hoist of mass 3000 kg is hauled vertically upwards by a cable, and the distance covered in 2 seconds from rest is 2 m. Find the tension in the cable, assuming a constant value. NCTEC

8 An engine hauls a train of mass 270 tonnes up an incline of 1 in 300, and at a certain instant the speed is 72 km/h. If the draw-bar power is 400 kW, calculate the resistance in newtons per tonne due to friction, etc. (a) assuming uniform speed, and (b) if there is a deceleration of 0·02 m/s². NCTEC

9 A locomotive exerts a constant pull on a train of mass 400 tonnes up an incline of 1 in 200 measured along the slope, and in 3·2 km the speed drops from 81 to 72 km/h. If frictional resistances are constant at 60 N/tonne, find the pull of the locomotive. NCTEC

10 Determine the power exerted by an engine of mass 100 tonnes, when at a given instant it is pulling a train of mass 200 tonnes at 36 km/h up an incline of 1 in 100 with an acceleration of 0·2 m/s^2. Frictional resistance to motion is 40 N/tonne for engine and train.

Estimate the instantaneous acceleration of the train at a later instant when the engine is exerting 400 kW and travelling at 54 km/h on the level against the same frictional resistances. NCTEC

11 The shortest distance in which a motor car travelling at 100 km/h on a level road can be brought to rest is 50 m. If the motor car is travelling at the same speed up an incline of 1 in 20, find the shortest distance in which it can be brought to rest, assuming the braking force to remain the same. NCTEC

12 A motor car has a mass of 1·5 tonnes. On a certain throttle setting and in second gear the car can accelerate at the rate of 3·6 km/h per second on the level road. If the car is running at 36 km/h at this setting when it comes on to a gradient of 1 in 8, what is the maximum distance it can run up the hill before the driver must change gear? You are to assume that the tractive effort is kept constant by the throttle during the ascent, and that the minimum permissible speed in second gear is 9 km/h. Frictional resistances on flat and gradient are equal, and may be neglected. NCTEC

13 A body moving at 10 m/s is acted upon by a force constant in magnitude and direction for 0·12 seconds, and then moves at 25 m/s in a direction at 45° to the original direction. If the mass of the body is 2 kg, find the magnitude and direction of the force. NCTEC

14 State the second and third laws of motion.

A body of mass 5 kg is sliding down a plane inclined at 60° to the horizontal. What is the force normal to the plane?

A train of mass 400 tonnes is hauled by a constant tractive effort of 5000 N, and at the end of 60 seconds the speed has increased by 18 km/h. Find the resistance to motion, assuming it to be constant. NCTEC

15 The work done in raising a body slowly and steadily through a height of H m is W joules, and when raised with a uniform acceleration of a m/s^2 the work done is 1·05 W joules. Calculate the value of the acceleration, a, during the lift. NCTEC

16 A pulley, of mass with its spindle, etc. 0·5 kg, is suspended from a spring balance. A cord hangs over the pulley with a weight F on one end, and a weight 1·15F on the other hand. When the system is allowed to move freely, the reading on the spring balance is 38 N. Calculate (a) the value of F, (b) the acceleration of the system, (c) the time taken to move 1 m from rest, and (d) the kinetic energy after this time. You may ignore the rotational inertia of the pulley. EMI

17 A cage of mass 1000 kg is lowered down a mine shaft which is 1500 m deep. The cage moves with uniform acceleration for 10 seconds, then with a constant velocity for 50 seconds, and finally retards at a uniform rate for 15 seconds, at the end of which time it rests on the bottom of the shaft. Calculate the tensions in the hoisting cable during the three stages. UEI

18 State Newton's second law of motion. A force F gives a body of mass M an acceleration a. Deduce an expression connecting these quantities.

An engine hauls a train of mass 300 tonnes up an incline of 1 in 300. When the speed of the train is 54 km/h, the draw-bar power developed is 400 kW. Find the resistance of the track in newtons per tonne mass of the train, assuming (a) uniform speed, and (b) an acceleration of 0·02 m/s^2. UEI

19 Find the least power of an engine which is able in 4 minutes to generate in a train of mass 100 tonnes a velocity of 54 km/h on a level track, the resistance due to friction, etc. being equal to 32 N/tonne and the pull of the engine being assumed constant. UEI

20 A train of mass 500 tonnes attains a speed of 72 km/h in 5 minutes from rest. Assuming constant acceleration and a uniform resistance of 50 N/tonnes, find the power at the instant the speed is 54 km/h.

If now the power is cut off, find the braking force required in addition to the original resistance to bring the train to rest in 500 m. UEI

21 A pull of 80 kN is exerted in hauling a mass of 300 tonnes up a gradient of 1 in 80. If the tractive resistance on the level is 60 N/tonne, find the acceleration of the load, and the power required at 36 km/h. IMECHE

22 The total load on the driving wheels of a locomotive is 550 kN, and the coefficient of adhesion—or friction—is to be taken as 0·17. If there is a tractive resistance of 50 N/tonne of train mass, determine the maximum mass (in tonnes) of train that can be accelerated from 54 to 72 km/h in 2 minutes on an up gradient of 1 in 110; and the power expended in pulling this train at the higher speed after acceleration ceases. IMECHE

23 A vehicle travels 500 m along a level road at a steady 96 km/h against a total resistance of 1000 N. It passes on to a rising gradient of 1 in 25. The speed steadily falls to 72 km/h, the total resistance and driving torque remaining constant.

Calculate the distance travelled up the incline during this deceleration, the time taken for the whole distance, the power developed at 96 km/h and at 72 km/h, and the total work done.

The vehicle has a mass of 2000 kg. ULCI

24 A locomotive is drawing a train of mass 300 tonnes at a speed of 96 km/h when it reaches an incline of 1 in 200 which is 3 km long. The locomotive exerts a constant pull and the speed has fallen to 72 km/h by the time the locomotive reaches the top of the incline. If the frictional resistances are constant at 60 N/tonne, calculate (a) the power exerted by the locomotive at the speed of 72 km/h, and (b) the acceleration in m/s^2 on the level beyond the incline. NCTEC

25 A truck of mass 5000 kg is to be hauled up an inclined track by means of a capstan. The incline rises 1 m vertically for every 10 m measured along the incline, and the surface resistances amount to a force of 500 N. If the truck starts from rest and reaches a speed of 36 km/h by uniform acceleration in 40 seconds, calculate the tension in the cable.

Find the tension in the cable if the speed is uniformly reduced to 9 km/h over the subsequent 50 m length of track.

Assuming that the cable brakes when the speed reaches 36 km/h, how far would the truck proceed up the track? ULCI

Chapter 5

Torque and Angular Motion

The problems which we have been considering in connection with the forces required to accelerate masses are very similar to those associated with the angular acceleration of rotating masses. We know from experience that the application of a force at some distance from the centre of rotation of a wheel will cause the wheel to rotate. The applied *torque*, which is the product of the force and its perpendicular distance from the axis of the wheel, causes the wheel to rotate in the direction of the torque.

We require to know the relationship between the applied torque and the subsequent acceleration of the wheel.

Our first difficulty arises from the fact that various parts of the wheel are moving with different velocities. Those parts on the rim are moving much faster than those nearer to the hub. In the case of linear motion, all parts of the mass were in fact moving with the same linear velocity.

Let us consider the case of a mass rotating at the end of an arm, about a fixed centre (fig.5.1). If we consider motion in a horizontal plane, we shall avoid some out-of-balance issues, if not all of them. We shall neglect any effect which the mass of the arm will have.

Let M = the mass, in kg;
r = the radius of the arm, in m;
F = the force applied at the end of the arm, in N;
T = the applied couple or torque = Fr Nm;
α = the angular acceleration of the arm, in rad/s².

The mass will move with an acceleration a such that

$$F = \frac{M}{a}$$

But linear acceleration = angular acceleration × radius

$$a = \alpha r$$
$$\therefore F = M\alpha r$$

Multiplying both sides by r,

$$Fr = Mr^2\alpha$$
$$\therefore T = Mr^2\alpha$$
$$\text{torque} = Mr^2 \times \text{angular acceleration}$$

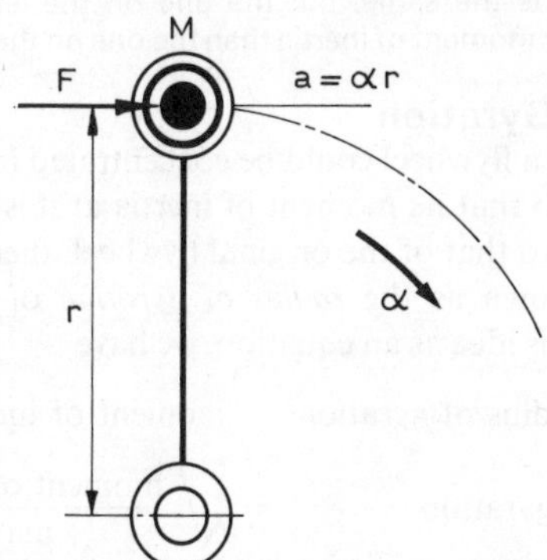

Fig.5.1 Torque and angular motion

The product (mass × radius²) is known as the *moment of inertia* of the mass about the axis of rotation. It is sometimes called the second moment of mass, the first moment of mass being the product (mass × radius). The moment of inertia of a mass is concerned not only with the magnitude of the mass but also with its position with regard to a defined axis. The moment of inertia of a rotating body bears a similar relationship to angular motion as does mass to linear motion.

Now consider the case of a rotating flywheel (fig.5.2), which is made up of a number of masses similar to the one with which we have just been dealing. A corresponding force is acting on each mass at its own radius; so that for any one mass we can say

$$\text{force} = \text{mass} \times \text{acceleration}$$
$$F = M \times \alpha r$$

and $$Fr = Mr^2.\alpha$$

If we add a number of similar expressions together, indicating them in turn with suffices 1, 2, 3, etc., we have:

$$F_1r_1 + F_2r_2 + F_3r_3 + \ldots = M_1r_1^2\alpha + M_2r_2^2\alpha + M_3r_3^2\alpha + \ldots$$
$$= (M_1r_1^2 + M_2r_2^2 + M_3r_3^2 + \ldots)\alpha$$

We use the Greek letter $\sum$ to stand for the expression 'the sum of all the quantities such as . . .'. Thus $\sum Fr$ means 'the sum of all the quantities such as F_1r_1 and F_2r_2, etc.'

Using this notation, we can rewrite the equation in this form:

$$\sum Fr = \sum Mr^2 \times \alpha$$

$\sum Fr$ is the total applied torque on the wheel, and $\sum Mr^2$ is the moment of inertia of the whole wheel about the axis of rotation. The letter I is the symbol for moment of inertia.

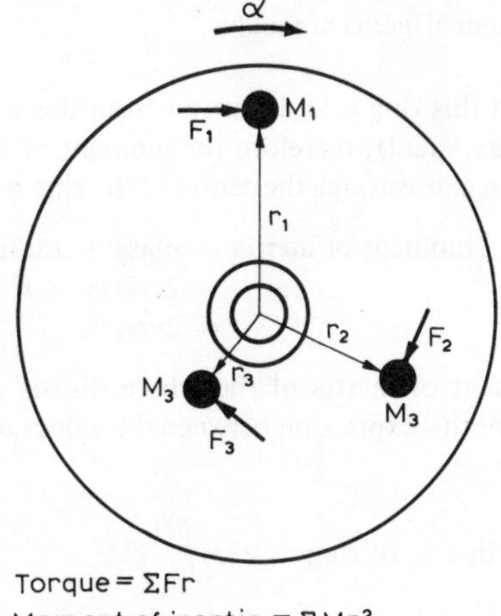

Fig.5.2 Moment of inertia

The fundamental relationship for angular motion can be written

torque = moment of inertia × angular acceleration

Units

The moment of inertia of a mass, being the product of mass and radius², is expressed in 'kg m²' units. With the angular acceleration measured in rad/s², we have the torque expressed in 'N m' units.

Torque = moment of inertia × angular acceleration

N m = kg m² × rad/s²

Moment of Inertia of Annular Ring and Disc

Let R_1 = outside radius, in m;
R_2 = inside radius, in m;
D = outside diameter, in m;
d = inside diameter, in m;
t = thickness, in m;
ρ = density of material, in kg/m³.

Considering a thin ring, radius r, width δr (fig.5.3),

$$\text{volume of ring} = 2\pi r\delta r t \text{ m}^3$$
$$\text{mass of ring} = 2\pi r\delta r t \text{ kg}$$

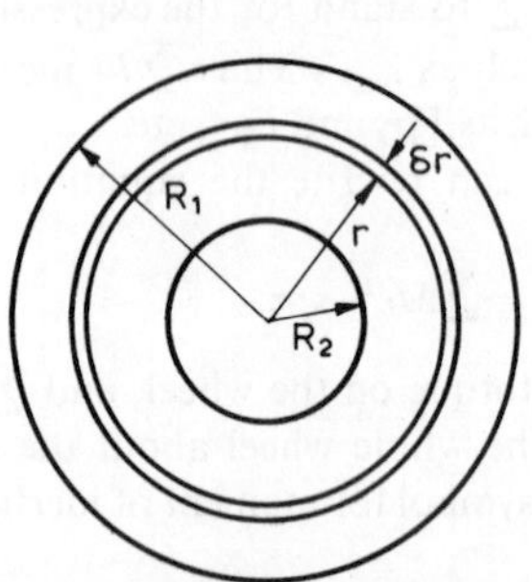

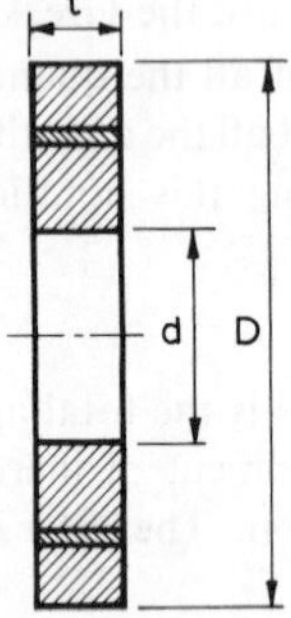

Fig.5.3 Moment of inertia of annulus

Each part of this ring is at distance r from the axis (assuming that δr is very small); therefore the moment of inertia of the ring about an axis through the centre of the ring is given by

$$\begin{aligned}\text{moment of inertia} &= \text{mass} \times \text{radius}^2\\ &= 2\pi r\delta r t\rho \times r^2\\ &= 2\pi t\rho r^3\delta r\end{aligned}$$

The moment of inertia of the whole disc is given by the integration of this expression between the values of $r = R_2$ and $r = R_1$.

$$\begin{aligned}\text{Moment of inertia of ring} &= 2\pi t\rho\int_{R_2}^{R_1} r^3 dr\\ &= 2\pi t\rho\left[\frac{r^4}{4}\right]_{R_2}^{R_1}\\ &= \frac{\pi t\rho}{2}(R_1^4 - R_2^4)\\ &= \pi t\rho(R_1^2 - R_2^2)\left(\frac{R_1^2 + R_2^2}{2}\right)\end{aligned}$$

But $\pi(R_1^2 - R_2^2)t\rho$ is equal to the mass of the whole ring.

$$\therefore \text{ Moment of inertia of annular ring} = \text{mass} \times \frac{R_1^2+R_2^2}{2}$$

Expressing in terms of diameters, moment of inertia of annular ring

$$= \frac{\text{mass}}{2}\left[\left(\frac{D}{2}\right)^2 + \left(\frac{d}{2}\right)^2\right]$$
$$= \frac{\text{mass}\,(D^2 + d^2)}{8}$$

If the ring is solid, i.e. if R_2 and d are equal to zero, then

$$\text{moment of inertia of solid disc} = \frac{\text{mass} \times R^2}{2}$$
$$= \frac{\text{mass} \times \text{diameter}^2}{8}$$

The importance of the position of the mass relative to the axis of rotation is illustrated in fig.5.4. The two wheels have the same mass and the same outside diameter, but in the case of one wheel the mass is concentrated at the outside, whilst in the other case it is towards the centre. The moment of inertia of the first wheel is much greater than that of the second.

If you examine flywheels, you will find that practically all of them will have been designed on the principle of keeping the mass as far away from the axis of rotation as possible.

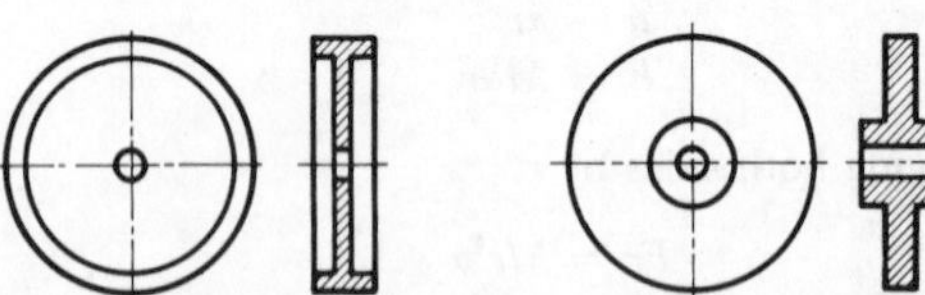

Fig.5.4 Importance of distribution of mass—the mass of each wheel is the same, but the one on the left has a much greater moment of inertia than the one on the right.

Radius of Gyration

If the mass of a flywheel could be concentrated into a thin ring of radius k, so that its moment of inertia at this radius would still be equal to that of the original flywheel, then the radius k would be known as the *radius of gyration* of the flywheel. Expressing this idea as an equation, we have

$$\text{mass} \times \text{radius of gyration}^2 = \text{moment of inertia of wheel}$$

$$\text{Radius of gyration} = \sqrt{\frac{\text{moment of inertia}}{\text{mass}}}$$

In symbols, $I = Mk^2$

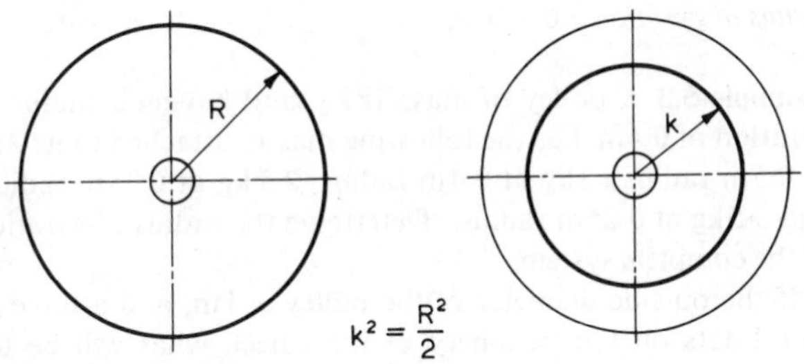

Fig.5.5 Radius of gyration of solid disc

Figure 5.5 indicates two wheels which have the same mass and the same moment of inertia; but in the one case the whole of the mass has been concentrated at the radius of gyration of the flywheel.

In the case of the solid disc of outside radius R, the radius of gyration about the axis of rotation is given by $R/\sqrt{2}$. This can be established as follows:

$$\text{moment of inertia of solid disc} = \text{mass} \times \frac{R^2}{2}$$

also $\quad \text{moment of inertia} = \text{mass} \times \text{radius of gyration}^2$

$$\therefore \text{radius of gyration}^2 = \frac{R^2}{2}$$

$$k = \frac{R}{\sqrt{2}}$$

It is possible to determine the radius of gyration and moment of inertia of other solids in similar ways, but for our present purpose a consideration of the annular ring and the solid disc will be sufficient.

Work Done by a Torque

A similar expression to the one stating that 'work done is equal to force multiplied by linear displacement' is used for angular motion.
In this case,

$$\begin{aligned}\text{work done} &= \text{torque} \times \text{angular displacement (rad)}\\ &= T\theta\,\text{Nm}\\ &= T\theta\,\text{joules}\end{aligned}$$

$$\begin{aligned}\text{Power} &= \text{work done per second}\\ &= \text{torque} \times \text{angular displacement per second}\\ &= \text{torque} \times \text{angular velocity}\\ &= T\omega\,\text{Nm/s}\\ &= T\omega\text{ watts}\end{aligned}$$

Work Done by a Variable Torque

When we were dealing with forces, particularly with varying forces, we saw that it was possible to draw a force diagram plotted with 'distance moved' on the x-axis. The area enclosed by the diagram represented the work done by the force.

In the same way we can obtain the amount of work done by a variable torque if we plot the value of this torque with the angular distance moved through as the x-axis. If the units of the torque are in newton metres, and the units of the angular motion are in radians, then the area of the diagram represents the work done in joules. From a diagram of this type it is possible to determine the power developed by the engine. We should require to know the angle turned through per second, in other words the speed of the engine.

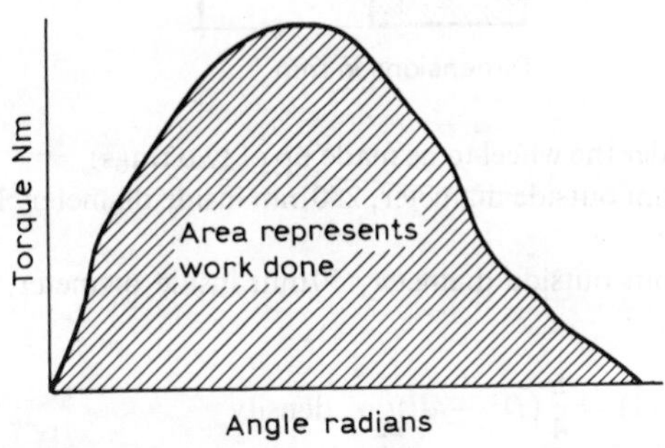

Fig.5.6 Torque-angular displacement diagram

Example 5.1 A wheel whose mass is 50 kg and radius of gyration 600 mm is rotating at 200 rev/min. A retarding torque of 80 Nm is applied to the wheel. Determine the time taken to bring the wheel to rest.

$$\begin{aligned}\text{Moment of inertia} &= \text{mass} \times \text{radius of gyration}^2\\ &= 50 \times 0{\cdot}6^2\\ &= 18\,\text{kgm}^2\end{aligned}$$

$$\text{Torque} = \text{moment of inertia} \times \text{angular acceleration}$$

$$80 = 18\alpha$$

$$\alpha = 4{\cdot}44\,\text{rad/s}^2$$

$$200\text{ rev/min} = \frac{200}{60} \times 2\pi = 20{\cdot}9\text{ rad/s}$$

$$\begin{aligned}\omega_2 &= \omega_1 + \alpha t\\ \omega_2 &= 0\\ \omega_1 &= 20{\cdot}9\\ \alpha &= -4{\cdot}44\text{ (retardation)}\\ t &= ?\\ \therefore 0 &= 20{\cdot}9 - 4{\cdot}44t\\ t &= 4{\cdot}7\text{ seconds}\end{aligned}$$

i.e. The wheel will come to rest in 4·7 seconds.

Example 5.2 Determine the moment of inertia and the radius of gyration about the axis of rotation for the wheel shown in fig.5.7. The density of the material can be taken as 7000 kg/m³.

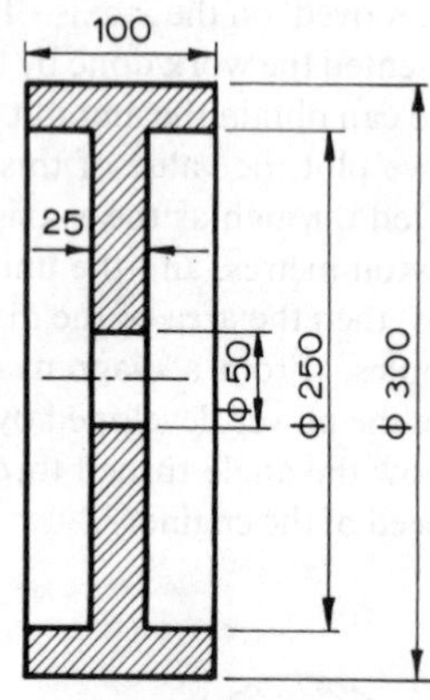

Fig.5.7

Dimensions in mm

Consider the wheel to be made up of two rings:

1 300 mm outside diameter, 250 mm inside diameter, 100 mm wide;

2 250 mm outside diameter, 50 mm inside diameter, 25 mm wide.

$$\text{Mass of (1)} = \frac{\pi}{4}(D^2 - d^2)t \times \text{density}$$

$$= \frac{\pi}{4}(0{\cdot}3^2 - 0{\cdot}25^2)0{\cdot}1 \times 7000$$

$$= 15{\cdot}1\,\text{kg}$$

$$\text{Mass of (2)} = \frac{\pi}{4}(0{\cdot}25^2 - 0{\cdot}05^2)0{\cdot}025 \times 7000$$

$$= 8{\cdot}25\,\text{kg}$$

$$\text{Total mass of wheel} = 15{\cdot}1 + 8{\cdot}25$$

$$= 23{\cdot}35\,\text{kg}$$

$$\text{Moment of inertia of disc} = \text{mass} \times \left(\frac{R^2 + r^2}{2}\right)$$

$$\text{Moment of inertia of (1)} = 15{\cdot}1\left(\frac{0{\cdot}15^2 + 0{\cdot}125^2}{2}\right)$$

$$= 0{\cdot}288\,\text{kgm}^2$$

$$\text{Moment of inertia of (2)} = 8{\cdot}25\left(\frac{0{\cdot}125^2 + 0{\cdot}025^2}{2}\right)$$

$$= 0{\cdot}067\,\text{kgm}^2$$

$$\text{Total moment of inertia of wheel} = 0{\cdot}288 + 0{\cdot}067$$

$$= 0{\cdot}355\,\text{kgm}^2$$

$$= \text{mass} \times \text{radius of gyration}^2$$

$$\therefore 0{\cdot}355 = 23{\cdot}35k^2$$

$$k^2 = 0{\cdot}0152$$

$$k = 0{\cdot}123\,\text{m}$$

i.e. The moment of inertia of the wheel is 0·355 kg m², and the radius of gyration is 0·123 m.

Example 5.3 A pulley of mass 18 kg, and having a radius of gyration of 0·4 m, has the following masses attached to it: 2 kg at 0·5 m radius, 3 kg at 0·4 m radius, 2·5 kg at 0·35 m radius, and 3·5 kg at 0·25 m radius. Determine the radius of gyration of the complete system.

If the outside diameter of the pulley is 1 m, and a force of 250 N acts on the periphery of the wheel, what will be the angular acceleration of the system? NCTEC

Mass (kg)	*Radius* (m)	*Radius*² (m²)	*Mass* × *radius*² (kgm²)
18	0·4	0·16	2·88
2	0·5	0·25	0·50
3	0·4	0·16	0·48
2·5	0·35	0·12	0·30
3·5	0·25	0·06	0·21
Total 29			Total 4·37

$$\text{Radius of gyration, } k = \sqrt{\frac{\text{moment of inertia}}{\text{mass}}}$$

$$= \sqrt{\frac{4{\cdot}37}{29}}$$

$$= 0{\cdot}39\,\text{m}$$

$$\text{Applied torque} = \frac{250 \times 1}{2} = 125\,\text{Nm}$$

$$\text{Moment of inertia of system} = \text{mass} \times \text{radius of gyration}^2$$

$$= 29 \times 0{\cdot}39^2$$

$$= 4{\cdot}4\,\text{kgm}^2$$

$$\text{Angular acceleration} = \frac{\text{torque}}{\text{moment of inertia}}$$

$$= \frac{125}{4{\cdot}4}$$

$$= 28{\cdot}5\,\text{rad/s}^2$$

i.e. The radius of gyration is 0·39 m, and the angular acceleration is 28·5 rad/s².

Example 5.4 The total mass of a small flywheel and axle is 28 kg. The axle is horizontal and 60 mm in diameter. A cord is wound round the axle, and a mass is attached to the free end. The system is held at rest, and then released. When a mass of 0·3 kg is attached to the flywheel, if started, it revolves with uniform angular velocity. With a mass of 2·5 kg attached, it falls from rest through a vertical distance of 2·5 m in 17·2 seconds, and then the mass is detached. Determine (a) the radius of gyration of the flywheel and axle, and (b) the time taken for the flywheel to come to rest after the mass is detached. ULCI

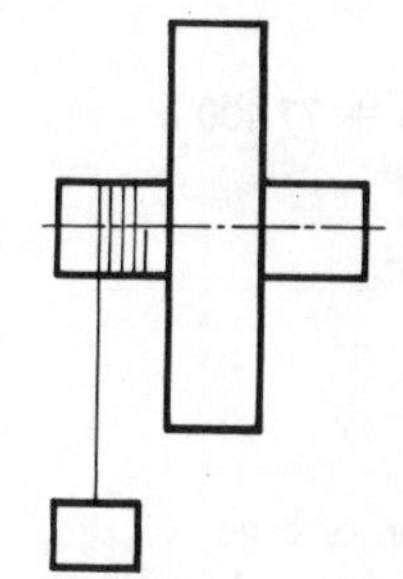
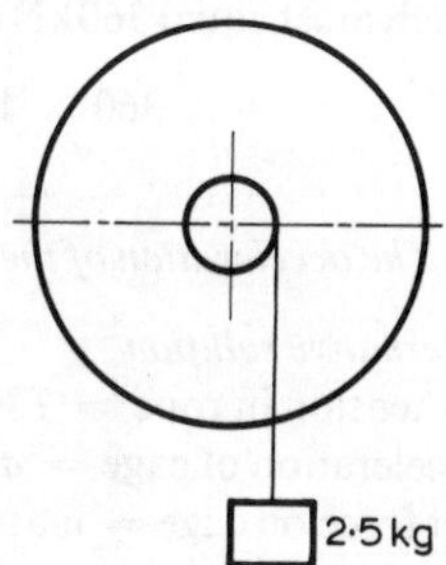

Fig.5.8

A diagrammatic arrangement is shown in fig.5.8.

Acceleration of 2·5 kg mass:

$$s = ut + \tfrac{1}{2}at^2$$
$$s = 2{\cdot}5\,\text{m}$$
$$u = 0 \text{ (starts from rest)}$$
$$t = 17{\cdot}2\,\text{seconds}$$
$$a = ?$$
$$2{\cdot}5 = 0 + \tfrac{1}{2}a \times 17{\cdot}2^2$$
$$a = 0{\cdot}0169\,\text{m/s}^2$$

$$\text{Acceleration of flywheel} = \frac{a}{r}$$

$$= \frac{0{\cdot}0169}{0{\cdot}030}$$

$$= 0{\cdot}565\,\text{rad/s}^2$$

Let F N = tension in cord whilst 2·5 kg mass is falling.
Then $2{\cdot}5g - F$ = resultant force on 2·5 kg mass (down).
Equation of motion for 2·5 kg mass:

$$2{\cdot}5 \times 9{\cdot}81 - F = 2{\cdot}5 \times 0{\cdot}0169$$
$$F = 24{\cdot}458\,\text{N}$$

of which 0·3 × 9·81 N is required to overcome the frictional and windage resistances.

Hence force in cord to accelerate flywheel = 24·458 − 2·943 = 21·515 N

This produces an accelerating torque of 21·515 × 0·030 N m

$$= 0{\cdot}6454\,\text{N m}$$

Equation of motion for flywheel:

torque = moment of inertia × angular acceleration

$$\text{Moment of inertia of flywheel} = \frac{\text{torque}}{\text{angular acceleration}}$$

$$= \frac{0{\cdot}6454}{0{\cdot}565}$$

$$= 1{\cdot}14\,\text{kg m}^2$$

Moment of inertia = mass × radius of gyration²

$$\text{Radius of gyration} = \sqrt{\frac{1{\cdot}14}{28}}$$

$$= 0{\cdot}202\,\text{m}$$

Speed of flywheel when weight is detached:

$$\omega_2 = \omega_1 + \alpha t$$
$$\omega_2 = ?$$
$$\omega_1 = 0$$
$$\alpha = 0{\cdot}565\,\text{rad/s}^2$$
$$t = 17{\cdot}2 \text{ seconds}$$
$$\omega_2 = 0 + 0{\cdot}565 \times 17{\cdot}2$$
$$= 9{\cdot}72 \text{ rad/s}$$

Friction torque is equivalent to 0·3 × 9·81 N at 30 mm radius, i.e. to a torque of 0·3 × 9·81 × 0·030 = 0·088 29 N m. This torque will bring the wheel to rest.

$$\text{Torque} = I\alpha$$
$$0{\cdot}088\,29 = 1{\cdot}14\alpha$$
$$\alpha = 0{\cdot}077\,5\,\text{rad/s}^2$$
$$\omega_2 = \omega_1 + \alpha t$$
$$\omega_2 = 0$$
$$\omega_1 = 9{\cdot}72\,\text{rad/s}$$
$$\alpha = -\,0{\cdot}0775 \text{ (retardation)}$$
$$t = ?$$
$$0 = 9{\cdot}72 - 0{\cdot}0775t$$
$$t = 126\,\text{seconds}$$

i.e. The radius of gyration of the flywheel is 0·202 m, and the flywheel will come to rest in 2 minutes 6 seconds.

Example 5.5 The winding drum in a drive for a pit cage has a mass of 20 tonnes, and is 7·6 m in diameter. Its radius of gyration is 3 m. The total mass of the loaded cage and rope is 8 tonnes. Frictional effects are equal to a torque of 200 N m at the drum shaft, and a force of 450 N at the cage. Calculate the acceleration of the cage when a torque of 360 kN m is applied to the drum shaft. NCTEC
(See fig.5.9).

The applied torque will:
a) overcome friction,
b) balance the weight of the cage, and
c) accelerate the system.

a) Torque to overcome friction:

(1) at drum = 200 N m

$$\text{(2) at cage} = 450 \times \frac{7{\cdot}6}{2} = 1710\,\text{N m}$$

Total frictional torque = 1910 N m.

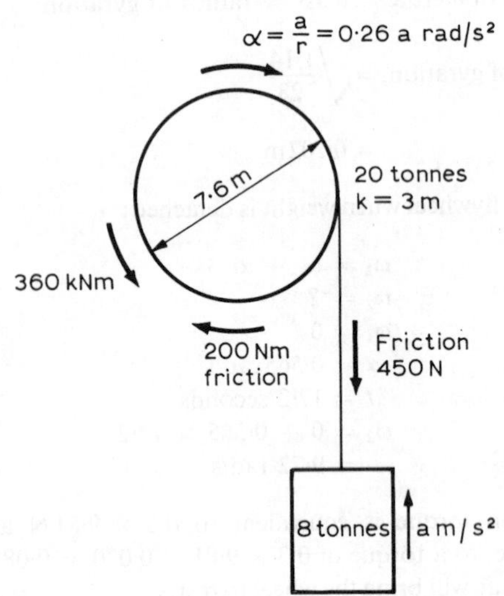

Fig.5.9

b) Torque to balance weight of cage, i.e. torque to hold cage, is equal to

$$\text{weight of cage} \times \text{drum radius} = 8 \times 1000 \times 9{\cdot}81 \times \frac{7{\cdot}6}{2}\ \text{Nm}$$

$$= 299\,000\,\text{Nm}$$

c) Torque to accelerate:

Let a = acceleration of cage in m/s²

then $\frac{a}{r} = \frac{2a}{7{\cdot}6} = 0{\cdot}26a\,\text{rad/s}^2$ is the drum acceleration.

(1) Mass of drum $= 20 \times 1000\,\text{kg}$

Moment of inertia $= Mk^2$
$= 20 \times 1000 \times 3^2$
$= 180\,000\,\text{kgm}^2$

Torque to accelerate $= I\alpha$
$= 180\,000 \times 0{\cdot}26a$
$= 47\,000a\,\text{Nm}$

(2) Force in rope to accelerate cage = mass × acceleration
$= 8 \times 1000a$
$= 8000a\,\text{N}$

$$\text{Torque to produce this force} = 8000a \times \frac{7{\cdot}6}{2}$$

$$= 30\,400a\,\text{Nm}$$

Total torque required $= 1910 + 299\,000 + 47\,000a + 30\,400a$

$= 300\,910 + 77\,400a\,\text{Nm}$

which must equal 360 kN m

$$\therefore\ 360 \times 1000 = 300\,910 + 77\,400\,a$$
$$a = 0{\cdot}77\,\text{m/s}^2$$

i.e. The acceleration of the cage is 0·77 m/s².

Alternative solution

Let tension in rope $= T$ N

Acceleration of cage $= a\,\text{m/s}^2$

Net force on cage = mass × acceleration of cage
= tension in rope − frictional force − weight of cage

$$T - 450 - 8000 \times 9{\cdot}81 = 8000 \times a$$
$$T - 78\,930 = 8000\,a \quad . \quad . \quad . \quad (1)$$

Net torque on drum = M of I × angular acceleration of drum

$$360\,000 - \frac{7{\cdot}6T}{2} - 200 = 20\,000 \times 3^2 \times \frac{2 \times a}{7{\cdot}6}$$

$$94\,800 - T = 12\,500\,a \quad . \quad . \quad . \quad . \quad (2)$$

Adding (1) and (2),

$$94\,800 - 78\,930 = 20\,500\,a$$
$$a = 0{\cdot}77\,\text{m/s}^2$$

i.e. The acceleration of the cage is 0·77 m/s².

Example 5.6 Figure 5.10 is the graph of the torque on a crankshaft of an engine, plotted on a base of angle turned through by the crankshaft. Find the average torque and the work done in one revolution of the crankshaft. If the speed of the engine is constant at 200 rev/min, find the average power transmitted.

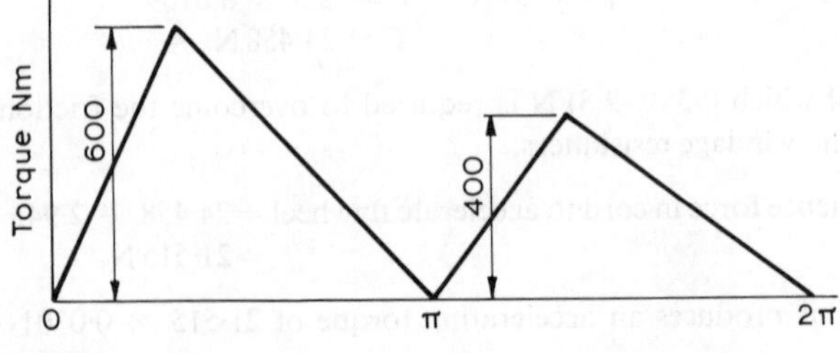

Fig.5.10

The work done in one revolution is represented by the area under the two triangles. (Note that one revolution compares with the 2π radian shaft angle.)

Area of the triangles $= (\frac{1}{2}\pi \times 600) + (\frac{1}{2}\pi \times 400)$
$= 300\pi + 200\pi$
$= 500\pi$

Work done per rev $= 500\pi\,\text{Nm}$
$= 1571\,\text{Nm}$

$$\text{Mean torque} = \frac{\text{work done per revolution}}{\text{base}}$$

$$= \frac{500\pi}{2\pi}$$

$$= 250\,\text{Nm}$$

$$\text{Average power} = \text{torque} \times \text{angular velocity (rad/s)}$$

$$= 250 \times \frac{200}{60} \times 2\pi \text{ watts}$$

$$= 5{\cdot}24\,\text{kW}$$

i.e. The work done per revolution = 1571 Nm, the mean torque = 250 Nm, and the average power = 5·24 kW.

Friction Torque

We have previously seen that a friction force equal to μW will tend to oppose the movement of a body, whose weight is W, over a rough horizontal surface, where μ is the coefficient of friction between the body and the surface. A similar condition applies in the case of a shaft rotating in a bearing. For the present we shall neglect any tendency for the shaft to climb round the bearing. The journal load, F, on the bearing (which might act along any radius, depending upon the nature of the loads on the shaft) produces a friction force, μF, tangential to the shaft. To overcome this force, a torque equal to (friction force × radius of shaft) has to be applied to the shaft.

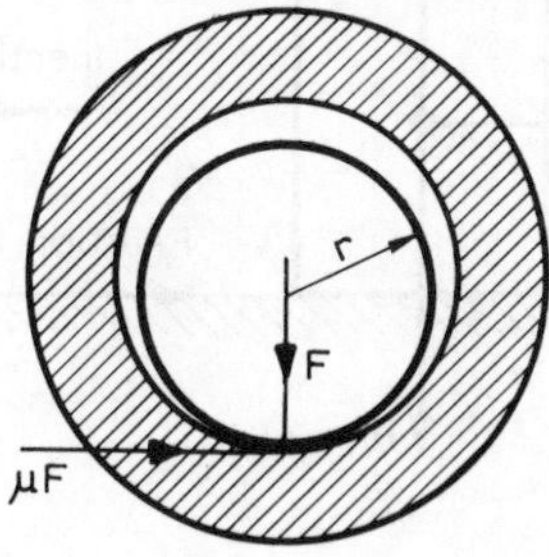

Fig.5.11 Friction torque

$$\text{Friction torque} = \mu Fr \text{ Nm, if } r \text{ is in metres.}$$

Consequently, if the shaft is running at ω rad/s, the power absorbed in overcoming the friction is given by

$$\text{power} = \text{torque} \times \text{angular velocity}$$

$$= \mu Fr \times \omega$$

$$= \mu F\omega r \text{ watts}$$

Example 5.7 Calculate the frictional torque, in Nm, resisting the rotation of a shaft 150 mm in diameter, the load on the journal being 40 kN, and the coefficient of friction between the shaft and its bearing being 0·05. If the shaft revolves at 200 rev/min, what is the power absorbed in friction?

$$\text{Journal load} = 40 \times 1000\,\text{N}$$

$$\text{Resisting frictional force} = 40\,000\mu\,\text{N}$$

$$= 40\,000 \times 0{\cdot}05\,\text{N}$$

$$= 2000\,\text{N}$$

$$\text{Frictional torque} = \text{force} \times \text{radius}$$

$$= 2000 \times \frac{150}{2 \times 1000}$$

$$= 150\,\text{Nm}$$

$$\text{Power absorbed in friction} = \text{torque} \times \text{angular velocity}$$

$$= 150 \times \frac{200}{60} \times 2\pi \text{ joules/s}$$

$$= 1000\pi \text{ joules/s}$$

$$= 3142 \text{ watts}$$

i.e. Power absorbed in friction = 3·14 kW

Combined Linear and Angular Motion

The motion of a solid body in space is often a combination of linear movement and angular movement, referred to as combined translation and rotation of a body. For example, the wheel of a car is moving forward and rotating in a clockwise direction at the same time. We shall be concerned with motion in two directions only, although the principles involved in the analysis of the motion apply to general movement in three dimensions.

The solution of this type of problem depends on dividing the motion into two parts:

1 The linear motion of the centre of gravity of the body.

The resultant force acting on the body = mass × acceleration of c of g in the direction of the force

2 The angular motion of the body about its centre of gravity.

The resultant torque acting about the c of g = M of I about c of g × angular acceleration in direction of torque

Example 5.8 A cylinder of radius 100 mm and 20 kg mass rolls from rest down an inclined plane which is 5 m high and 10 m long. What will be the linear speed of the cylinder at the bottom of the plane?

Forces acting on cylinder (fig.5.12):

1 gravitational force, $Mg = 20 \times 9{\cdot}81$ N;
2 normal reaction of plane, R;
3 frictional force, F.

Equations of linear motion down the plane:

$$\text{Net force acting down plane} = Mg \sin\theta - F$$

$$= 20 \times 9{\cdot}81 \times \frac{5}{10} - F$$

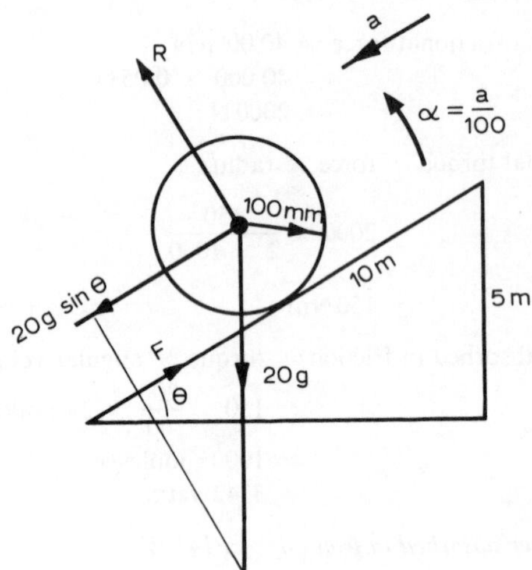

Fig.5.12

Force = mass × acceleration = $98{\cdot}1 - F$ N

$$\therefore\ 98{\cdot}1 - F = 20\,a \quad . \quad . \quad . \quad . \quad . \quad (1)$$

where a is the linear acceleration of the cylinder.

Equation of angular motion of cylinder:

$$\text{Net torque acting on cylinder} = F \times \frac{100}{1000}$$

$$= 0{\cdot}1\,F\,\text{Nm}$$

Torque = M of I × angular acceleration

$$0{\cdot}1\,F = Mk^2 \times \alpha$$

$$k^2 = \frac{R^2}{2} = \frac{0{\cdot}1^2}{2} \text{ for cylinder}$$

$$\alpha = \frac{a}{r} = \frac{a}{0{\cdot}1}$$

$$0{\cdot}1\,F = 20 \times \frac{0{\cdot}1^2}{2} \times \frac{a}{0{\cdot}1}$$

$$F = 10a \quad . \quad . \quad . \quad . \quad . \quad . \quad . \quad . \quad . \quad . \quad (2)$$

From equations (1) and (2).

$$98{\cdot}1 - 10a = 20a$$

$$a = \frac{98{\cdot}1}{30}$$

$$= 3{\cdot}27\,\text{m/s}^2$$

Distance travelled, s = 10m.
Initial velocity, u = 0m²/s.

Final velocity, v, is given by

$$v^2 - u^2 = 2as$$

$$v^2 = 2 \times 3{\cdot}27 \times 10$$

$$v = 8{\cdot}1\,\text{m/s}$$

i.e. Linear velocity of cylinder at base of slope is 8·1 m/s.
An alternative method of solution to this type of problem is shown in example 6.1.

Inertial Forces and D'Alembert's Principle

Newton's third law of motion states that to every action there is always an equal and opposite reaction. A force applied to a mass with the purpose of accelerating it is referred to as the accelerating force. Immediately this is applied, an equal and opposite internal force, known as an *inertial force*, is produced in the mass, and this force makes the mass resist any change of motion. The ultimate movement of the mass may be affected by frictional forces, which, like the accelerating force, act external to the mass. Other external forces acting on the mass would be the gravitational force and the normal reaction of the support. Any such external forces are sometimes defined as *impressed forces*; they are impressed on the mass from outside.

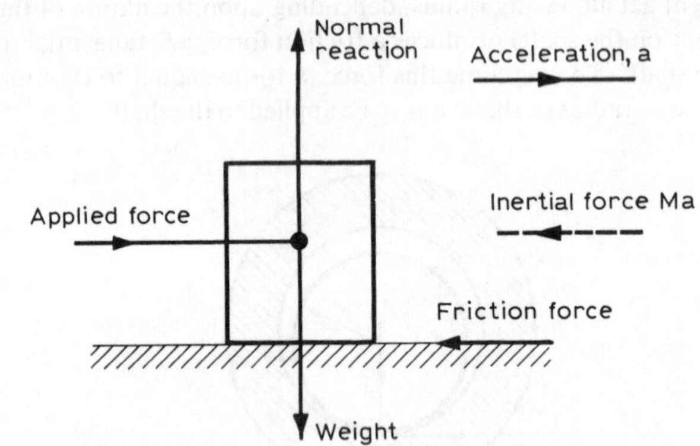

Fig.5.13

In 1743, a French scientist named D'Alembert established a very useful principle which bears his name, and which can be stated as *the resultant of the impressed forces acting on a mass and the resultant of the inertial forces within the mass are in equilibrium.* In this way we are able to consider a mass to be in dynamic equilibrium in a similar way to that of static equilibrium, and we can apply the conditions of equilibrium related to statics to an appropriate problem in dynamics.

Example 5.9 A body of mass 10kg is pulled along a level surface by a constant force, P, of 50N. The coefficient of friction between the body and the surface is 0·2. Determine the acceleration of the mass.

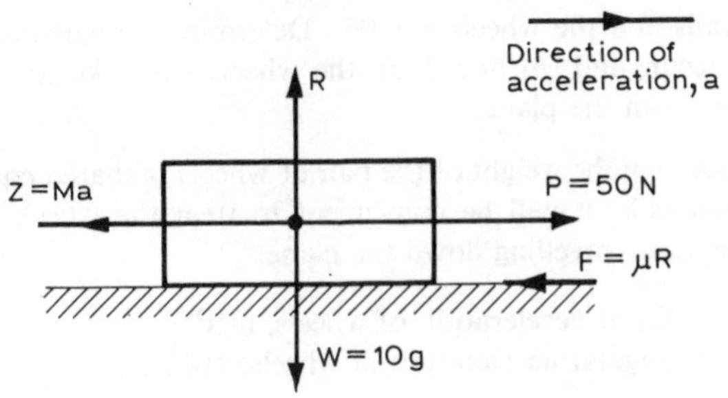

Fig.5.14

Let acceleration of mass = $a\,\text{m/s}^2$ in the same direction as P.

Forces acting on mass:
1 pull, $P = 50\,\text{N}$;
2 gravitational force, $W = 9{\cdot}81 \times 10 = 98{\cdot}1\,\text{N}$;
3 normal reaction of surface, $R = W = 98{\cdot}1\,\text{N}$;
4 friction force, $F = \mu R = 0{\cdot}2 \times 98{\cdot}1 = 19{\cdot}62\,\text{N}$;
5 inertial force, $Z = Ma = 10a\,\text{N}$ in a direction opposite to that of the acceleration.

The sum of the horizontal forces will be zero for equilibrium

$$\therefore P - F - Z = 0$$
$$50 - 19{\cdot}62 - 10a = 0$$
$$a = 3{\cdot}04\,\text{m/s}^2$$

i.e. The acceleration of the block is $3{\cdot}04\,m/s^2$.

Example 5.10 Figure 5.15 shows details of a uniform block carried on a lorry which is travelling towards the right. The block has a mass of 300 kg, is 1·2 m high, and has a base 0·5 m square. If the coefficient of friction between the block and the lorry is 0·3, determine the subsequent motion of the block if the lorry decelerates suddenly.

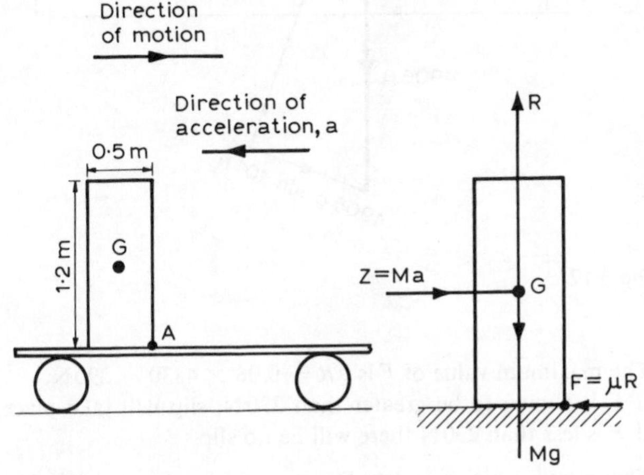

Fig.5.15

Lorry is moving towards the right and decelerating, i.e. accelerating in the direction of a.

Forces acting on block:
1 gravitational force = $M \times 9{\cdot}81\,\text{N}$
2 normal reaction of floor of lorry, $R = M \times 9{\cdot}81\,\text{N}$
3 frictional force, $F = \mu R$
$= 2943 \times 0{\cdot}3$
$= 883\,\text{N}$
4 inertial force, $Z = Ma$
$= 300a$ in a direction opposite to that of a.

Resolving horizontally,

$$300a = 883 \text{ for equilibrium}$$
$$a = 2{\cdot}94\,\text{m/s}^2$$

If a exceeds $2{\cdot}94\,\text{m/s}^2$, then $300a$ will be greater than 883, and the block will slide to the front of the lorry.

Rotation about A:

Since the block is uniform, c of g is $\frac{1{\cdot}2}{2} = 0{\cdot}6\,\text{m}$ above base.

Clockwise moment about A $= 300a \times 0{\cdot}6$
$= 180a\,\text{Nm}$

Anticlockwise moment about A $= 2943 \times \frac{0{\cdot}5}{2}$

$= 735{\cdot}75\,\text{Nm}$

When the block is on the point of overturning in the clockwise direction about A, R is zero, and

$$180a = 735{\cdot}75$$
$$a = 4{\cdot}09\,\text{m/s}^2$$

i.e. If the deceleration of the lorry exceeds $4{\cdot}09\,m/s^2$, the block will overturn clockwise. But, since 4·09 is greater than 2·94, the block will slide before it overturns.

Example 5.11 A hollow cylinder, 2 m outside diameter and having a mass of 2400 kg, radius of gyration 0·8 m, is rolled along a rough horizontal surface by means of a rope exerting a pull of 400 N (fig.5.16). What will be the linear acceleration of the cylinder, and the time taken to roll 15 m from rest?

Forces acting on wheel:
1 pull, $P = 400\,\text{N}$;
2 gravitational force, $Mg = 2400 \times 9{\cdot}81 = 23\,500\,\text{N}$;
3 reaction of surface, R;
4 friction force, F;
5 inertial force, $Z = 2400a\,\text{N}$ in direction opposite to a.

$$\text{Inertial torque on wheel} = Mk^2\alpha$$
$$= 2400 \times 0{\cdot}8^2\alpha$$
$$= 1540\alpha \text{ Nm in direction opposite to } \alpha.$$

By D'Alemberts principle, these forces and the torque produce equilibrium of the wheel.

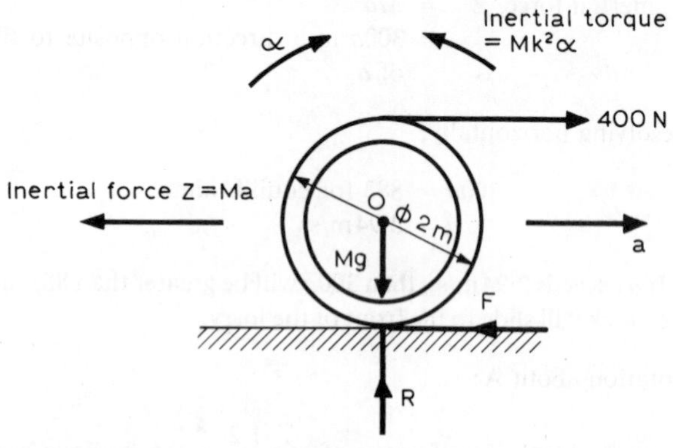

Fig.5.16

Moments about 0 give

$$400 \times 1 + F \times 1 - 1540\alpha = 0$$
$$400 + F - 1540a = 0 \text{ (since } \alpha = a/1) \quad . \quad . \quad (1)$$

Forces parallel to plane.

$$400 - F - 2400a = 0 \quad . \quad . \quad . \quad . \quad . \quad . \quad . \quad (2)$$

From (1) and (2),

$$800 - 3940a = 0$$
$$a = \frac{800}{3940} = 0{\cdot}2 \text{ m/s}^2$$

Time to roll 15m from rest

$$s = ut + \tfrac{1}{2}at^2$$
$$15 = 0 + \tfrac{1}{2} \times 0{\cdot}2t^2$$
$$t = 12{\cdot}2 \text{ seconds}$$

i.e. The linear acceleration of the cylinder is $0{\cdot}2\,m/s^2$, and the time taken to roll 15m from rest is 12·2 seconds.

Example 5.12 A pair of wheels, whose mass is 500kg and radius of gyration is 0·4m, starts from rest to travel on rails down a plane inclined at 10° to the horizontal. The radius of the wheels is 0·45m, and the coefficient of friction between the rails and the wheels is 0·06. Determine (*a*) whether slip will occur, and (*b*) how long the wheels will take to travel 100m down the plane.

a) Although the weight of the pair of wheels is shared equally by two rails, it will be convenient to treat the wheels as a single mass travelling down the plane.

Let a = linear acceleration of wheels, m/s²;
α = angular acceleration of wheels, rad/s².

Forces acting on wheels:

1 gravitational force, $Mg = 500 \times 9{\cdot}81 = 4905$N;
2 reaction of rails, $R = 4905 \cos 10° = 4830$N;
3 friction force, F;
4 inertial force, $Z = Ma = 500a$N in direction opposite to a.

$$\text{Inertial torque on wheels} = Mk^2\alpha$$
$$= 500 \times 0{\cdot}4^2\alpha$$
$$= 80\alpha \text{ Nm in direction opposite to } \alpha.$$

By D'Alembert's principle, these forces and the torque produce equilibrium of the wheels.

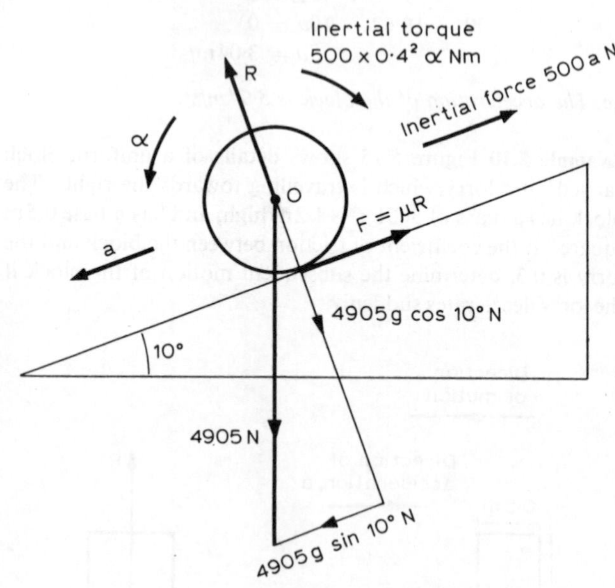

Fig.5.17

The maximum value of F is $\mu R = 0{\cdot}06 \times 4830 = 290$N.
If F is shown to be greater than 290N, slip will take place.
If F is less than 290N there will be no slip.

The relationship between linear and angular acceleration, $\alpha = a/0{\cdot}45$, will be valid only if there is no slip.

Resolving forces parallel to the plane,

$$4905 \sin 10° - F - 500a = 0 \quad . \quad . \quad . \quad . \quad (1)$$

Moments about 0:

$$F \times 0{\cdot}45 - 500 \times 0{\cdot}4^2\alpha = 0$$
$$F = 177{\cdot}8\alpha \quad . \quad . \quad . \quad (2)$$

Substituting this value of F into (1),

$$a = 1{\cdot}7 - 0{\cdot}36\alpha \quad . \quad . \quad . \quad . \quad . \quad (3)$$

If there is no slip then $\alpha = a/0{\cdot}45$.
Substituting into (3) gives $\alpha = 2{\cdot}1$, and this value in (2) gives F equal to 373·4 N, which is greater than the limiting value of 290 N. Therefore slip will take place, and the value of $F =$ 290 N must be used in (1) to determine the value of the acceleration a.
Substituting into (1),

$$4905 \sin 10° - 290 - 500a = 0$$

which gives $a = 1{\cdot}1 \text{ m/s}^2$

b) Time taken to travel from rest 100 m down the plane:

$$s = ut + \tfrac{1}{2}at^2$$
$$100 = 0 + \tfrac{1}{2}1{\cdot}1\,t^2$$
$$t = 13{\cdot}4 \text{ seconds}$$

i.e. The wheels will slip whilst turning whilst they move down the plane, taking 13·4 seconds to cover the 100 m. If the rails were made less greasy, i.e. the value of μ increased, then a value would be reached when the wheels would not slip.

Example 5.13 A uniform rod, mass 2 kg, length 3 m, is supported at one end, and is free to move in a vertical plane. A horizontal force of 10 N is applied at a point 2·5 m from the support, as shown in fig.5.18. Determine the angular acceleration of the rod, and the horizontal and vertical reactions at the support. At what distance from the support will the force have to be applied so that the horizontal reaction will be zero?

The c of g will have a linear acceleration of a, and the rod will have an angular acceleration of α about the support.
$\bar{x}$ is distance from support to c of g of rod (the mid point).

Forces acting on rod:

1 applied force, $P = 10$ N;
2 gravitational force, $W = M \times 9{\cdot}81 = 19{\cdot}62$ N;
3 reactions R_H and R_V at support;
4 inertial force, $Z = Ma = 2a$ in a direction opposite to that of a.

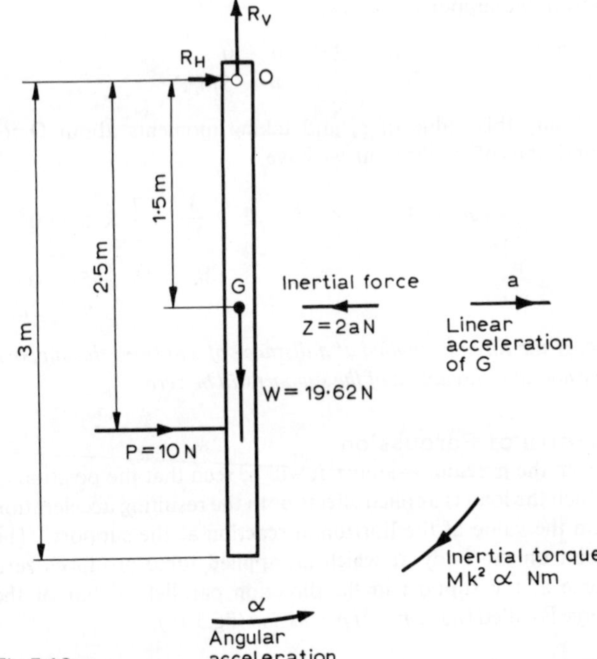

Fig.5.18

In addition there is an inertial torque, $Mk^2\alpha$, acting in a direction opposite to that of the angular acceleration α. Note that k is the radius of gyration of the rod about the c of g, O; $k^2 = l^2/12$ for a uniform rod.

By D'Alembert's principle, these forces and the torque produce equilibrium of the body.

Sum of anticlockwise torque and moments about O is zero.

$$10 \times 2{\cdot}5 - 2a \times 1{\cdot}5 - 2 \times \frac{3^2}{12} \times \frac{2a}{3} = 0 \quad . \quad . \quad . \quad . \quad (1)$$

$$a = 6{\cdot}25 \text{ m/s}^2$$

$$\alpha = \frac{a}{\bar{x}} = \frac{6{\cdot}25}{1{\cdot}5}$$

$$= 4{\cdot}16 \text{ rad/s}^2$$

Sum of horizontal forces is zero.

$$10 - 2a + R_H = 0 \quad . \quad . \quad . \quad . \quad . \quad (2)$$
$$R_H = 12{\cdot}5 - 10$$
$$= 2{\cdot}5 \text{ N}$$

Sum of vertical forces is zero.

$$R_H = 19{\cdot}62 \text{ N}$$

i.e. The angular acceleration of the rod is 4·16 rad/s², the horizontal reaction is 2·5 N and the vertical reaction is 19·62 N.

For the condition when $R_H = 0$, let P be applied at distance h from the support.

From (2) $\quad 10 - 2a + 0 = 0$

$$a = 5\,\text{m/s}^2$$

Using this value of a, and taking moments about O for conditions of equilibrium, we have

$$10h - 2 \times 5 \times 1{\cdot}5 - 2 \times \frac{3^2}{12} \times \frac{2}{3} \times 5 = 0$$

$$10h - 15 - 5 = 0$$

$$h = 2\,\text{m}$$

i.e. If the force is applied at a distance of 2 m from the support, the horizontal reaction of the support will be zero.

Centre of Percussion

From the previous example, it will be seen that the position at which the load is applied affects both the resulting acceleration and the value of the horizontal reaction at the support. The point on the body at which an applied force produces zero force at the support in the direction parallel to that of the force is called the *centre of percussion* (fig.5.19).

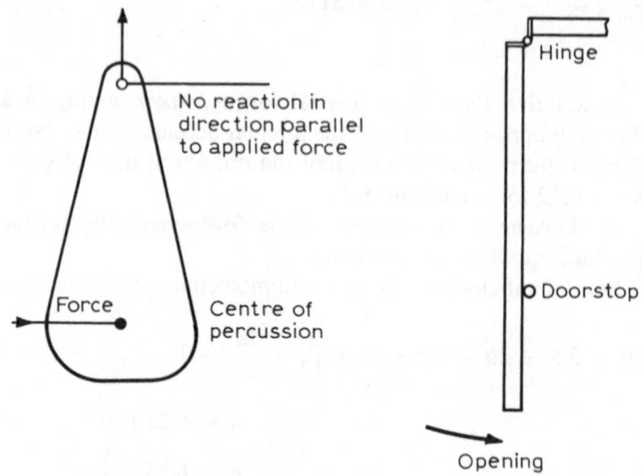

Fig.5.19 Centre of percussion

This is obviously of importance in the design of many engineering components, and it also has some other interesting applications in everyday life. The design of a cricket bat is such that it is intended that the ball will be struck at the bat's centre of percussion, which is roughly at 2/3 of its length from the place where it is gripped. In this way there will be little reaction experienced by the hands, and the resulting motion of the ball will have been achieved in an apparently effortless manner. On the other hand, if the ball strikes at a point other than the centre of percussion, the familiar stinging is felt by the hands.

Another use of the idea of the centre of percussion is the application of the doorstop. If a door strikes the stop at the centre of percussion of the door, i.e. two-thirds of its width from the hinge, no horizontal reaction will be experienced by the hinge. If the stop is placed at any other point, contact with the stop will tend to pull the hinge out of the wall or door.

Further applications of the idea of the centre of percussion will be seen in studies on vibrations.

Exercise 5

1–3 Determine the moment of inertia and the radius of gyration about the axis of rotation of the flywheels whose sections are given in fig.5.20. Density 7000 kg/m³.

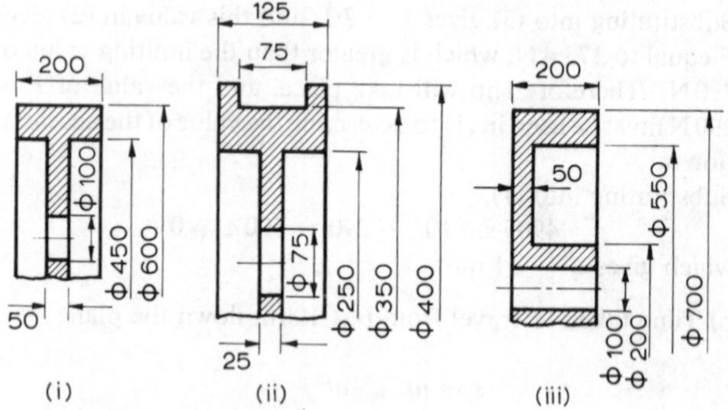

Fig.5.20

4 A pulley whose mass is 45 kg, and which has a radius of gyration of 0·5 m, has the following masses attached to it: 4·5 kg at 650 mm radius, 7 kg at 600 mm radius, 9 kg at 250 mm radius, and 11 kg at 750 mm radius. Determine the radius of gyration of the complete system.

5 What is the function of a flywheel?

A mass of 18 kg attached to a cord which is wrapped round the 50 mm diameter spindle of a flywheel descends, and thereby causes the flywheel to rotate. If the weight descends 1·8 m in 10 seconds, and the friction of the bearing is equivalent to a force of 14 N at the circumference of the spindle, find the moment of inertia of the flywheel. If it weighs 981 N, what is its radius of gyration? NCTEC

6 A flywheel of mass 450 kg has a radius of gyration of 600 mm. What steady tangential force, acting 300 mm from the axis of rotation, will in 10 seconds set up a speed of 6 rev/min against an opposing frictional couple of 2·7 N m? If the force is then removed, how long will it take for the wheel to come to rest? NCTEC

7 Explain the terms 'angular velocity' and 'angular acceleration', and state what is meant by the radius of gyration of a flywheel.

A flywheel of mass 5 tonnes, and having a radius of gyration of 2·5 m, is acted upon by a constant torque which produces an acceleration of 2 rad/s². Find (a) the rev/min 4 seconds after the angular velocity was 5 rad/s, (b) the number of revolutions turned in the 4 seconds, and (c) the magnitude of the torque. NCTEC

8 In order to turn a flywheel in its bearings against friction, it is found necessary to exert a couple of 475 N m. The mass of the flywheel is 5 tonnes and the radius of gyration is 1·1 m. If the driving power is cut off when the wheel is running at 350 rev/min, find how long it will take, and how many revolutions it will make in coming to rest. NCTEC

9 A flywheel has a mass of 1400 kg and a radius of gyration of 1·2 m. When running at 300 rev/min, the driving torque is removed, and the wheel comes to rest in 80 seconds. Calculate the work done against friction per revolution, if it is constant throughout.

Calculate also the frictional torque. NCTEC

10 An experimental flywheel is in the form of a rim, 300 mm outside diameter and 200 mm inside, and weighs 285 N. It is mounted on a horizontal spindle 20 mm diameter, and is rotated by a weight attached to a cord passing round the spindle. A mass of 2 kg in excess of that required for friction is attached to the cord, and it falls 1·5 m from rest before the cord becomes detached. Calculate the maximum speed in rev/min attained by the wheel. Neglect the effect of the web and spindle on the inertia of the wheel.

Note. The radius of gyration, k, of a solid disc of diameter D about an axis through its centre of gravity is given by $k^2 = D^2/8$. NCTEC

11 A lift of mass 1500 kg is raised by means of a rope passing round a drum. The drum is 1·5 m in diameter, has a mass of 750 kg, and a radius of gyration of 600 mm. Find the tension in the rope, and the torque supplied to the drum when the lift ascends with an acceleration of 150 mm/s². Neglect the friction in the drum bearings. NCTEC

12 Two masses of 10 kg and 8 kg are connected to the ends of a cord passing over a solid circular disc of uniform thickness. The mass of the disc is 12 kg, and its diameter is 600 mm. Determine the acceleration of the masses, and the tension in the two portions of the cord when the masses are moving freely. The disc can be assumed to be mounted on frictionless bearings. NCTEC

13 A wheel of mass 70 kg, radius of gyration 300 mm, and outside diameter 1 m is mounted with its axle horizontal. Due to bearing friction, the wheel comes to rest from a speed of 500 rev/min after making 120 revolutions. When the wheel is running at 500 rev/min, a wooden brake block is pressed against the rim of the wheel with a force of 65 N, the coefficient of friction between the wood and the wheel being 0·4. Determine the number of revolutions which the wheel will make in coming to rest. NCTEC

14 A small flywheel is keyed to a horizontal axle 50 mm in diameter, and the total mass is 30 kg. A cord is wound round the axle, and a mass of 2·25 kg is attached to the free end. The system is held at rest, and then released, and the weight takes 12·5 seconds to fall through a height of 2 m. Assuming that the frictional torque on the axle remains constant, and is equivalent to 0·25 kg attached to the cord, determine (a) the angular acceleration of the flywheel, and (b) the effective radius of gyration of the flywheel and axle. ULCI

15 A flywheel, 2·25 m in diameter, has a mass of 5 tonnes, and a radius of gyration of 1 m. By means of a brake block applying a constant pressure on the rim, the flywheel is slowed down from 300 to 120 rev/min whilst the wheel turns through 140 revolutions. The coefficient of friction between the brake block and the flywheel rim is 0·30. Determine (a) the time taken to bring the flywheel to rest, (b) the normal force between the brake block and the rim, assuming this force remains constant. ULCI

16 A load of mass 36 kg is raised by a rope round a drum 750 mm in diameter. The drum and rigidly attached wheels which rotate with it have a mass of 45 kg, and combined have a radius of gyration of 350 mm. What torque will be required to give the suspended load an upward acceleration of 1 m/s²? IMECHE

17 The drum of a goods hoist has a mass of 900 kg. It has an effective diameter of 1·5 m, and a radius of gyration of 600 mm. The loaded cage weighs 5·4 kN, and its frictional resistance in the vertical line of travel is 270 N. A maximum acceleration of 600 mm/s² is required. Determine (a) the necessary driving torque on the drum, (b) the tension in the rope during acceleration, and (c) the power developed at the steady speed of 3·6 m/s. IMECHE

18 A and B are two trucks which are coupled together. A has a mass of 5 tonnes, and B of 3 tonnes, and they are hauled together up an incline of 1 in 20 by means of a rope attached to A, which is the leading truck. This rope, which is parallel to the incline, passes round a drum which is at the top of the incline. The drum has a mass of 4500 kg, an effective diameter of 2·5 m, and a radius of gyration of 1 m.

The road resistance is 110 N/tonne, and there is a friction torque of 170 N m on the drum shaft.

If the trucks are to move uphill with an acceleration of 2 m/s², find the torque required on the drum shaft.

19 Write down the symbolic form of Newton's Second Law as applied to a rotating body. Explain the meaning of the symbols involved, and the respective units to be employed for consistency.

A rope passes over a pulley 1 m in diameter which has a mass of 70 kg and a radius of gyration of 300 mm. A mass of 700 kg is attached to one end of the rope, and a mass of 450 kg to the other end. Determine the force which must be applied to the rope in order to give the two masses an acceleration of 1·5 m/s², the heavier mass ascending.

Neglect the weight of the rope. ULCI

20 Figure 5.21 is a graph of the torque (twisting moment) on the crankshaft of an engine, plotted against a base of angle turned through by the shaft. Find the average torque, and the work done in one revolution of the crankshaft. If the speed of the engine is constant at 300 rev/min, find the average power transmitted NCTEC

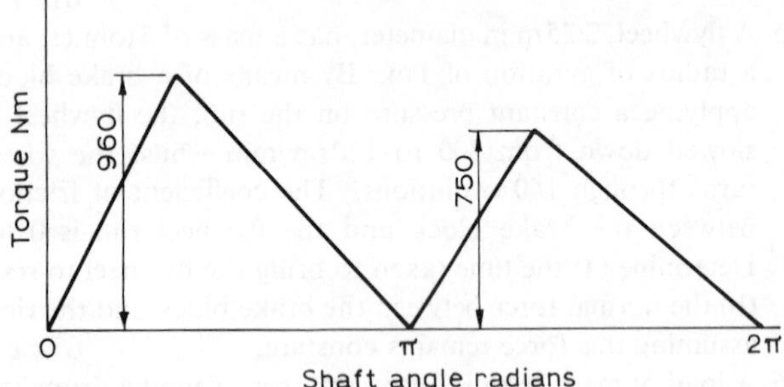

Fig.5.21

21 Define torque.

In a motor car having wheels 750 mm in diameter, the speed ratio between the engine shaft and the rear axle is 5 to 1. If, at a uniform speed of 50 km/h, the resistance to motion is 1000 N, calculate the torque and power at the engine shaft, assuming 30 per cent of the power to be lost between the engine and the wheels. NCTEC

22 What is meant by 'coefficient of friction'?

A shaft journal is 300 mm in diameter, and is subjected to a normal load of 150 kN when turning at 85 rev/min. If 10 kW is lost in friction, calculate the frictional torque in N m, and the coefficient of friction. NCTEC

23 Define the coefficient of friction and the angle of friction. State the laws of friction.

Find, for a speed of 2000 rev/min, the loss in power due to friction in a bearing which has a rubbing diameter of 50 mm and a rubbing length of 80 mm. The force of friction in the bearing may be taken as $0{\cdot}0045\, dl\sqrt{v}$ N, when $d =$ diameter of bearing in mm, $l =$ length of bearing in mm, $v =$ speed of rotation in m/s. NCTEC

24 (a) Calculate the frictional torque in N m resisting the rotation of a shaft journal 100 mm in diameter, the load on the journal being 20 kN, and the coefficient of friction between the shaft and the bearing being 0·06.

(b) If the shaft revolves at 150 rev/min, what is the power absorbed in friction? UEI

25 Define the term 'coefficient of friction'.

The coefficient of friction for a shaft rotating in a bearing at 200 rev/min is 0·02. The shaft diameter is 150 mm, and the load on the bearing is 20 kN. Calculate: (a) the friction torque on the shaft, (b) the power lost in friction at the bearing, (c) the heat generated by friction in the bearing per min. ULCI

26 Figure 5.22 (i) shows a cylinder of mass 2 kg, radius 250 mm and radius of gyration 200 mm being pulled along a rough horizontal plane by a force of 15 N. The force acts at the axis of the cylinder, and parallel to the plane.

Determine the linear acceleration of the cylinder if there is no slipping.

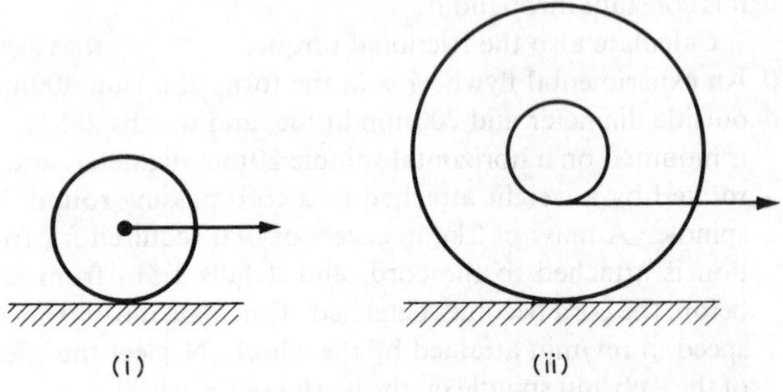

Fig.5.22

27 Figure 5.22 (ii) shows a cable drum being drawn along a rough horizontal plane by means of the cable, which is pulled horizontally with a force of 4 N. The drum has a mass of 4 kg, a radius of 750 mm, and flanges of radius 2 m. Its moment of inertia is 9 kg m^2.

Find the linear acceleration of the drum, and the minimum value of the coefficient of friction, if the drum just rolls without slipping.

28 A cylinder of mass 7·5 kg, radius 2 m, and moment of inertia 4·5 kg m^2 stands on a rough plane inclined at 30° to the horizontal.

Find the linear acceleration of the cylinder, and the coefficient of friction, if the drum just rolls without slipping.

What would be the linear acceleration if the coefficient of friction were 0·01?

Chapter 6

Energy

Energy stored in a body is an indication of the capacity of the body to do work. When work is done on a body there is a corresponding increase of energy, an increase which is measured in joules, and which is equal to the amount of work done on the body. Mechanical energy has three different forms.

1 *Potential energy*, i.e. energy due to the position or height of the body above a datum line. To lift a mass of M kg, whose weight is Mg N, through a vertical distance of h m would require Mgh joules of work to be done. This work is stored in the body as potential energy. Notice that in considering potential energy we are concerned with weights or forces, and not masses.

2 A rather special kind of potential energy is known as *strain energy*. If a spring is compressed or strained by a force, then the work which had to be done in straining the spring is stored in it as strain energy. A force of F N would compress the spring a distance x, although during the compression the necessary force would increase uniformly from 0 to F N, giving an average value of $\frac{1}{2}F$ N. Hence the work done will be $\frac{1}{2}Fx$ joules. The same reasoning is used for all materials which follow Hooke's law of elasticity.

3 *Kinetic energy*, i.e. energy due to motion. In order to make a mass M move with a velocity v, starting from rest, a force must be applied to produce the necessary acceleration. This force will do work on the body, and the work done will be stored in the body as *kinetic energy of translation*, or linear kinetic energy.

Acceleration to produce velocity v in distance s from rest ($u = 0$):

$$v^2 - 0^2 = 2as$$

$$a = \frac{1}{2}\frac{v^2}{s}$$

Force to produce this acceleration = mass × acceleration

$$= M \times \frac{1}{2}\frac{v^2}{s}$$

Work done by force = force × distance

$$= \frac{\frac{1}{2}Mv^2}{s} \times s$$

$$= \frac{1}{2}Mv^2$$

This work is stored in the body as kinetic energy of translation. Hence the kinetic energy of translation of a mass M moving with velocity v is $\frac{1}{2}Mv^2$.

Similarly in the case of angular motion. A body whose moment of inertia is I is rotating at a speed of ω rad/s after turning through an angle of θ radians from rest.

Acceleration of body is given by

$$\omega^2 - 0^2 = 2\alpha\theta$$

$$\alpha = \frac{\omega^2}{2\theta} \text{ rad/s}^2$$

Torque to provide this acceleration $= I\alpha$

$$= \frac{I\omega^2}{2\theta}$$

Work done by torque = torque × angle turned through in radians

$$= \frac{I\omega^2}{2\theta} \times \theta$$

$$= \frac{1}{2}I\omega^2$$

This work is stored in the rotating body as *kinetic energy of rotation*. Hence the kinetic energy of a mass, moment of inertia I, rotating at ω rad/s is $\frac{1}{2}I\omega^2$.

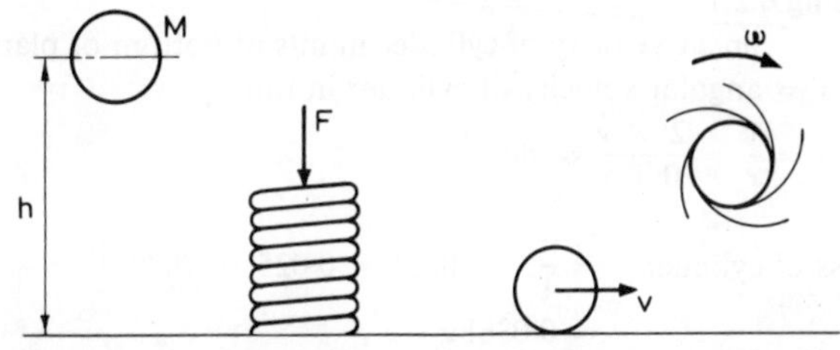

Fig.6.1 Energy—simple forms

Conservation of Energy

The principle of conservation of energy states that *energy cannot be created or destroyed, but can be converted from one form to another*. This means that, unless some external force is applied, or external resistance overcome, the sum of the energies possessed by a body at any instant will remain constant.

The general expression connecting energy and work done can be written

work done by external force = change of energy + work done against resistances

This is the basis of an alternative analysis of the power distribution of a machine, referred to on page 35.

The power of a machine is used to overcome:

a) external resistances or loads,
b) frictional effects within the machine, and
c) to increase the energy of both the machine and the load.

Example 6.1 A solid cylinder 25 mm diameter and 25 mm long is allowed to roll from the top of a plane 1·2 mm long inclined at an angle of 20° to the horizontal. Determine the linear velocity of the cylinder on reaching the bottom of the plane. Neglect any frictional resistances, and assume no slip. Take the density of the material as 7000 kg/m³.

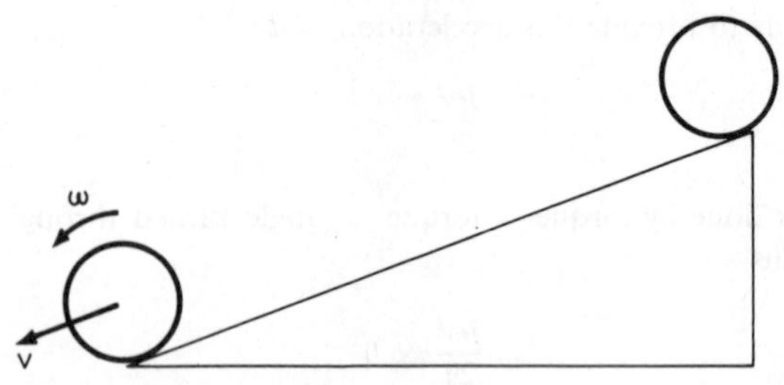

Fig.6.2 From potential to kinetic energy

The energy equation of motion is

Top of plane *Bottom of Plane*

$$\text{Potential energy} = \text{kinetic energy of translation} + \text{kinetic energy of rotation}$$

(See fig.6.2.)

Let v = linear velocity of cylinder in m/s at bottom of plane.

ω = angular velocity of cylinder in rad/s.

$$\omega = \frac{v}{r} = \frac{2 \times v}{0{\cdot}025} = 80v$$

$$\text{Mass of cylinder} = \frac{\pi}{4} \times 0{\cdot}025^2 \times 0{\cdot}025 \times 7000$$
$$= 0{\cdot}086\,\text{kg}$$

$$\text{Weight of cylinder} = 0{\cdot}086 \times 9{\cdot}81 = 0{\cdot}84\,\text{N}$$

$$I \text{ for solid cylinder} = \text{mass} \times k^2$$
$$= \text{mass} \times \frac{r^2}{2}$$
$$= \tfrac{1}{2} \times 0{\cdot}086 \times (0{\cdot}025/2)^2$$
$$= 6{\cdot}7 \times 10^{-6}\,\text{kgm}^2$$

$$\text{Height of plane} = 1{\cdot}2 \sin 20° = 0{\cdot}41\,\text{m}$$

$$\text{Potential energy at top of plane} = Mgh$$
$$= 0{\cdot}84 \times 0{\cdot}41$$
$$= 0{\cdot}345\,\text{J}$$

$$\text{Kinetic energy of translation} = \tfrac{1}{2}Mv^2$$
$$= \tfrac{1}{2} \times 0{\cdot}086v^2$$
$$= 0{\cdot}043v^2\,\text{J}$$

$$\text{Kinetic energy of rotation} = \tfrac{1}{2}I\omega^2$$
$$= \tfrac{1}{2} \times 6{\cdot}7 \times 10^{-6} \times (80v)^2$$
$$= 0{\cdot}0215v^2\,\text{J}$$

$$\text{Equation of energy: } 0{\cdot}345 = 0{\cdot}043v^2 + 0{\cdot}0215v^2$$
$$v^2 = \frac{0{\cdot}345}{0{\cdot}0645} = 5{\cdot}35$$
$$v = 2{\cdot}31\,\text{m/s}$$
$$\omega = 80v$$
$$= 80 \times 2{\cdot}31$$
$$= 184{\cdot}8\,\text{rad/s}$$

i.e. At the bottom of the plane, the cylinder will have a linear velocity of 2·31 m/s, and an angular velocity of 184·8 rad/s.

Example 6.2 A train, mass 250 tonnes, moving with a uniform velocity of 63 km/h along a horizontal track begins to climb up an inclined bank having a slope of 1 in 80. During the climb, the engine exerts a constant tractive force of 22 000 N, whilst the resistances to motion remain constant at 65 N/tonne. Determine how far the train will climb up the bank before coming to a standstill. Give your answer in km.

$$\text{Mass of train} = 250 \times 10^3\,\text{kg}$$

$$\text{Velocity of train} = \frac{63 \times 10^3}{60 \times 60}$$
$$= 17{\cdot}5\,\text{m/s}$$

Kinetic energy of train at bottom of incline

$$= \tfrac{1}{2}Mv^2$$
$$= \tfrac{1}{2} \times 250 \times 10^3 \times 17{\cdot}5^2$$
$$= 383 \times 10^5\,\text{J}$$

$$\text{Potential energy at bottom of incline} = 0\,\text{J}$$

Let x = distance travelled up the plane, in km.

$$\text{Vertical distance travelled} = \frac{1000x}{80}$$
$$= 12{\cdot}5x\,\text{m}$$

$$\text{Potential energy at end of climb} = Mgh$$
$$= 250 \times 10^3 \times 9{\cdot}81 \times 12{\cdot}5x\,\text{J}$$
$$= 30{\cdot}6x \times 10^6\,\text{J}$$

Kinetic energy at end of climb = 0 (engine at rest)

$$\text{Resistance to motion} = 65 \times 250$$
$$= 16\,250\,\text{N}$$

$$\text{Work done against resistance} = \text{force} \times \text{distance}$$
$$= 16\,250 \times 1000x$$
$$= 16{\cdot}25x \times 10^6$$

$$\text{Work done by tractive force} = 22\,000 \times 1000x$$
$$= 22x \times 10^6$$

Total energy at beginning of incline + work done by tractive force = total energy at end of incline + work done against resistance

$$38{\cdot}3 \times 10^6 + 22x \times 10^6 = 30{\cdot}6x \times 10^6 + 16{\cdot}25x \times 10^6$$
$$38{\cdot}3 = (30{\cdot}6 + 16{\cdot}25 - 22)x$$
$$x = 1{\cdot}54\,\text{km}$$

i.e. The train will travel 1·54 km up the plane before coming to rest.

Example 6.3 A projectile whose mass is 0·5 kg is fired with a velocity of 100 m/s at 60° to the horizontal. Determine its velocity after 2 seconds. This is an alternative solution to that indicated in Chapter 2.

Initial vertical component of velocity $= 100 \sin 60°$
$= 86{\cdot}6\,\text{m/s}$

Height of projectile after 2 seconds $= ut - \frac{1}{2}gt^2$
$= 86{\cdot}6 \times 2 - \frac{1}{2}g \times 2^2$
$= 153{\cdot}6\,\text{m}$

Mass of projectile = 0·5 kg
Kinetic energy of projectile at instant of firing
$= \frac{1}{2}Mv^2$
$= \frac{1}{2} \times 0{\cdot}5 \times 100^2\,\text{J}$
$= 2500\,\text{J}$

Potential energy at instant of firing = 0 J
Total energy of projectile = 2500 J
Neglecting any air resistance effects, we can say that during flight
potential energy + kinetic energy = constant
$= 2500\,\text{J}$

Potential energy after 2 seconds $= Mgh$
$= 0{\cdot}5 \times 9{\cdot}81 \times 153{\cdot}6$
$= 753\,\text{J}$

Kinetic energy after 2 seconds $= 2500 - 753$
$= 1747\,\text{J}$

Let v = velocity after 2 seconds, then

$$\tfrac{1}{2}Mv^2 = 1747$$
$$\tfrac{1}{2} \times 0{\cdot}5v^2 = 1747$$
$$v = 84\,\text{m/s}$$

Vertical component of velocity after 2 seconds:

$$v = u - gt$$
$$= 86{\cdot}6 \quad 2g$$
$$= 67\,\text{m/s}$$

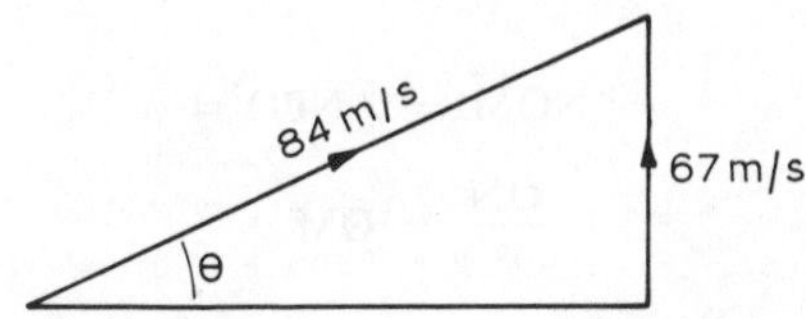

Fig.6.3

Note that this is positive, and therefore the projectile is still rising, with consequent upward inclination of velocity given by

$$\sin\theta = \frac{67}{84} = 0{\cdot}8$$

$$\theta = 53°$$

i.e. The velocity of projectile is 84 m/s, upwards at 53° to the horizontal.

Example 6.4 A uniform rod 3 m long, of mass 2 kg, swings about a fixed horizontal axis through one end. The centre of gravity of the rod is 1·5 m from the axis, and its radius of gyration about the axis is 1·75 m. The rod is at rest in a horizontal position, and is then released. Determine its kinetic energy and angular velocity when passing through the lowest position.

Moment of inertia of rod about support axis $= Mk^2$
$= 2 \times 1{\cdot}75^2$
$= 6{\cdot}12\,\text{kg m}^2$

Consider the datum line for the energies to pass through the lowest position of the centre of gravity (fig.6.4).

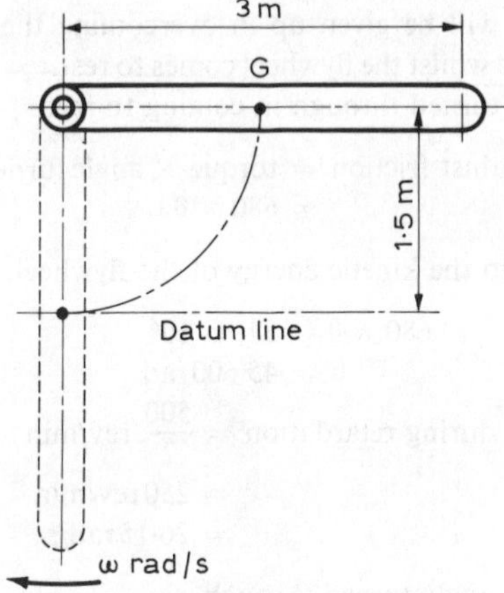

Fig.6.4

When the rod is at rest in the horizontal position, it has potential energy but no kinetic energy. In this position, the centre of gravity is 1·5 m above the datum line.

Potential energy $= Mgh$
$= 2 \times 9{\cdot}81 \times 1{\cdot}5$
$= 29{\cdot}43\,\text{J}$

Total energy of rod $= 29{\cdot}43 + 0$
$= 29{\cdot}43\,\text{J}$

which is constant through the swing. At the lowest position, the potential energy is zero (height of centre of gravity above datum line = 0).

∴ Kinetic energy at lowest point = 29·43 J.

Let ω = angular velocity of rod at lowest position.

$$\tfrac{1}{2}I\omega^2 = 29{\cdot}43$$
$$\tfrac{1}{2} \times 6{\cdot}12 \times \omega^2 = 29{\cdot}43$$
$$\omega = 3{\cdot}1\,\text{rad/s}.$$

i.e. At the lowest position, the kinetic energy is 29·43 J, and the angular velocity of rotation is 3·1 rad/s.

Example 6.5 A flywheel has a radius of gyration of 1·5 m and a mass of 10 tonnes. Find its kinetic energy when running at a speed of 500 rev/min. If a resisting torque of 680 N m is applied to the wheel, determine the time taken to bring it to rest.

$$\text{Moment of inertia of flywheel} = Mk^2 = 10 \times 10^3 \times 1{\cdot}5^2 = 2{\cdot}25 \times 10^4\,\text{kg}\,\text{m}^2$$

$$500\,\text{rev/min} = \frac{500 \times 2\pi}{60} = 52{\cdot}4\,\text{rad/s}$$

$$\text{Kinetic energy of flywheel} = \tfrac{1}{2}I\omega^2 = \tfrac{1}{2} \times 2{\cdot}25 \times 10^4 \times 52{\cdot}4^2 = 31 \times 10^6\,\text{J}$$

This energy will be given up in overcoming the frictional resisting torque whilst the flywheel comes to rest.
Let θ = angle turned through in coming to rest.

$$\text{Work done against friction} = \text{torque} \times \text{angle turned through} = 680 \times \theta\,\text{J}$$

Equating this to the kinetic energy of the flywheel,

$$680 \times \theta = 31 \times 10^6$$
$$\theta = 45\,600\,\text{rad}$$

$$\text{Average speed during retardation} = \frac{500}{2}\,\text{rev/min} = 250\,\text{rev/min} = 26{\cdot}15\,\text{rad/s}$$

$$\text{Time taken} = \frac{\text{angle turned through}}{\text{average velocity}} = \frac{45\,600}{26{\cdot}15} = 1740\ \text{seconds}$$

i.e. The flywheel comes to rest in 29 minutes.

Alternative solution

Resisting torque = moment of inertia × retardation

$$\text{Retardation} = \frac{\text{torque}}{I} = \frac{680}{2{\cdot}25 \times 10^4} = 0{\cdot}0302\,\text{rad/s}^2$$

Equation of motion:

$$\omega_2 - \omega_1 = \alpha t$$
$$\omega_2 = 0 \text{ (at rest)}$$
$$\omega_1 = 52{\cdot}4\,\text{rad/s}$$
$$\alpha = -\,0{\cdot}0302\,\text{rad/s}^2 \text{ (retarding)}$$
$$t = ?$$
$$0 - 52{\cdot}4 = -\,0{\cdot}0302t$$
$$t = 1740 \text{ seconds, as above.}$$

Fluctuation of Energy, and the Flywheel

In a reciprocating-type engine, the force on the piston due to explosion of gases or pressure of steam vapour is converted into a torque on the crankshaft by means of the connecting-rod and the crank mechanism. Figure 6·5 indicates the mechanism, in which OC is the crank and CP the connecting-rod.

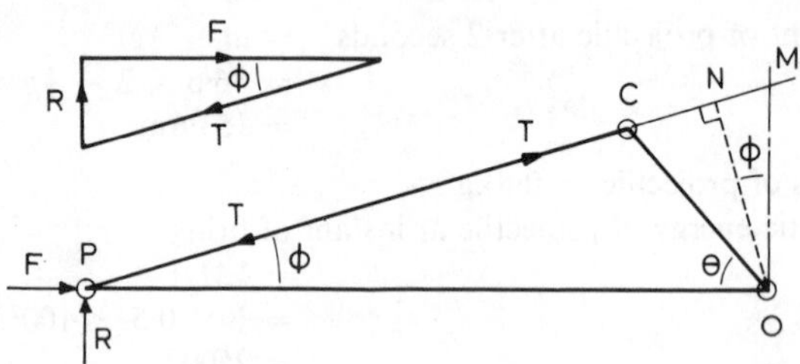

Fig.6.5 Forces on gudgeon pin of engine

A force, F, is produced on the piston, which in turn produces the thrust, T, in the connecting-rod. The third force acting at the piston P is the guide reaction R. From the triangle of forces for the point P it will be seen that

$$T = \frac{F}{\cos\phi}$$

where ϕ is the angle made by the connecting-rod and the horizontal.

Now the thrust, T, in the connecting-rod produces a turning moment on the crankshaft.

Torque produced by $T = T.\text{ON}$

where ON is drawn perpendicular to PC, produced if necessary.

$$\text{Hence torque} = \frac{F.\text{ON}}{\cos\phi}$$

Draw OM perpendicular to OP, and let PC produced cut this line in M. From the geometry of the figure it will be seen that

$$\angle\text{NOM} = \angle\text{NPO} = \phi$$

and that
$$\frac{\text{ON}}{\cos\phi} = \text{OM}$$

Thus the crankshaft torque produced by the force $F = F.\text{OM}$.

Since OM varies, it follows that the crankshaft torque produced by the mechanism will be a varying quantity. In fact, one of the disadvantages of the mechanism arises from the fact that the maximum force applied to the piston occurs near to the point in the stroke for which the crank and the connecting-rod are in the same straight line, when no torque can be transmitted.

The variation of torque can be represented on a diagram known as a turning-moment diagram, in which the torque is plotted against crank angle, θ, in radians. The area enclosed by this diagram will represent work done by the engine during the cycle of operations. Figure 6.6 illustrates the torque diagrams of some of the more common engines.

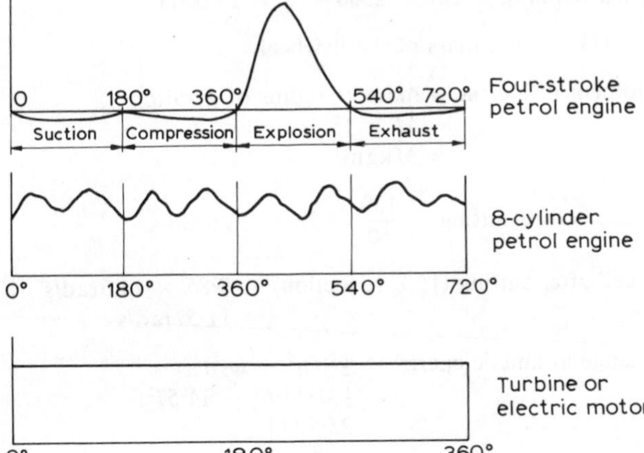

Fig.6.6 Typical turning-moment diagrams

1 Four-stroke single-cylinder engine (petrol, gas or oil). An explosion takes place in the cylinder once every four strokes, or once every two revolutions.
2 V8 engine, four-stroke. There are now eight cylinders, arranged in two banks and connected on the same crankshaft, so that now there are eight explosions in two revolutions, or four explosions in each revolution.
3 Turbine, electric motor, or Pelton (water) wheel. Here there is no crank and connecting-rod mechanism. The torque is practically constant throughout the whole of the revolution. It is here that the turbine is shown to great advantage.

Now at the end of the cycle of operation, the work done by the engine must just equal the work required to overcome the external load (including, of course, those additional quantities: friction and windage); otherwise the engine will either accelerate or slow down and stop if it produces more or less energy than is required. The function of the governor on an engine is to control variation in speed from cycle to cycle by allowing less or more of the working fluid to enter the cylinder. Assuming that the governor is operating satisfactorily, we can say that energy produced per cycle is equal to that demanded per cycle to overcome the load. Usually loads are variable quantities, and there may be a cyclic variation of the torque to overcome the load.

In fig.6.7 there are illustrated the two variable torques, and you should be quite clear in your minds as to the difference between them. The full line indicates the crankshaft torque produced by the engine, whilst the dotted line indicates the variable torque required to overcome the load. Now, in one

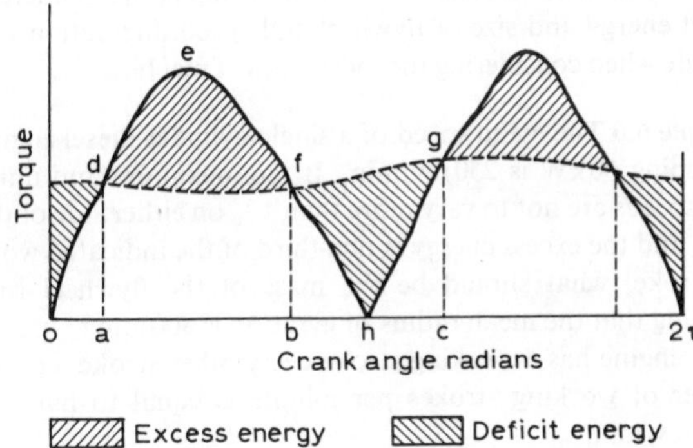

Fig.6.7 Turning-moment diagram and fluctuation of energy

complete 0 to 2π radians cycle, the area under the turning-moment diagram will be just equal to the area under the load-torque diagram, since the work done by the engine just equals work to overcome the load.

It will, however, be seen that during the cycle there are many variations involving excesses and deficiencies of energy supplied over energy required. For example, whilst the crank turns from angle *a* to angle *b*, the work done by the engine is represented by the area *adefb*, whilst the work required to overcome the load is represented by the area *adfb*. Thus the area *def* represents the excess work done by the engine.

Similarly, while the crank moves from angle *b* to angle *c*, the work done by the engine is represented by the area *bfh* plus the area *hgc*, whilst the work required to overcome the load is represented by the area *bfgc*. Thus area *fgh* represents the deficiency of work done by the engine during that portion of the cycle.

Throughout the day's run, this alternation of excess and deficiency of energy takes place many times per second, a characteristic of reciprocating engines which is one of the causes of excessive vibrations. The flywheel plays a very important part in engine operation, acting as a reservoir for the energy variation. When excess energy is supplied by the engine, it is stored as kinetic energy in the flywheel, whose speed, and consequently the engine speed, increases. Similarly, when the external load demands more energy than the engine can produce, the deficiency of the engine is made good by the supply of stored kinetic energy from the flywheel, whose speed then falls. There is thus a cyclic variation of engine speed which can be limited by the size of the flywheel. The larger the flywheel, the smaller the speed variation.

Thus, whilst both governor and flywheel control the speed of the engine, their particular functions are different. The governor keeps the speed of the engine at a nominal figure, say 300 rev/min, despite any variation in load. The flywheel cuts down the tendency of the engine to make rapid changes of speed during each revolution; it keeps the engine speed between two predetermined values, say 295 and 305 rev/min.

A more detailed analysis of the relationship between fluctuation of energy and size of flywheel and speed fluctuation will be made when considering the mechanics of machines.

Example 6.6 The mean speed of a single-cylinder diesel engine developing 60 kW is 250 rev/min. If the maximum and minimum speeds are not to vary more than 1 % on either side of the mean, and the excess energy is one-third of the indicated work per stroke, what should be the mass of the flywheel rim, assuming that the mean radius of gyration is 800 mm? UEI

The engine has a working stroke every other stroke, i.e. the number of working strokes per minute is equal to half the speed rev/min.

In this case, the engine has 125 working strokes per minute, i.e. $\frac{125}{60}$ per second.

$$\text{Work done per stroke} = \frac{60 \times 10^3 \times 60}{125} = 28\,800\,\text{J}$$

$$\text{Excess energy} = \tfrac{1}{3} \times 28\,800\,\text{J} = 9600\,\text{J}$$

This energy causes an increase in the speed of the flywheel.

$$250\,\text{rev/min} = 26{\cdot}2\,\text{rad/s}$$

Max. speed (ω_2) = $26{\cdot}2 + 0{\cdot}26 = 26{\cdot}46$ rad/s
Min. speed (ω_1) = $26{\cdot}2 - 0{\cdot}26 = 25{\cdot}94$ rad/s
Let I = moment of inertia of flywheel (kgm²) and M = mass of flywheel (kg).

$$\begin{aligned}\text{Change in kinetic energy} &= \tfrac{1}{2}I\omega_2^2 - \tfrac{1}{2}I\omega_1^2 \\ &= \tfrac{1}{2}I(\omega_2^2 - \omega_1^2) \\ &= \tfrac{1}{2}I(26{\cdot}46^2 - 25{\cdot}94^2)\,\text{J} \\ &= I\frac{(26{\cdot}46 + 25{\cdot}92)}{2}(26{\cdot}46 - 25{\cdot}9)\,\text{J} \\ &= I \times 26{\cdot}2 \times 0{\cdot}52\,\text{J} \\ &= 13{\cdot}6I\,\text{J}\end{aligned}$$

Equating this to the excess energy,

$$\begin{aligned}13{\cdot}6I &= 9600 \\ I &= 705\,\text{kgm}^2 \\ \therefore Mk^2 &= 705 \\ M \times 0{\cdot}8^2 &= 705 \\ M &= 1102\,\text{kg}\end{aligned}$$

i.e. Mass of flywheel rim necessary to control speed is 1102 kg.

Example 6.7 A shearing machine has to cut flat steel strips 100 mm wide by 25 mm thick, and it may be assumed that 6 joules of work are required per square millimetre cut. The flywheel, of radius of gyration 1 m, has a speed of 130 rev/min at the start of each cut. Assuming that the energy required for cutting is supplied wholly by the flywheel, and its speed reduction is not to exceed 15 % of the maximum, determine (a) the mass of flywheel necessary, and (b) the torque that must be applied to the flywheel so that it can regain full speed in the 3·3 seconds available. EMEU

a) Area to be cut = 100 × 25 = 2500 mm²
Work required to cut = 2500 × 6 = 15 000 J

Let M kg be the mass of the flywheel.

$$\begin{aligned}\text{Moment of inertia} &= \text{mass} \times \text{radius of gyration}^2 \\ &= M \times 1^2 \\ &= M\,\text{kgm}^2\end{aligned}$$

$$\text{Speed before cutting} = \frac{130}{60} \times 2\pi = 13{\cdot}6\,\text{rad/s}$$

$$\begin{aligned}\text{Speed after cutting (15\% reduction)} &= 0{\cdot}85 \times 13{\cdot}6\,\text{rad/s} \\ &= 11{\cdot}57\,\text{rad/s}\end{aligned}$$

$$\begin{aligned}\text{Change in kinetic energy} &= \tfrac{1}{2}I(\omega_1^2 - \omega_2^2) \\ &= \tfrac{1}{2}M(13{\cdot}6^2 - 11{\cdot}57^2) \\ &= 25{\cdot}5M\,\text{J}\end{aligned}$$

This will be equal to the work done in cutting.

$$\begin{aligned}25{\cdot}5\,M &= 15\,000 \\ M &= 590\,\text{kg}\end{aligned}$$

b) Acceleration required to attain full speed in 3·3 seconds:

$$\begin{aligned}\omega_1 - \omega_2 &= \alpha t \\ 13{\cdot}6 - 11{\cdot}57 &= 3{\cdot}3\alpha \\ \alpha &= 0{\cdot}615\,\text{rad/s}^2\end{aligned}$$

$$\begin{aligned}\text{Moment of inertia of flywheel} &= 590 \times 1^2 \\ &= 590\,\text{kgm}^2\end{aligned}$$

$$\begin{aligned}\text{Torque} &= I\alpha \\ &= 590 \times 0{\cdot}615 \\ &= 363\,\text{Nm}\end{aligned}$$

i.e. The mass of the flywheel is 590 kg, and the necessary torque is 363 Nm.

Example 6.8 Explain the function of the flywheel. A certain machine tool does its work intermittently. The machine is fitted with a flywheel of mass 180 kg; the mean diameter of the rim is 700 mm, and it runs at a speed of 400 rev/min between the operations. The machine is driven continuously by a motor, and each operation takes 8 seconds. When the machine is doing its work, the speed drops from 400 to 250 rev/min. Calculate the required minimum power of the motor when there are five operations performed per minute. How much energy is expended in performing each operation? ULCI

It is assumed that the mass of the flywheel is concentrated in the rim, and therefore the radius of gyration will be equal to the mean radius of the rim, i.e. $\frac{0{\cdot}7}{2}$ m.

Moment of inertia of flywheel $= 180 \times \left(\frac{0{\cdot}7}{2}\right)^2$

$= 22\,\text{kg m}^2$

Maximum speed of flywheel $= \frac{400 \times 2\pi}{60}$

$= 41{\cdot}9\,\text{rad/s}$

Minimum speed of flywheel $= \frac{250 \times 2\pi}{60}$

$= 26{\cdot}2\,\text{rad/s}$

Energy expended during operation $= \frac{1}{2}I\omega_1^2 - \frac{1}{2}I\omega_2^2$

$= \frac{1}{2}I(\omega_1^2 - \omega_2^2)$

$= \frac{1}{2} \times 22(41{\cdot}9^2 - 26{\cdot}2^2)$

$= 11\,800\,\text{J}$

Five operations per minute means a complete operational cycle of 12 seconds. During 8 seconds, work is done, and the flywheel gives up energy whilst its speed drops from 400 to 250 rev/min. There is then a 4-second period during which the motor has to supply the necessary energy to accelerate the flywheel from 250 to 400 rev/min, in readiness for the next operation.

Flywheel must receive 11 800 J of energy in 4 seconds.

∴ Motor must supply energy at the rate of $\frac{11\,800}{4} = 2950\,\text{J/s}$.

∴ Minimum power of motor is 2·95 kW

i.e. The energy expended in performing an operation is 11 800 J, the minimum power of the driving motor being 2·95 kW.

Exercise 6

The weight of a mass of M kg may be taken as 9·81 M newtons.

1 Determine the final linear velocity of a cylinder 50 mm in diameter, mass 0·5 kg, which is allowed to roll down a plane 1·5 m long inclined at 30° to the horizontal. Neglect any frictional resistances, and assume no slip.

2 Determine the kinetic energy of a four-wheel truck, total mass 9 kg, travelling at 3 m/s. Each wheel has a mass of 1 kg, and is 300 mm in diameter, having a radius of gyration of 100 mm.

3 A block of steel of mass 1 tonne is allowed to fall through a height of 2 m on to the end of a vertical steel pile, to drive it into the ground. If the ground resists penetration of the pile with a constant force of 200 kN, determine the distance which the pile is driven into the ground. You can assume that 25 % of the available energy is dissipated at the impact, and is not available for doing work on the pile.

4 The friction and windage resistance to motion of a diesel-electric train is equal to 44 N/tonne. The train, which is travelling at 90 km/h along a level track, comes to an ascending incline of one in a hundred. If the supply power is switched off, how far will the train travel up the incline before it comes to rest, assuming that the resistance remains constant?

5 The flywheel of a shearing machine has a mass of 1600 kg, and a radius of gyration of 670 mm. The speeds of the flywheel immediately before and after the cutting operation are 150 and 120 rev/min respectively. Calculate (a) the energy absorbed in the cutting operation, and (b) the torque required to build up the speed of the flywheel from 120 to 150 rev/min in $\frac{3}{4}$ second, assuming uniform acceleration. EMEU

6 A solid cast-iron flywheel is 1·2 m in diameter, and is of uniform thickness throughout. Its mass is 1700 kg. If this wheel attains a speed of 1200 rev/min from rest in 45 seconds, determine the torque applied, and its kinetic energy at this speed. Assume the frictional torque is constant, and equal to 16 N m. If the driving torque be now removed, calculate the kinetic energy of the wheel after a further 5000 revolutions. EMEU

7 What is the function of a flywheel? A flywheel of mass 360 kg has a radius of gyration of 600 mm. If the flywheel is rotating at 600 rev/min, determine what uniform torque will be required to bring it to rest in 30 seconds, and how many revolutions it will make before coming to rest. UEI

8 A petrol engine is running light at 500 rev/min when the ignition is cut out. The engine comes to rest in 50 revolutions. If the mass and radius of gyration of the rotating parts are 5·5 kg and 600 mm respectively, neglecting the inertia of all the other parts, find the power before switching off. What is the kinetic energy of the rotating parts at 500 rev/min?

9 Explain the terms angular velocity and angular acceleration, and state what is meant by the radius of gyration of a flywheel.

Find the energy stored in a flywheel of mass 4 tonnes rotating at 200 rev/min, if its radius of gyration is 1·2 m. Find also the uniform torque necessary to bring it to rest in $1\frac{1}{2}$ minutes. UEI

10 Explain the term 'moment of inertia', as applied to a rotating body.

A flywheel stores 13·5 kJ of energy when it rotates at 200 rev/min. What is its moment of inertia and the percentage of energy lost when its speed is reduced to 45 rev/min? If the time taken for the reduction is 2 minutes, find how many more revolutions the wheel will make before coming to rest, the retarding torque remaining constant. UEI

11 State what is meant by 'moment of inertia', as applied to a rotating body.

What must be the moment of inertia of a flywheel if the increased energy stored is 6·75 kJ when the speed of rotation is increased from 120 to 160 rev/min?

Find the torque that must be applied to bring about this change of speed in 10 seconds. UEI

12 Find the mass of a flywheel to give up 11 kJ of energy while the speed falls 5% from 180 rev/min. Radius of gyration 1·2 m.

Calculate also the constant torque necessary to increase the speed of the flywheel from zero to 180 rev/min in 4 minutes. NCTEC

13 State what you understand by the term 'radius of gyration', as applied to a rotating body. Calculate the energy stored by a flywheel rotating at 240 rev/min, if it has a mass of 8 tonnes, and a radius of gyration of 1·5 m. Find also the uniform torque required to bring the flywheel to rest in 2 minutes. NCTEC

14 A uniform rod, 2 m long, mass 1·4 kg, is free to swing about a fixed horizontal axis through one end. The rod is allowed to swing from an initial horizontal position. What will be its kinetic energy as it passes through its lowest position, and its angular velocity there? The centre of gravity is 1 m from the axis, and the radius of gyration about the axis is 1·2 m. NCTEC

15 By considering the work done in bringing a body of mass M kg uniformly from rest to velocity v m/s, derive the expression for kinetic energy $E = \frac{1}{2}Mv^2$.

A body of mass 7 kg falls freely from rest through a height of 9 m, when it breaks through a roof before continuing its fall. If 110 J of work are done in the break-through, calculate the speed at which the body emerges from the roof. NCTEC

16 A flywheel of mass 3650 kg and radius of gyration 1 m is acted upon by a constant torque. If the speed of the flywheel falls from 120 to 30 rev/min in 3 minutes, find (a) the magnitude of the torque, and (b) the loss of kinetic energy. NCTEC

17 If a body is rotating about a fixed axis, state the connection between an applied torque and the angular acceleration; hence derive an expression giving the kinetic energy of a rotating body.

The moment of inertia of a flywheel is equivalent to that of a mass of 275 kg rotating at a radius of 0·5 m. If the speed of the flywheel falls from 780 to 600 rev/min, calculate the loss of energy. NCTEC

18 (a) Derive, from first principles, an expression for the kinetic energy of a body of moment of inertia I, which is rotating about a fixed axis with angular velocity ω. State clearly the units for each term in the derived expression.

(b) A bullet of mass 85 kg travelling at 200 m/s will penetrate 125 mm into a fixed block of wood. Determine the velocity with which the bullet will emerge if fired into a block of similar wood 50 mm thick.

You may assume that the resistance of the wood is uniform, and that it has the same value in each case. NCTEC

19 A machine press is worked by an electric motor delivering 2·25 kW continuously. At the start of an operation, a flywheel of moment of inertia 30 kgm² on the machine is rotating at 240 rev/min. The pressing operation requires 4 kJ of energy, and occupies 1·0 second. Determine (a) the reduction in speed of the flywheel after each pressing, and (b) the number of pressings that can be made in 1 hour. Neglect friction losses. ULCI

20 The excess energy to be stored in each cycle by the flywheel of an engine is obtained from a graph of the turning moment on the crankshaft plotted against the crank angle, the scales used being 10 mm = 300 N/m and 10 mm = 20°. If the excess energy to be stored is represented on the diagram by an area of 2600 mm², determine (a) the fluctuation of energy, and (b) the fluctuation of speed as a percentage above and below the mean speed. The mass of the flywheel is 160 kg, it has a radius of gyration of 530 mm, and the mean speed is 400 rev/min.

Also determine the moment of inertia of the additional flywheel required to keep the fluctuation of speed within $\pm 1\%$ of the mean speed. ULCI

21 A rope passes over a pulley, and attached to each end is a mass of 5·5 kg. An additional mass of 1·8 kg is added to one end, and the resulting motion is 4·3 m in the first 5 seconds. The pulley is 600 mm in diameter, and of mass 55 kg.

Calculate the tension in the rope on each side of the pulley, the moment of inertia and radius of gyration of the pulley, and the energy stored in the pulley after 5 seconds. ULCI

22 A punching machine has a flywheel which stores energy used in punching holes. The mass of the flywheel is 440 kg, and this can be considered as concentrated in the rim, whose inner and outer radii are 365 mm and 485 mm respectively. When punching 20 mm diameter holes in 20 mm thick steel plates, the speed of the flywheel drops from 240 to 180 rev/min, and 75% of the energy drop is used in punching the hole.

Determine the average force exerted on the plate. NCTEC

23 Prove that the kinetic energy of a rotating body is given by $\frac{1}{2}I\omega^2$, where I is the moment of inertia about the axis of rotation, and ω is the angular velocity.

The flywheel of a punching machine has a mass of 160 kg, and a radius of gyration of 750 mm. During the punching stroke, the speed of revolution decreases from 150 to 80 rev/min. If 80% of the available energy is available for punching, determine the maximum plate thickness through which a 25 mm diameter hole can be punched. Take the ultimate shear stress of the plate to be 370 N/mm². ULCI

Chapter 7

Impulse and Momentum

The ideas of impulse and momentum are very closely related. We speak of the impulse of a force, and the momentum of a mass. An impulsive force is usually a force applied for a very short interval of time, e.g. the sharp blow of a hammer, an explosion, or the impact of two billiard balls.

If a force F acts during an interval δt (we use δt rather than t to suggest a small interval of time, although δt may have any value we choose) the impulse of the force is measured by the product $F\delta t$. The units are newton seconds.

Momentum of a mass has been defined already. It is equal to the product of the mass of the body and the velocity with which it may be moving.

Consider a mass of M kg (its weight will be Mg N) moving with velocity v_1. A force F N is applied to this mass for a period of δt seconds, at the end of which time the velocity has increased to v_2.

The acceleration produced by the force $= \dfrac{\text{force}}{\text{mass}} = \dfrac{F}{M}$ m/s²

The velocity at the end of this period $= v_2 = v_1 + a\delta t$

$$v^2 = v_1 + \frac{F}{M}\delta t$$

Multiplying by M, and rearranging, $F\delta t = Mv_2 - Mv_1$

The expression on the left of the equation is equal to the impulse of the force, whilst that on the right is the change of momentum that has taken place. Thus we obtain the fundamental relationship between impulse and momentum:

impulse of a force is equal to change of momentum produced. (Reminder: force is equal to rate of change of momentum.)

Conservation of Momentum

If two elastic bodies, A and B, travelling in the same direction [fig.7.1 (i)], collide, the force which A exerts on B is equal and opposite to the force which B exerts on A, since action and reaction are equal and opposite. Let this force be F [fig.7.1 (ii)]. The duration of the collision is very short, and is equal to δt; therefore an impulsive force acts on A, and causes a corresponding change of momentum. Similarly, an impulsive force acts on B, causing a corresponding change of momentum. But the impulse of the force is the same in each case, and equal to $F\delta t$. It follows that the magnitudes of the change in momentum of A and of B will be equal.

Now it will be clear from fig.7.1 (i) that the force will tend to reduce A's velocity and increase B's. Consequently, the momentum of A will be increased by the same amount as the momentum of B is decreased. In other words, the sum of the momentum before the impact will be equal to the sum of the momentum after impact. This leads to the idea of the conservation of momentum, which implies that *the total momentum before impact is equal to the total momentum after impact.*

Warning

It will be found that, except in the theoretical case of perfectly elastic bodies, there is always a loss of kinetic energy after impact, and students should guard against any tendency to solve problems of this type by suggesting that the energy before impact is equal to the energy after impact. A certain amount of energy is required to make the sound of the impact, other energy appears in the form of heat, whilst deformation of the bodies at contact is produced only at the expense of kinetic energy.

Collision of Elastic Bodies

The general behaviour of bodies in collision involves the elasticity of the bodies concerned, and introduces a coefficient known as the *coefficient of restitution*. If a perfectly elastic body is dropped on to a perfectly hard, rigid slab, theoretically it should return to the same height from which it was dropped. This means that the velocity after impact would be equal and opposite to that before impact. On the other hand, if a perfectly non-elastic body (putty is a good example) is dropped on to the slab, there would be no rebound, and the velocity after impact would be zero. The rebound of any other type of body will lie somewhere between these two examples.

The relationship governing velocity before and after impact is given as follows.

If two bodies collide, their relative velocity after impact is equal to their relative velocity before impact multiplied by a coefficient of restitution whose value, depending upon the elasticity of the material, lies between −1 for a perfectly elastic body and 0 for a non-elastic body.

Relative velocity after impact $= -C \times$ relative velocity before impact.

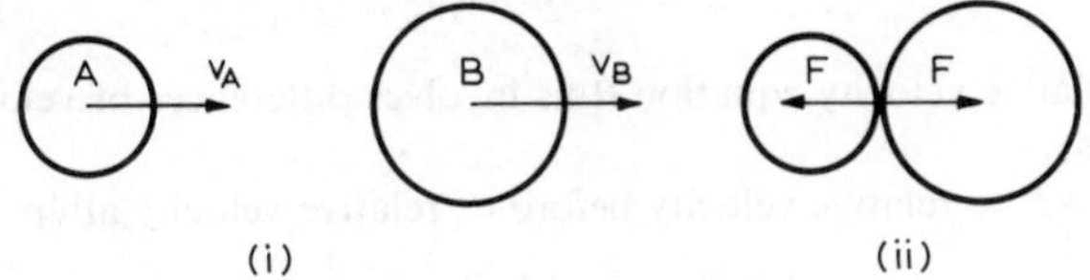

Fig.7.1 Impulse and collision

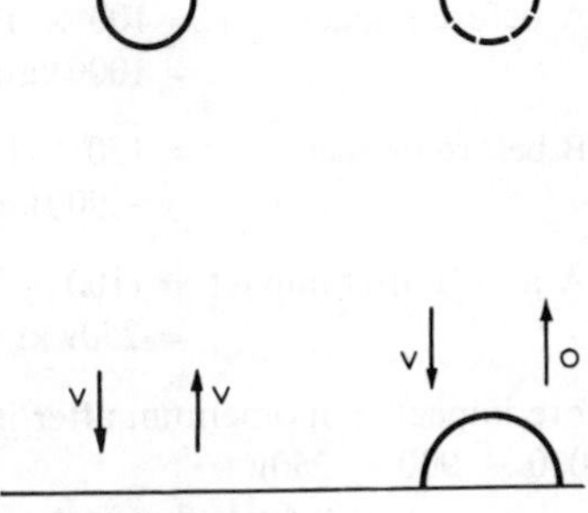

Fig.7.2 Perfectly elastic and perfectly plastic

Problems dealing with impact are solved by the use of two laws.

1 Momentum:

total momentum before = *total momentum after*

2 Relative velocity:

relative velocity after = $-C \times$ *relative velocity before*

(REMINDER. In practice, kinetic energy after impact is less than kinetic energy before.)

One important conclusion which is reached in our consideration of impulse and momentum is that the momentum of a body or system of bodies can be changed only by the application of an external force. *Any collision between the bodies themselves will not affect the total momentum possessed by them.* An internal explosion in a body moving through space, such as a shell or rocket, will break the body into a number of small pieces, each with their own individual velocities and momentum. But the sum of the momentum of these smaller bodies will still be equal to the momentum of the original. Theoretically, the centre of gravity of the system of smaller bodies will continue in the same path as that described by the larger body before the explosion.

Example 7.1 Two trucks travelling in the same straight line collide, and remain locked together after impact. Truck A has a mass of 100 kg and has a velocity of 10 m/s due east. Truck B has a mass of 150 kg and has a velocity of 6 m/s due west. Determine the magnitude and direction of the velocity of the trucks after impact.

What is the total kinetic energy of the trucks (a) before impact, and (b) after impact? Account for any difference between (a) and (b). NCTEC

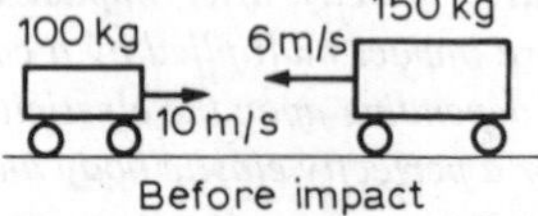

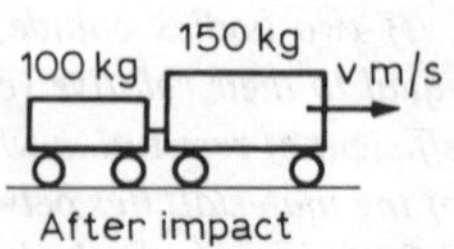

Fig.7.3

Easterly direction considered positive.

Let v = velocity of trucks after impact.

Momentum of A before impact $= 100 \times 10$
$= 1000$ kg m/s

Momentum of B before impact $= 150 \times (-6)$
$= -900$ kg m/s

Momentum of A and B after impact $= (100 + 150)v$
$= 250v$ kg m/s

Momentum before impact = momentum after impact

$$1000 - 900 = 250v$$
$$v = 0{\cdot}4 \text{ m/s due east}$$
(since v is positive)

Kinetic energy before impact $= \frac{1}{2}Mv^2$

for truck A $= \frac{1}{2} \times 100 \times 10^2$ J
$= 5$ kJ

for truck B $= \frac{1}{2} \times 150 \times 6^2$ J
$= 2{\cdot}7$ kJ

Total kinetic energy before impact $= (5 + 2{\cdot}7)$ kJ
$= 7{\cdot}7$ kJ

Kinetic energy after impact:

for truck A + truck B $= \frac{1}{2}(100 + 150) \times 0{\cdot}4^2$ J
$= 0{\cdot}02$ kJ

Loss of kinetic energy $= 7{\cdot}7 - 0{\cdot}02$ kJ
$= 7{\cdot}68$ kJ

i.e. The velocity after impact is 0·4 m/s due east. Total energy before impact is 7·7 kJ, whilst total energy after impact is 0·02 kJ.

The difference represents energy which would be dissipated in the form of heat and sound energy at the impact.

Direction of velocity is important in the momentum equations, but it does not affect the energy equation. Energy is not a vector quantity.

Example 7.2 Two perfectly elastic spheres are travelling in the same straight line. A has a mass of 5 kg and has a velocity of 2 m/s due east, whilst B, mass 3 kg, has a velocity of 4 m/s due west. Determine the velocity of the spheres after collision, and the loss of kinetic energy following the impact.

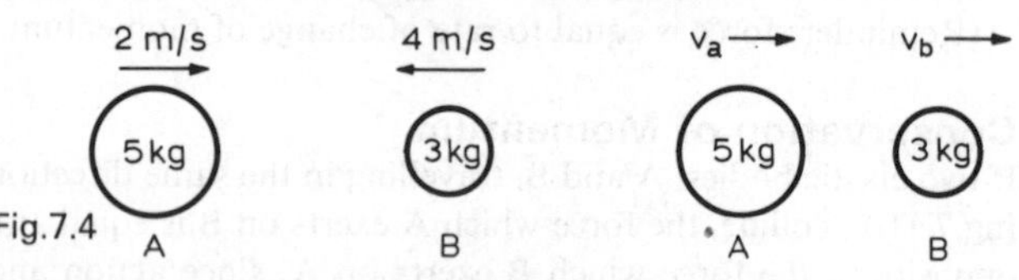

Fig.7.4

Easterly direction considered positive.

Coefficient of restitution is -1 for perfectly elastic materials.

Let v_A = velocity of A after impact,
v_B = velocity of B after impact.

It is assumed that these velocities are both easterly in direction; actual direction will be indicated by sign of velocity. Momentum equation (note direction of velocities fig.7.4):

Before impact After impact

$$(5 \times 2) + (3 \times -4) = 5v_A + 3v_B$$
$$-2 = 5v_A + 3v_B \quad . \quad . \quad . \quad (1)$$

Relative velocity equation (this involves differences of velocities):

$-1 \times$ relative velocity before = relative velocity after

$$-1 \times [2-(-4)] = v_A - v_B$$
$$-6 = v_A - v_B \quad . \quad . \quad . \quad (2)$$

Solution of (1) and (2) gives $v_A = -2\frac{1}{2}$
$v_B = +3\frac{1}{2}$

i.e. After impact, A is travelling at $2\frac{1}{2}$ m/s due west, and B at $3\frac{1}{2}$ m/s due east.

Change of kinetic energy.

Kinetic energy before impact $= \frac{1}{2}(5 \times 2^2) + \frac{1}{2}(3 \times 4^2) = 34\,\text{J}$

Kinetic energy after impact $= \frac{1}{2}(5 \times 2\frac{1}{2}^2) + \frac{1}{2}(3 \times 3\frac{1}{2}^2) = 34\,\text{J}$

Loss of kinetic energy $= 34 - 34 = 0\,\text{J}$.

i.e. There is no loss of kinetic energy (since the spheres are perfectly elastic).

Example 7.3 Explain briefly the principle of the conservation of linear momentum.

A pile driver, mass 1 tonne, falls freely through a distance of 5 m before striking the pile, mass 0·5 tonnes. When the pile is nearly fully driven, the average resistance is 700 kN. Determine the penetration per blow at that stage, and evaluate the kinetic energy lost at impact. IMECHE

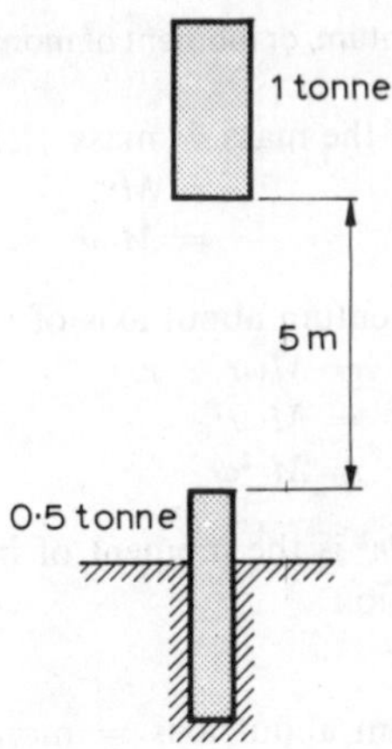

Fig.7.5

Striking velocity of driver $= \sqrt{2gh}$ (from $v^2 = u^2 + 2as$)
$= \sqrt{2g \times 5}$
$= 9{\cdot}9\,\text{m/s}$

Momentum of pile driver before impact $= 9{\cdot}9 \times 10^3\,\text{kg m/s}$

Momentum of pile before impact $= 0$ (at rest)

Total momentum before impact $= 9{\cdot}9 \times 10^3\,\text{kg m/s}$

Let v = common velocity after impact, m/s;
x = penetration of pile into ground, m.

Momentum after impact $= (1 + 0{\cdot}5)10^3 \times v$
$= 1{\cdot}5 \times 10^3 v$

Equating momentum before impact to momentum after,

$$1{\cdot}5 \times 10^3 v = 9{\cdot}9 \times 10^3$$
$$v = 6{\cdot}6\,\text{m/s}$$

Kinetic energy after impact $= \frac{1}{2}Mv^2$
$= \frac{1}{2}(1 + 0{\cdot}5) \times 10^3 \times 6{\cdot}6^2$
$= 32{\cdot}6\,\text{kJ}$

Work done against resistance = force × distance
$= 700 \times 10^3 \times x\,\text{J}$

Equating this to the kinetic energy,

$$32{\cdot}6 \times 10^3 = 700 \times 10^3 x$$
$$x = 0{\cdot}0468\,\text{m}$$

Kinetic energy before impact = kinetic energy of pile driver
= potential energy of pile driver before releasing
$= Mgh$
$= 1 \times 10^3 \times 9{\cdot}81 \times 5\,\text{J}$
$= 49{\cdot}05 \times 10^3\,\text{J}$

Kinetic energy lost at impact $= 49{\cdot}05 - 32{\cdot}6\,\text{kJ}$
$= 16{\cdot}45\,\text{kJ}$

i.e. Penetration into ground is 46·8 mm, and loss of energy at impact is 16·45 kJ.

Example 7.4 Two bodies of mass 5 kg and 3 kg respectively hang on light strings 2 m long, side by side and just in contact. The heavier body is drawn aside, keeping the string taut, until its centre of gravity is raised through a vertical distance of 600 mm. It is then released, and on impact the two masses adhere. Calculate (a) the velocity of the 5 kg mass just before impact, (b) the common velocity immediately after impact, (c) the loss of kinetic energy on impact, (d) the vertical height through which the centre of gravity of the combined system will rise, and (e) the tension in the string carrying the 5 kg mass just before impact. EMEU

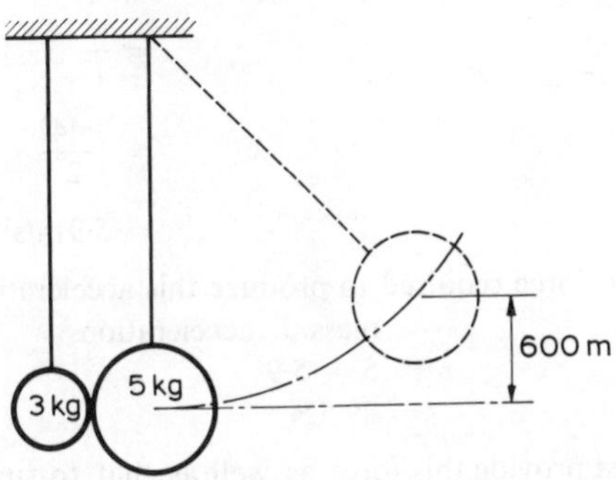

Fig.7.6

a) Velocity of 5 kg mass just before impact

$$= \sqrt{2gh}$$
$$= \sqrt{2 \times 9{\cdot}81 \times 0{\cdot}6}$$
$$= 3{\cdot}44\,\text{m/s}$$

b) Let v = common velocity after impact.

Momentum before impact = momentum after impact

$$(5 \times 3{\cdot}44) + (3 \times 0) = (5 + 3)v$$
$$v = 2{\cdot}15\,\text{m/s}$$

c) Kinetic energy before impact = kinetic energy of 5 kg mass
= potential energy of 5 kg mass before release

$$= Mgh$$
$$= 5 \times 9{\cdot}81 \times 0{\cdot}6$$
$$= 29{\cdot}43\,\text{J}$$

Kinetic energy after impact $= \frac{1}{2}(5 + 3) \times 2{\cdot}15^2$

$$= 18{\cdot}5\,\text{J}$$

Loss of energy at impact $= 29{\cdot}43 - 18{\cdot}5$

$$= 10{\cdot}93\,\text{J}$$

d) Let h m = vertical height through which combined system rises.

Potential energy of system $= Mgh$

$$= (5 + 3) \times 9{\cdot}81 \times h$$
$$= 78{\cdot}48h\,\text{J}$$

This must equal kinetic energy of system immediately after impact.

$$78{\cdot}48h = 18{\cdot}5$$
$$h = 0{\cdot}236\,\text{m}$$

Centre of gravity of combined system will rise 236 mm.

e) Tension in string. This is concerned with motion in a circle, and the student may wish to leave this part of the solution until he has dealt with that portion of the syllabus in the next chapter. For completeness, the whole solution is presented.

Centripetal acceleration of the 5 kg mass just before impact

$$= \frac{v^2}{r}$$
$$= \frac{3{\cdot}44^2}{2}$$
$$= 5{\cdot}9\,\text{m/s}^2$$

Centripetal force required to produce this acceleration

$$= \text{mass} \times \text{acceleration}$$
$$= 5 \times 5{\cdot}9$$
$$= 29{\cdot}5\,\text{N}$$

String must provide this force as well as that to support the 5 kg mass.

Total tension in string $= 29{\cdot}5 + (5 \times 9{\cdot}81)$

$$= 78{\cdot}55\,\text{N}$$

i.e. The velocity of the 5 kg mass before impact is 3·44 m/s, the common velocity after impact is 2·15 m/s, the loss in kinetic energy on impact is 10·93 J, the combined system rises 236 mm after impact, and the tension in the string of the 5 kg mass just before impact is 78·55 N.

Angular Momentum

The mass M shown in fig.7.7 is rotating at the end of an arm, length r, with angular velocity ω. Its linear velocity, v, is given by ωr.

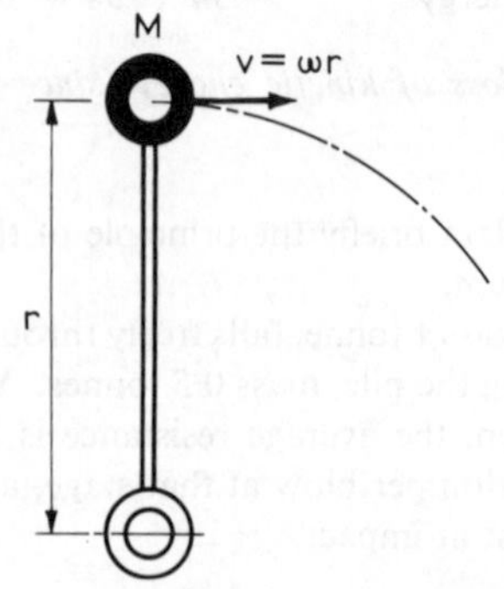

Fig.7.7 Angular momentum, or moment of momentum

Linear momentum of the mass = mass × linear velocity

$$= Mv$$
$$= M\omega r$$

Moment of this momentum about axis of rotation

$$= M\omega r \times r$$
$$= M\omega r^2$$
$$= Mr^2\omega$$

But the product Mr^2 is the moment of inertia of the mass about the axis of rotation.

Hence,

moment of momentum about axis = moment of inertia × angular velocity

We can consider a solid wheel to be made up of a number of small masses each having its own linear velocity.

Total moment of momentum of masses

$$= M_1r_1^2\omega + M_2r_2^2\omega + M_3r_3^2\omega + \ldots$$
$$= (M_1r_1^2 + M_2r_2^2 + M_3r_3^2 + \ldots)\omega$$
$$= \sum Mr^2 . \omega$$

But $\sum Mr^2$ is the moment of inertia of the wheel about its axis of rotation. Hence,

moment of momentum of wheel = moment of inertia about axis × angular velocity

The expression 'moment of momentum' is sometimes called the *angular momentum*.

Rate of change of angular momentum
$= \text{rate of change of } I\omega$
$= I \times \text{rate of change of angular velocity}$
$= I \times \text{angular acceleration}$

which is equal to the torque causing the change.

Hence we have the fundamental expression:

torque = rate of change of angular momentum

In the case of angular impact, such as two gear-wheels being suddenly brought into mesh, the same principle is applied as that which has been established for linear impact. The total angular momentum before impact is equal to the total angular momentum after impact. Care must be used in determining the angular velocities of the wheels after impact. These velocities will be dependent upon the diameter of the wheels or the number of teeth in the wheels. Only in the case of equal-sized wheels will there be the common 'after impact' velocity which we noticed in all linear problems not involving rebound.

Example 7.5 Define moment of momentum. A flywheel and shaft of 500 kg total mass and 1·2 m radius of gyration are rotating in fixed bearings at 300 rev/min. By means of a clutch on the shaft, another similar system of flywheel and shaft of 2000 kg total mass and 600 mm radius of gyration is suddenly connected to the first shaft. If the second flywheel and shaft are initially at rest, find the new common speed of rotation, and the loss in kinetic energy in the system, due to the connection. EMEU

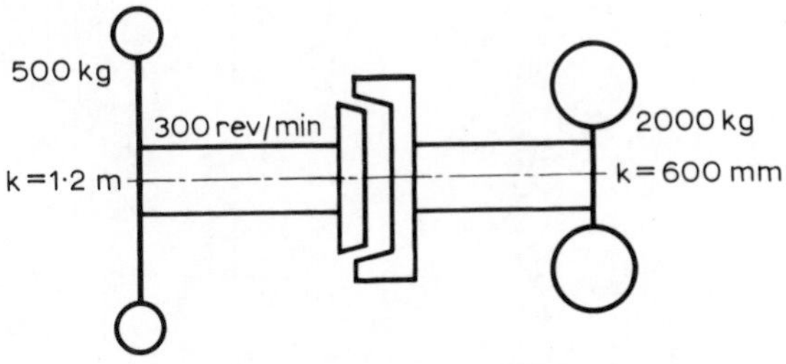

Fig.7.8

Moment of inertia of 1st flywheel $= Mk^2$
$= 500 \times 1{\cdot}2^2$
$= 720\,\text{kg}\,\text{m}^2$

Moment of inertia of 2nd flywheel $= 2000 \times 0{\cdot}6^2$
$= 720\,\text{kg}\,\text{m}^2$

Let N = common angular velocity (rev/min) after connection.

Angular momentum before connection = angular momentum after connection

$$(720 \times 300) + (720 \times 0) = (720 + 720)N$$
$$N = 150\,\text{rev/min}$$

Notice that there is no need to change rev/min into rad/s, since the change would have to be made to both sides of the equation; but this technique must be used with care!

Kinetic energy before connection $= \frac{1}{2}I\omega^2$

$$= \tfrac{1}{2} \times 720 \times \left(\frac{300 \times 2\pi}{60}\right)^2$$
$$= 356 \times 10^3\,\text{J}$$

Kinetic energy after connection

$$= \tfrac{1}{2} \times (720 + 720)\left(\frac{150 \times 2\pi}{60}\right)^2$$
$$= 178 \times 10^3\,\text{J}$$

Loss in kinetic energy due to connection

$$= 356 \times 10^3 - 178 \times 10^3\,\text{J}$$
$$= 178\,\text{kJ}$$

i.e. The common speed is 150 rev/min, and the loss of energy is 178 kJ.

Exercise 7

1 Two trucks travelling in the same straight line collide, and remain locked together after impact. Truck A, mass 1000 kg, has a velocity 2 m/s due west. Truck B, mass 800 kg, has a velocity of 1·5 m/s due east. Determine the magnitude and direction of the velocity of the trucks after impact.

2 Two perfectly elastic spheres are travelling in the same straight line. A has a mass of 8 kg and a velocity of 4 m/s due north, whilst B has a mass of 5 kg and a velocity of 6 m/s due south. Determine the velocity of the spheres after collision, and the loss of kinetic energy following the impact.

3 Two perfectly elastic spheres, each of mass 0·5 kg, are on a horizontal table. A is at rest, and is struck by B, which is travelling due north with a velocity of 20 m/s. Determine the subsequent motion of the two spheres.

4 A pile driver, mass $1\frac{1}{2}$ tonnes, falls freely through a distance of 2 m on to the pile, mass $\frac{1}{2}$ tonne. When the pile is nearly fully driven, the average resistance to motion is 800 kN. Determine the penetration at this stage, and the kinetic energy lost at impact.

5 A block of wood of mass 23 kg is suspended by a cord. A bullet of mass 23 g is fired into the block with a horizontal velocity of 500 m/s. Calculate the common velocity after impact, the loss of energy at impact, and the height to which the block rises above its original position.

6 State the third law of motion and illustrate it by an example.
A 20 tonne truck, moving at 14·4 km/h, collides with a stationary 10 tonne truck, and the two move on together.

Calculate the common velocity, and the loss of kinetic energy due to impact. NCTEC

7 A railway truck of mass 10 tonnes is moving at 10·8 km/h on a level track when it collides with a stationary truck of mass 2 tonnes, and they move on together. Calculate the loss of kinetic energy due to the impact, and explain what happens to this lost energy. NCTEC

8 A railway truck of mass 20 tonnes collides at a speed of 7·2 km/h with a stationary truck of mass 12 tonnes. If the two trucks move on together, find (a) the common velocity, and (b) the kinetic energy lost due to impact. NCTEC

9 A body of mass 250 kg and having an initial velocity of 600 mm/s is acted upon by a constant force of 90 N acting in the direction of motion for 2 minutes. Calculate the gain of momentum by the body, and the work done by the force. NCTEC

10 A target of mass 11 kg is suspended by a cord. A bullet of mass 11 g, moving horizontally at a speed of 500 m/s, strikes the target. Calculate (a) the common velocity after impact, (b) the loss of energy at impact, and (c) the height to which the target rises above its original position. EMEU

11 A truck of mass 10 tonnes starts from rest and runs down an incline of 1 in 80 for 30 seconds, when it reaches a level track, along which it runs for 10 seconds before colliding with a stationary truck of mass 20 tonnes. The two trucks then move on with a common velocity.

Determine their velocity immediately after impact, and also the total distance travelled by the lighter truck up to the point of impact. The frictional resistance of the 10 tonne truck can be assumed constant at 550 N. NCTEC

Chapter 8

Motion in a Circular Path

We have established already the fact that a body is subjected to an acceleration when it changes its velocity. This acceleration is still present, even though the change in velocity is only one of direction; in this case we have to obtain the vectorial difference between the original and the final velocities. A particular case of this type of change of velocity occurs in motion in a circular path.

Consider the particle A travelling in a circular path of radius r with centre O (fig.8.1). Its velocity will always be tangential to the path, and will therefore be changing in direction; we shall, however, consider that the magnitude of the velocity remains constant and equal to v m/s. The time taken for A to travel to B is a very small interval (say 1/100 second or, if you like, much smaller still).

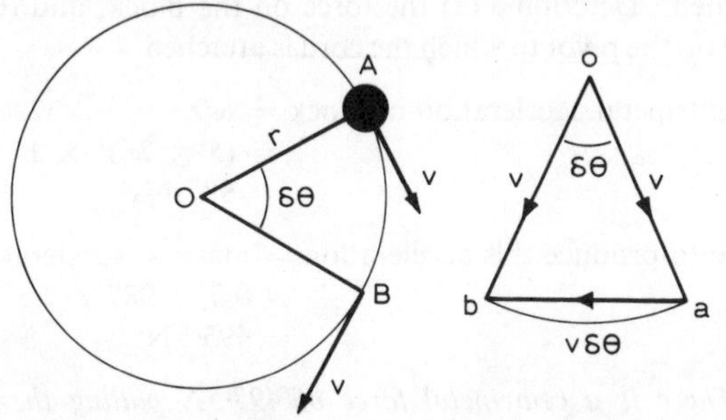

Fig.8.1 Motion in a circle. The direction of the velocity of A is constantly changing. It is therefore subject to a special acceleration known as *centripetal acceleration*.

It is usual to denote a small interval of time by the letters δt. Let the angle between the lines AO and BO be $\delta\theta$ radians (and since we think of δt as being very small, A and B will be very near together, and $\delta\theta$ will be a small angle).

Now draw the velocity triangle; ***oa*** represents the velocity at A, ***ob*** represents the velocity at B, and ***ab*** represents the difference between these velocities. Since ***oa*** is perpendicular to OA, and ***ob*** is perpendicular to OB, the angle between ***oa*** and ***ob*** will be the same as between OA and OB, which was the very small angle $\delta\theta$. We now require the length of *ab*. If we draw an arc *ab* from centre *o*, then, provided $\delta\theta$ is small, we shall not be able to tell the difference between the length of the arc *ab* and the length of the straight line *ab*.

Arc length *ab* = radius × angle in radians

$= \boldsymbol{oa} \times \delta\theta$

$\boldsymbol{ab} = v\delta\theta$

Change in velocity = final velocity − original velocity

$= \boldsymbol{ob} - \boldsymbol{oa}$

$= \boldsymbol{ab}$

$= v\delta\theta$ in δt seconds

$$\text{Change in velocity per second} = \frac{v\delta\theta}{\delta t}\ \text{m/s}^2$$

But $\dfrac{\delta\theta}{\delta t}$ angular velocity of the radius OA (rad/s)

$$= \omega = \frac{v}{r}$$

$$\text{Change in velocity per second} = v\,\frac{v}{r} = \frac{v^2}{r}$$

Since $v = \omega r$, we can write

$$\frac{v^2}{r} = \frac{\omega^2 r^2}{r} = \omega^2 r$$

i.e. Acceleration of A $= \dfrac{v^2}{r}$ *or* $\omega^2 r$.

Direction of Acceleration

Since $\delta\theta$ is very small, the sum of the two angles $\angle bao$ and $\angle abo$ must be nearly 180°, and since the triangle is isosceles, each angle must be practically 90°. The smaller we make $\delta\theta$, the more correct does this statement become. This means that the direction of the line *ab* is nearly perpendicular to line *oa*.

The direction of the acceleration is perpendicular to the direction of the velocity. It is therefore acting along the radius towards the centre of the circle, O. For this reason it is known as a *centripetal acceleration.*

Summarising, we can say that when a body is moving with velocity v m/s along a circular path of radius rm, it has an acceleration of v^2/r m/s² towards the centre of the circle, this acceleration being known as the centripetal acceleration.

Centripetal Force

Now it is a fundamental idea in mechanics that we never get an acceleration unless we have a force producing it. Let us, then, consider a mass of Mkg travelling round a circular path of radius rm with velocity vm/s (fig.8.2). This mass will be subjected to an acceleration v^2/r always acting towards the centre of the circle. Consequently, there must be a force acting on the mass in the direction of this acceleration.

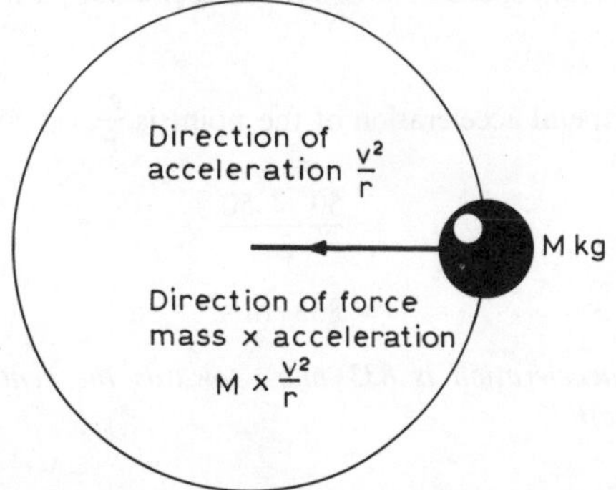

Fig.8.2 Centripetal force. The centripetal acceleration and the centripetal force producing it are all directed towards the centre of rotation.

Force = mass × acceleration

$$= \frac{Mv^2}{r} \text{ newtons}$$

or, alternatively, $= Mr\omega^2$ newtons

This force is known as the *centripetal force*, and it will always have to be applied in order to make the body move in a circular path.

When you make a mass travel in a circular path at the end of a string, the string is pulling the mass into the circular path all the time; otherwise the mass would move off in a straight line. But while the string is pulling the mass towards the centre, it is also true that there is an equal and opposite reaction on your hand at the centre. This opposite reaction is known as the *centrifugal force*. It is equal in magnitude to the centripetal force, and exists only as an equal and opposite reaction to this centripetal force. It is an example of the inertial force which was discussed along with D'Alembert's principle.

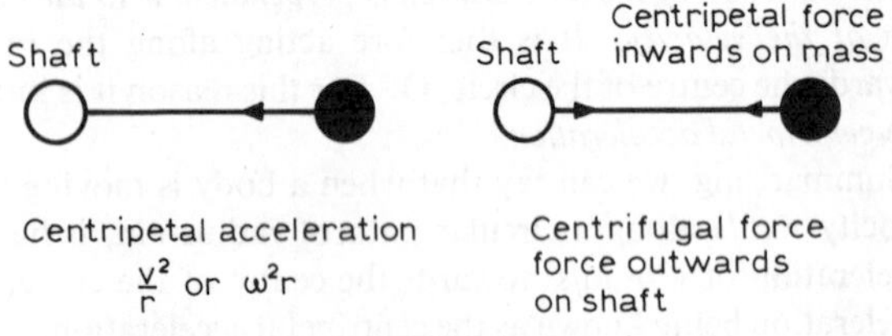

Fig.8.3 Centripetal and centrifugal. As the mass is whirled around the shaft, it experiences a centripetal acceleration towards the centre of the shaft. There must therefore be a force known as a *centripetal force*, pulling the mass towards the centre of rotation. The shaft experiences an equal and opposite reaction, known as a *centrifugal force*.

Example 8.1 Determine the acceleration of a point moving with a constant speed of 50 m/s round a circular path of radius 3 m.

The centripetal acceleration of the point is $\frac{v^2}{r}$.

$$= \frac{50 \times 50}{3}$$

$$= 833\tfrac{1}{3}\,\text{m/s}^2$$

i.e. The acceleration is $833\frac{1}{3}$ *m/s², towards the centre of the circular path.*

Example 8.2 A flywheel 2 m in diameter is rotating at 400 rev/min. What is the acceleration of a point on the rim of the wheel?

The centripetal acceleration of a point on the rim is $\omega^2 r$.

$$\omega = \frac{400}{60} \times 2\pi \,\text{rad/s}$$

$$= 41{\cdot}9\,\text{rad/s}$$

$$r = 1\,\text{m}$$

$$\text{Centripetal acceleration} = 41{\cdot}9^2 \times 1$$

$$= 1757\,\text{m/s}^2$$

i.e. The acceleration of a point on the rim is 1757 m/s², towards the centre of the flywheel.

Example 8.3 A block, mass $\frac{1}{2}$ kg, attached to one end of a cord 1 m long, is caused to rotate at 5 rev/s on a smooth horizontal table about a pivot to which the other end of the cord is attached. Determine (a) the force on the block, and (b) the force on the pivot to which the cord is attached.

a) Centripetal acceleration of block $= \omega^2 r$

$$= (5 \times 2\pi)^2 \times 1$$

$$= 987\,\text{m/s}^2$$

Force to produce this acceleration = mass × acceleration

$$= 0{\cdot}5 \times 987$$

$$= 493{\cdot}5\,\text{N}$$

i.e. There is a centripetal force of 493·5 N pulling the block towards the centre of the circle.

b) *There is a force of the same magnitude, 493·5 N, but opposite in direction, which the cord exerts on the pivot.* This force will tend to cause the pivot to deflect towards the block. This force is the centrifugal force.

Example 8.4 The maximum safe load which a piece of string can carry is 360 N. The string is used to swing a mass of 1 kg in a horizontal circle at a radius of 0·75 m. What is the greatest velocity which the mass can have without breaking the string?

Let v m/s = linear velocity of mass,

then $\frac{Mv^2}{r}$ = centripetal force in string to pull the mass into a circular path.

Maximum permissible value of this force will be 360 N.

$$\frac{Mv^2}{r} = 360$$

$$\frac{1 \times v^2}{0{\cdot}75} = 360$$

$$v^2 = 360 \times 0{\cdot}75 = 270$$

$$v = 16{\cdot}45\,\text{m/s}$$

This is equal to an angular velocity of $\frac{16{\cdot}45}{0{\cdot}75} = 22$ rad/s, or 210 rev/min.

i.e. Maximum velocity of mass is 16·45 m/s, or 210 rev/min.

Conical Pendulum

In its simplest form the conical pendulum consists of a mass suspended from a fixed point by a cord, and moving on a circular path in a horizontal plane, whilst the cord generates the sloping surface of a cone (fig.8.4).

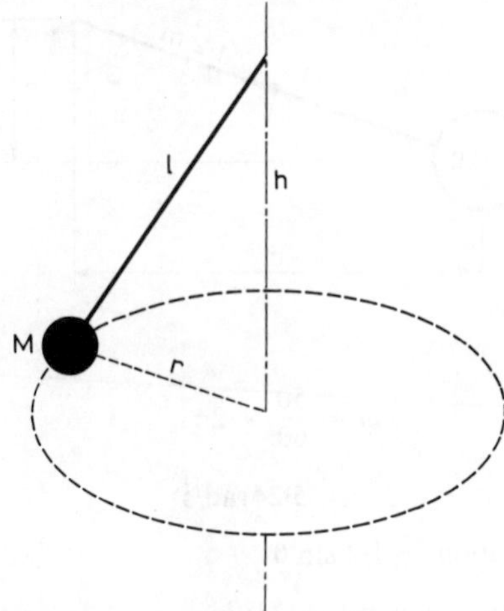

Fig.8.4 Conical pendulum. The mass, *M*, at the end of the inclined arm rotates in a horizontal circular path. The height of the pendulum, *h*, is dependent only upon the speed of rotation.

Consider a mass M supported by a cord, length l, moving with constant angular velocity ω on a path of radius r. If h is the height of the pendulum, the cord will make angle θ with the vertical, where $\tan\theta$ is equal to r/h. The centripetal acceleration of the mass is $\omega^2 r$, and the force required to produce this acceleration will be mass $\times$ acceleration or $M\omega^2 r$. This force is provided by the horizontal component of the tension T in the cord. The vertical component of this tension T will be equal to the weight of the mass, Mg (fig.8.5).

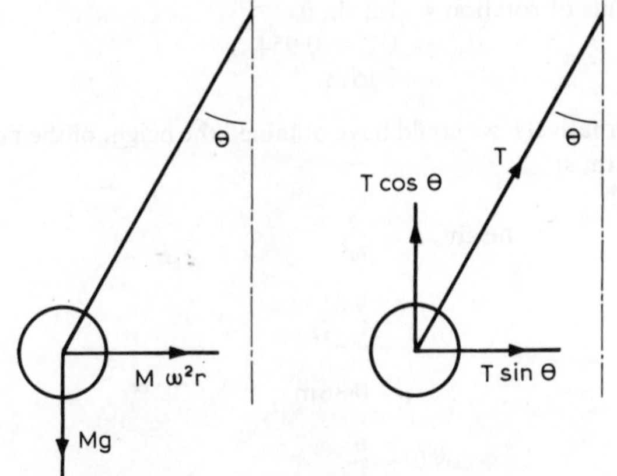

Fig.8.5 Conical pendulum. The horizontal component of the tension, *T*, in the cord provides the necessary centripetal force. The vertical component of *T* supports the rotating mass.

$$\text{Horizontal component} = T\sin\theta = M\omega^2 r \quad . \quad . \quad . \quad (1)$$

$$\text{Vertical component} = T\cos\theta = Mg \quad . \quad . \quad . \quad . \quad (2)$$

Dividing (1) by (2), we get

$$\frac{\sin\theta}{\cos\theta} = \frac{\omega^2 r}{g}$$

or

$$\tan\theta = \frac{\omega^2 r}{g}$$

But

$$\tan\theta = \frac{r}{h}$$

$$\therefore \frac{r}{h} = \frac{\omega^2 r}{g}$$

$$\omega^2 = \frac{g}{h}$$

or

$$\omega = \sqrt{\frac{g}{h}}\ \text{rad/s}$$

or

$$n = \frac{60}{2\pi}\sqrt{\frac{g}{h}}\ \text{rev/min}$$

From the above expression, it follows that the speed of rotation of a conical pendulum is dependent solely on the height of the pendulum, h, and is independent of the weight of the mass and the length of the cord. Thus, if the pendulum is rotating steadily at 100 rev/min, its height will be 89 mm whatever the length of the cord. (Obviously the cord must be longer than 89 mm; if not, then the pendulum cannot operate at 100 rev/min.)

The fact that the corresponding height changes with a change of speed was used by James Watt in his early design of a governor to control the speed of his steam engines. The governor was driven directly by the engine, so that the speed of the governor was proportional to the speed of the engine. By means of a linkage, the change in height was transferred to the steam-control valve, so that, when an increase of speed lifted the governor sleeve, the motion was used to close the steam valve, and thus reduce the engine speed. Similarly, when the speed was reduced, due to an increase in load, then the height of the governor increased, and the linkage opened the steam valve. More steam was thus supplied to the engine, with a corresponding increase in speed. In this way it was possible to keep the engine speed within a predetermined range. Various modifications were made later, in order to increase the efficiency of the arrangement, but later developments still made use of the variation of governor height due to change of speed.

Example 8.5 Determine, from first principles, the change in height of a conical pendulum when the speed falls from 200 to 160 rev/min.

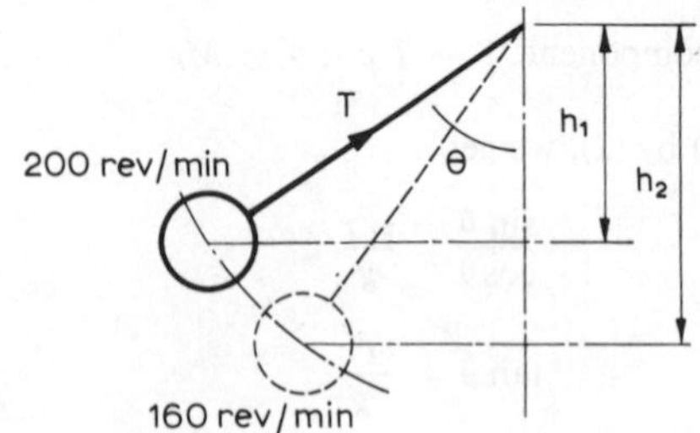

Fig.8.6

Let M = magnitude of rotating mass
T = tension in cord,
r = radius of rotation,
h = height of governor,
n = velocity of rotation (revs/min),
θ = inclination to vertical, and
ω = velocity of rotation.

Centripetal force required to make mass travel in circular path

$$= M\omega^2 r$$

This must equal horizontal component of T.

$$\therefore\ T \sin\theta = M\omega^2 r$$

Also $$T\cos\theta = Mg$$

$$\tan\theta = \frac{\omega^2 r}{g}$$

But $$\tan\theta = \frac{r}{h}$$

$$\therefore\ \frac{r}{h} = \frac{\omega^2 r}{g}$$

$$h = \frac{g}{\omega^2}$$

Let h_1 be height of pendulum when speed is ω_1.
h_2 be height of pendulum when speed is ω_2.
Then change in height is

$$h_2 - h_1 = \frac{g}{{\omega_2}^2} - \frac{g}{{\omega_1}^2}$$

$$= g\,\frac{{\omega_1}^2 - {\omega_2}^2}{{\omega_1}^2 . {\omega_2}^2}$$

$$= \left(\frac{60}{2\pi}\right)^2 g\,\frac{{n_1}^2 - {n_2}^2}{{n_1}^2 . {n_2}^2}$$

$$= \frac{3600 \times 9{\cdot}81\,(200^2 - 160^2)}{4\pi^2 \times 200^2 \times 160^2}$$

$$= 0{\cdot}0126\,\text{m}$$

i.e. When the speed changes from 200 to 160 rev/min, the height of the pendulum increases by 12·6 mm.

Example 8.6 A mass of 1·5 kg is suspended from a swivel point by a string 1·2 m long (fig.8.7). The mass revolves in a horizontal circular path at 50 rev/min. What is the tension in the string, and what is the radius of rotation of the mass?

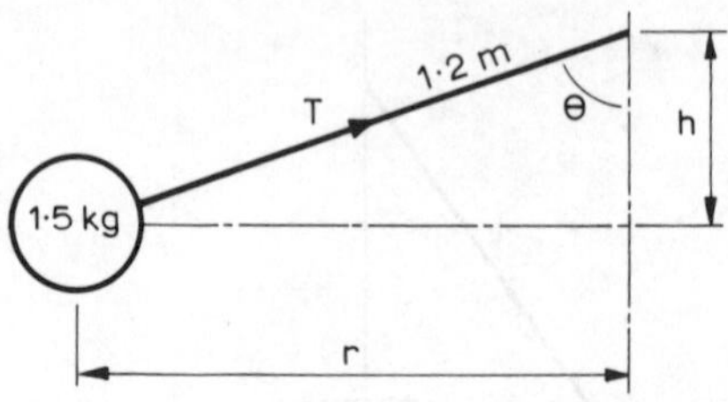

Fig.8.7

$$\omega = \frac{50}{60} \times 2\pi$$

$$= 5{\cdot}24\,\text{rad/s}$$

Radius of rotation = $1{\cdot}2 \sin\theta$

Centripetal force required = $M\omega^2 r$
$= 1{\cdot}5 \times 5{\cdot}24^2 \times 1{\cdot}2 \sin\theta$
$= 49 \sin\theta$

Let T = tension in the string,

then $T \sin\theta = 49 \sin\theta$
$T = 49\,\text{N}$

Vertical component of T is equal to the weight of the mass.

$$T\cos\theta = Mg$$

$$\cos\theta = \frac{Mg}{T} = \frac{1{\cdot}5 \times 9{\cdot}81}{49} = 0{\cdot}30$$

$$\theta = 72°\,30'$$

Radius of rotation = $1{\cdot}2 \sin\theta$
$= 1{\cdot}2 \times 0{\cdot}954$
$= 1{\cdot}15\,\text{m}$

Alternatively, we could have obtained the height of the pendulum thus:

$$\text{height, } h = \frac{g}{\omega^2}$$

$$= \frac{9{\cdot}81}{5{\cdot}21^2}$$

$$= 0{\cdot}36\,\text{m}$$

$$\cos\theta = \frac{h}{l}$$

$$= \frac{0{\cdot}36}{1{\cdot}2}$$

$$= 0{\cdot}30, \text{ as before.}$$

The value of T could then be obtained by the relationship $T\cos\theta = Mg$.

i.e. The tension in the string is equal to 49 N, and the radius of rotation is 1·15 m.

Balancing of Rotating Masses

Single rotating mass. If a mass of M kg at a radius of r m is fastened to a shaft rotating at ω rad/s, there is a centrifugal force of $M\omega^2 r$ newtons acting outwards on the shaft, which produces an out-of-balance effect on the shaft, which will be very detrimental to the efficient running of the machine, producing excessive wear on the bearings, and setting up vibrations.

To balance the shaft, it will be necessary to place a balancing mass (called a balance weight) immediately opposite the original mass M, so that the centrifugal force on the shaft due to the balancing mass will be equal and opposite to that set up by the mass M.

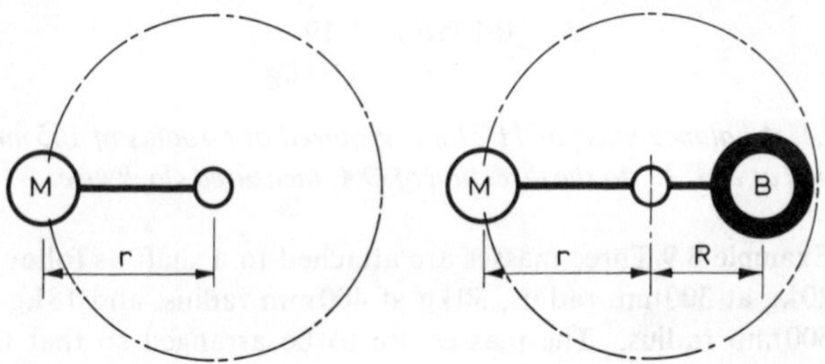

Fig.8.8 Balancing mass

If B kg is the mass of the balancing mass, which is placed at radius R m, then the centrifugal force will be $B\omega^2 R$, so that for balance

$$B\omega^2 R = M\omega^2 r$$
$$B.R = M.r$$

The product of the mass and the radius must therefore be the same for the balancing mass and the original out-of-balance mass. The product $B.R$ or $M.r$ is referred to as a *mass moment*.

Several rotating masses. If there are several rotating masses connected to the shaft at different radii, but all in one plane perpendicular to that of the shaft, then each sets up centrifugal forces on the shaft. It will be necessary to supply only one balancing mass, whose magnitude can be determined by means of a force diagram. Since all the masses are connected to the same shaft, they have a common angular velocity, ω. We need not calculate the magnitude of the centrifugal force, but deal only with mass moment products.

Three masses, A, B, and C kg, are fastened to the shaft at radii a, b, and c metres respectively, their angular positions being as shown in fig.8.9. We are to determine the size of a balance mass, M kg, to be placed at radius r m to balance the system. The method is as follows.

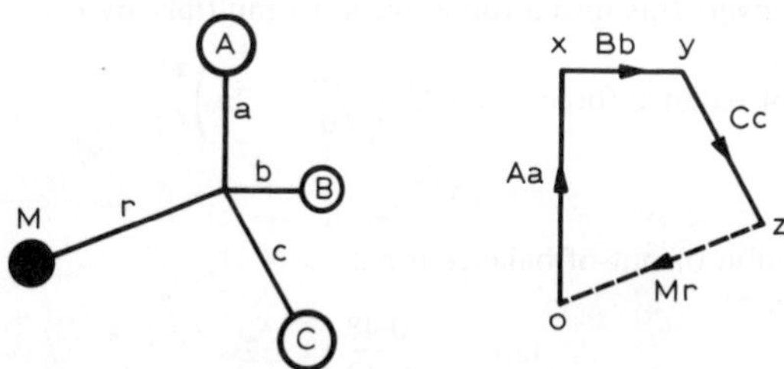

Fig.8.9 Balancing several masses by a single balance mass

1 Calculate the mass moment for each mass.
2 Draw the vector diagram for these mass moments:
Commencing at o, draw ***ox*** to represent $A.a$
xy to represent $B.b$
yz to represent $C.c$
3 The closing line ***zo*** (from z to o) indicates the magnitude and direction of the balancing mass moment $M.r$.
4 Measure ***zo*** to scale and, knowing r, calculate the value of M.

Note the line ***oz*** (from o to z) gives the magnitude and direction of the 'out-of-balance' mass moment. To convert this into a force, we must multiply by ω^2.

Example 8.7 A circular plate revolving about its centre at 150 rev/min has a mass of 10 kg attached at a radius of 40 mm, and a mass of 8 kg at a radius of 60 mm. The angle between the weights is 90°. Determine the magnitude and direction of the out-of-balance force on the shaft.

The position of the masses is shown in fig.8.10.

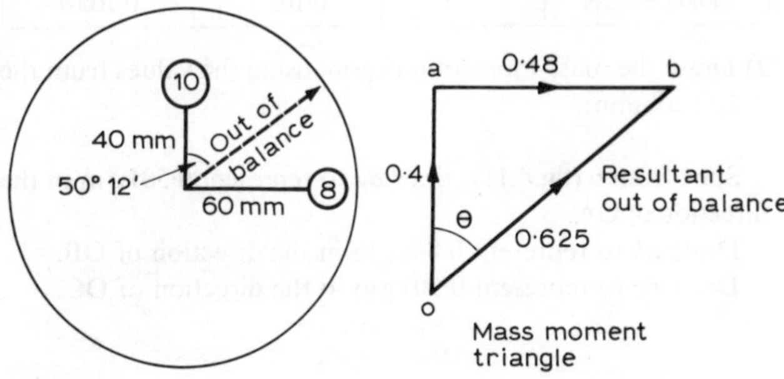

Fig.8.10

Mass moment of 10 kg = 10 × 0·04 = 0·4 kg m.
Mass moment of 8 kg = 8 × 0·06 = 0·48 kg m.

Draw ***oa*** in the direction of the 40 mm arm, to represent 0·4 kg m.

Draw ***ab*** in the direction of the 60 mm arm, to represent 0·48 kg m.

The resultant out-of-balance mass moment is given by the line ***ob***, which represents 0·625 kg m.

To convert this into a force, we must multiply by ω^2.

$$\text{Out of balance force} = 0{\cdot}625\left(\frac{150}{60}\times 2\pi\right)^2$$

$$= 155\,\text{N}$$

Direction of out-of-balance force:

$$\tan\theta = \frac{0{\cdot}48}{0{\cdot}40} = 1{\cdot}2$$

$$\theta = 50°\,12'$$

i.e. The out-of-balance force of 155 N makes an angle of 50° 12′ with the 40 mm arm, as shown.

Example 8.8 A circular disc rotates on a spindle through its centre O, and carries attached masses, respectively of amounts 5, 7, and 10 kg at positions A, B, and C. OA = 100 mm, OB = 120 mm, OC = 90 mm, and the angular positions measured clockwise from OA are, respectively, 0°, 60°, and 150°. Determine the unbalanced force on the spindle at a speed of 250 rev/min, and the magnitude and angular position of a mass at a radius of 105 mm to give balance when rotating. IMECHE

1) Construct the following table.

Reference	*Mass* kg	*Radius* m	*Mass moment* kg m
OA . . .	5	0·10	0·50
OB . . .	7	0·12	0·84
OC . . .	10	0·09	0·90
balance mass	*B*	0·105	0·105*B*

2) Draw the mass-moment polygon, using the values from the last column.

Start from *o* (fig.8.11); draw ***oa*** to represent 0·50 kg m in the direction of OA.

Draw ***ab*** to represent 0·84 kg m in the direction of OB.
Draw ***bc*** to represent 0·90 kg m in the direction of OC.

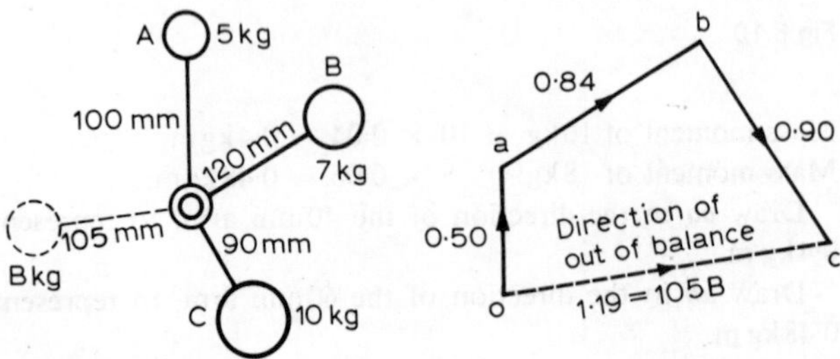

Fig.8.11

Join *oc*.

Then ***oc*** represents the out-of-balance mass moment on the shaft.

According to the scale of the diagram, ***oc*** represents 1·19 kg m.

$$\text{Out-of-balance force on shaft} = Mr\omega^2$$

$$= \boldsymbol{oc}.\omega^2$$

$$= 1{\cdot}19\left(\frac{250}{60}\times 2\pi\right)^2$$

$$= 815\,\text{N}$$

Position of balance mass:
This is shown dotted on the left of the diagram in fig.8.11. It is placed in the direction of ***co*** (opposite to the out-of-balance force).

The value of the balancing mass moment is given in the last column of the above table, and is equal to 0·105 *B* kg m.

$$0{\cdot}105B = 1{\cdot}19$$

$$B = 11{\cdot}3\,\text{kg}$$

i.e. A balance mass of 11·3 kg is required at a radius of 105 mm, and at 263° 12′ to the direction of OA, measured clockwise.

Example 8.9 Three masses are attached to a shaft as follows: 20 kg at 300 mm radius, 30 kg at 400 mm radius, and 18 kg at 500 mm radius. The masses are to be arranged so that the shaft is in balance. Determine the angular position of the masses relative to the 20 kg mass. All the masses are in the same plane (fig.8.12).

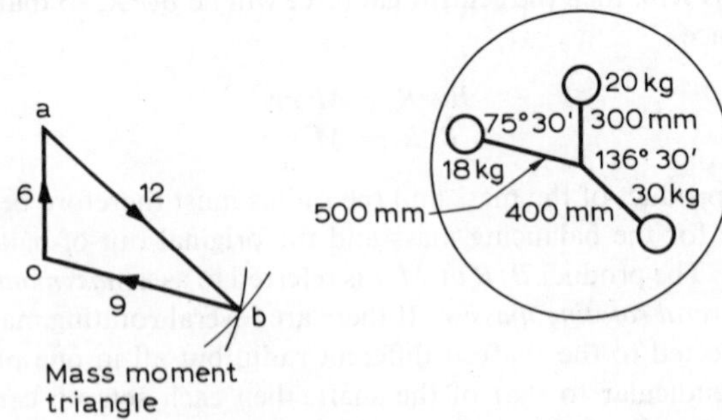

Fig.8.12

1) Construct the following table.

Mass kg	*Radius* m	*Mass moment* kg m
20	0·3	6
30	0·4	12
18	0·5	9

2) Since the masses are in equilibrium, there will be no out-of-balance mass moment, and therefore the mass-moment diagram will be a closed triangle whose sides are proportional to the values in the last column.

Draw ***oa*** to represent the 6 kg m in any convenient direction.

With *a* as centre, and radius equal to 12 kgm, draw an arc of circle.

With *o* as centre, and radius equal to 9 kgm, draw an arc of circle intersecting the first arc at *b*.

Join *ab* and *bo*. Then the triangle *oab* is the required mass-moment triangle, which gives the relative directions of the three masses.

3) Draw the 400 mm arm parallel to ***ab***.

Draw the 500 mm arm parallel to ***bo***.

Measure the angles between the arms.

The angle between 20 kg and 30 kg is 136° 30′, clockwise.

The angle between 20 kg and 18 kg is 75° 30′, anticlockwise.

Note. To avoid confusion in these problems, it is always advisable to indicate the angular positions of the masses on a diagram.

Stability of Vehicle on Circular Path

In order that a vehicle may travel on a horizontal circular path, it has to be subject to an adequate centripetal force determined by the conditions of speed and the radius of curvature of the path. Since the required force can be obtained only from the points of contact of the vehicle with the ground, i.e. the wheels, two important effects may take place:

1 The vehicle may skid, i.e. it may continue in a straight line instead of moving in the circular path.

2 The vehicle may overturn.

Tendency to Skid

If the weight of the vehicle is Mg newtons, and the coefficient of friction between the vehicle and the ground is μ, then the maximum horizontal force which can be obtained by frictional contact is μMg (fig.8.13). Hence the greatest centripetal force which can be brought into action is μMg. If conditions are such that a centripetal force greater than μMg is required, the vehicle will be unable to maintain motion in the circular path of the required radius, and it will consequently skid. Motion will be maintained provided that Mv^2/r is less than μMg. This gives the limiting condition that

$$\frac{Mv^2}{r} = \mu Mg$$

or $$v = \sqrt{\mu g r} \text{ for maximum safe velocity}$$

or $$r = \frac{v^2}{\mu g} \text{ for minimum safe radius}$$

Thus, if the coefficient of friction between the wheels and the road is 0·3, then the minimum radius on which the car can be driven at 50 km/h is about 66 m. The car cannot corner at a smaller radius than this, since the necessary centripetal force cannot be supplied by the friction contact. On the other hand, if the car is approaching a corner of 30 m radius, the maximum velocity with which it can safely manoeuvre the corner is about 33 km/h. Any attempt to corner faster would result in a skid.

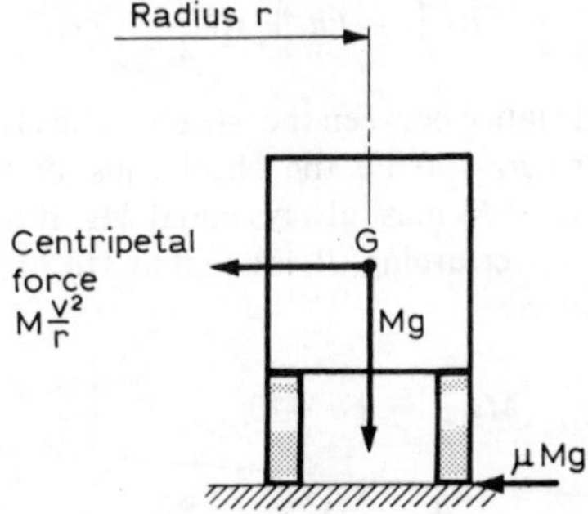

Fig.8.13 Stability of vehicle on circular path. Necessary centripetal force is provided by frictional contact between road and wheels. Vehicle will skid when required centripetal force is greater than maximum available friction force.

Tendency to Overturn

When the vehicle is at rest, the reactions of the road wheels will normally be equally distributed. The two off-side wheels will share half the weight of the vehicle, and the two near-side wheels will share the other half. When the vehicle is travelling round a circular path, the loading distribution will change, although the sum of the wheel reactions will always be equal to the weight of the vehicle. The vehicle is on the point of overturning when the reaction on the inner wheels is equal to zero.

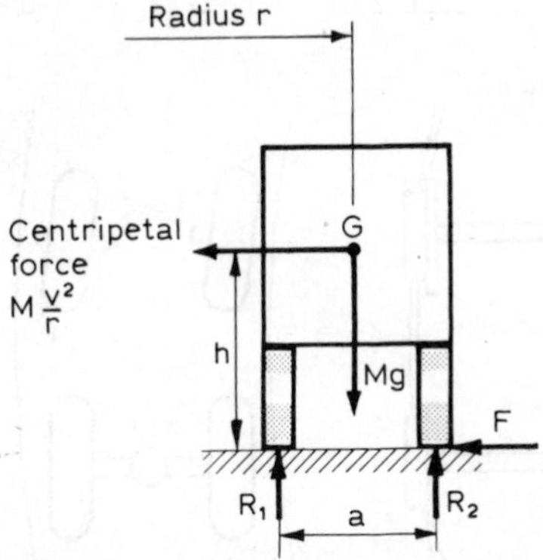

Fig.8.14 Overturning of vehicle on circular path. Friction force may be sufficient to provide necessary centripetal force, but design of vehicle may be such that it will overturn if its speed is too high on the corner. Vehicle is on the point of overturning when the reaction on the inner wheel, R_1, is zero, i.e. when reaction on outer wheel is Mg.

In order to make the vehicle shown in fig.8.14 travel in a circular path, a centripetal force Mv^2/r must be applied. We have just seen that this force is supplied by frictional contact, represented by F, in the case of a road vehicle. Taking moments about the centre of gravity of the vehicle, whose height above the ground is h, we have

$$R_2 \frac{a}{2} = Fh + R_1 \frac{a}{2}$$

where a is the distance between the wheels. The critical condition occurs when $R_1 = 0$, i.e. the wheel is just on the point of lifting. Since $R_1 + R_2$ must always equal Mg, it follows that, on the instant of overturning, R_2 is equal to Mg. The equation can thus be written

$$Mg \frac{a}{2} = Fh + 0$$

$$Mg \frac{a}{2} = \frac{Mv^2}{r} h$$

or $$v = \sqrt{\frac{agr}{2h}} \text{ for maximum velocity}$$

or $$r = \frac{2v^2h}{ag} \text{ for minimum radius}$$

If this velocity is exceeded, or this radius reduced, the vehicle will overturn.

It will be seen that the value of v can be increased considerably if h is made small, and a made large. This is the principle behind the design of racing cars.

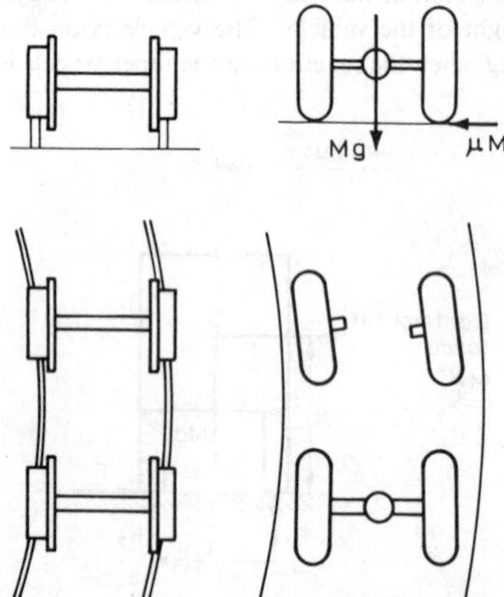

Fig.8.15 Friction and flanges. Road vehicles rely on good frictional contact between wheels and road for safe negotiation of bends. Rail vehicles rely on the flanges of the metal tyres. These make it virtually impossible for a rail vehicle to skid on a corner.

In the case of locomotives, flanges are provided on the wheels for the purpose of guiding them along the rails. The flanges considerably augment the effect of friction. In fact, the reaction between the flanges and the rail provides the necessary centripetal forces, with consequent wear of the flanges. The result of this is that the locomotive cannot skid on a corner in the same way that a car can. It is, however, subject to the same tendency to overturn if the speed is excessive.

Banking of Roads and Racing Tracks

In order to allow vehicles to travel safely at greater speeds round corners, it is the usual practice to bank the corner, i.e. to lift the outer curve with respect to the inner curve. A similar procedure is adopted on railway tracks, it being usual in this case to speak of the 'super-elevation' of the track; this simply means the difference in height between the outer and inner rails.

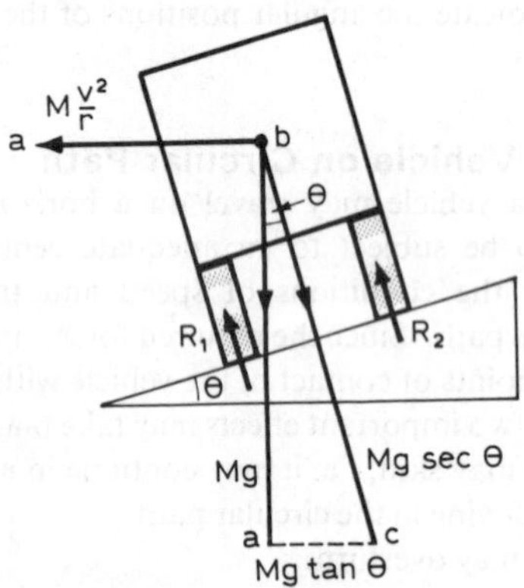

Fig.8.16 Banking of tracks. If the road or track is banked, it is possible to eliminate side thrust on the wheel or flanges. The reactions R_1 and R_2 support the normal component, Mg sec θ, of the weight of the vehicle. The horizontal component, Mg tan θ, provides the necessary centripetal force.

It will be seen from fig.8.16 that the weight of the vehicle on the inclined banking has two components:

bc $= Mg \sec\theta$ normal to the banking, and

ca $= Mg \tan\theta$ acting horizontally towards the centre of the curved path.

This ***ca*** component provides the necessary centripetal force for the vehicle. It is obtained without causing any side thrust on the wheels of the vehicle.

Hence $$ca = Mg \tan\theta = \frac{Mv^2}{r}$$

$$\tan\theta = \frac{v^2}{gr}$$

It is usual to make angle θ suitable for an estimated average velocity, v, any increase of which would still produce a tendency to skid. It will be noticed that in the above statement the effect of the contact friction is neglected. Its effect will be to counteract any tendency to skid resulting from the imprecise adjustment of the banking in relation to the speed.

Having obtained a suitable value for θ, the super-elevation of a railway line will be $d \sin \theta$, where d is the gauge of the track, the standard value of which in this country is 1·44m (4 ft 8½ inches).

Example 8.10 A motor-cyclist rounding an unbanked corner of 400m radius leans at an angle of 5°51′ from the vertical. What is his speed in kilometres per hour? If the total mass of the man and machine is 150kg and the coefficient of friction between his tyres and the road is 0·6, what is his maximum speed without slipping?

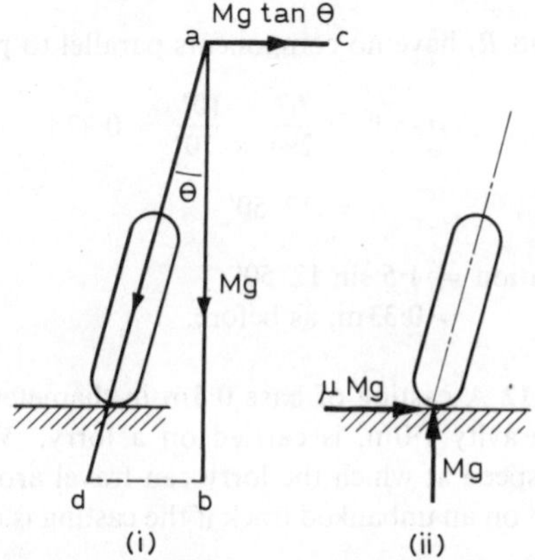

Fig.8.17 Stability of cyclist on circular path

The cyclist leans over to such an angle as will provide the necessary centripetal force [fig.8.17(i)]. The combined weight of the cyclist and machine is made up of the two components:

ac, acting horizontally towards the centre of the curved path;

ad, acting along the line of cyclist's inclination.

$ac = Mg \tan 5°51' = 0{\cdot}1025\,Mg.$

In order to turn the corner, the value of ***ac*** must be $\dfrac{Mv^2}{r}$.

Hence $$0{\cdot}1025M \times 9{\cdot}81 = \frac{Mv^2}{400}$$

$$v = \sqrt{400 \times 0{\cdot}1025 \times 9{\cdot}81}$$
$$= 20\text{m/s or } 72\text{km/h}$$

At the point of contact with the ground, the normal force will be Mg, and the greatest frictional resistance to movement will be μMg. This will also be the greatest centripetal force available to help the cyclist turn the corner [fig.8.17(ii)].

$$\mu Mg = \frac{Mv^2_{max}}{r}$$

$$v_{max} = \sqrt{\mu gr}$$
$$= \sqrt{0{\cdot}6 \times 9{\cdot}81 \times 400}$$
$$= 48{\cdot}6\text{m/s or } 175\text{km/h}$$

i.e. The original speed of the cyclist is 72km/h, whilst the maximum safe speed on the corner will be 175km/h.

Example 8.11 A 30 tonne truck is travelling at 36km/h round a curved track of 45m radius. The rails are in a horizontal plane, and are 1·5m apart. If the centre of gravity of the truck is 2m above the rails, determine the vertical reaction of each of the rails, stating clearly which reaction applies to the inner rail.

Calculate the super-elevation of the outer rail if the side thrust is to be eliminated at this speed. NCTEC

$$36\text{km/h} = 10\text{m/s}$$

Centripetal force required to make truck move in circular path

$$= \frac{Mv^2}{r}$$

$$= \frac{30 \times 10^3 \times 10^2}{45}\text{N}$$

$$= 67\text{kN}$$

This force is provided by the thrust of the rail against the wheel flanges.

Let R_1 and R_2 be the vertical reactions of the rails, R_1 applying to the inner rail, and R_2 to the outer rail (fig.8.18).

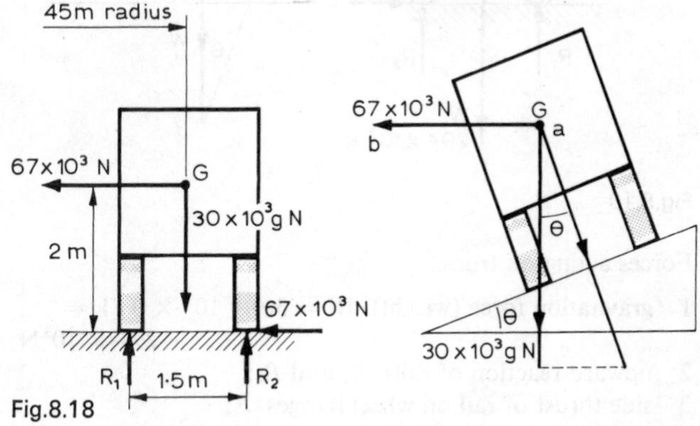

Fig.8.18

Taking moments about the centre of gravity, we have

$$(R_2 - R_1)\,0{\cdot}75 = 67 \times 10^3 \times 2$$

But $$R_2 + R_1 = 30 \times 10^3 \times 9{\cdot}81$$

Adding $$2R_2 = 9{\cdot}81 \times 30 \times 10^3 + \frac{67 \times 2 \times 10^3}{0{\cdot}75}$$

$$R_2 = 236{\cdot}5\,\text{kN}$$
$$R_1 = 57{\cdot}8\,\text{kN}$$

Let θ = inclination of track, then $1{\cdot}5 \sin\theta$ = super-elevation of the outer rail.

The inclination of the track must be such as to make the horizontal component ***ab*** of the weight of the truck equal to the necessary centripetal force.

i.e. $$67 \times 10^3 = 30 \times 10^3 \times 9{\cdot}81 \tan\theta$$

$$\tan\theta = \frac{67}{30 \times 9{\cdot}81} = 0{\cdot}228$$

$$\theta = 12°\,50'$$

$$\text{Super-elevation} = 1{\cdot}5 \sin 12°\,50' = 0{\cdot}333\,\text{m}$$

i.e. Without banking, the vertical reaction of the inner rails is 57·8 kN and of the outer rails 236·5 kN. The required super-elevation of the outer rail to eliminate side thrust is 333 mm.

Alternative solution using D'Alembert's principle

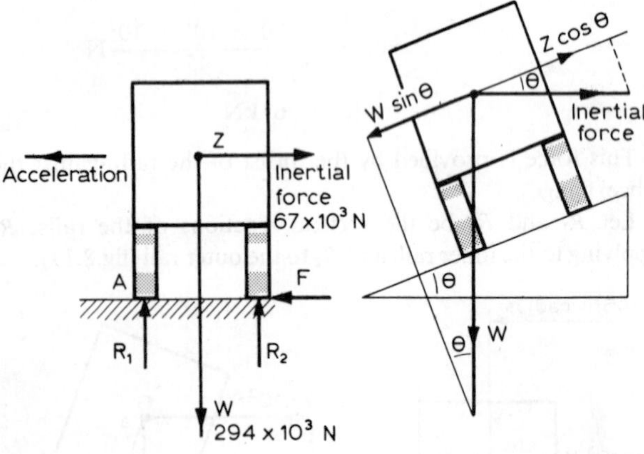

Fig.8.19

Forces acting on truck:

1 gravitation force (weight), $W = 30 \times 10^3 \times 9{\cdot}81 = 294 \times 10^3\,\text{N}$;
2 upward reaction of rails, R_1 and R_2;
3 side thrust of rail on wheel flanges, F;
4 inertial force (centrifugal force), $Z = Mv^2/r = 67 \times 10^3\,\text{N}$, direction opposite to that of the centripetal acceleration.

Take moments about A. Their sum must be zero for equilibrium.

$$294 \times 10^3 \times \frac{1{\cdot}5}{2} + 67 \times 10^3 \times 2 - R_2 \times 1{\cdot}5 = 0$$
$$R_2 = 236{\cdot}5\,\text{kN}$$
as before

Sum of vertical forces must be zero for equilibrium:

$$R_1 + R_2 - 294 \times 10^3 = 0$$
$$R_1 = 57{\cdot}8\,\text{kN, as before.}$$

Sum of horizontal forces must be zero for equilibrium:

$$F - 67 \times 10^3 = 0$$
$$F = 67\,\text{kN}$$

Forces acting on truck while on banked track:

1 gravitation force (weight), $W = 294 \times 10^3\,\text{N}$;
2 reaction of rails perpendicular to plane, R_1 and R_2;
3 this time there will be no side thrust, i.e. $F = 0$;
4 inertial force (centrifugal force), $Z = 67 \times 10^3\,\text{N}$.

Resolve forces parallel to the plane. The sum of components will be zero for equilibrium.

$$67 \times 10^3 \cos\theta = 294 \times 10^3 \sin\theta = 0$$

R_1 and R_2 have no components parallel to plane.

$$\tan\theta = \frac{67 \times 10^3}{294 \times 10^3} = 0{\cdot}228$$
$$= 12°\,50'$$

$$\text{Super-elevation} = 1{\cdot}5 \sin 12°\,50' = 0{\cdot}33\,\text{m, as before.}$$

Example 8.12 A casting of base 0·5 m in diameter, height to centre of gravity 1·0 m, is carried on a lorry. What is the maximum speed at which the lorry can travel around a 30 m radius bend on an unbanked track if the casting is not to overturn?

Let M = mass of casting,
v = velocity of lorry.

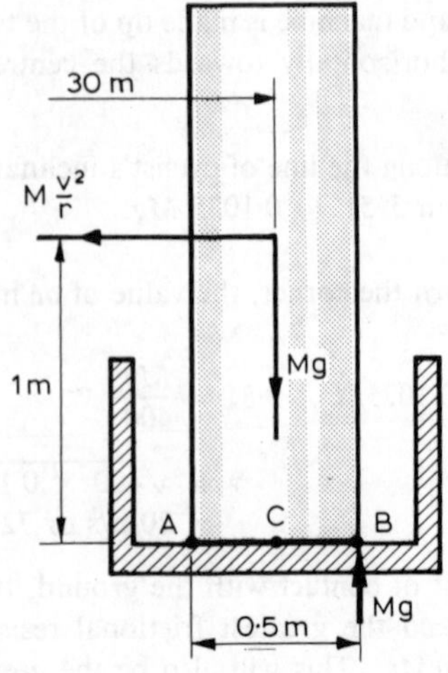

Fig.8.20

When the casting is on the point of overturning, the whole of the load Mg will be on corner B (fig.8.20), producing an equal reaction.

Take moments about C.

$$Mg \times \frac{0{\cdot}5}{2} = \frac{Mv^2}{30} \times 1{\cdot}0$$
$$v^2 = 73{\cdot}6$$
$$v = 8{\cdot}58\,\text{m/s}$$
$$= 30{\cdot}9\,\text{km/h.}$$

i.e. The lorry must not exceed a speed of 30·9 km/h around the 30 m radius bend.

Gyroscopic Effects

It may be useful at this point to mention another important effect which is observed in this type of motion, an effect known as the *gyroscopic effect*. If you hold a cycle wheel so that it is rotating in a vertical plane, and then attempt to turn its axle in a horizontal plane, you will immediately notice a resistance to such motion. The wheel will try to turn in such a direction as to bring itself in a horizontal plane with its axis vertical. If you have not experienced this resistance you would be well advised to carry out the experiment. Alternatively, you may have noticed similar effects with a small model gyroscope.

This gyroscopic effect is noticed in varying degrees every time wheels which are rotating in one plane are made to turn, or to *precess*, to use the correct term, in another plane. Thus, cycle, motor car, and engine wheels, including flywheels, steam turbines in ships, and jet turbines in planes, are all subject to this apparently capricious gyroscopic effect, which, in general, adds to the problem of stability on circular paths. A more detailed review of this aspect must wait until a later stage of study, particularly in mechanics of machines.

Stress in a Flywheel Rim

A rotating flywheel, in common with all rotating discs, is subject to tensile stresses in its rim. These stresses are necessary to provide the required centripetal forces. If the rim stresses exceed the safe working stress of the material, the flywheel is in danger of bursting. The bursting of flywheels, and more particularly of grinding wheels from the same cause, presents one of the occasional industrial dangers associated with engineering.

Consider a flywheel where:

r = mean radius of rim, in m;
A = cross-sectional area of rim, in m²;
v = velocity of rim (sometimes known as peripheral velocity), in m/s;
ρ = density of material, in kg/m³;
F = tangential force caused by centripetal effects, in N;
δ = stress due to F, in N/m².

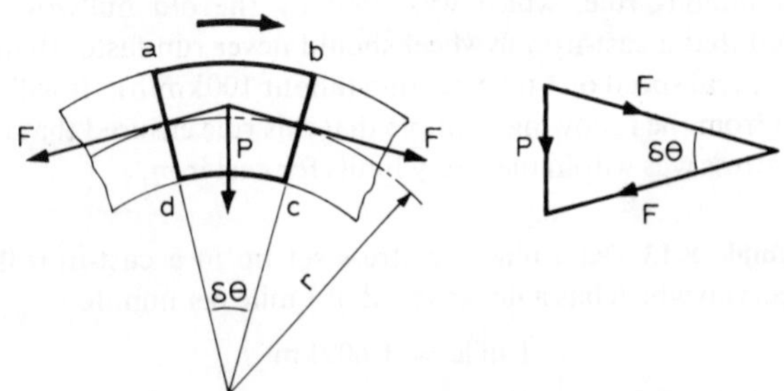

Fig.8.21 Stress in flywheel rim. In order to provide the necessary centripetal force P, there must be a series of forces such as F. These forces produce stresses in the rim, which will fracture if the tensile strength of the material is exceeded.

A small portion of the rim, whose front elevation is shown as *abcd*, length δx m, subtends an angle $\delta\theta$ at the centre of the flywheel (fig.8.21).

Volume of this portion $= A\delta x\,\text{m}^3$
But $\delta x = r\delta\theta$ (arc = radius × angle in radians)
Volume of portion $= Ar\delta\theta\,\text{m}^3$
Mass of portion $= \rho Ar\delta\theta\,\text{kg}$

$$\text{Centripetal acceleration of portion} = \frac{v^2}{r}\ \text{m/s}^2$$

Centripetal force required to produce this acceleration

$$P = \text{mass} \times \text{acceleration}$$
$$= \rho Ar\delta\theta \times \frac{v^2}{r}$$
$$= \rho Av^2\delta\theta \quad \ldots \quad (1)$$

This force P is the radial component of the tangential force F acting on the planes indicated by *ad* and *bc*.

From the force diagram it will be seen that

$$P = F\delta\theta \text{ (using arc = radius × angle)}$$
$$F = \frac{P}{\delta\theta}$$
$$= \frac{\rho Av^2\delta\theta}{\delta\theta} \text{ from equation (1)}$$
$$= \rho Av^2\,\text{N}$$

This force F causes a tensile stress on the radial sections such as *ad* and *bc*.

$$\text{Tensile stress} = \frac{\text{force}}{\text{area}} = \frac{F}{A}$$
$$= \frac{\rho Av^2}{A}$$

i.e. Tensile stress in rim $= \rho v^2$

A famous rule, which was used by the old millwrights, stated that a cast-iron flywheel should never run faster than a peripheral speed of 1 mile per min (about 100 km/h). It will be seen from the following example that this rule ensured that the rim stress was within the safety limits for cast iron.

Example 8.13 Determine the stress set up in a cast-iron flywheel rim which has a linear speed of 1 mile per minute.

$$1 \text{ mile} = 1{\cdot}609\,\text{km}$$

Speed of rim $= 26{\cdot}8\,\text{m/s}$

ρ for cast iron $= 7{\cdot}25 \times 10^3\,\text{kg/m}^3$

$$\begin{aligned} \text{Stress} &= \rho v^2 \\ &= 7{\cdot}25 \times 10^3 \times 26{\cdot}8^2 \\ &= 5200 \times 10^3\,\text{N/m}^2 \end{aligned}$$

i.e. Rim stress set up with peripheral speed of 1 mile per minute is 5·2 N/mm².

Example 8.14 Establish an expression for the stress produced in a thin rotating rim due to centrifugal force.

A thin steel rim, 1·2 m diameter and 125 mm wide, is made of steel plate 16 mm thick. Determine the maximum permissible speed, in revolutions per minute, of the rim if the tensile strength of the steel is 495 N/mm² and a factor of safety of 9 is used. Density of steel $= 7{\cdot}8 \times 10^3\,\text{kg/m}^3$.

The rim is made in two halves, and fastened by two bolts in single shear, one each side of each joint. Determine the minimum diameter of the bolts if the shear stress in the bolts is not to exceed 70 N/mm². ULCI

Rim stress $= \rho v^2$

$$\begin{aligned} \text{Allowable stress} &= \frac{\text{tensile strength}}{\text{factor of safety}} \\ &= \frac{495 \times 10^6}{9} \\ &= 55 \times 10^6\,\text{N/m}^2 \end{aligned}$$

$$\begin{aligned} \text{Stress in rim} &= 7{\cdot}8 \times 10^3 \times v^2 \\ &= 55 \times 10^6 \\ \therefore v &= 84\,\text{m/s} \end{aligned}$$

$$\begin{aligned} \text{Maximum angular velocity of rim} &= \frac{84 \times 60}{0{\cdot}6 \times 2\pi} \\ &= 1336\,\text{rev/min} \end{aligned}$$

Force in rim producing centripetal effects

$$\begin{aligned} &= \text{stress} \times \text{area of rim} \\ &= 55 \times 10^6 \times 0{\cdot}125 \times 0{\cdot}016 \\ &= 110 \times 10^3\,\text{N} \end{aligned}$$

This force will set up shear stresses in the bolts. Each bolt will have to withstand a load of 110 kN.

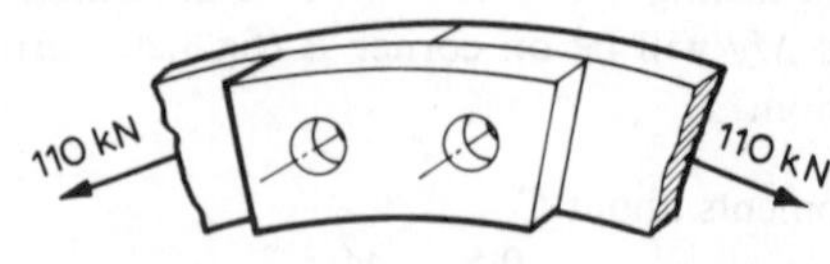

Fig.8.22

$$\begin{aligned} \text{Area of bolt} &= \frac{\text{load}}{\text{stress}} = \frac{110 \times 10^3}{70 \times 10^6} \\ &= 1{\cdot}57 \times 10^{-3}\,\text{m}^2 \\ &= 1570\,\text{mm}^2 \end{aligned}$$

$$\begin{aligned} \text{Diameter of bolt} &= \sqrt{\frac{4 \times 1570}{\pi}} \\ &= 44{\cdot}8\,\text{mm} \end{aligned}$$

i.e. The maximum safe speed of the rim is 1336 rev/min; the minimum diameter of the bolts is 44·8 mm.

Exercise 8

1 A point P is moving around a circular path with a velocity of 3 m/s. If the radius of the path is 1·2 m, what is the magnitude and direction of the acceleration of P?

2 The crank-pin of an engine is 0·45 m from the crank-shaft, which is rotating uniformly at 200 rev/min. What is the acceleration of the crank-pin?

3 In a machine, a horizontal arm 0·6 m long is driven by a vertical shaft, and makes 600 rev/min in a horizontal plane. A 4·5 kg block is attached to the free end of the arm. Determine (a) the force on the block, and (b) the force on the vertical shaft due to the rotation of the block.

4 Show that the 'height' of a conical pendulum is dependent only upon the speed of rotation.

A roundabout has a number of carriages hung from a rotating roof by means of chains 3·6 m long. The upper ends of the chains are attached to the roof on a pitch circle of 3·0 m radius. Find the greatest speed at which the roundabout can operate if the angle which the chains make with the vertical is not to exceed 20°. UEI

5 A locomotive, mass 60 tonnes, is rounding a curve of 200 m radius at 48 km/h when the power is suddenly shut off. The total resistance to motion is then 50 kN. Calculate the radial and tangential accelerations immediately after the power was shut off, and the radial pressure between the wheels and the rails. To what angle would the track have to be banked in order to reduce the radial pressure to zero when the train is running at 48 km/h? UEI

6 State what is meant by centripetal acceleration.

A spring 300 mm long extends 25 mm when loaded with a force of 10 N. A 0·225 kg mass is attached to one end, and is caused to rotate at 3 rev/s, on a smooth horizontal table, about a point to which the other end of the spring is attached. Find the tension of the spring, and the radius of the circle. UEI

7 Explain why there must be a radial force on a body which moves with uniform velocity in a circle.

The height of the centre of gravity of a locomotive is 2 m above rail level. Find the speed in km/h at which it would become unstable on a horizontal curve without super-elevation. The mean radius of the curve is 245 m, and the distance between the rails is 1·5 m. UEI

8 Derive an expression for the acceleration of a body moving in a circular path with constant speed.

A truck running on level rails which are 1·44 m apart has to turn a curve of 45 m radius. If the centre of gravity of the truck is 0·75 m above the rails, what is the greatest velocity with which it may take the curve without overturning? UEI

9 Prove that a body moving in a circular path of radius r m, with a velocity of v m/s possesses an inward radial acceleration of v^2/r m/s^2.

Find the maximum speed at which a motor cyclist can travel around a banked curve of radius 55 m without slipping, if the angle of banking is 15°, and the coefficient of friction between the wheels and the bank is 0·4. Assume that the rider and cycle remain in one plane. UEI

10 Explain the difference between centripetal and centrifugal force.

A stone of mass 0·225 kg is whirling in a vertical circle at the extremity of a string 0·6 m long. Find the least velocity of the stone, and the tension in the string at the highest position and at the lowest position when the stone just completes the circle. UEI

11 Obtain an expression for the acceleration of a body moving in a circle at constant speed.

A train travels at 80 km/h on a curve of 400 m radius. If the gauge of the track is 1·5 m, calculate the elevation of the outer above the inner rail so that there shall be no flange pressure. UEI

12 A vehicle having a wheel track 1·5 m wide is running on level ground round a curve of 60 m radius. If the centre of gravity is 0·7 m above the ground, calculate the speed in km/h at which the vehicle will tend to overturn. NCTEC

13 A vehicle has its centre of gravity 1·06 m above the ground, and the wheel track is 1·2 m wide. Determine the minimum speed in km/h at which the car will overturn when rounding an unbanked curve of 45 m radius. NCTEC

14 Show how the banking of the track on a railway curve reduces the side thrust between the wheel flanges and the rails. Calculate a suitable value for the super-elevation of a track of 1·44 m gauge on a radius of 180 m if the maximum safe speed is to be 65 km/h. NCTEC

15 Explain why there must be a radial force acting on a body which moves with uniform velocity in a circle. A railway on a curve of 800 m radius has a gauge of 1·4 m. By how much must the outer rail be raised if there is to be no side thrust on the wheels at 72 km/h? NCTEC

16 An electric tramcar turns a sharp corner of mean radius 9 m at a speed of 16 km/h, the road being horizontal. Find the greatest height of the centre of gravity in order that the inner wheels may not leave the rails. The gauge is 1·37 m. NCTEC

17 Derive an expression for the acceleration of a body moving with constant speed in a circular path.

A motor car is travelling around a flat circular track of radius 9 m at 24 km/h, and is just on the point of skidding. What is the coefficient of friction between wheels and road? NCTEC

18 In a conical pendulum, find the change of height when the speed falls from 90 to 60 rev/min. If you use a formula, show how it is derived. NCTEC

19 A ball is suspended from a string attached to a swivel joint, and revolves in a horizontal circular path with constant angular velocity. Show that the vertical height from the centre of the ball to the point of suspension is independent of the length of the string.

If the ball has a mass of 1 kg, and revolves at 50 rev/min at the end of a string 1 m long, find the tension in the string. NCTEC

20 A tramcar, of mass 12 tonnes, is moving round a curve of 45 m mean radius at a speed of 32 km/h, the plane of the rails being horizontal, and the gauge 1·07 m. The centre of gravity of the car is 1·5 m above the rails. Determine the vertical pressure on the inner and outer rails.

If the side of the car is taken as equivalent to a rectangle 4·25 m high (measured from the ground) and 6 m long, find the least wind pressure, in N/m^2, which would overturn the car when rounding a curve at 32 km/h. ULCI

21 Deduce an expression for the height of a conical pendulum when rotating at an angular speed of ω rad/s.

The arm of a simple conical pendulum is 0·6 m, and the pendulum bob has a mass of 1·4 kg. Determine the height of the pendulum, and the tension in the arm when rotating at 75 rev/min. What increase in speed, in revolutions per minute, is necessary to reduce the height by 10%? Neglect the mass of the arm. ULCI

22 A four-wheeled, two-axled vehicle travels at a uniform speed of 56 km/h round a horizontal curve of 120 m radius. The distance between the wheel tracks is 1·8 m, the centre of gravity of the vehicle is on the vertical through the centre of the wheel-base, and 1·5 m above the ground, and the total mass of the vehicle is 16 tonnes.

Determine (a) the vertical pressure on each of the inner and outer wheels, and (b) the maximum velocity at which the vehicle can negotiate the curve without overturning. ULCI

23 Deduce an expression for the height of a conical pendulum when rotating at an angular speed of ω rad/s.

The arm of a simple conical pendulum is 0·75 m, and the pendulum bob has a mass of 1·6 kg. When the pendulum rotates at 80 rev/min, determine (a) the radius at which the bob rotates, and (b) the tension in the arm. Neglect the mass of the arm. ULCI

24 A cylinder, which can be considered as a thin shell, is made of steel plate 16 mm thick and 2·1 m in diameter. The cylinder is subjected to an internal pressure of 550 kN/m², and is rotated about a horizontal axis at 300 rev/min. Determine (a) the hoop stress produced in the material due to the pressure, (b) the hoop stress produced due to the rotation, and (c) the factor of safety used in the design of the cylinder. The tensile strength and the density of the steel used are 450 N/mm² and 7800 kg/m³ respectively. ULCI

25 The string of a conical pendulum is 1·25 m long, and can just support a mass of 12 kg without breaking. If the mass of the pendulum bob is 5 kg, determine the radius of the circle described by the bob, and the maximum speed, in revolutions per minute, that the bob can make without breaking the string. ULCI

26 How high above the rails may the centre of gravity of a loaded truck be, when standing on a level track, without danger of overturning at 96 km/h, on a curve of 120 m radius, where the outer rail is 150 mm above the inner rail? The gauge is 1·5 m. IMECHE

27 A bend in a road is banked at an angle arctan 0·2, and has a mean radius of 76 m. If the coefficient of friction between the tyres and the road is 0·6, determine the speed of a car travelling round this bend when side slip is imminent. ULCI

28 Explain briefly the meaning of the terms 'centrifugal force' and 'centripetal force'.

Show that the vertical height of a conical pendulum rotating at constant speed is independent of the length.

A ball of mass 1 kg is suspended by a string 1 m long, and revolves in a horizontal plane at 50 rev/min. Determine the tension in the string. NCTEC

Chapter 9

Simple Harmonic Motion

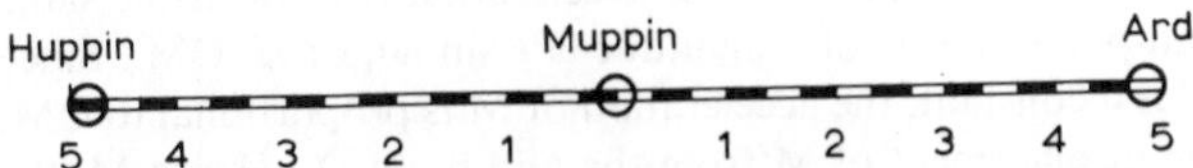

Fig.9.1 Huppin, Muppim, and Ard railway

Let us examine the strange performance of the 17·45 train which runs from Huppin to Ard via Muppim. The two terminii are 10 kilometres apart, and no doubt you know that Muppim is exactly mid-way, i.e. 5 kilometres from either station. The train is fitted with a speedometer, recording both speed and distance travelled, and also with a meter which records acceleration. The motion of the train is to be such that its acceleration is proportional to the distance moved from the mid-point of the railway (which you may remember is Muppim). Let us sit in front of the meters, and record the value of the acceleration of the train at the end of each kilometre travelled from Muppim. Here is the result.

Distance from Muppim, km	1	2	3	4	5
Acceleration, m/s²	0·06	0·12	0·18	0·24	0·30

As the distance increases, the acceleration increases in proportion. You may think that the accelerations are very small compared with the more dignified Victoria Line accelerations of 0·9 m/s²; nevertheless, our train travels the 5 kilometres in approximately 10 minutes, and arrives at the terminus, Ard, with a speed of nearly 60 km/h.

Now of course this is serious: the train arrives at 60 km/h, and shows no sign of slowing down. In fact, its acceleration is higher now than at any point on the run, and the farther the train travels from Muppim (which you remember is the mid-point of the railway line), then the greater becomes its acceleration. The result of this alarming journey, in which the 17·45 rushes through Ard at 60 km/h, with both velocity and acceleration increasing, must surely be a tragic one. (If you study the matter carefully, you will find that 10 minutes later the train will be travelling at 500 km/h, and will certainly never be seen again.)

Now let us make one very small but tremendously important change in the conditions under which the train travels from Huppin to Ard via Muppim.

We shall still insist that the magnitude of the acceleration shall be proportional to the distance from the mid-point of the line, i.e. we shall get the same acceleration readings as before; but we now stipulate that the direction of the acceleration must always be towards the mid-point of the line (which is Muppim) so that, while the train travels from one terminus towards the mid-point, the acceleration is in the same direction as the velocity, which therefore increases. On going beyond the mid-point, the direction of the acceleration is reversed, whilst the direction of the velocity remains the same. The train therefore begins to retard, until it comes to rest at the terminus. But here the acceleration reaches its greatest value, and therefore the train immediately begins its return journey, with its velocity increasing to a maximum whilst passing through the mid-point, and then decreasing to zero at the opposite terminus. This oscillating, backward-and-forwards motion will be continued indefinitely under identical conditions. The movement of the train is constrained between the two termini. The time taken to travel the total 10 kilometres is 15½ minutes, and the train passes through the mid-point, Muppim, at 60 km/h (which is rather lamentable, since the usefulness of Muppim as a station is therefore negligible, although on further reflection it will be seen that since the train stops only for an instant at either terminus, making it extremely difficult for anyone to board the train, the problem of leaving it is practically eliminated).

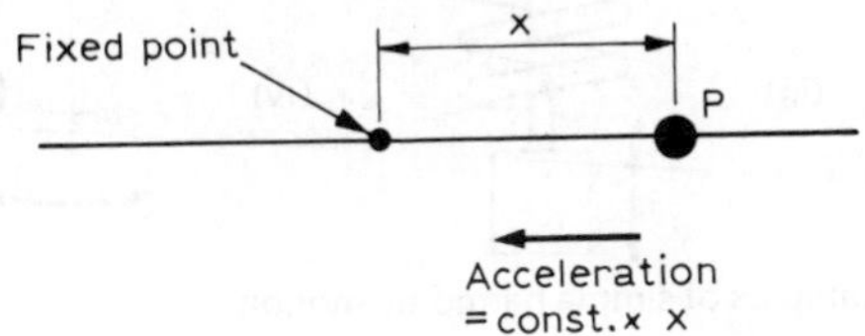

Fig.9.2 Simple harmonic motion. P moves so that its acceleration is always proportional to its distance from the fixed point.

Now under these conditions, the train is said to be moving with *simple harmonic motion.* It is a form of motion which is of immense importance. It is the basis of all work on vibrations, a vast subject in the field of engineering. It is essential that you get a very clear conception of the nature of simple harmonic motion, and that you are familiar with the various definitions associated with it.

We shall define simple harmonic motion along a straight line in the following words:

A body which moves so that its acceleration is:
a) *proportional to the distance moved from a fixed point in its path, and*
b) *always directed towards that point*
is said to move with simple harmonic motion.

There are many examples of simple harmonic motion (fig. 9.3). (The usual abbreviation for these words is S.H.M.)

The motion of the piston in a cylinder is approximately S.H.M. In fact, if the connecting-rod were of infinite length, then the motion would actually be S.H.M.

A follower operated by a circular cam whose axis of rotation is displaced from the geometrical centre of the cam will move with S.H.M.

A mass hung from a spring will vibrate in a vertical direction, and will move with S.H.M.

The bob at the end of a swinging pendulum moves with S.H.M., provided that the pendulum does not swing through too great an angle.

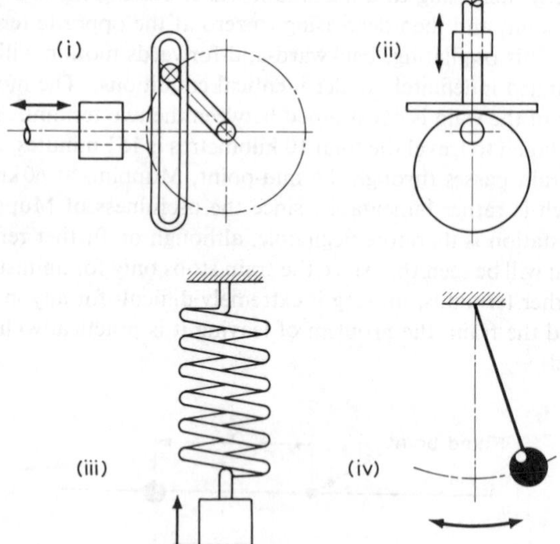

Fig.9.3 Examples of simple harmonic motion

Calculations in connection with ships rolling at sea are based on the assumption that the motion of the ship's roll is S.H.M.

Consider the motion of a point P (fig.9.4) moving in a circular path of radius r with a constant angular velocity ω rad/s. The radial line OP will have moved through angle ωt from the vertical in t seconds. M is the foot of a perpendicular drawn from P on to OX, the horizontal axis through O. OM is equal to $r \sin \omega t$.

The centripetal acceleration of P is $\omega^2 r$, and the horizontal component of this is $\omega^2 r \sin \omega t$, directed towards the axis OY. Hence a plan view of the motion of P would indicate a point moving backwards and forwards along a straight line, so that at any instant its displacement from the mid-point is given by

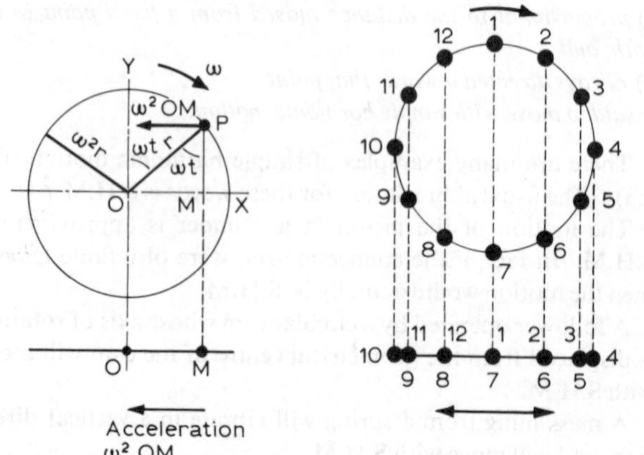

Fig.9.4 and 9.5 The projection on to a straight line of a point P moving with uniform speed on a circular path is an example of simple harmonic motion.

OM, or $r \sin \omega t$, and whose acceleration is towards the same mid-point, and is of magnitude $\omega^2 r \sin \omega t$, or ω^2 OM. Since ω^2 is a constant, the acceleration of M is proportional to OM, the displacement of M from the mid-point O. Hence M, the projection of the point P, is moving with simple harmonic motion.

Now P makes $\frac{\omega}{2\pi}$ rev/s, and it will be obvious that M must make the same number of complete 'backward-and-forward' motions or oscillations per second as P makes rev/s. This number of oscillations per second is known as the *frequency* of the motion. The time taken for one oscillation is known as the *periodic time*. If M makes $\frac{\omega}{2\pi}$ oscillations per second, then the time taken for one oscillation will be $\frac{2\pi}{\omega}$ seconds.

The unit of frequency is the *hertz* (Hz). A frequency of one hertz is equal to one oscillation or cycle per second.

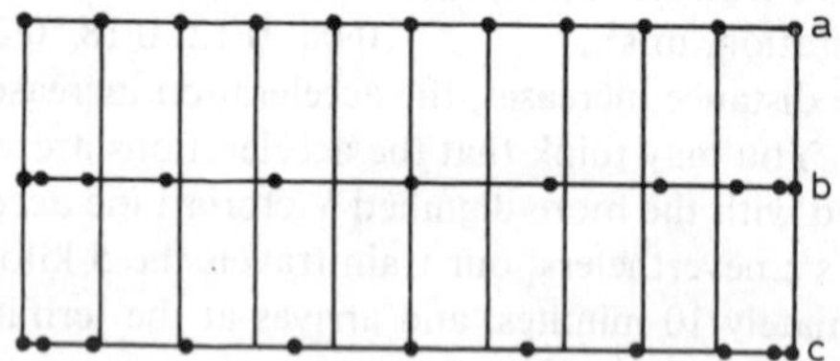

Fig.9.6 Three basic types of motion. In each case the point travels through the same distance. It moves with uniform velocity in case *a*, with uniform acceleration in case *b*, and with simple harmonic motion in case *c*. By comparing the position of the points after equal intervals of time, you can obtain some idea of the nature of the motion in each case.

Mathematical Approach to Simple Harmonic Motion

The definition of simple harmonic motion, already stated as 'motion in which a body moves so that its acceleration is proportional to its distance x from a fixed point in its path, and is directed towards that point,' can be expressed mathematically thus:

$$\frac{d^2x}{dt^2} = -\omega^2 x \quad . \quad . \quad . \quad (1)$$

i.e. the acceleration (d^2x/dt^2) is equal to some constant (ω^2) multiplied by the displacement (x), and also the acceleration is measured in the opposite direction (−) to that in which we are measuring the displacement (x), which, incidentally, is measured from the mid-point of the oscillation. Regarding the choice of the constant (ω^2), any letter might have been chosen, but we shall see that there are such strong resemblances between the equations derived and those for motion in a circle that there are advantages in using ω^2 in both cases. The square in ω^2 is used to avoid too many square-root signs occurring in the resulting equations.

Consider the expression $x = a \sin \omega t$, in which a and ω are constants; this expression gives us the value of the displacement x in terms of time t. If we differentiate this expression with respect to t, we obtain an expression for the velocity which, when differentiated again, gives an expression for acceleration.

Displacement $\quad x = a \sin\omega t \quad . \quad . \quad . \quad . \quad (2)$

Velocity $\quad v = a\omega \cdot \cos\omega t \quad . \quad . \quad . \quad . \quad (3)$

$$\text{Acceleration } \frac{dv}{dt} = \frac{d^2x}{dt^2} = -a\omega . \omega \sin\omega t$$

$$= -a\omega^2 \sin\omega t$$

$$= -\ \omega^2(a \sin\omega t)$$

$$= -\ \omega^2 x$$

which is the fundamental equation for simple harmonic motion Hence the displacement equation for simple harmonic motion is

$$x = a \sin\omega t$$

where the constant ω occurs in the expression

$$\text{acceleration} = -\omega^2 \times \text{displacement}$$

Since the maximum value of $\sin \omega t$ is equal to 1, the maximum value of x is a. This is known as the *amplitude* of the oscillation, and is the greatest distance which the body travels from the mid-point of its motion.

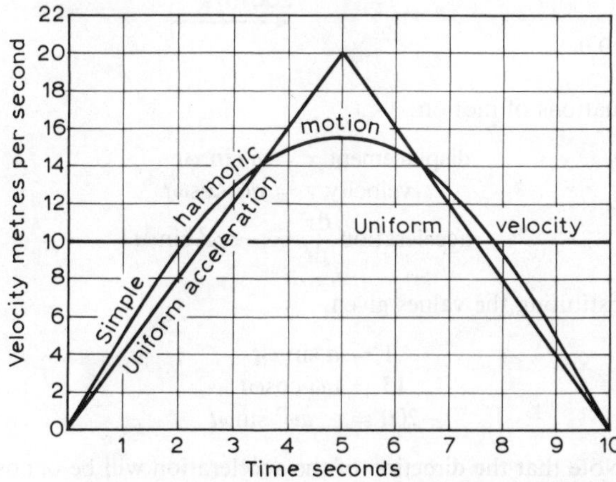

Fig.9.7 Three basic forms of motion. This diagram allows a further comparison between the uniform velocity, uniform acceleration, and the simple harmonic forms of motion. Assuming that the particles moving with uniform acceleration and with simple harmonic motion are at rest at the beginning and end of their motion, it will be seen that, in order to travel through the same distance in the same time, the maximum velocity of the particle moving with uniform acceleration will be $2v$, whilst that of the particle moving with S.H.M. will be $\pi v/2$, where v is the uniform velocity of the third particle.

The value of $\sin\omega t$ is equal to $\sin(\omega t + 360°)$ or $\sin(\omega t + 2\pi)$, which can be written as $\sin \omega(t + 2\pi/\omega)$. Therefore, when t is increased by $2\pi/\omega$ seconds, the value of x is unchanged, i.e. the body is passing through the same point in its path, and is travelling in the same direction. This value of $2\pi/\omega$ is the *periodic time* of the oscillation.

Since the frequency is always equal to (1/periodic time), the value of the frequency becomes $\omega/2\pi$ per second or $\omega/2\pi$ Hz.

From equation (1) we can express the value of ω as $\sqrt{\frac{\text{acceleration}}{\text{displacement}}}$, remembering that the direction of the acceleration will be opposite to that of the displacement. Hence we make sure that we are not troubled with the square root of a negative quantity. Substituting this value of ω into the expressions for periodic time and frequency, we get

$$\text{periodic time} = 2\,\pi\sqrt{\frac{\text{displacement}}{\text{acceleration}}} \text{ seconds}$$

and $$\text{frequency} = \frac{1}{2\pi}\sqrt{\frac{\text{acceleration}}{\text{displacement}}} \text{ hertz}$$

Example 9.1 A particle moves with simple harmonic motion between two points 1 m apart. The frequency of the oscillation is 4 Hz. Determine (a) the periodic time for the oscillation, (b) the maximum velocity and acceleration, and (c) the velocity and the acceleration of the particle when it is 300 mm from one end of the motion (fig.9.8).

a) Periodic time $= \dfrac{1}{\text{frequency}} = \dfrac{1}{4} = 0{\cdot}25$ seconds

b) Equation of motion is $x = a \sin \omega t$
where a is the amplitude $= \frac{1}{2} = 0{\cdot}5$ m

ω is given by $\quad \text{frequency} = \dfrac{\omega}{2\pi}$ Hz

$$\frac{\omega}{2\pi} = 4$$

$$\therefore \omega = 8\pi$$

Equation for motion is $x = 0{\cdot}5 \sin 8\pi t$

$$\text{Velocity } v = \frac{dx}{dt} = 4\pi \cos 8\pi t$$

The maximum value of this velocity occurs when $\cos 8\pi t$ is equal to 1, and equals 4π or 12·57 m/s. This will occur at the mid-point of the stroke.

$$\text{Acceleration} = \frac{dv}{dt} = -32\pi^2 \sin 8\pi t$$

The maximum value of this acceleration occurs when $\sin 8\pi t$ is equal to 1, and equals $32\pi^2$ or 316 m/s^2. This will occur at either end of the stroke.

c) When the particle is 0·3 m from one end, it is 0·2 m from the mid-point of the stroke. Hence the displacement, x, is equal to 0·2 m.

$$0{\cdot}2 = 0{\cdot}5 \sin 8\pi t, \text{ using the displacement equation}$$

$$\sin 8\pi t = 0{\cdot}4$$

$$\cos 8\pi t = \sqrt{(1 - \sin^2 8\pi t)} = \sqrt{(1 - 0{\cdot}4^2)} = 0{\cdot}916$$

Velocity at this instant is $4\pi \cos 8\pi t$ m/s

$$= 4\pi \times 0{\cdot}916 \text{ m/s} = 11{\cdot}5 \text{ m/s}$$

Acceleration at this instant is $-32\pi^2 \sin 8\pi t$ m/s²

$$= -32\pi^2 \times 0{\cdot}4 \text{ m/s}^2 = -126{\cdot}4 \text{ m/s}^2$$

The negative sign implies that the acceleration is in the opposite direction to that in which we are measuring the displacement.

Alternative Solution

Consider the motion of the particle between A and B as the projection of the motion of P round a circular path of radius 0·5 m. P will make 4 rev/s, which is equivalent to an angular velocity of $4 \times 2\pi = 8\pi$ rad/s.

The linear velocity of P will be ωr, or $8\pi \times 0{\cdot}5$, which is 4π m/s. The velocity, at any instant, of the particle moving between A and B will be the horizontal component of P's velocity at the same instant. When P is moving through the point C, so that the particle is at the corresponding point C′, the velocity of P will be in the direction of AB, and therefore the velocity of the particle at this instant will be equal to the whole of P's velocity, i.e. 4π or 12·57 m/s.

Similarly for the acceleration. The acceleration of P is ωr^2, or $(8\pi)^2 \times 0{\cdot}5$, which is $32\pi^2$ m/s² radially towards O. The corresponding acceleration of the particle will be the horizontal component of P's acceleration at the same instant.

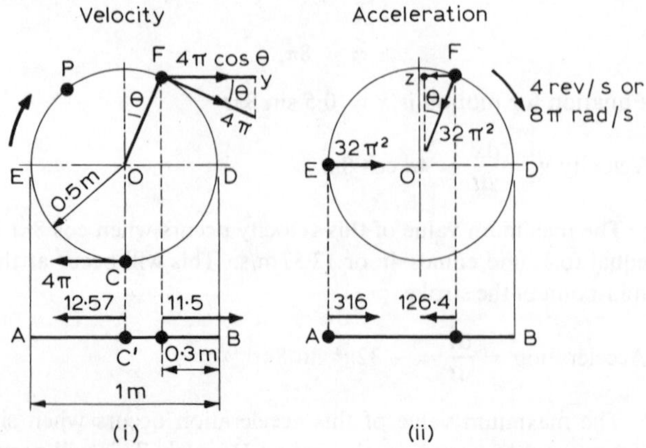

Fig.9.8

When P is passing through E and D, so that the particle is at the corresponding point A or B, the acceleration will be in the direction of AB, and therefore the acceleration of the particle at these points will be equal to the whole of P's acceleration, i.e. $32\pi^2$ or 316 m/s².

When the particle is 0·3 m from B, P is at F. The component of P's velocity in the AB direction is given by **F*y***, fig.9.8 (i), and is equal to $4\pi \cos \theta$. $\sin \theta$ is 2/5, or 0·4, giving $\cos \theta$ equal to 0·916. Hence the required component of P's velocity is $4\pi \times 0{\cdot}916$, or 11·5 m/s.

The component of P's acceleration in the AB direction is given by **F*z***, fig.9.8 (ii), and is equal to $32\pi^2 \sin \theta$, or $32\pi^2 \times 0{\cdot}4$, which is 126·4 m/s², as before.

Example 9.2 A mass of 20 kg moves with simple harmonic motion. At a displacement of 1 m from the centre of oscillation, the velocity and acceleration of the body are 15 m/s and 200 m/s² respectively (fig.9.9).

Determine (a) the number of oscillations made per minute, (b) the amplitude of the motion, and (c) the force required to overcome the inertia of the body when at the extremities of the oscillation. ULCI

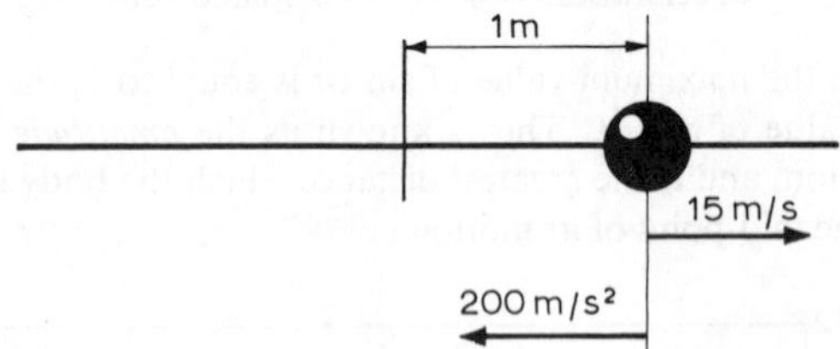

Fig.9.9

Equations of motion:

$$\text{displacement } x = a \sin \omega t$$

$$\text{velocity } v = a\omega \cos \omega t$$

$$\text{acceleration } \frac{dv}{dt} = -a\omega^2 \sin \omega t$$

Substituting the values given,

$$1 = a \sin \omega t \quad \dots \quad (1)$$

$$15 = a\omega \cos \omega t \quad \dots \quad (2)$$

$$-200 = -a\omega^2 \sin \omega t \quad \dots \quad (3)$$

Note that the direction of the acceleration will be opposite to that of the displacement, since the motion is simple harmonic.

Dividing (3) by (1), we have

$$-200 = \frac{-a\omega^2 \sin \omega t}{a \sin \omega t} = -\omega^2$$

$$\omega^2 = 200. \quad \dots \quad (4)$$

$$\text{Frequency of motion} = \frac{\omega}{2\pi}$$

$$= \frac{\sqrt{200}}{2\pi} \text{ Hz}$$

$$= \frac{\sqrt{200}}{2\pi} \times 60 \text{ oscillations per minute}$$

$$= 135 \text{ oscillations per minute}$$

Value of amplitude, a.

Multiplying (1) by ω and squaring,

$$\omega^2 = a^2\omega^2 \sin^2\omega t$$

Squaring (2), $\quad 225 = a^2\omega^2\cos^2\omega t$

Adding, $\quad \omega^2 + 225 = a^2\omega^2(\sin^2\omega t + \cos^2 \omega t)$
$\quad = a^2\omega^2$, since $\sin^2\omega t + \cos^2\omega t = 1$

Substituting $\omega^2 = 200$ from (4),

$$200 + 225 = 200a^2$$
$$a = 1{\cdot}46\text{m}$$

i.e. Amplitude of vibration is 1·46 m.

Force to overcome inertia at extremity of motion, when displacement of body equals amplitude

$$x = a = 1{\cdot}46$$

But $\quad x = a \sin \omega t$

hence $\sin \omega t$ must equal 1.

$$\text{Acceleration} = -a\omega^2 \sin \omega t$$
$$= -1{\cdot}46 \times 200 \times 1$$
$$= -292\,\text{m/s}^2$$

Force to overcome inertia of body = mass × acceleration
= 20 × 292
= 5840 N

i.e. The frequency of motion is 135 oscillations per minute, the amplitude is 1·46 m, and the force to overcome inertia of body at the extremity of the oscillation is 5·84 kN.

Motion of Mass Supported by Spring

Figure 9.10(i) indicates a mass of M kg supported by a spring whose stiffness is e N/m, i.e. a spring which requires a force of e newtons in order to stretch it 1 m. When the M kg mass is attached, the spring will stretch Mg/e metres; this is known as the static deflection of the spring. The mass will be in equilibrium under the action of its own weight, Mg, downwards, and the spring tension, which must equal Mg upwards.

Now let the mass be displaced downwards from this equilibrium position by an amount x [fig.9.10(ii)]. The forces acting on the mass will now be:

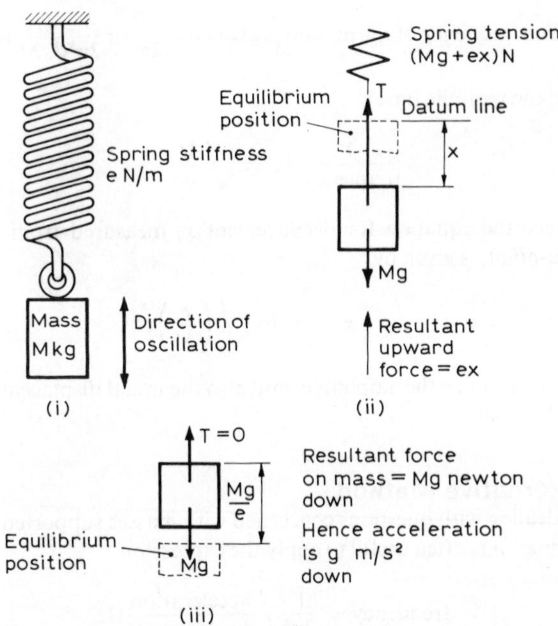

Fig.9.10 Mass suspended from spring. This is a very important case of simple harmonic motion. Throughout the motion there is a continual transference of energy. The interchange is between the strain energy of the spring and the kinetic energy of the mass.

1 tension in the spring T. Before displacing the mass, this tension would be Mg newtons. For every metre increase in length of the spring, the tension will increase by e newtons. If the spring is stretched x metres (since the mass has been displaced x metres), then the increase in spring tension is ex newtons, and the total spring tension will be $Mg + ex$ newtons.

2 dead-weight, Mg newtons, of the mass acting downward.

Resultant downward force on the mass is $Mg - (Mg + ex) = -ex$ newtons. Notice that we have calculated the resultant force in the same direction as that in which the mass was displaced, i.e. downwards. This direction is important.

The equation for motion is

$$\text{force} = \text{mass} \times \text{acceleration}$$
$$-ex = M \times \text{acceleration}$$

$$\text{Acceleration} = -\left(\frac{e}{M}\right)x$$
$$= -kx$$

where k is a constant equal to $\left(\frac{e}{M}\right)$ or $\frac{g}{\text{static deflection}}$, since Mg/e is equal to the static deflection. Hence the acceleration is proportional to the displacement, and acts towards the midpoint of the motion. Therefore the mass is moving with simple harmonic motion.

The frequency of the motion is given by $\frac{\sqrt{k}}{2\pi}$ or $\frac{1}{2\pi}\sqrt{\frac{e}{M}}$ Hz,

and the periodic time is

$$\frac{1}{\text{frequency}} = 2\pi\sqrt{\frac{M}{e}}$$

Hence the equation for displacement x, measured from the mid-point, is given by

$$x = a \sin\sqrt{\left(\frac{e}{M}\right)}t$$

where a will be the amplitude, and also the initial displacement of the mass.

Alternative Method

In dealing with questions concerned with masses supported by springs, it is often useful to apply the expression

$$\text{frequency} = \frac{1}{2\pi}\sqrt{\frac{\text{acceleration}}{\text{displacement}}}\text{Hz}$$

This can be used if we know the value of the acceleration for a particular displacement. Referring again to fig.9.10(iii), let the mass be lifted until all the tension is taken out of the spring. In view of the fact that the spring stretched an amount Mg/e when the mass was attached, it follows that the mass will have to be lifted by an amount Mg/e to relieve the spring of tension. When this has been done, the only force on the mass will be its own weight Mg, since the spring has no effect on it now. If the resultant force acting on the mass is equal to its own weight, then the acceleration produced will be equal to $g\,\text{m/s}^2$

Hence we can say that the acceleration will be $g\,\text{m/s}^2$ when the displacement is Mg/e metres.

$$\text{Frequency of motion} = \frac{1}{2\pi}\sqrt{\frac{\text{acceleration}}{\text{displacement}}}$$

$$= \frac{1}{2\pi}\sqrt{\frac{g}{Mg/e}}$$

$$= \frac{1}{2\pi}\sqrt{\frac{e}{M}}\ \text{Hz, as before.}$$

Example 9.3 A vertical helical spring is attached to a rigid support at its upper end, and carries at the other end a body of mass 20kg, which causes an extension of 30mm. This body is pulled down a further 20mm, and is then released (fig.9.11). Calculate (a) the initial acceleration of the body, (b) the velocity when the body attains its original position, (c) the velocity and acceleration of the body when it is 10mm above its original position, and (d) the time for the body to make one complete oscillation. IMECHE

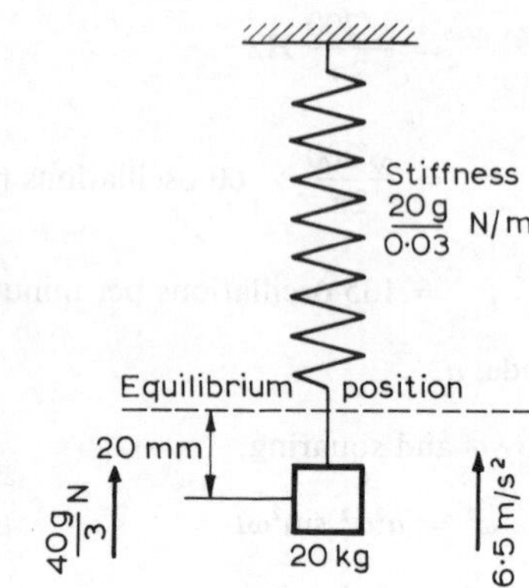

Fig.9.11

a) Initial acceleration of body.

$$\text{Spring stiffness} = \frac{20g}{0{\cdot}03}\ \text{N/m}$$

Forces acting on body.

1 Spring force. Originally $20g$N, then increased by stiffness × extension.

$$\text{Spring force} = \left(20g + \frac{20g \times 0{\cdot}02}{0{\cdot}03}\right)\text{N}$$

$$= \frac{100g}{3}\ \text{N upwards}$$

2 Gravitational force. $20g$N downwards.

$$\text{Resultant force} = \frac{100g}{3} - 20g$$

$$= \frac{40g}{3}\ \text{N upwards}$$

Equation of motion.

$$\text{Force} = \text{mass} \times \text{acceleration}$$

$$\frac{40g}{3} = 20 \times \text{acceleration}$$

$$\text{Acceleration} = \frac{40g}{60} = 6{\cdot}54\,\text{m/s}^2\ \text{upwards}$$

b) At the extremities of motion

$$v = 0$$

$$\therefore a\omega \cos\omega t = 0$$

$$\therefore \cos\omega t = 0$$

and $\sin\omega t = 1$

Equation for acceleration.

$$\text{Acceleration} = -a\omega^2 \sin \omega t$$

$$-6{\cdot}54 = -0{\cdot}02\omega^2.1$$

$$\omega^2 = 327$$

Velocity, $v = a\omega \cos\omega t$

When body passes through the original position (which is the mid-point of the oscillation) there is no acceleration,

$$\therefore \sin \omega t = 0$$
$$\therefore \cos \omega t = 1$$

$$\text{Velocity} = 0{\cdot}02\sqrt{327} \times 1$$
$$= 0{\cdot}362\,\text{m/s}$$

(iii) Velocity and acceleration when displaced 10mm.
Displacement equation:

$$x = a \sin \omega t$$
$$0{\cdot}01 = 0{\cdot}02 \sin \omega t$$
$$\sin \omega t = 0{\cdot}5$$
$$\therefore \cos \omega t = 0{\cdot}866$$

$$\text{Velocity} = a\omega \cos \omega t$$
$$= 0{\cdot}02\sqrt{327} \times 0{\cdot}866$$
$$= 0{\cdot}313\,\text{m/s}$$

$$\text{Acceleration} = -a\omega^2 \sin \omega t$$
$$= -0{\cdot}02 \times 327 \times 0{\cdot}5$$
$$= 3{\cdot}27\,\text{m/s}^2$$

(iv) Periodic time $= 2\pi\sqrt{\dfrac{\text{displacement}}{\text{acceleration}}}$

$$= 2\pi\sqrt{\frac{0{\cdot}01}{3{\cdot}27}}$$

$$= 0{\cdot}347\,\text{s}$$

i.e. The initial acceleration is 6·54 m/s², and the periodic time is 0·347 seconds. When the body passes through the original position, its velocity is 0·362 m/s. When the displacement is 10 mm above the mid-point, the velocity is 0·313 m/s, and the acceleration is 3·27 m/s².

Motion of a Simple Pendulum

A simple pendulum is defined as a heavy concentrated mass suspended from a rigid support by an inextensible cord. The pendulum, with a mass M, is shown in fig.9.12 having moved through an angle θ from the mid-position OA. If the length of the pendulum is l, then the mass has moved through a distance Am equal to θl, θ being measured in radians. There are two forces acting on the mass:

1 its own weight, Mg, vertically downwards, and
2 the tension T in the cord.

Resolving the weight into two components, we have $Mg \cos \theta$, represented by ***mp***, and $Mg \sin \theta$, represented by ***pn***. It will be seen that the tension, T, in the cord will be equal to $Mg \cos \theta$, so that we have a force $Mg \sin \theta$ acting in the opposite direction to that in which the mass is moving. It is, in fact,

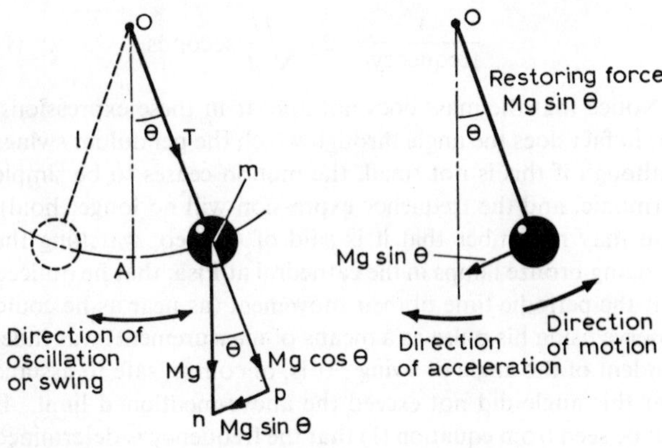

Fig.9.12 The simple pendulum

trying to restore the pendulum to its original vertical position. For this reason this force is sometimes referred to as the restoring force. The acceleration produced by this restoring force is given by:

$$\text{force} = \text{mass} \times \text{acceleration}$$
$$Mg \sin \theta = M \times \text{acceleration}$$
$$\text{acceleration} = g \sin \theta$$

Now if the angle of swing is small, i.e. not greater than 14° either side of the mid-position, $\sin \theta$ has practically the same value as θ measured in radians (see Appendix 1). We can write, therefore,

$$\text{acceleration} = g\theta$$

provided that θ is not greater than approximately 14°.

The displacement, Am, or x, $= \theta l$

$$\theta = \frac{x}{l}$$

$$\text{Acceleration} = \frac{g}{l}\,x$$

Since g and l are constant (at least for the place in which the pendulum is swinging), it follows that the acceleration is proportional to the displacement x, and, since the force is directed towards A, it also follows that the acceleration will be directed towards this mid-point A. Hence the two conditions for simple harmonic motion are satisfied. A pendulum therefore swings with simple harmonic motion provided that the angle of swing is small, i.e. not greater than approximately 14°. In this case the constant ω in the frequency expression will be equal to $\sqrt{(g/l)}$, so that the frequency of the motion will be given by

$$\text{frequency} = \frac{\omega}{2\pi} \text{ or } \frac{1}{2\pi}\sqrt{\frac{g}{l}}\ \text{Hz}$$

and the periodic time is

$$\frac{1}{\text{frequency}} = 2\pi\sqrt{\frac{l}{g}} \text{ seconds} \quad . \quad . \quad . \quad (1)$$

Notice that the mass does not appear in these expressions, nor in fact does the angle through which the pendulum swings (although if this is not small, the motion ceases to be simple harmonic, and the frequency expression will no longer hold). You may remember that it is said of Galileo, watching the swinging bronze lamps in the cathedral at Pisa, that he noticed that the periodic time of their movement (as near as he could observe using his pulse as a means of measurement) was independent of the angle of swing. It is, of course, safe to assume that this angle did not exceed the above-mentioned limit. It will be seen from equation (1) that the frequency is determined by the length, l, of the cord.

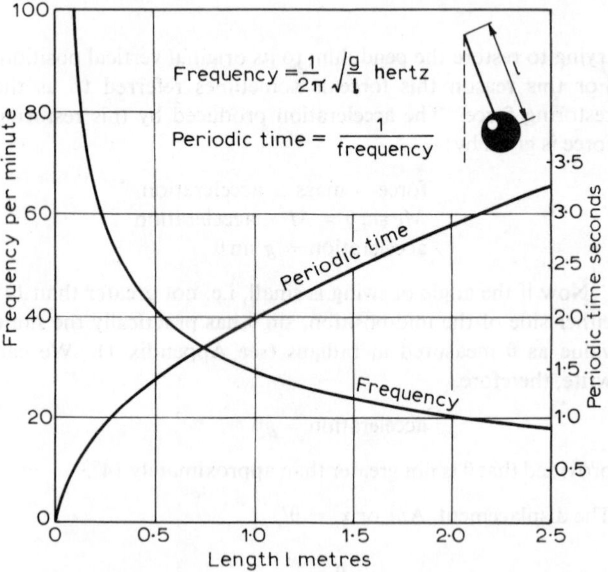

Fig.9.13 Frequency and periodic time of pendulum. The frequency of vibration of a simple pendulum is dependent solely upon the length of the pendulum.

Example 9.4 A pendulum which was intended to beat seconds (i.e. have a periodic time of 2 seconds) is found to lose 4 seconds in 1 hour. By how much must the pendulum be shortened in order that it may beat exact seconds?

Length of pendulum to beat seconds:

$$\text{Periodic time} = 2\pi\sqrt{\frac{l}{g}}$$

$$2 = 2\pi\sqrt{\frac{l}{g}}$$

$$l = \frac{9{\cdot}81}{\pi^2} = 0{\cdot}9938\,\text{m}$$

In 1 hour the pendulum should have made 3600/2 or 1800 complete swings.

But it made only 1800 − (4/2) = 1798 swings; hence its periodic time was 3600/1798 seconds.

Let l_1 be the actual length of the pendulum,

then $$2\pi\sqrt{\frac{l_1}{g}} = \frac{3600}{1798}$$

From (1) $$2\pi\sqrt{\frac{l}{g}} = \frac{3600}{1800}$$

Dividing these two equations, we have

$$\sqrt{\frac{l_1}{l}} = \frac{1800}{1798}$$

$$\frac{l_1}{l} = \left(\frac{1800}{1798}\right)^2$$

$$= \left(1 + \frac{2}{1798}\right)^2$$

Now the Binomial theorem states that, if x is small compared with 1, then $(1 + x)^n$ is approximately equal to $1 + nx$.

Thus $\left(1 + \frac{2}{1798}\right)^2$ is approximately equal to

$$1 + \frac{2 \times 2}{1798} = 1 + \frac{2}{899}$$

$$\therefore \frac{l_1}{l} = 1 + \frac{2}{899}$$

$$\frac{l_1}{l} - 1 = \frac{2}{899}$$

$$\frac{l_1 - l}{l} = \frac{2}{899}$$

$$l_1 - l = \frac{2}{899} \times 0{\cdot}9938 = 0{\cdot}002\,21\,\text{m}$$

i.e. The pendulum must be shortened by 2·21 mm in order to cause it to beat seconds accurately.

Exercise 9

1 Determine the number of complete oscillations per minute which will be made by a pendulum whose length is 1·2 m.

2 A clock pendulum is required to make 4 beats per second. Determine the length of the pendulum.

3 What will be the length, in millimetres, of a simple pendulum which will make one complete oscillation in 2 seconds, i.e. a pendulum to beat seconds?

4 Find an expression for the acceleration, at displacement x from its mid-position, of a body moving in a straight line with simple harmonic motion.

The piston of an engine has a stroke of 1 m, and the reciprocating parts have a mass of 250 kg. If the crankshaft makes 250 rev/min, find the force to overcome the inertia of the reciprocating parts at the ends of the stroke, and also the inertial force and the velocity of the reciprocating parts when the crank has turned 30° from either dead-centre. UEI

Note. In solving this example, you are to assume that the piston is moving with simple harmonic motion.

5 Show that the bob of a simple pendulum moves with simple harmonic motion with a period $2\pi\sqrt{(l/g)}$, provided that the amplitude is small.

Find the length of a clock pendulum which will make three complete beats per second. If the clock loses 1 second per hour, what change is required in the length of the pendulum? UEI

6 In the case of simple harmonic motion, define what are meant by periodic time, amplitude, and maximum velocity.

A helical spring carries a mass of 20 kg at its lower end, and the spring stretches 25 mm when supporting 10 kg. When the mass is set oscillating vertically, the amplitude of the oscillations is 37·5 mm. Calculate (a) the periodic time of the oscillation, and (b) the maximum velocity. UEI

7 Derive an expression for the periodic time of a body moving in a straight line with simple harmonic motion.

The stiffness of a helical spring is 2200 N/m of extension. Find its periodic time of vibration when supporting a mass of 4·55 kg.

If the mass is initially displaced 12·5 mm, what would be its maximum velocity during its motion? UEI

8 A part of a machine moves with simple harmonic motion, making 200 complete oscillations in a minute. Its mass is 4·55 kg. Find (a) the accelerating force upon it, and its velocity in metres per second, when it is 75 mm from mid-stroke, and (b) the maximum accelerating force if its total stroke is 225 mm. UEI

9 Define simple harmonic motion.

A point starts from rest at a distance of 0·4 m from the centre of its path, and moves with simple harmonic motion. If, in its initial position, the acceleration is 1·2 m/s², find (a) its velocity when at a distance of 0·2 m from the centre, and when passing through the centre, and (b) its periodic time. UEI

10 State the meaning of amplitude, displacement, and period in connection with simple harmonic motion.

The velocities of a point moving with simple harmonic motion are 11 m/s and 3 m/s when 0·75 m and 2 m respectively from the centre of its path. Find its period and amplitude. UEI

11 A body moves with simple harmonic motion. Obtain an expression for the periodic time in terms of the acceleration and the displacement of the body from the mid-position.

A body of mass 9 kg moves with simple harmonic motion with frequency of 75 complete oscillations per minute. At the maximum displacement, the acceleration of the body is 14·4 m/s². Determine (a) the amplitude of the oscillation, and (b) the displacement of the body from the mid-position when the force acting on the body is 67 N. ULCI

12 A body moves with simple harmonic motion along a straight line. Prove that the acceleration at any point is directly proportional to the displacement of the point from the mid-point of the motion.

Assuming that a piston moves with simple harmonic motion, and that its stroke is 0·375 m, determine the velocity of the piston, and the force necessary to overcome the inertia of the reciprocating parts when the crank has turned through 45° from inner dead-centre. The reciprocating parts have a mass of 90 kg, and the crankshaft makes 240 rev/min. ULCI

13 When a mass is suspended vertically by a helical spring, the length of the spring is found to increase by 62·5 mm. If the mass is pulled 50 mm below its position of rest, and then released, determine the time taken for one complete oscillation of the mass. Calculate also the acceleration and velocity of the mass when it is 31·25 mm from its position of rest. ULCI

14 Define simple harmonic motion. A helical spring with a free length of 0·25 m has one end fixed, and a mass of 4·55 kg attached to the other end. The spring and mass hang vertically. The mass is pulled down until the length of the spring is 0·295 m, and is then released. Show that the motion of the mass is simple harmonic. Also, if the mass makes 195 complete oscillations per minute, determine (a) the stiffness of the spring in kilonewtons per metre, and (b) the amplitude of the motion. ULCI

15 Show that the periodic time for a body moving with simple harmonic motion is given by

$$T = 2\pi\sqrt{\frac{\text{displacement}}{\text{acceleration}}}$$

The crankshaft of an engine rotates at 300 rev/min, and the piston stroke is 450 mm. The mass of the reciprocating parts is 68 kg, and the piston can be assumed to move with simple harmonic motion. When the crank has turned through 40° from inner dead-centre, determine (a) the velocity of the piston, and (b) the inertial force exerted by the reciprocating parts. ULCI

16 (a) Define simple harmonic motion. A mass is suspended from the end of a spring, and caused to vibrate. Show that its motion satisfies your definition of simple harmonic motion.

(b) A particle, mass 0·34 kg, vibrates with simple harmonic motion of amplitude 50 mm. The maximum accelerating force acting on the particle is 18 N. Determine (i) the frequency of vibration, (ii) the maximum velocity of the particle, and (iii) the acceleration at 12·5 mm from the mean position. EMEU

17 Obtain an expression for the acceleration of a body moving with simple harmonic motion, in terms of the frequency and displacement from the mean position.

A body starts from rest at a distance of 3·6 m from the centre of its path, and moves with simple harmonic motion. It starts with an acceleration of 0·9 m/s². Calculate the velocity when 2·4 m from the centre of its path. Calculate also the maximum velocity, and the periodic time of the motion. EMEU

18 The piston of an engine is assumed to move with simple harmonic motion; the engine makes 300 rev/min, the crank is 200 mm long, and the piston has a mass of 5·5 kg. Calculate the following: (a) the accelerating force on the piston at the end of the stroke, (b) the accelerating force on the piston at quarter stroke, and (c) the velocity of the piston at quarter stroke. EMEU

19 Define simple harmonic motion, and establish the formula for periodic time. A spring of elastic force 1·75 kN/m extension is suspended vertically, and two equal masses of 3·6 kg each are attached to the lower end. One of these masses is suddenly removed, and the system oscillates. Determine (a) the amplitude and frequency of the oscillation (b) the velocity and acceleration of the mass when passing through the half-amplitude position, and (c) the energy of the oscillation, in joules. IMECHE

20 A body has simple harmonic motion of frequency f Hz, and amplitude a. Obtain expressions for the velocity and acceleration when at x from the mid-position.

The plunger of a single-acting pump has a diameter of 0·25 m, and a mass of 180 kg. It is so driven that it moves with simple harmonic motion over the stroke length of 0·5 m, completing 200 double strokes—suction and delivery—per minute. Determine the velocity of the plunger, and the driving force acting on it when it is 50 mm from the end of the delivery stroke, if the pressure in the cylinder is then 415 kN/m². IMECHE

21 A body of mass 40 kg oscillates in a straight horizontal line, with simple harmonic motion of amplitude 76 mm. When the body is 50 mm from the centre of oscillation, the force acting on the body is 157 N. Determine (a) the periodic time of the motion, and (b) the velocity of the body. ULCI

22 A body is acted upon by a force proportional to its distance from a fixed point, the force being directed towards the fixed point. Name the motion, and give an engineering example.

If the greatest force is 29·5 N, and the greatest distance from the fixed point is 12·5 mm, calculate the greatest velocity. The body has a mass of 4 kg.

Calculate also the acceleration at 6·25 mm from the fixed point. ULCI

23 Show that, for a body moving with simple harmonic motion, the periodic time is independent of the amplitude.

A slider in a mechanism moves with simple harmonic motion in a straight line. At distances of 1·2 m and 0·9 m from the mid-position, the respective velocities are 1·8 m/s and 2·4 m/s. Determine the amplitude of the motion, and the shortest time taken by the slider in moving from an extreme position to a point mid-way between this position and the centre of oscillation. ULCI

Chapter 10

Forces and Frameworks

By way of a summary of work covered in an earlier stage, we may state that the general conditions for equilibrium of a body under the action of a system of co-planar forces (i.e. forces all in one plane) are:

1 the algebraic sum of the components of the forces must be zero in any two directions, and
2 the algebraic sum of the moments of all the forces about any point must be zero.

The implication of these two conditions is that, since the resultant force is zero, there will be no resultant linear acceleration; and since the resultant moment is zero, there will be no resultant angular acceleration.

Whilst any two directions could be chosen in which to take components in the first condition, it is usual to take vertical and horizontal components. Incidentally, the graphical implication of this condition is that the vector diagram for the forces is a closed polygon.

Space Diagram

A diagram on which all the forces are indicated in their correct position is known as a *space diagram.*

Bow's Notation

The graphical solution of problems in statics is considerably helped by the use of Bow's notation. The forces are referred to by two capital letters, placed one in each space on either side of the force in the space diagram. Thus, if the spaces on either side of the force are lettered A and B, the force is referred to as *AB*, and the corresponding vector on the force diagram is referred to as ***ab*** (fig.10.1). In this way it is possible to deal with a whole system of forces.

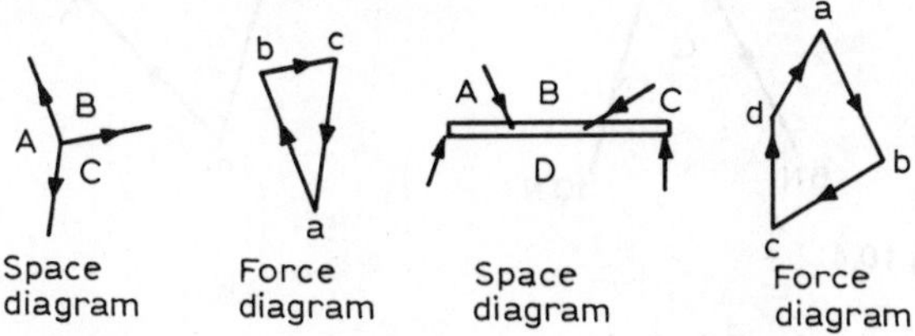

Fig.10.1 Space and force diagrams

Lami's Theorem

The special case of *three* forces in equilibrium is covered by the application of Lami's theorem.

Firstly, the line of action of the three forces must pass through one point; and, secondly, the forces will be represented by the three sides of a triangle. Three such forces are shown in fig.10.2. The angles between the forces are α, β, and γ. It will be seen that the angles of the vector triangle are $(180 - \alpha)$, $(180 - \beta)$, and $(180 - \gamma)$. Applying the sine rule to this vector triangle, we have

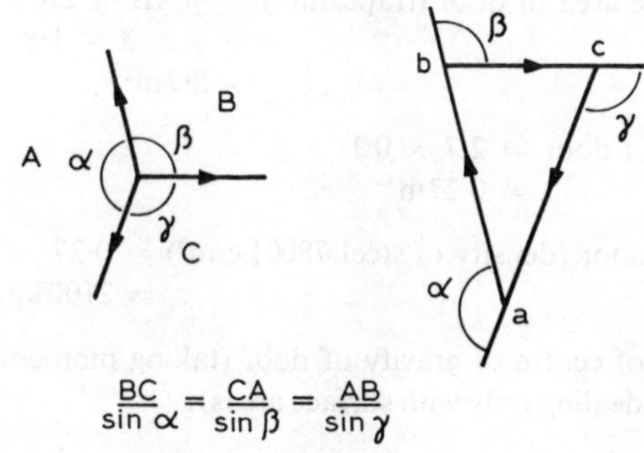

Fig.10.2 Lami's theorem

$$\frac{bc}{\sin(180 - \alpha)} = \frac{ca}{\sin(180 - \beta)} = \frac{ab}{\sin(180 - \gamma)}$$

or, since $\sin(180 - \alpha) = \sin\alpha$,

$$\frac{bc}{\sin\alpha} = \frac{ca}{\sin\beta} = \frac{ab}{\sin\gamma}$$

Referring to the space diagram,

$$\frac{BC}{\sin\alpha} = \frac{CA}{\sin\beta} = \frac{AB}{\sin\gamma}$$

In words:
if three planar forces acting on a body are in equilibrium, each is proportional to the sine of the angle between the other two.

Example 10.1 A steel door is 100 mm thick, and is shaped as shown in fig.10.3, angles CDA and DAB being right angles, and the lengths of the sides being AB = 1·2 m, CD = 1·8 m, and DA = 1·8 m. The door is hung with a pin joint at O, and a roller at P, so that it swings with the side DC in the horizontal plane. (The distances AO and PD are 0·3 m.)
a) Determine the forces acting at O and P, and their horizontal and vertical components.
b) If a clockwise twisting moment of 560 N m is applied in the plane ABCD, at the point C, calculate the forces then acting at O and P. IMECHE

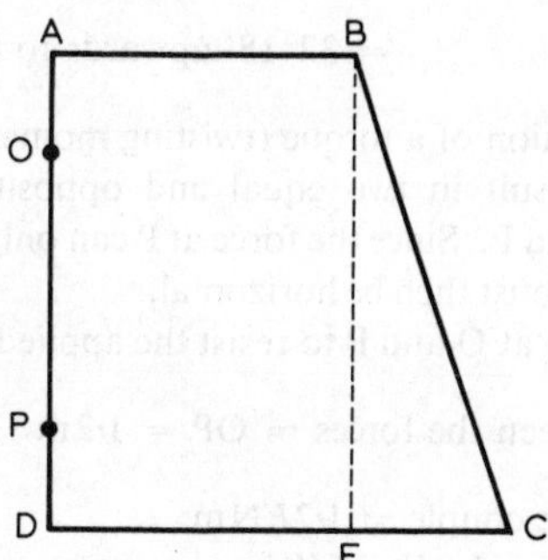

Fig.10.3

a) Surface area of door (trapezium) $= \frac{1}{2}(AB + DC) \times AD$
$= \frac{1}{2} \times 3 \times 1{\cdot}8$
$= 2{\cdot}7\,m^2$

Volume of door $= 2{\cdot}7 \times 0{\cdot}1$
$= 0{\cdot}27\,m^3$

Mass of door (density of steel $7800\,kg/m^3$) $= 0{\cdot}27 \times 7800$
$= 2100\,kg$

Position of centre of gravity of door (taking moments about AD, and dealing only with surface areas):

Moment of rectangle
sides AD and AB $= 1{\cdot}8 \times 1{\cdot}2 \times 0{\cdot}6$
$= 1{\cdot}296$

Moment of triangle BEC $= \frac{1}{2}(0{\cdot}6 \times 1{\cdot}8) \times (1{\cdot}2 + 0{\cdot}2)$
$= 0{\cdot}756$

Moment of total trapezium $= 2{\cdot}7 \times \bar{x}$
$2{\cdot}7\bar{x} = 1{\cdot}296 + 0{\cdot}756$
$\bar{x} = 0{\cdot}76$m from AD

The force at P will be horizontal, since there is a roller at P. To find the magnitude of this force, take moments about O (OP = 1·2m).

$$P \times 1{\cdot}2 = 2100 \times 9{\cdot}81 \times 0{\cdot}76$$
$$P = 13\,100\,N$$

The horizontal force at O will be equal and opposite to that at P (since there are no other horizontal forces acting on the door).

Horizontal force acting at O = 13 100N

The vertical force at O must equal the total weight of the door, since these are the only two vertical forces acting on the door.

Vertical force at O = 20 600N

Resultant force at O $= \sqrt{20\,600^2 + 13\,100^2}$
$= 24\,400\,N$

Inclination of resultant $= \arctan \dfrac{13\,100}{20\,600}$

$= 32°18'$ upwards to the vertical

b) The application of a torque (twisting moment) in the plane ABCD will result in two equal and opposite forces being applied at O and P. Since the force at P can only be horizontal, the force at O must then be horizontal.

Let the force at O and P to resist the applied torque be FN.

Distance between the forces = OP = 1·2m

Moment of the couple $= 1{\cdot}2F$ Nm
$1{\cdot}2F = 560$
$F = 467\,N$

Since the applied twisting moment is clockwise, the forces at O and P must produce an anticlockwise couple,

i.e. force at O must be to the left,
force at P must be to the right.

Total force at P = 13 100 + 467
= 13 567N to the right

Horizontal component at O = 13 100 + 467
= 13 567N to the left

Total force at O $= \sqrt{20\,600^2 + 13\,567^2}$
$= 24\,700\,N$

Inclination of the resultant $= \arctan \dfrac{13\,567}{20\,600}$

$= 33°11'$ upwards to the vertical

Note. The point of application of the 560Nm twisting moment does not affect the resulting forces at O and P.

Example 10.2 In connection with a certain balancing problem, it is required to determine the magnitude of two forces, A and B, so that the four forces shown in fig.10.4 will be in equilibrium.

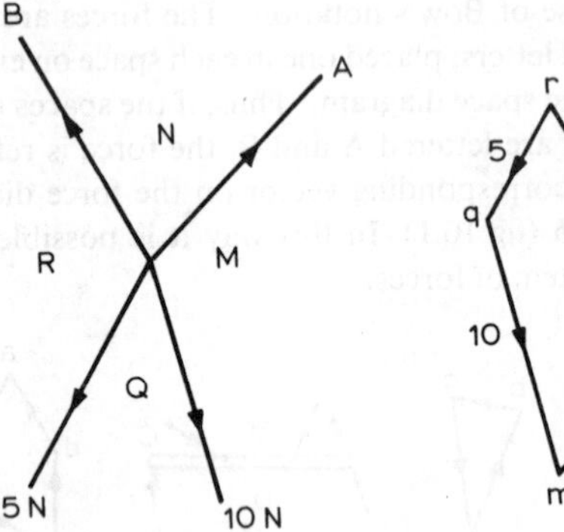

Fig.10.4

Solution by Calculation

First, express the position of each force by the angle which it makes with the horizontal datum line, measured in the anti-clockwise direction.

Force	*Angular displacement from horizontal*
A	45°
B	120°
5N	240°
10N	285°

The algebraic sum of the horizontal components will be zero, and the algebraic sum of the vertical components will be zero, since the forces are to be in equilibrium.

Horizontal components

$A \cos 45° + B \cos 120° + 5 \cos 240° + 10 \cos 285° = 0$

$A \cos 45° - B \cos 60° - 5 \cos 60° + 10 \cos 75° = 0$

$0{\cdot}7071A - 0{\cdot}5B - 2{\cdot}5 + 2{\cdot}588 = 0$

$0{\cdot}7071A - 0{\cdot}5B + 0{\cdot}088 = 0$ . . . . (1)

Vertical components

$A \sin 45° + B \sin 120° + 5 \sin 240° + 10 \sin 285° = 0$

$A \sin 45° + B \sin 60° - 5 \sin 60° - 10 \sin 75° = 0$

$0{\cdot}7071A + 0{\cdot}866B - 4{\cdot}33 - 9{\cdot}659 = 0$

$0{\cdot}7071A + 0{\cdot}866B - 13{\cdot}989 = 0$ . . . . . . (2)

Subtracting equation (1) from (2),

$$1{\cdot}366B = 14{\cdot}077$$
$$B = 10{\cdot}316\,\text{N}$$

Substituting into equation (1),

$$0{\cdot}7071A - 0{\cdot}5 \times 10{\cdot}32 + 0{\cdot}088 = 0$$
$$0{\cdot}7071A = 5{\cdot}072$$
$$A = 7{\cdot}17\,\text{N}$$

i.e. Force A is 7·17 N, and force B is 10·32 N.

Graphical Solution

1 Draw the space diagram, and insert the letters M, N, R, and Q in the spaces between the forces, in accordance with Bow's notation.
2 Commencing at *r*, draw ***rq*** to represent the 5 N force *RQ* in magnitude and direction.
3 Draw ***qm*** to represent the 10 N force in magnitude and direction.
4 Through *m*, draw a line parallel to force *A* (or force *MN*). The length of this line will not be known, since the magnitude of *A* is unknown.
5 Through *r*, draw a line parallel to force *B* (or force *NR*), so that this line intersects the line drawn in (4) in the point *n*.
6 Then ***mn*** and ***nr*** represent in magnitude and direction the forces *A* and *B*.

Note. The arrows must all point in the same direction (in this case anticlockwise) in the force diagram.

By measurement, force A is 7·17 N, and force B is 10·32 N.

Example 10.3 A garden roller, 500 mm in diameter and weighing 1400 N, rests on a level path. Find the magnitude and direction of the minimum pull required on the handle to pull the roller up a step 50 mm high. IMECHE

When the roller is on the point of moving over the corner of the step, it is in equilibrium under the action of three forces [fig.10.5(i)]:

1 the pull, *P*;
2 the gravitational force (weight), *Mg*;

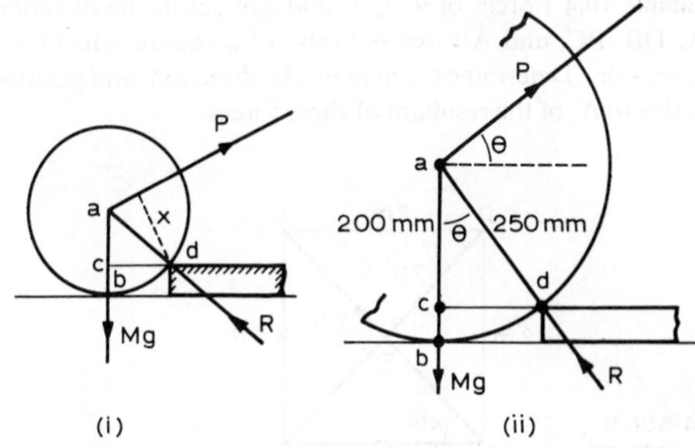

Fig.10.5

3 the reaction of the step, *R*. Notice that the ground reaction has been reduced to zero when the roller is about to move.

Since *R* is unknown, we can eliminate it by taking moments about a point in its line of action, e.g. the corner of the step.

Moment about the corner of the step, *d*:

$$Px = Mgh$$

where *x* and *h* are the lengths of lines drawn from *d* perpendicular to *P* and *Mg*.

Now
$$ac = ab - bc$$
$$= 250 - 50$$
$$= 200\,\text{mm}$$
$$cd = \sqrt{250^2 - 200^2} = 150\,\text{mm}$$
$$Px = 1400 \times 150$$
$$P = \frac{210\,000}{x}\,\text{N}$$

The minimum value of *P* occurs when *x* is maximum; but the maximum value of *x* is 250 mm, and occurs when the line of action of *P* is perpendicular to *ad*.

$$\text{Minimum } P = \frac{210\,000}{250} = 840\,\text{N}$$

The direction of the pull must be inclined at angle θ to the horizontal, as shown in fig.10.5(ii). It will be seen that angle *dac* is also equal to θ, and that, from the triangle *acd*,

$$\cos\theta = \frac{ac}{ad} = \frac{200}{250}, \text{ giving } \theta = 36°52'$$

i.e. The minimum pull required to move the roller over the step is 840 N, and its direction, is 36° 52′ to the horizontal, in the direction shown.

Example 10.4 Forces of 9, 7, 5, and 6N act in the directions CA, DB, BC, and AB, respectively, of a square ABCD of 2 metres side. Determine the magnitude, direction, and position, relative to A, of the resultant of these forces.

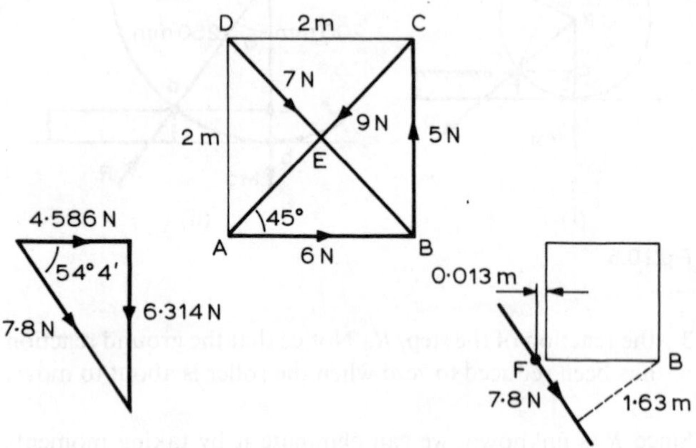

Fig.10.6

The magnitude and direction of the resultant can be obtained by resolving the forces into their horizontal and vertical components; the horizontal and vertical components of the resultant force will equal the algebraic sum of the respective horizontal and vertical components of the given forces.

Resolve horizontally: to the right considered positive.

$$6 + 7\cos 45° - 9\cos 45° = 6 - 2\cos 45°$$
$$= 6 - 1{\cdot}414$$
$$= 4{\cdot}586\text{N to the right}$$

Resolve vertically: downwards considered positive.

$$9\sin 45° + 7\sin 45° - 5 = 16\sin 45° - 5$$
$$= 11{\cdot}314 - 5$$
$$= 6{\cdot}314\text{N downward}$$

These two components are now considered vectorially, giving the resultant force of magnitude $\sqrt{6{\cdot}314^2 + 4{\cdot}586^2} = 7{\cdot}8\text{N}$ inclined at angle θ to the horizontal, where

$$\tan\theta = 6{\cdot}314/4{\cdot}586 = 1{\cdot}38;\ \text{i.e. } \theta = 54°4'.$$

The position of the resultant can be obtained by taking moments about a suitable point. The moment of the resultant about any point is equal to the algebraic sum of the moments of the given forces about the same point.

If we choose B as our reference point, we shall find that the moment of three of the forces about B is zero, since three of the forces pass through B.

Take moments about B, and let x be the perpendicular distance from B to the line of action of the resultant.

Moment of forces B = 9 × BE (note that BE is perpendicular to the line of action of the 9N force)

$$= 9 \times 1{\cdot}414$$
$$= 12{\cdot}72\text{Nm anticlockwise}$$

The resultant force, 7·8N, must be placed so that its moment about B will be 12·72Nm anticlockwise.

$$7{\cdot}8x = 12{\cdot}72$$
$$x = 1{\cdot}63\text{m}$$

Note that $\text{BF} = \dfrac{1{\cdot}63}{\sin 54°4'} = 2{\cdot}013\text{m}$

i.e. The resultant is 7·8N, inclined at 54°4′ to AB, as shown, cutting BA produced 13mm from A.

Note. A graphical solution to this problem is given in example 10·8.

Example 10.5 A bar ACDB in a framework is 5m long. It is inclined at 60° to the horizontal – B above A. At A, a force P acts, unknown in direction and magnitude. At C, 2m from A, a force of 150N acts vertically downwards. At D, 1·5m from B, a force Q acts at an angle of 60° to the line of the bar (i.e. 30° to the vertical). At B, a force of 300N acts vertically downwards. Determine, analytically or graphically, the magnitude and directions of P and Q to satisfy the conditions of equilibrium. IMECHE

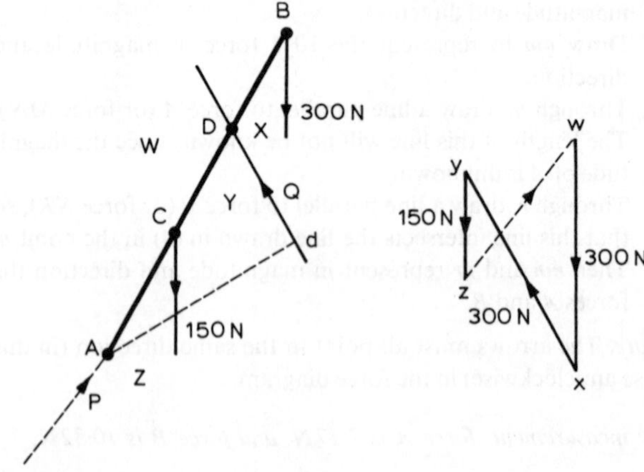

Fig.10.7

Magnitude of Q (fig.10.7).
Take moments about A.

$$\text{Perpendicular distance A}d = \text{AD}\cos 30°$$
$$= 3{\cdot}5 \times 0{\cdot}866$$
$$= 3{\cdot}03\text{m}$$

$$(300 \times 5\cos 60°) + (150 \times 2\cos 60°) = Q \times 3{\cdot}03$$
$$Q = 300\text{N}$$

Graphical Solution

The spaces between the forces have been lettered W, X, Y, and Z, in accordance with Bow's notation. The force diagram is constructed with

wx representing 300 N (force at B),
xy representing 300 N (force at D),
yz representing 150 N (force at C).

The closing line, *zw*. represents the force P at A.
Hence, P = 242 N at 51°44′, upwards to the horizontal. Q = 300 N.

Analytical Solution

Let P be inclined at θ to the horizontal, all angles being measured in an anticlockwise direction.
Thus the forces at B and C make 270° with zero direction, the force at D makes 120° with zero direction.

Horizontal components

$$300 \cos 270° + 300 \cos 120° + 150 \cos 270° + P \cos\theta = 0$$
$$0 + 150 + 0 + P\cos\theta = 0,$$
$$P\cos\theta = 150 \quad . \quad . \quad . \quad . \quad (1)$$

Vertical components

$$300 \sin 270° + 300 \sin 120° + 150 \sin 270 + P \sin\theta = 0$$
$$-300 + 259{\cdot}8 - 150 + P\sin\theta = 0$$
$$P\sin\theta = 190{\cdot}2 \quad . \quad . \quad . \quad . \quad (2)$$

Dividing (2) by (1),

$$\tan\theta = \frac{190{\cdot}2}{150} = 1{\cdot}268$$

$$\theta = 51°44'$$

Substituting into (1),

$$P \cos 51°44' = 150$$

$$P = \frac{150}{0{\cdot}6193}$$

$$= 242\,\text{N}$$

Note. An alternative graphical solution to this problem is indicated in example 10.12.

Funicular Polygon

Consider, now, three forces M, P, and Q, which are all acting in one plane, but which do not pass through the same point. We are asked to determine the magnitude, direction, and position of the resultant of these forces. We can determine the magnitude and direction of the resultant by the usual method of drawing the force diagram. But, before we can decide the position in which the resultant acts, it will be necessary to draw another diagram, which is known as the *link* or *funicular polygon*.

If all the forces passed through one point, then, of course, the resultant would also pass through this point; in which case there would be no need to construct a link polygon.

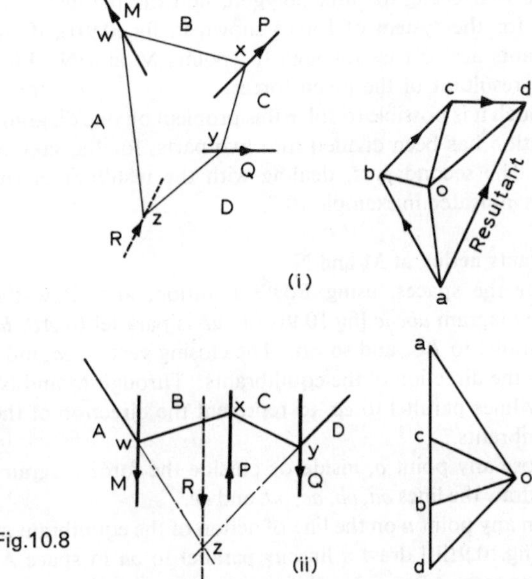

Fig.10.8

The construction is carried out as follows [fig.10.8(i)].

1 Draw the force diagram, *abcd*, in the usual way, and obtain the magnitude and direction of the resultant force, R, as given by the vector ***ad***.
2 Choose any point o, either inside or outside the force diagram, and join o to each corner of the force diagram.
3 From any point w, in the line of action of force M, draw a line in space A, parallel to the line *oa*.
4 From the point w, draw the line *wx* in space B, parallel to line ***ob***, and cutting force P in the point x. (You may have to produce the line of action of the forces to get the necessary intersection.) This procedure is continued until lines have been drawn in all the spaces. The lines parallel to *oa* and *od* can now be produced until they meet in z.
5 The resultant of the forces will pass through the point z. Through z, draw a line parallel to *ad*, to represent the resultant force R.

The diagram *wxyz* is the *link* or *funicular polygon*.

Resultant of Parallel Forces

The construction, fig.10.8(ii), is similar to that outlined above. The point o must, of course, be outside the force diagram, which in this case is a vertical straight line. In order to get the intersection point z, it will normally be necessary to project the line in spaces A and D backwards.

For the example given, the resultant will have the magnitude and direction as given by the vector ***ad***, and its position will be given by its having to pass through the point z.

The use of the funicular polygon to determine the direction of reactions is indicated in examples 10.13 and 10.14.

Example 10.6 Using the link polygon, find the parallel equilibrants for the system of forces shown in fig.10.9(i), if the equilibrants are to pass through the points M and N. Find also the resultant of the given forces. NCTEC

Although it is possible to solve this problem on one diagram, the solution has been divided into two parts, for the sake of clarity. The second part, dealing with the resultant of the forces, is indicated in example 10.7.

Equilibrants acting at M and N

1 Letter the spaces, using Bow's notation, and draw the force diagram *abcde* [fig.10.9(iii)]. ***ab*** is parallel to *AB*, ***bc*** is parallel to *BC*, and so on. The closing vector, ***ea***, indicates the direction of the equilibrants. Through M and N, draw lines parallel to ***ea***, to represent the direction of the equilibrants.

2 Choose any point *o*, inside or outside the force diagram, and draw the lines *oa*, *ob*, *oc*, *od*, and *oe*.

3 From any point *u* on the line of action of the equilibrant at M, [fig.10.9(ii)] draw a line *uv* parallel to *oa* in space A, cutting force AB, produced if necessary, at *v*.

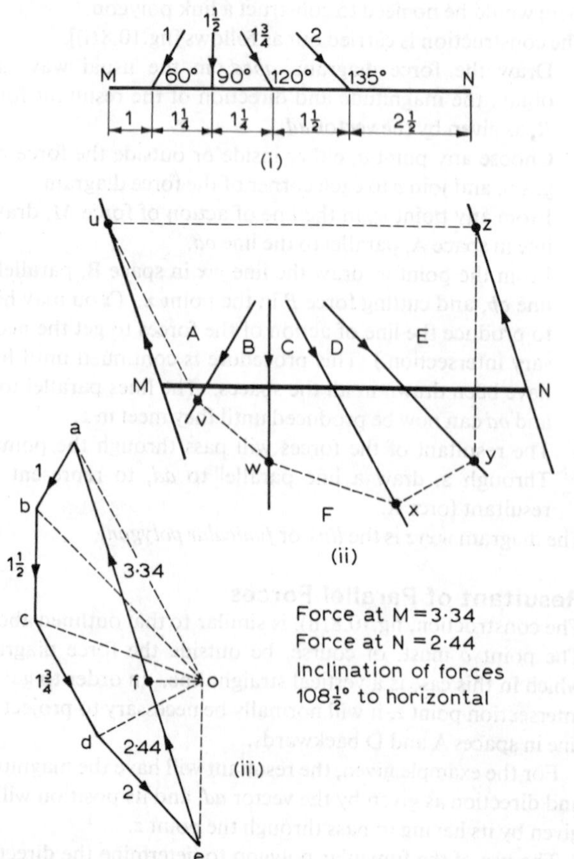

Fig.10.9

4 From *v* draw the line *vw* in space B, parallel to *ob*. Note the relationship between space A and *oa*, and between space B and *ob*.

5 Repeat this construction until the last line has been drawn: the line *yz* parallel to *oe* in space E.

6 Join the points *u* and *z*, and through *o* draw a line *of* parallel to *uz* cutting the vector *ea* in *f*.

7 Then ***ef*** represents the magnitude and direction of the equilibrant *EF* at N, and ***fa*** represents the magnitude and direction of the equilibrant *FA* at M.

Hence the equilibrant at M is 3·34 units, and that at N is 2·44 units. Both equilibrants are inclined at 108½° to the horizontal, the angle being measured in the same manner as that used for the forces in the space diagram.

Example 10.7 Using the link polygon, determine the resultant of the system of forces shown in fig.10.10(i). NCTEC

Note. This is the second part of the problem given in example 10.6. The division into two portions has been made for the purpose of clarity.

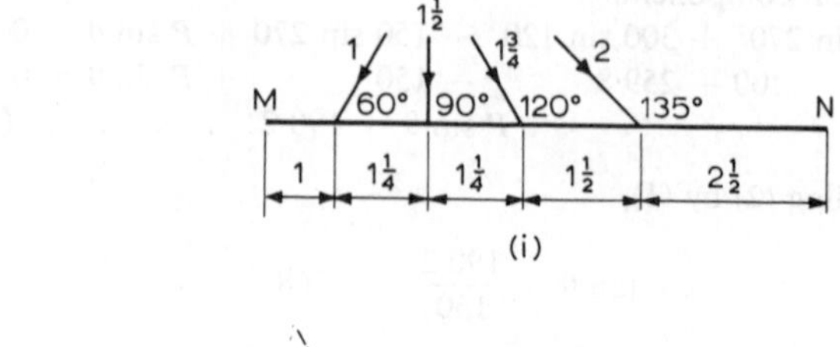

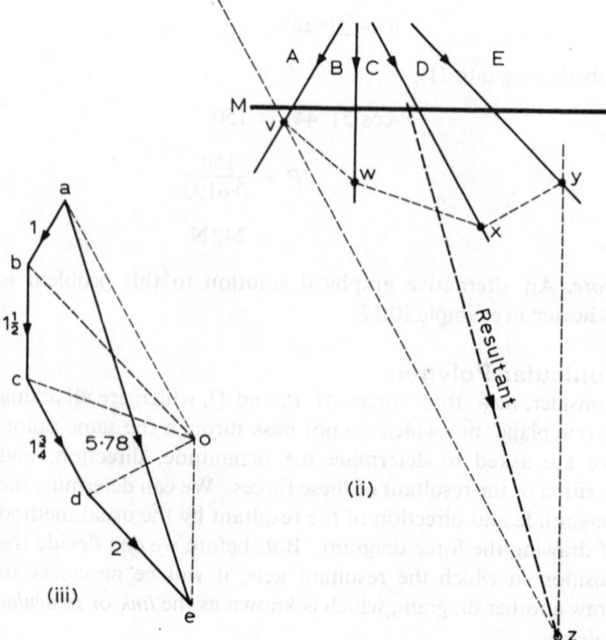

Fig.10.10

Resultant of forces

1 Letter the spaces, using Bow's notation, and draw the force diagram *abcde* [fig.10.10(iii)]. ***ab*** is parallel to *AB*, *bc* is parallel to *BC*, and so on.

2 The vector ***ae*** (drawn from the starting-point to the finishing point) represents the *resultant* of the given forces in magnitude and direction.

3 In order to determine the position of the resultant, it is necessary to draw the link polygon. Choose any point *o*, inside or outside the force diagram, and draw the lines *oa*, *ob*, *oc*, *od*, and *oe*.

4 From any point *v* on the line of action of force *AB* (produced if necessary), draw a line parallel to *oa* in space A. This line will ultimately have to be produced, to intersect another line in the point *z* [fig.10.10(ii)].

5 From *v*, draw the line *vw* in space B, parallel to *ob*. Then draw the line *wx* in space C, parallel to *oc*. Note the relationship between space *B* and *ob*, and between space C and *oc*.

6 Repeat this construction until the last line has been drawn: the line through the point *y* parallel to *oe* in space E. Produce this line until it meets the line in space A (passing through point *v*). The point of intersection is *z*.

7 The resultant of the given forces will pass through the point *z*. Through *z* draw a line parallel to ***ae*** to represent the position and direction of the resultant of the given forces. Measure the distance from M to the point where the resultant cuts the line MN.

Hence the resultant is a force of 5·78 units, inclined at 108½° to the horizontal in the direction shown. It cuts the line MN between M and N, 3·15 units from M.

Example 10.8 Forces of 9, 7, 5, and 6N act in the directions CA, DB, BC, and AB, respectively, of a square ABDC of 2 metres side. Determine the magnitude, direction, and position, relative to A, of the resultant of these forces.

The space diagram indicated in fig.10.11(i) is drawn directly from the specification of the forces in the question. Figure 10.11(ii) shows the same set of forces, with the exceptions that their lines of action terminate at the corners of the square, and all the forces are drawn so that their general direction is the same; in this case they all point towards the centre of the square, rather than away from the centre. This re-drawing of the forces in no way alters their effect upon the square; it will, however, be found to be much easier to letter up the diagram using Bow's notation if this modification has been made.

1 Letter the spaces between the forces, using Bow's notation [fig.10.11(iii)]. Draw the force diagram *mnrst* [fig.10.11 (iv)]. ***mn*** is parallel to MN, ***nr*** is parallel to NR, and so on.

2 The vector ***mt*** (drawn from starting-point to finishing-point) represents the resultant of the given forces, in magnitude and direction.

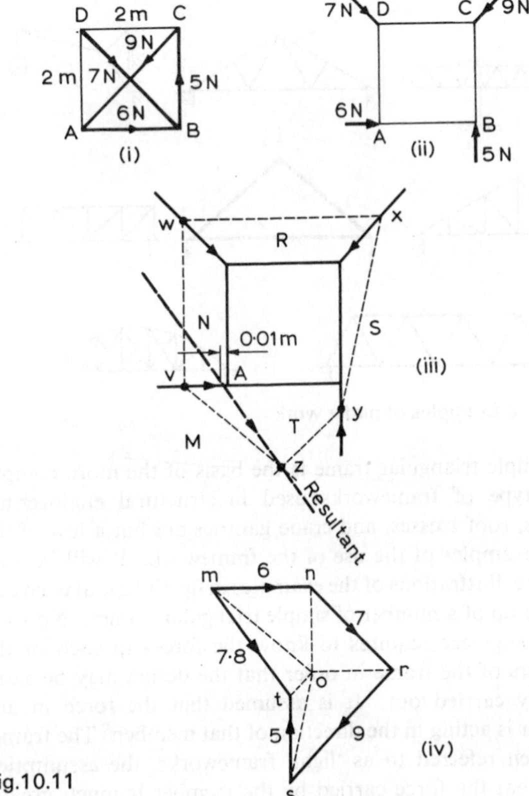

Fig.10.11

3 In order to find the position of the resultant, it is necessary to draw the link polygon. Choose any point *o*, inside or outside the force diagram, and draw the lines *om*, *on*, *or*, *os*, and *ot*.

4 From any point *v* on the line of action of MN, draw a line parallel to *om* in space M. This line will ultimately have to be produced, to intersect another line in *z* [fig.10.11(iii)].

5 From *v*, draw the line *vw* in space N, parallel to *on*. Then draw *wx* parallel to *or* in space R.

6 Repeat this construction until the last line has been drawn: the line through the point *y* parallel to *ot* in space T. Produce this line to intersect the line in space M (passing through point *v*) in the point *z*.

7 The resultant of the given forces passes through the point *z*. Through *z*, draw a line parallel to ***mt***, to represent the position and direction of the resultant of the given forces. Measure the distance from A to the point where the resultant cuts the side AB of the square.

Hence resultant is 7·8 N, inclined at 54°4′ to AB, as shown, cutting BA produced 10 mm from A.

Note. This is a graphical solution to the problem solved analytically in example 10.4.

Frameworks

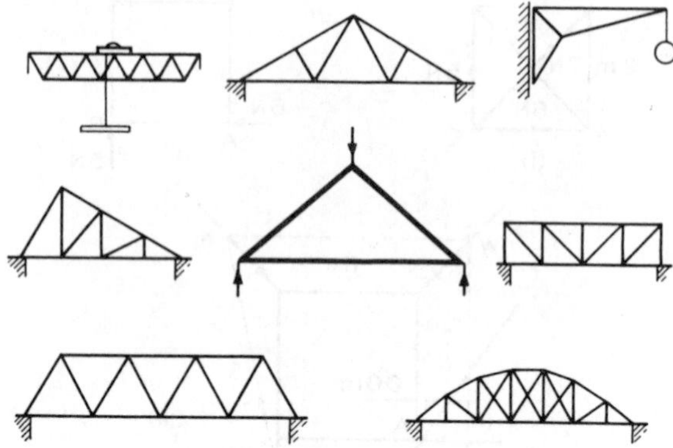

Fig.10.12 Examples of girder work

The simple triangular frame is the basis of the more complicated type of frameworks used in structural engineering. Bridges, roof trusses, and crane gantries are but a few of the many examples of the use of the framework. It will be seen from the illustrations of the examples in fig.10.12 that each one is made up of a number of simple triangular frames. Now the design engineer requires to know the forces in each of the members of the frame in order that the design may be satisfactorily carried out. It is assumed that the force in any member is acting in the direction of that member. The frames are often referred to as 'light' frameworks, the assumption being that the force carried by the member is much greater than the weight of the member. It follows that a diagram of the lay-out of the frame is really a space diagram of a series of forces. Some of these forces are external, such as the loads and the reactions; others are internal, such as the forces within the members themselves.

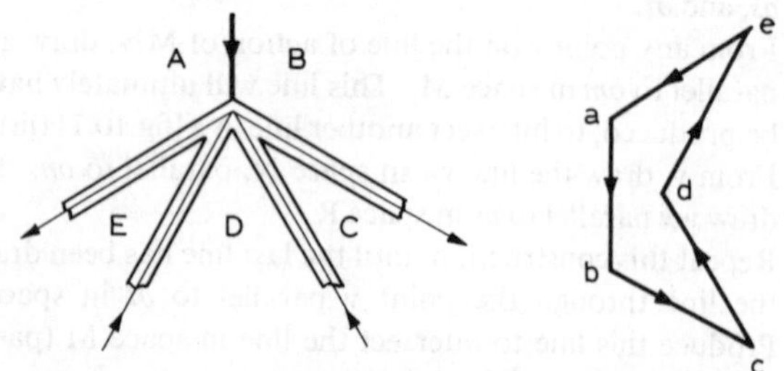

Fig.10.13 Forces in frameworks. All the forces acting at any point in a framework are in equilibrium, and can be represented by a closed vector polygon.

Consider a point where a number of these forces meet, as shown in fig.10.13. It will be realised that, in effect, we have a number of forces in equilibrium acting at a point, and a vector diagram can be drawn for these forces. In fact, a separate vector diagram could be drawn for the group of forces acting at each of the junctions of the frame. In practice, however, only one diagram is drawn, in which all the separate vector diagrams are incorporated. The method of drawing this diagram, and the determination from it of the magnitude and nature of the force in the member, is illustrated in the series of examples following.

Directions of Reactions

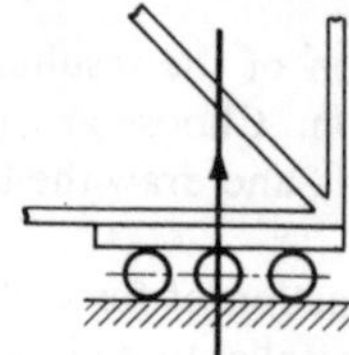

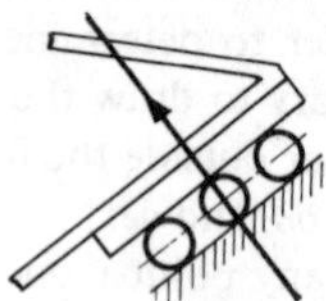

Fig.10.14 Reaction of roller support. To allow for temperature variation, structures are often supported on rollers. The reaction of the roller support is always perpendicular to the support, as indicated.

It is usual to support one end of a framework by a hinge, and the other end upon rollers; in this way, changes of size due to temperature variation can be accommodated. It is assumed that the reaction of the roller support will always be perpendicular to the line joining the centres of the rollers (fig.10.14); generally the rollers are in a horizontal plane, and the reaction is vertical. The reaction of the hinge can be in any direction, but must be governed by the condition required to maintain the whole structure in equilibrium (fig.10.15). If the external loads are vertical, and the roller reaction is vertical, then the hinge reaction will be vertical.

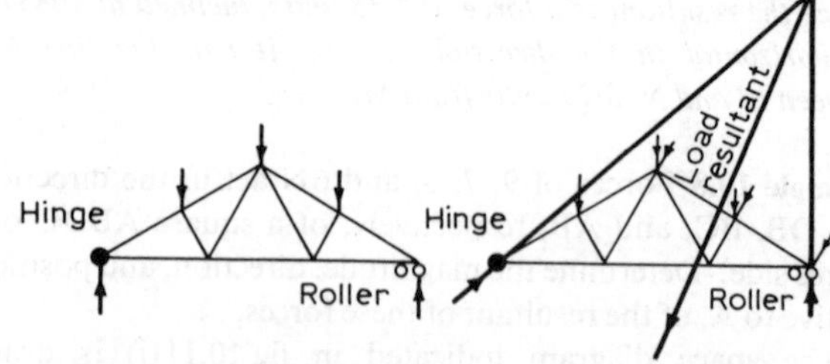

Fig.10.15 Reaction of hinge support. The reaction which comes through the hinge can be in any direction. The important principle is that the reaction of the two supports, and the resultant of the external loads, must all pass through one point.

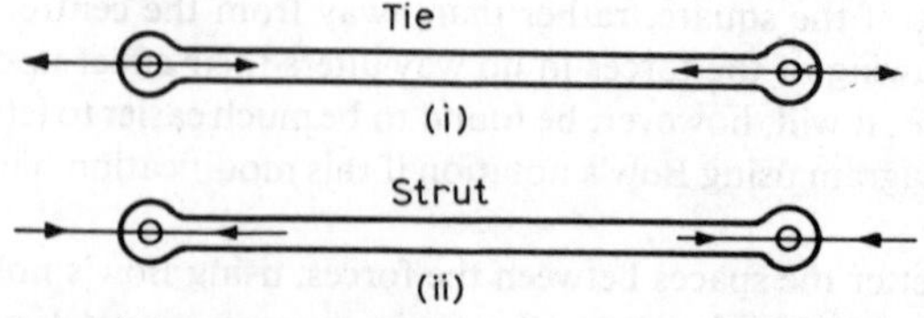

Fig.10.16 The difference between the tie and the strut. The tie exerts an inward pull at either end, to prevent the pins being pulled apart by the tensile loads. The strut exerts an outward force at either end, to prevent the compressive loads pushing the pins together.

If, on the other hand, the resultant of all the external loads is inclined, then the line of action of the hinge reaction must pass through the point of intersection of this resultant and the line of action of the reaction at the roller support.

Example 10.9 Draw the complete force diagram for the whole of the Warren girder shown in fig.10.17. Determine the magnitudes of the forces in members KL, CL, and LM only, and state whether they are in compression or tension EMEU

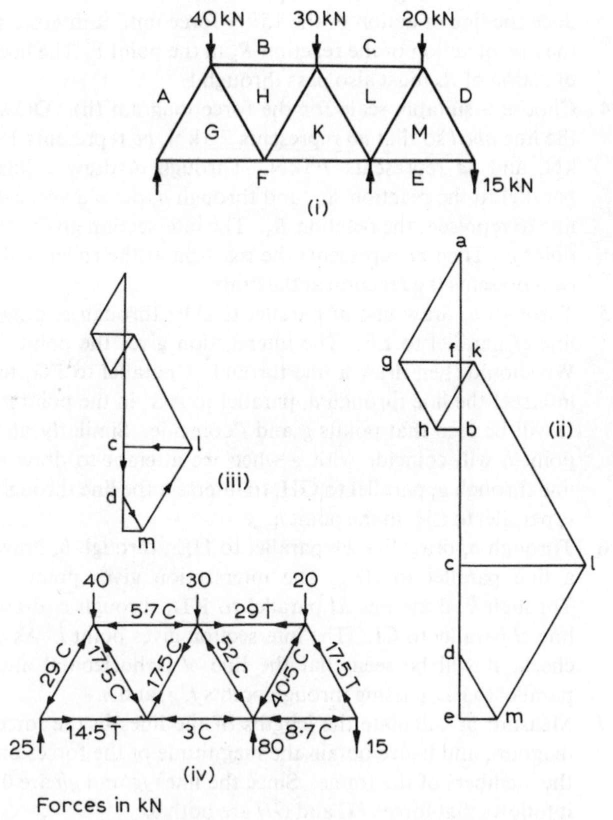

Fig.10.17

1 Draw to scale the space diagram, showing the directions of the various members of the frame.
2 Calculate the reactions in a similar manner to that of a simply supported beam. The triangles are equilateral, so the 40kN load acts over the mid-point of the base of the left-hand triangle, which could be assumed to have sides of length 2 units. Hence the 40kN load acts at a distance of 1 unit from the left-hand support. Similarly, the 30kN load acts at 3 units, the 20kN load 5 units, and the 15kN load 6 units from the left-hand support. By taking moments, the values of the reactions become $R_a = 25$kN and $R_b = 80$kN.
3 Using Bow's notation, indicate with a capital letter the space between each force and truss member.
4 Choose a suitable scale for the force diagram, and draw the line *abcde* to represent the vertical external forces and reactions, fig.10.17(ii).
5 The adjoining spaces to space G are A and F. Both these letters are already on the force diagram. Through the point *a*, draw a line parallel to AG; and through the point *f*, draw a line parallel to FG. The intersection gives the point *g*, so that ***ag*** represents the force *AG*, and ***gf*** represents the force *FG*.
6 Through *g*, draw *gh* parallel to GH; and through *b*, draw *bh* parallel to BH. The intersection gives the point *h*.
7 Through *h*, draw a line parallel to HK; and through *f*, draw *fk* parallel to FK. The intersection gives the point *k*.
8 Through *k*, draw the line *kl* parallel to KL; and through *c*, draw the line *cl* parallel to CL. The intersection gives the point *l*.
9 Through *l*, draw the line *lm* parallel to LM; and through *e*, draw the line *em* parallel to EM. The intersection gives the point *m*.
10 Through *d*, draw a line parallel to DM. This should pass through the point *m*.
11 Measure or calculate the lengths of the lines in the force diagram, and hence obtain the magnitude of the forces in the members of the frame.
12 Obtain the direction of the forces acting at the different points of the frame. As an example, the forces acting at the top right-hand corner of the frame are dealt with in diagram (iii). Starting at *c*, follow round the points *c*, *d*, *m*, *l*, and back to *c*. This direction has been chosen because *cd* is in the direction of the 20kN force acting at the top right-hand corner. The arrows as shown in diagram (iii) should all point in the same forward direction, with the arrow *cd* pointing *down*. Transfer these arrows to the scale diagram (iv). Repeat for all other points in the frame. Remember that arrows at either end of any member must point in the opposite direction. If the arrows point towards each other, the member is in *tension*; if the arrows point away from each other, the member is in *compression*.
13 Indicate the magnitudes and natures of the various forces on the scale diagram (iv).

Since the question asks for the forces in only three specific members, it would, of course, be necessary only to indicate these values, and state:

force in KL = 52*kN* – *compressive force*,
force in CL = 29*kN* – *tensile force*,
force in LM = 40·5*kN* – *compressive force*.

Example 10.10 The roof truss shown in fig.10.18 is supported on rollers at one end, and through a hinge at the other end. Determine the magnitudes and directions of the reactions when the truss is carrying the loading shown. Determine also the forces in the members, distinguishing between tension and compression.

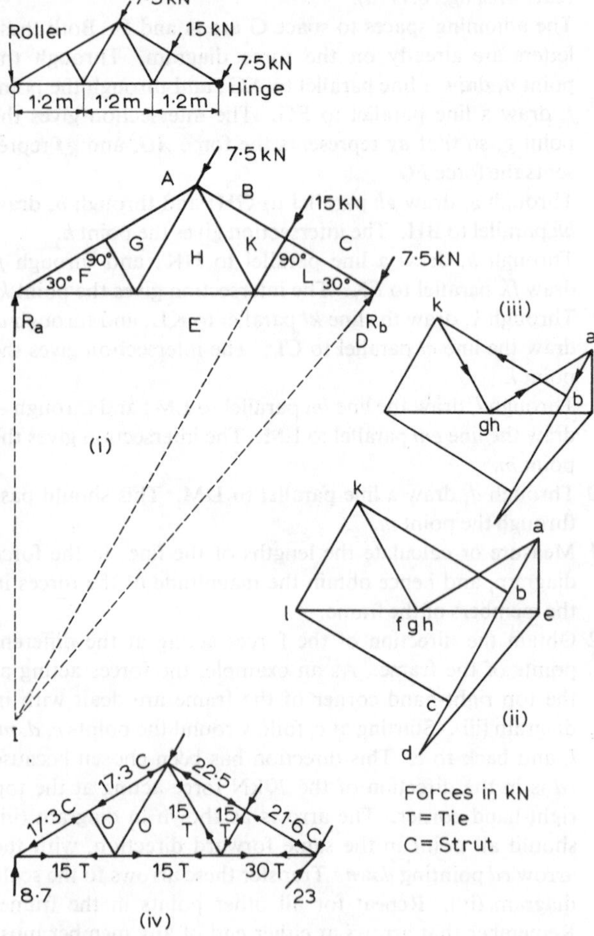

Fig.10.18

1 Draw, to scale, the space diagram, showing the directions of the various members of the frame.

2 Using Bow's notation, indicate with a capital letter the space between each force.

3 Since the three external loads acting on the right-hand portion of the truss are symmetrically placed, it follows that the resultant of these loads will coincide with the 15 kN, the force *BC*. The magnitude of this resultant will be 30 kN, although we do not need to know this actual value. Since the resultant of these loads, together with the two reactions, must pass through one point, the direction of the reaction at the right-hand support can be obtained. Produce the line of action of the 15 kN force until it intersects the line of action of the reaction R_a in the point I. The line of action of R_b must also pass through I.

4 Choose a suitable scale for the force diagram (ii). Draw the line *abcd* so that ***ab*** represents 7·5 kN, ***bc*** represents 15 kN, and ***cd*** represents 7·5 kN. Through *d*, draw a line parallel to the reaction R_b; and through *a*, draw a vertical line to represent the reaction R_a. The intersection gives the point *e*. Then ***de*** represents the reaction at the roller, and ***ea*** represents the reaction at the hinge.

5 Through *a*, draw line *af* parallel to AF; through *e*, draw line *ef* parallel to EF. The intersection gives the point *f*. We should then draw a line through *f*, parallel to FG, to intersect the line through *a*, parallel to AG, in the point *g*. It will be seen that points *g* and *f* coincide. Similarly, the point *h* will coincide with *g* when we attempt to draw a line through *g*, parallel to GH, to intersect the line through *e*, parallel to EH, in the point *h*.

6 Through *h*, draw line *hk* parallel to HK; through *b*, draw a line parallel to BK. The intersection gives point *k*. Through *k*, draw line *kl* parallel to KL; through *c*, draw line *cl* parallel to CL. The intersection gives point *l*. As a check, it will be seen that the line *el* is horizontal and parallel to EL, passing through points *f*, *g*, and *h*.

7 Measure or calculate the lengths of the lines in the force diagram, and hence obtain the magnitude of the forces on the members of the frame. Since the lines *fg* and *gh* are 0, it follows that forces *FG* and *GH* are both 0.

8 The directions of the forces acting at any point are obtained as before. The example given in diagram (iii) deals with the forces acting at the vertex of the truss. The direction of *ab* is *down* to the *left*, since the force *AB* is down to the left. This indicates the way around the figure *abkgh*.

9 Indicate the magnitude and nature of the forces on the scale diagram (iv).

Note. The use of the funicular polygon to determine the directions of the reactions is illustrated in example 10.14.

Example 10.11 Figure 10.19 shows a pin-jointed structure loaded at the point D, and hinged at the point A. The structure is maintained with DA horizontal by the pull in the horizontal chain EC. Determine the pull in the chain, and the force in each member of the structure, stating whether it is a tie or a strut. ULCI

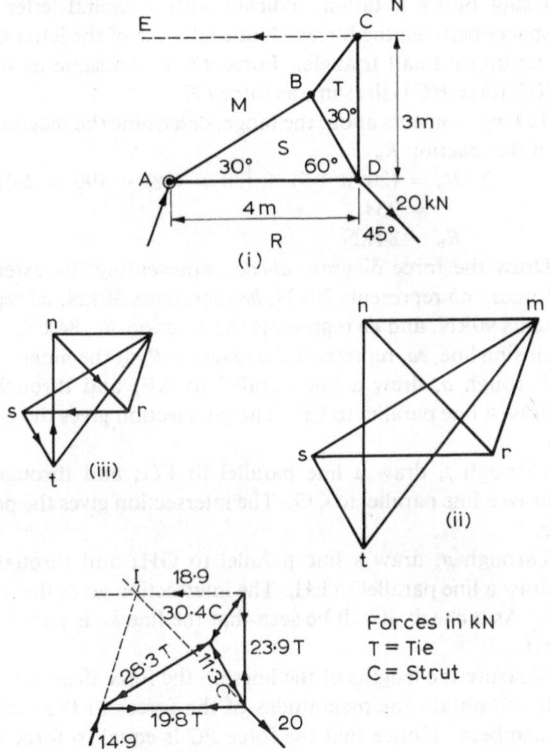

Fig.10.19

1 Draw, to scale, the space diagram, showing the directions of the various members of the frame.
2 Using Bow's notation, indicate with a capital letter the spaces between the forces. The letter M indicates the space between the reaction at A and the horizontal pull in the chain.
3 Since all three external forces (20kN, the reaction at A, and the pull in chain) must pass through one point, the direction of *RM* can be determined. Produce the line of action of the 20kN force until it meets the line of action of the chain in the point I [diagram (iv)]. The line of action must also pass through I. Draw the reaction at A so that it will pass through I.
4 Choose a suitable scale for the force diagram (ii). Draw ***nr*** to represent 20kN. Draw ***rm*** parallel to the reaction at A, and draw ***nm*** parallel to EC, intersecting at *m*. Then ***rm*** represents the reaction at A, and ***mn*** represents the pull in the chain.
5 Through *n*, draw ***nt*** parallel to NT; through *m*, draw ***mt*** parallel to MT; the intersection gives the point *t*. Through *t*, draw ***ts*** parallel to TS; and through *m* draw ***ms*** parallel to MS. As a check, the line *rs* should be parallel to RS.
6 Measure or calculate the lengths of the lines in the force diagram, and hence obtain the magnitude of the forces on the members of the frame.
7 The directions of the forces acting at any point are obtained as before. The example given in diagram (iii) deals with the forces acting at the point D. The direction *nr* is *down* to the *right*, since the force *NR* is down to the right. This indicates the way around the figure ***nrst***.
8 Indicate the magnitude and nature of the forces on the scale diagram (iv).

Example 10.12 This is a graphical solution to example 10.5 on page 94. The student should refer to this example for details of the question.

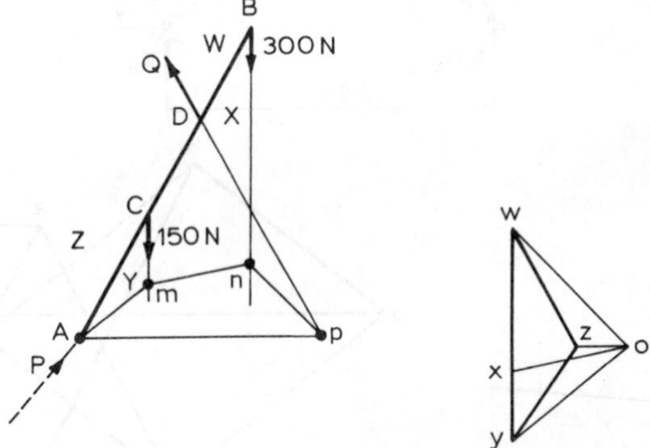

1 Draw, to scale, the space diagram, indicating the various forces.
2 Using Bow's notation, indicate with a capital letter the spaces between the forces. Forces *P* and *Q* are indicated by letters *YZ* and *ZW*.
3 Draw the load line ***wxy***, in which ***wx*** represents the 300N force at B and ***xy*** the 150N force at C.
4 Choose any point *o*, and join *o* to *w*, *x*, and *y*.
5 Since the reaction at A must pass through A, it follows that, although the general direction of the reaction is unknown, we can identify one point, viz. A, on its line of action. From A, draw the line A*m* in space Y, parallel to *oy*. Draw the line *mn* in space X, parallel to *ox*. Draw the line *np* in space W, parallel to *ow*.
6 Join *pA*, and draw a line through *o*, parallel to *pA*. Let this line meet the line through *w*, parallel to force *Q*, at *z*. Join *yz*.
7 Then ***yz*** represents the reaction at A, and ***zw*** represents the force *Q*.

Example 10.13 A pin-jointed structure is in the form of two equal inverted triangles with a common base in the top member PR, 1·2 m long — R to the right of P. The vertices of the triangles are at S and T, 1·5 m below PR — T to the right of S. The length of ST is 2·8 m; S is a hinged support and T a roller support. There are thus five members in all, S and T not being directly connected.

A load of 30 kN acts vertically downward at P, together with a horizontal force of 20 kN directed towards the right. At R, a force of 90 kN acts vertically downwards. Determine the forces in all the members of the frame, stating whether they are tensile or compressive. IMECHE

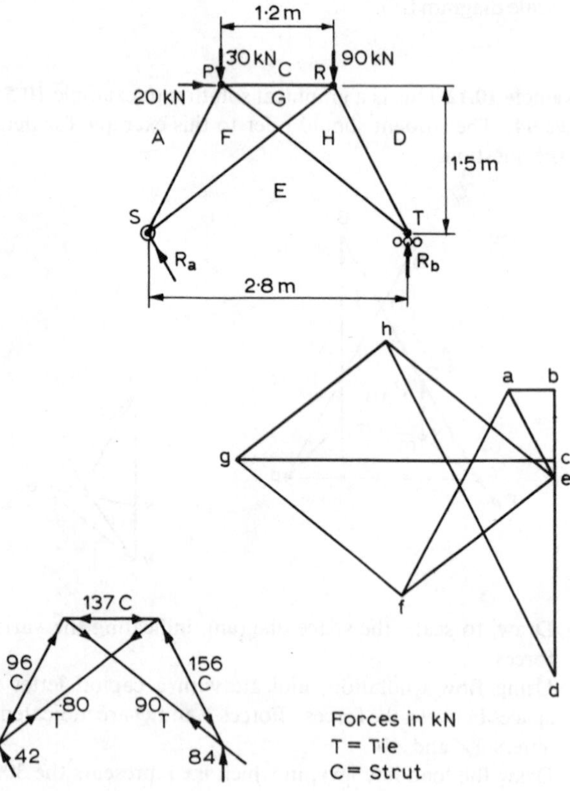

Fig.10.20

1 Draw, to scale, the space diagram, showing the directions of the various members of the structure (fig.10.20). The reaction at the right-hand side will be vertical, since the support is on rollers. The reaction at the hinge can be in any direction, and will be determined from the force diagram.

2 Using Bow's notation, indicate with a capital letter the spaces between the forces. Notice the use of the letter G in the upper small triangle. Force *FG* is the same as force *HE*; force *HG* is the same as force *FE*.

3 Taking moments about the hinge, determine the magnitude of the reaction R_b

$$2{\cdot}8R_b = (20 \times 1{\cdot}5) + (30 \times 0{\cdot}8) + (90 \times 2{\cdot}0)$$
$$= 234$$
$$R_b = 84\,\text{kN}$$

4 Draw the force diagram *abcde*, representing the external forces. ***ab*** represents 20 kN, ***bc*** represents 30 kN, ***cd*** represents 90 kN, and ***de*** represents the reaction R_b, 84 kN. The closing line, ***ea***, represents the reaction R_a at the hinge.

5 Through *a*, draw a line parallel to AF; and through *e*, draw a line parallel to EF. The intersection gives the point *f*.

6 Through *f*, draw a line parallel to FG; and through *c*, draw a line parallel to CG. The intersection gives the point *g*.

7 Through *g*, draw a line parallel to GH; and through *e*, draw a line parallel to EH. The intersection gives the point *h*. As a check, it will be seen that the line *he* is parallel to HE.

8 Measure the lengths of the lines on the force diagram, and hence obtain the magnitudes of the forces in the various members. Notice that the force *FG* is equal to force *HE*, and that force *HG* is the same as force *FE*.

9 Determine the directions of the forces at the different points in the frame, in the manner outlined in the previous examples.

10 Indicate the magnitudes and natures of the forces on the scale diagram at the bottom of fig.10.20.

Example 10.14 This is a graphical solution to an example of the type shown on page 95, to which the student should refer for details.

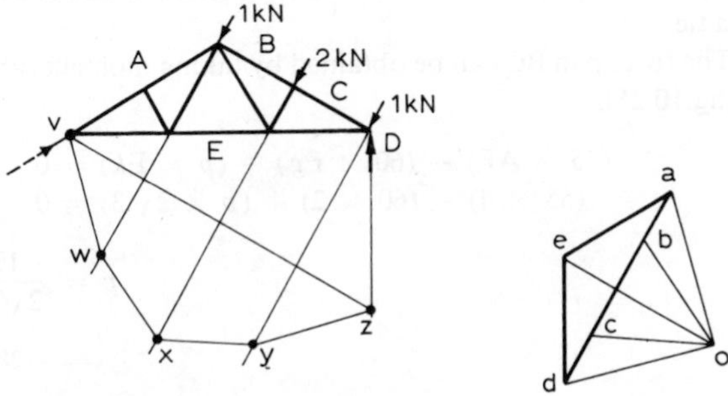

Fig.10.21

1 Draw, to scale, the space diagram, indicating the directions of the various members of the frame.

2 Using Bow's notation, indicate with a capital letter the spaces between each force.

3 Draw the load line *abcd*, and the vertical through *d* to represent the direction of the reaction *DE* (the length of *de* is not known).

4 Since the reaction at the left-hand support must pass through the point *v*, this is the starting point of the construction. From *v*, draw *vw* in space A, parallel to *oa*. Draw *wx* in space B, parallel to *ob*. Draw *xy* in space C, parallel to *oc*. Draw *yz* in space D, parallel to *od*.

5 Join *zv*, and draw a line through *o* parallel to *zv*. Let this line meet the vertical through *d* at *e*. Join *ae*.

6 Then ***de*** and ***ea*** represent the reactions at the right- and left-hand supports respectively.

Example 10.15 Figure 10.22 shows a loaded truss, hinged at the left-hand support, and supported on rollers at the right-hand support. All the loads are given in newtons. Draw a force diagram to a suitable scale, and tabulate the forces acting in the members, distinguishing between ties and struts.

NCTEC

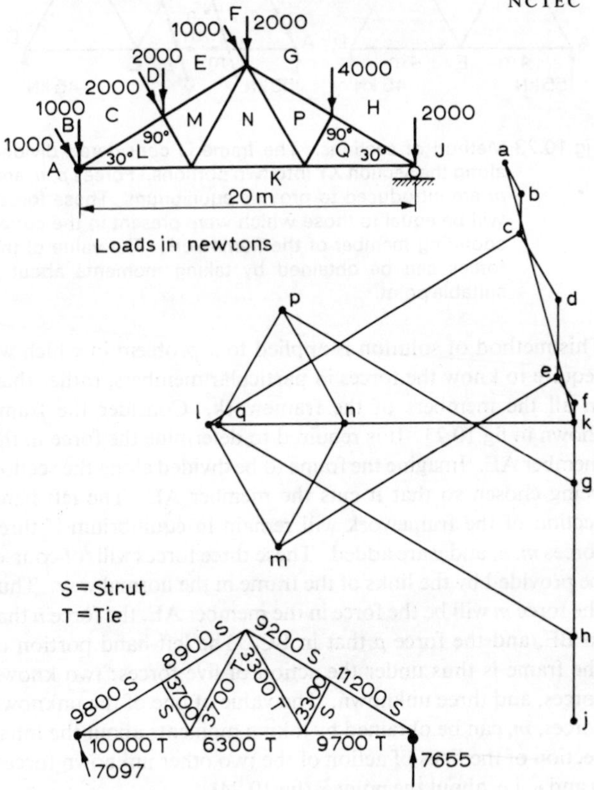

Fig.10.22

This is a more elaborate example than the ones indicated previously. The method of solution is, however, the same as before, and the student is recommended to compare his result with that drawn out opposite.

After the reactions have been calculated in the usual way, the load line *abcdefghijk* should be drawn, and then, commencing at the point *c*, the various force triangles can be constructed.

The reaction at the right-hand support is 7655 N.

The forces in the different members are as follows:

Ties (T)		*Struts (S)*	
LK	10 000	*CL*	9800
NK	6300	*EM*	8900
QK	9700	*GP*	9200
MN	3700	*HQ*	11200
NP	3300	*ML*	3700
		PQ	3300

All forces are in newtons.

Method of Sections

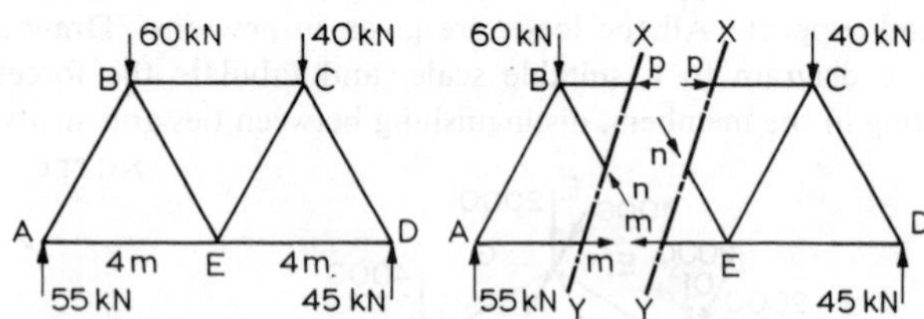

Fig.10.23 Method of sections. The frame is considered divided along the section XY into two portions. Forces p, n, and m are introduced to provide equilibrium. These forces will be equal to those which were present in the corresponding member of the framework. The value of the forces can be obtained by taking moments about a suitable point.

This method of solution is applied to a problem in which we require to know the forces in particular members, rather than in all the members of the framework. Consider the frame shown in fig.10.23. It is required to determine the force in the member AE. Imagine the frame to be divided along the section being chosen so that it cuts the member AE. The left-hand section of the framework will remain in equilibrium if three forces m, n, and p are added. These three forces will, of course, be provided by the links of the frame in the normal way. Thus the force m will be the force in the member AE, the force n that in BE, and the force p that in BC. The left-hand portion of the frame is thus under the action of five forces: two known forces, and three unknown. The value of one of the unknown forces, m, can be obtained by taking moments about the intersection of the lines of action of the two other unknown forces, p and n, i.e. about the point B (fig.10.24).

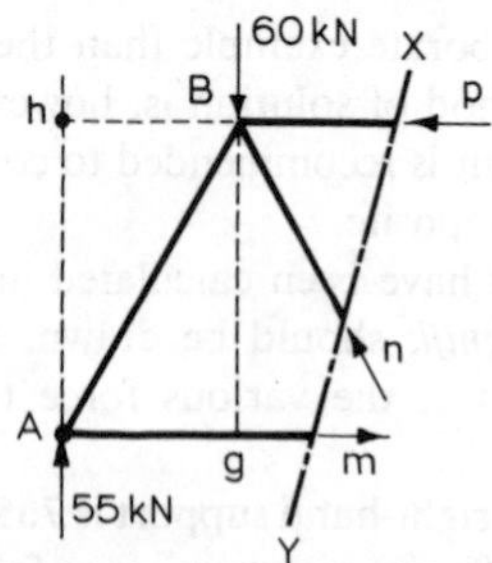

Fig.10.24 To find force m, take moments about B.

$$(55 \times Bh) + (m \times Bg) = 0$$
$$(55 \times 2) + (m \times 2\sqrt{3}) = 0$$
$$m = \frac{-110}{2\sqrt{3}}$$
$$= 31{\cdot}7\,\text{kN}$$

The negative sign indicates that the moment of m about B must be anticlockwise.

To maintain equilibrium, it will be seen that the force m acts away from A, i.e. the member AE is in tension, and is acting as a tie.

The force p in BC can be obtained by taking moments about E (fig.10.25).

$$(55 \times AE) - (60 \times Eg) + (p \times Ek) = 0$$
$$(55 \times 4) - (60 \times 2) + (p \times 2\sqrt{3}) = 0$$
$$p = \frac{-100}{2\sqrt{3}}$$
$$= -28\,\text{kN}$$

hence the moment of p about A is anticlockwise, i.e. p acts towards B, so that BC is in compression, acting as a strut.

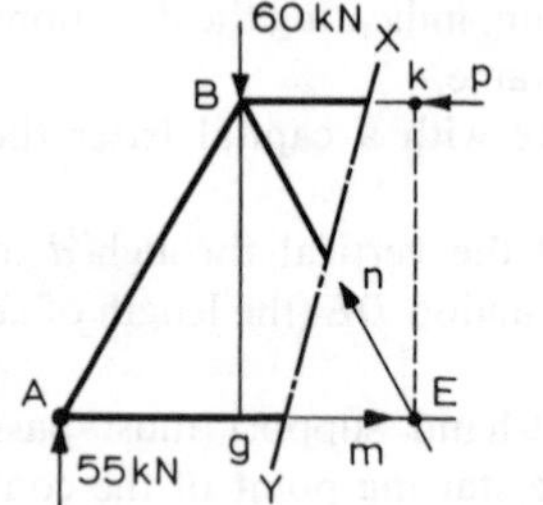

Fig.10.25 To find force p, take moments about E.

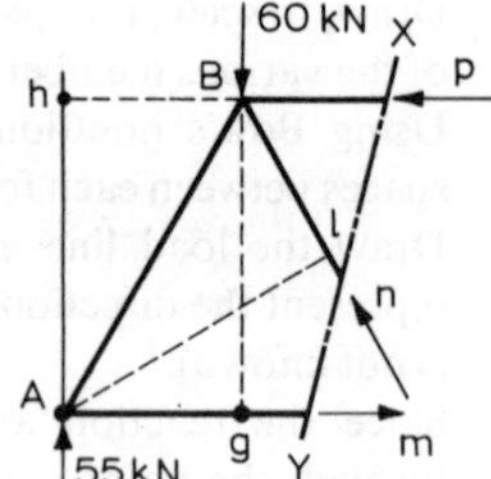

Fig.10.26 To find force n, take moments about A.

Finally, taking moments about A, the force n can be obtained (fig.10.26).

$$(60 \times Ag) - (p \times Ah) + (n \times Al) = 0$$
$$(60 \times 2) - (28 \times 2\sqrt{3}) + (2\sqrt{3} \times n) = 0$$
$$n = \frac{-20}{2\sqrt{3}}$$
$$= 5{\cdot}8\,\text{kN}$$

The negative sign indicates that the moment of n about A is anticlockwise, i.e. n acts towards B, so that BE is in compression, acting as a strut.

Note. It will be seen that in all these calculations the unknown force has been assumed to act in a direction giving a clockwise moment about the reference point. This assumption will be correct if the sign of the force turns out to be positive. Its direction will, however, be required to be reversed if the sign of the force is negative. It should be possible, after a little practice, to put down the correct direction of many of the forces after an inspection of the space diagram.

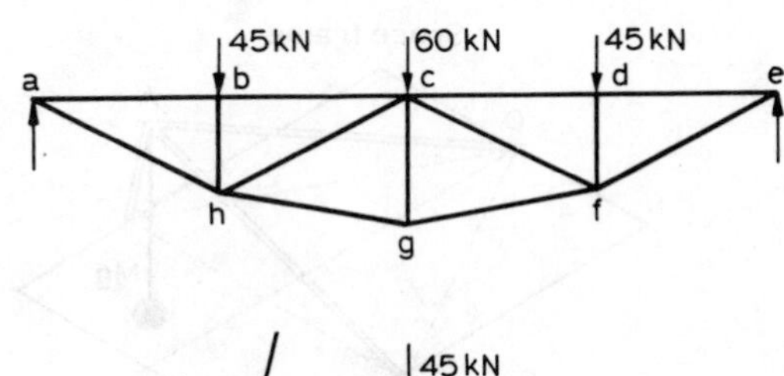

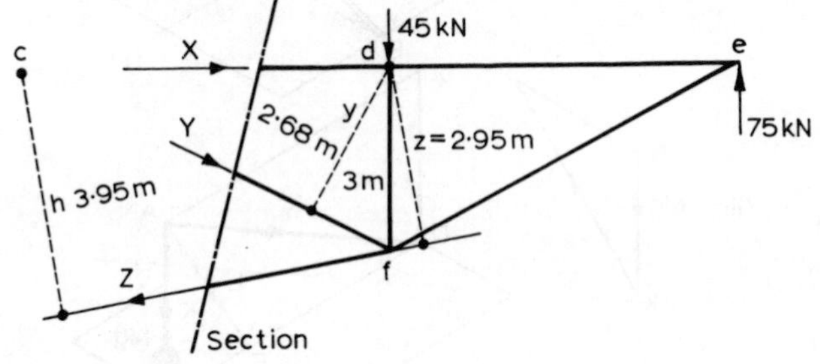

Fig.10.27

Example 10.16 Figure 10.27 gives details of a loaded frame, which is freely supported at the ends. Using the method of sections, determine the magnitudes and natures of the forces in member *cd*, and in member *fg*.

$$ab = bc = cd = de = 6\text{m};\ gc = 4\text{m};\ bh = df = 3\text{m}$$

1 Moments about *a* give the reaction at *e*.

$$24R_e = (6 \times 45) + (12 \times 60) + (18 \times 45)$$
$$R_e = 75\text{kN}$$

Let *X*, *Y*, and *Z* be the forces in members *cd*, *cf*, and *fg*, respectively.

2 To determine the value of these forces, take a section as shown, on which five forces are acting to produce equilibrium.

3 Take moments about the intersection of *Y* and *Z*, to obtain the value of *X*.

$$X \times 3 = 75 \times 6$$
$$X = 150\text{kN}$$

acting towards *d*, i.e. putting *cd* in compression.

4 Take moments about the intersection of *X* and *Y*, to obtain the value of *Z*. The perpendicular distance *h* must be measured or calculated. Its length is 3·95 m.
Moments about *c* give

$$(Z \times 3{\cdot}95) + (45 \times 6) = (75 \times 12)$$
$$Z = 159{\cdot}5\text{kN}$$

acting away from *f*, i.e. putting member *fg* in tension.

5 Take moments about *d*, to obtain the value of *Y*.
Perpendicular distances *y* and *z* must be measured or calculated; *y* is 2·68 m, and *z* is 2·95 m.

$$159{\cdot}5 \times 2{\cdot}95 - 75 \times 6 = Y \times 2{\cdot}68$$
$$Y = 7{\cdot}66\text{kN}$$

towards *f*, i.e. putting member *cf* in compression.

Note. If any of the values of the forces become negative, it simply means that you have indicated the wrong direction of the force on your diagram. Its direction should be changed before deciding whether the member is in compression or tension.

Force in cd is 150 kN, compressive.
Force in cf is 7·66 kN, compressive.
Force in fg is 159·5 kN, tensile.

Space Frames

A space frame is one in which the members are in different planes, as distinct from the single-plane type of framework which we have just been considering. For example, a tripod is a space frame, and is in fact the simplest of such frames (we are to have in mind the camera type, rather than the chemical type associated with the bunsen burner). Figure 10.28(i) indicates a tripod arrangement in which the line of action of the load falls outside the triangular base BCD. This arrangement is sometimes known as 'shear legs'. The shorter members, AB and AC, are equal in length.

To determine the forces in each member due to the load, consider the vertical plane containing the back leg and the load, as shown in diagram (ii). Another member, AE, is introduced to provide equilibrium. This additional member, shown dotted, replaces the two short legs. We now have a case of three co-planar forces in equilibrium. The magnitude and nature of these forces can be determined by means of the force diagram (iii).

> ***hk*** represents the load.
> ***kl*** represents the thrust in the new member, AE.
> ***lh*** represents the pull in the back leg, AD.

Thus we obtain the value of the force in AE to produce equilibrium. Consider now the inclined plane containing the two short legs, diagram (iv). Note that AE has been chosen so that this member also lies in the plane of the two short legs. We now require to know the value of the force in each of these members, AB and AC, such that their combined effect will equal that of AE. It is necessary to know the true inclination of AB and AC. This is shown in diagram (v), which is the view in the direction of the arrow, which is drawn perpendicular to the inclined plane.

Force diagram (vi) is drawn so that ***qr*** is the resultant of ***qp*** and ***pr***, the forces in members AB and AC; by calculation or measurement, it is possible to determine the magnitude of the forces which they represent.

You will notice that it is possible to combine the two force diagrams, since ***qr*** and ***kl*** represent the same force; they appear to be in different directions, since the viewpoint has been changed.

Care must be taken to obtain the ***true*** inclination of members of the frames which are in the inclined plane, such as AB and AC in this example.

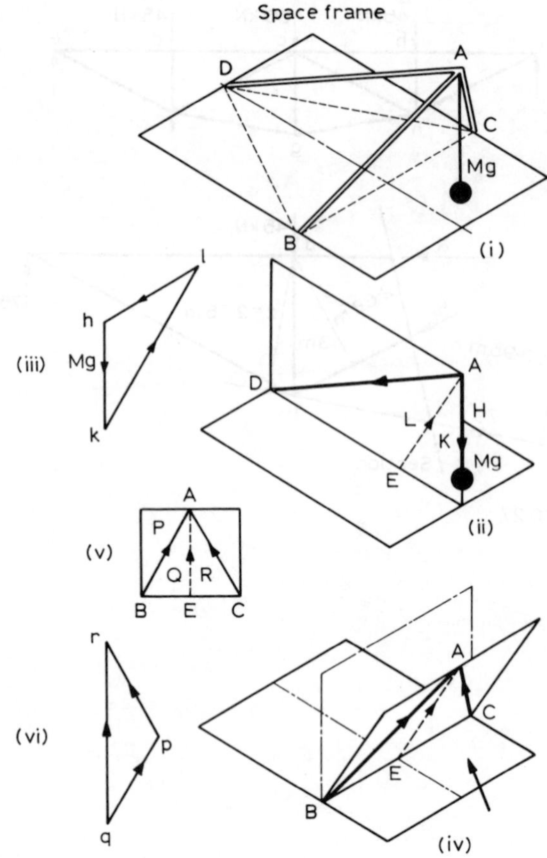

Fig.10.28

Example 10.17 Two legs of a tripod are each 13 m long, the third leg being 12·5 m long. If the feet of the legs lie on the corners of an equilateral triangle of side 10 m lying in a horizontal plane, find the forces in each leg when a body of weight of 50 kN is suspended from the apex of the tripod. ULCI

Problems of this type present two different aspects, and we must become familiar with both.

1 From a solid geometry point of view, it is necessary to be able to construct the correct figure, obtaining the correct inclinations and lengths of the various members of the framework.
2 Having represented the space frame, it is necessary to determine the respective forces from the applied mechanics point of view.

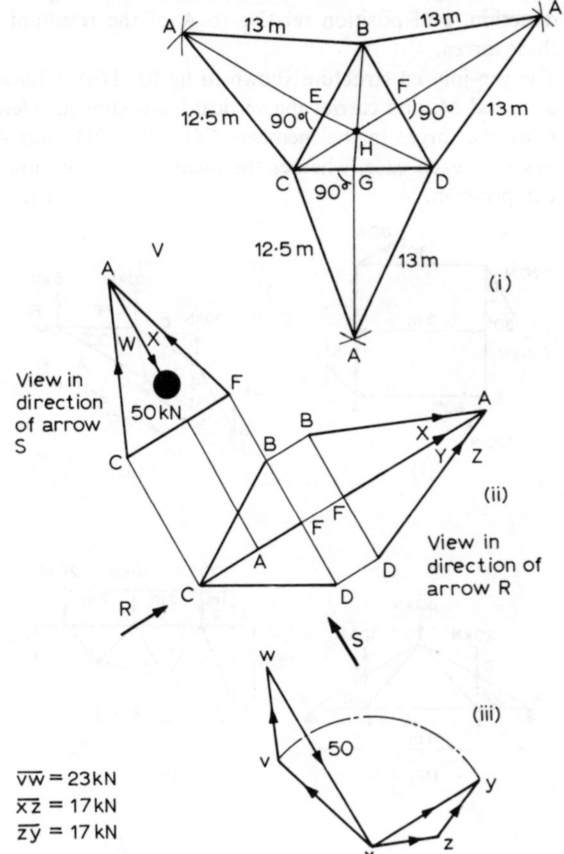

Fig.10.29

1 Representation of the tripod. The triangle BCD is drawn to scale to represent the base of the frame [fig.10·29(i)]. Triangle ABD is drawn with AB and AD each representing 13 m. This triangle is the true view of the side of the tripod standing on base BD. Similarly, triangles ABC and ACD are drawn with AB and AD representing 13 m, and AC representing 12·5 m. You will realise that if each of these three constructed triangles could be folded along their base, so that the three A's came together, you would have the solid model of the tripod. The plan of the vertex of the frame would be the point H.

Perpendiculars are dropped from each point A on to the respective base, meeting in points, E, F, and G; and these points are joined to the opposite apex of triangle BCD. It will be seen that these lines intersect at the point H.

2 Referring to diagram (ii), we have a reproduction of the plan of the tripod, the legs BA and DA being omitted for clarity. A vertical plane is chosen to include the short leg CA, the 50 kN load, and an imaginary member FA. These members are shown, as seen in the direction of the arrow S, by the triangle CAF on the left-hand side of diagram (ii). We require to know the value of the force in the imaginary member FA to provide equilibrium. Letter the spaces V, W, and X; and draw the vector diagram *vwx* as in diagram iii.

wx is drawn to represent the 50 kN load,
xv is drawn parallel to FA (i.e. *XV*),
vw is drawn parallel to CA (i.e. *VW*).

Intersection gives the point *v*, so that ***xv*** represents the force in FA, and ***vw*** represents the force in CA.

3 The force in the imaginary member FA is provided in the actual tripod by the members BA and DA. The triangle BAD on the right-hand side of diagram (ii) is a view in the direction of the arrow R, but giving the true lengths of BA, DA, FA, and, of course, BD. Letter the spaces X, Y, and Z. Draw vector ***xy*** in the direction of FA (i.e. *XY*), and of length equal to ***xv*** (note geometrical construction). Both these vectors, ***xv*** and ***xy***, represent the same force; the difference in direction is due to the different projection of the same member. Draw ***xz*** parallel to BA, and ***zy*** parallel to DA, intersecting at *z*; then ***xy*** is the resultant of ***xz*** and ***zy***.

4 By calculation or measurement, determine the magnitude of the forces represented by ***vw***, ***xz***, and ***zy***, which will give the value of the forces in CA, BA, and DA, respectively.

Hence the force in the short legs CA = 23 kN, the force in the long legs BA and DA = 17 kN each, and all the legs are in compression.

Example 10.18 Determine the forces in the wall support indicated in elevation and plan in fig.10.30(i) and (ii) when supporting a load of 100 N.

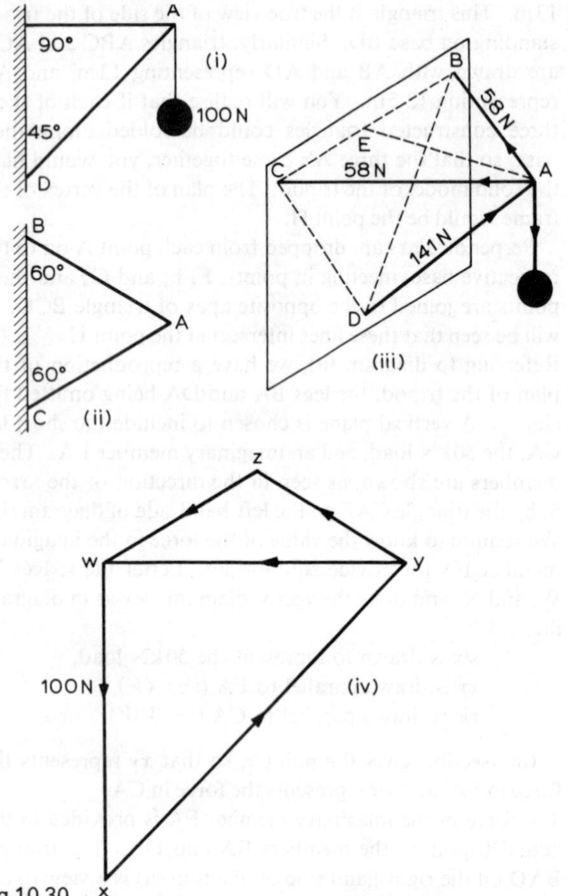

Fig.10.30

Diagram (iii) illustrates the arrangement of the frame in depth.

1 Consider a vertical plane which includes the 100 N load, the stay AD, and a new member, AE [shown dotted in diagram (iii)], introduced to provide equilibrium. This member temporarily replaces AB and AC.
2 Draw, to scale, the vector wx, to represent the 100 N load.
3 Through x, draw xy parallel to AD, to represent the direction of the force in AD; and through w, draw a vector parallel to AE (which is horizontal); the intersection gives point y. Then

   xy represents the thrust in stay AD, and
   yw represents the pull required at A in the direction of imaginary member AE.

4 This pull is in fact provided by ties AB and AC, such that their resultant is the force represented by vector yw.

   Through y, draw a line parallel to AB [as shown in plan (ii)]; and through w, draw a line parallel to AC; the intersection gives the point z. Then

   yz represents the force in AB, and
   zw represents the force in AC.

   Note particularly the direction of these forces with respect to the force represented by yw. yw is the resultant of yz and zw.

5 Measure or calculate the length of the lines in the force diagram, and indicate the value of the force which they represent on the space diagram (iii).

Hence the thrust in AD is 141 N;
the tension in AB and AC is 58 N each;
AD acts as a strut, and AB and AC each as ties.

Exercise 10

1 Figure 10.31 (i) shows a pin-jointed square frame, with loads acting at each corner. Determine the magnitude, direction, and position relative to A of the resultant of these forces.

2 The pin-jointed structure shown in fig.10.31 (ii) is hinged at L and M, and carries the vertical loads shown. Determine the forces in the members CG, GH, DH, and AI. State, in each case, whether the member is in tension or compression. ULCI

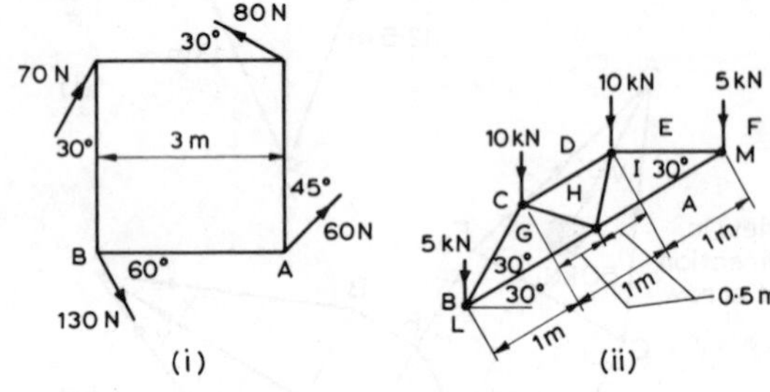

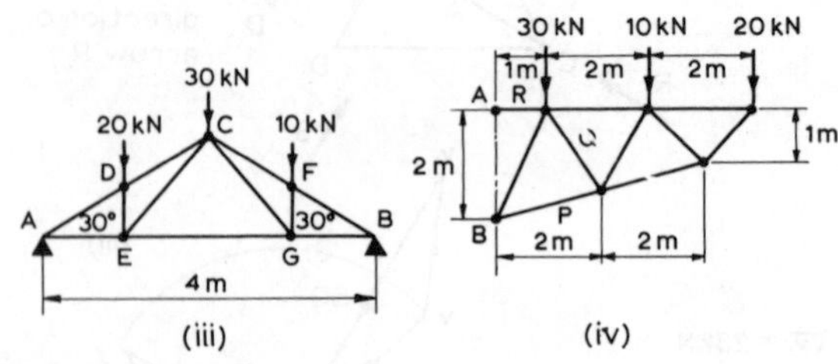

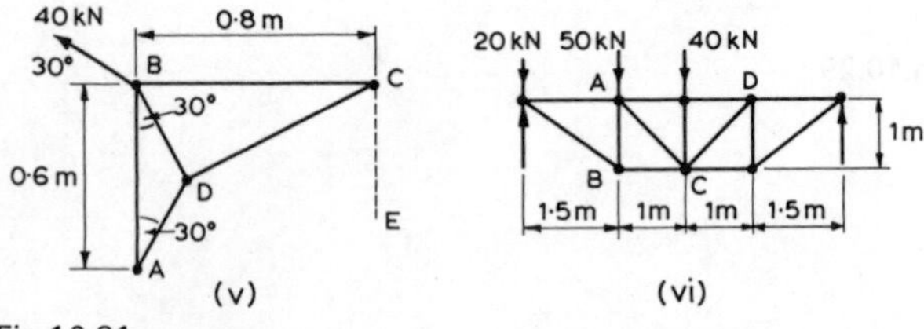

Fig.10.31

3 Figure 10.31 (iii) shows a pin-jointed structure which is simply supported at A and B. AB is horizontal. D and F are mid-points of AC and CB, respectively. DE and FG are vertical. The structure carries vertical loads of 10, 20, and 30 kN at F, D, and C, respectively. For the loaded structure, determine (a) the magnitude of the reaction at B, (b) the magnitude of the forces in the members AD, EC, and FG, stating whether the respective member is a tie or a strut. ULCI

4 The pin-jointed cantilever frame shown in fig.10.31 (iv) is hinged to a vertical wall at A and B, and loaded as shown. Determine the forces in the members P, Q, and R. State in each case whether the member is in tension or compression. ULCI

5 Figure 10.31 (v) shows a pin-jointed structure, loaded at the point B, and hinged at the point A. The structure is maintained with AB vertical by the pull in the vertical chain EC. BC is horizontal. Determine (a) the pull in the chain, (b) the magnitude and direction of the reaction at the hinge A, (c) the forces in the members AB and DC. State whether the member is in tension or compression. ULCI

6 Figure 10.31 (vi) shows a pin-jointed structure carrying vertical loads at the points shown, and simply supported at the ends. Determine the forces in the members AB, BC, and CD, and state whether the member is a tie or a strut. ULCI

7 Draw the complete force diagram for the whole of the Warren girder shown in fig.10.32 (i). Determine the magnitude of the forces in members, KL, CL, and LM only, and state whether they are in compression or tension. EMEU

8 Draw the force diagram for the frame loaded as shown in fig.10.32 (ii), and indicate the magnitude and sense of the force in each member. Calculate also the change in length of the member AE if its cross-sectional area is 200 mm², and Young's modulus of elasticity for the material is 210 GN/m². EMEU

9 Draw the force diagram for the frame loaded as shown in fig.10.32 (iii), and indicate the magnitude and sense of the force in each member. EMEU

10 Forces of 9, 7, 5, and 6 N act on the directions CA, DB, BC, and AB, respectively, of a square ABCD of 50 mm side. Determine graphically the magnitude, direction, and position relative to A of the resultant of these forces. UEI

11 Determine graphically, or otherwise, the forces in the members of the Warren girder shown in fig.10.32 (iv). All angles are 60°. UEI

12 The roof truss shown in fig.10.32 (v) is supported on rollers at one end, and through a hinge at the other end. With the aid of a funicular polygon, determine the magnitudes and directions of the reactions when the truss is carrying the loading shown.

Determine also the forces in the members PQ, RS, and PR, distinguishing between tension and compression. UEI

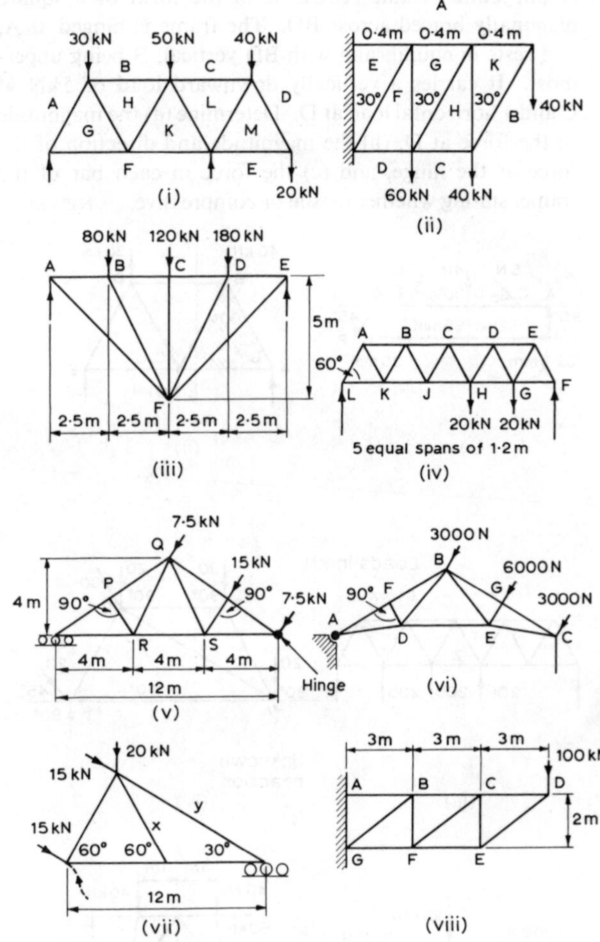

Fig.10.32

13 The roof truss shown in fig.10.32 (vi) consists of two principal rafters, AB and BC, inclined at 30° to the horizontal. AF = FB = BG = GC, and the span AC = 4 m. DE is 1 m vertically below the apex B. Loads as shown are applied perpendicular to BC at points B, G, and C. The truss is pinned at A, and the reaction at C is vertical. Determine the reaction at C, the magnitude and direction of the reaction at A, and the load in DE. UEI

14 In the framework loaded as in fig.10.32 (vii), the right-hand end is supported on rollers, the reaction at this end being therefore vertical. Determine the reactions at the supports, and draw the force diagram for the framework. Write down the forces in the members marked x and y, differentiating between struts and ties. UEI

15 Draw the force diagram for the cantilever frame shown in fig.10.32 (viii), and tabulate the forces in each member, stating whether tensile or compressive. UEI

16 A pin-jointed frame ABCD is in the form of a square diagonally braced across BD. The frame is hinged at A, and rests in equilibrium with BD vertical, B being uppermost. It carries a vertically downward load of 5 kN at C and a horizontal load at D. Determine (a) the magnitude of the force at D, (b) the magnitude and direction of the force at the hinge, and (c) the force in each bar of the frame, stating whether tensile or compressive. NCTEC

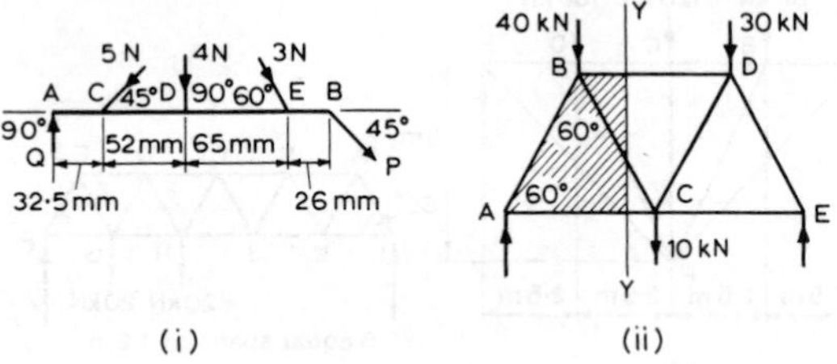

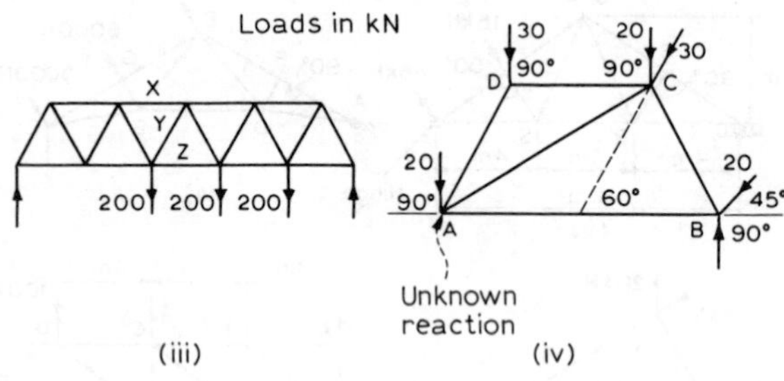

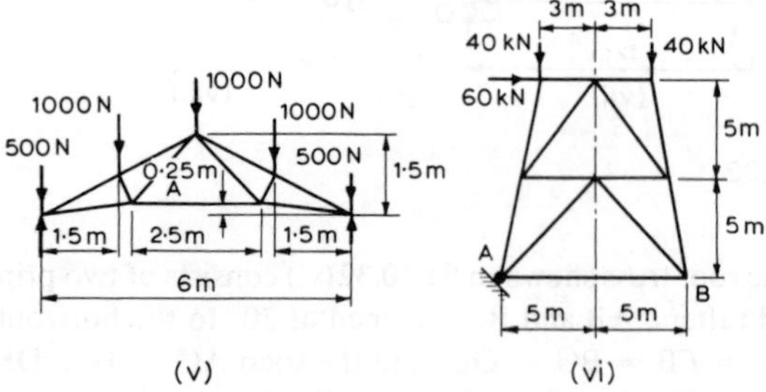

Fig.10.33

17 The rod AB is acted on by forces as shown in fig.10.33 (i). Find graphically the forces P and Q required to keep the rod in equilibrium. Also find, by means of a link polygon, the resultant of the forces acting at C, D, and E, measuring and stating its distance from A and its inclination to the rod. Note that the direction of force P is shown only diagrammatically. (Space or direction diagram, scale full size. Force scale: 10 mm to N.) NCTEC

18 A hinged frame ABCDE, in which all the bars are of equal length, is loaded as shown in fig.10.33 (ii). Using the method of sections (i.e. by considering the equilibrium of the shaded portion), calculate the forces in the bars BD, BC, and AC. A graphical method is not required. NCTEC

19 Calculate the magnitudes and natures of the forces in the members, X, Y, and Z of the Warren girder shown in fig. 10.33 (iii). Each of the angles in the girder is 60°. The loads are given in kN.

20 In the pin-jointed framework shown in fig.10.33 (iv), the members AB, BC, CD, and DA are 2·4, 1·0, 1·2, and 1·0 m long, respectively, the quadrilateral ABCD being symmetrical about the vertical centre-line through AB. Find graphically the supporting forces, and the amount and kind of force in all the members of the framework. Write on the members of the frame the forces in them, and indicate compressive forces by minus signs. NCTEC

21 Draw the complete force diagram for the roof truss shown in fig.10.33 (v). Tabulate your results, and indicate which are tension and compression members respectively. Check the member marked A by taking moments. NCTEC

22 Find by graphical methods the forces in the pin-jointed frame shown in fig.10.33 (vi). The reaction at B is vertical. Indicate on the space diagram the kind of force in each member, using C for compression and T for tension. NCTEC

23 Figure 10.34 (i) shows a loaded roof truss resting on a roller at X, and hinged at Y. Determine, by graphical methods, the reactions at X and Y, and indicate on the space diagram the magnitude and kind of force in each member, using C for compression and T for tension.

24 A pin-jointed frame has the forces acting as shown in fig. 10.34 (ii). Determine graphically (a) the magnitude of the resultant force, (b) the line of action of the resultant. NCTEC

25 In a tripod, the lengths of each of the legs, OA, OB, and OC, are 1·8 m. The lines joining their feet are AB = 1·2 m, BC = 1 m, and AC = 0·9 m. When a load of 15 kN is suspended from the apex O, determine graphically the force in each leg. Choose your own scales. NCTEC

26 The frame shown in fig.10.34 (iii) is pin-jointed throughout. The frame is supported by a pin at P, and rollers at Q. Determine the forces in the four members meeting at R. ULCI

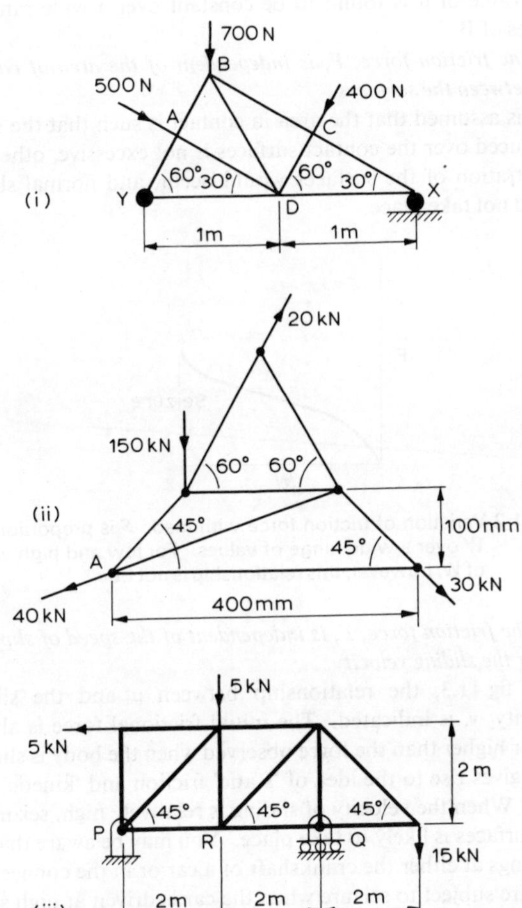

700 N
B
500 N
A
400 N
C
60°
30°
60°
30°
Y
D
X
(i)
1m
1m
20 kN
150 kN
60°
60°
(ii)
45°
100 mm
45°
A
30 kN
40 kN
400 mm
5 kN
5 kN
2 m
45°
45°
45°
P
R
Q
15 kN
2 m
2 m
2 m
(iii)

Fig.10.34

Chapter 11

Friction

A horizontal force P newtons (fig.11.1) is applied to a block of weight W newtons resting on a rough horizontal surface. The force P is insufficient to move the block. There are four forces now acting on the block:

1 the weight of the block acting vertically down;
2 the horizontal pull, P;
3 the vertical reaction of the surface, R upwards;
4 the horizontal friction force, F, due to the roughness of the surface.

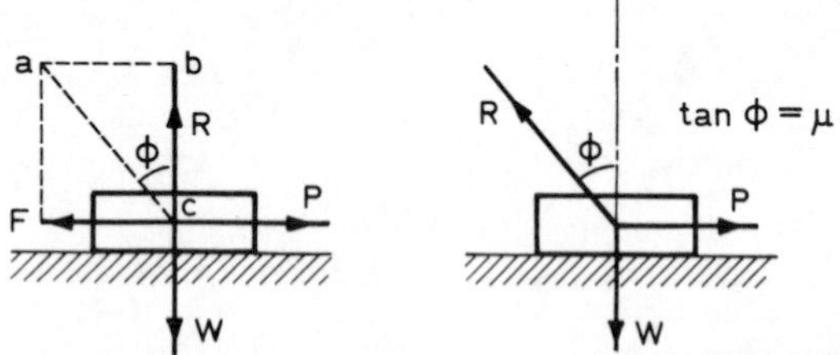

Fig.11.1 Friction. The force of friction, F, opposes the motion of the block. F increases as P increases, until F reaches a maximum value, beyond which it cannot go. This maximum value depends upon the nature of the surfaces in contact, the two materials in contact, and the weight of the sliding block.

Since the block is in equilibrium, W and R will be equal and opposite, and F and P will be equal and opposite.

Now let the pull P be increased. There will be an automatic and corresponding increase in F, such that F and P are still equal. But whilst P can go on increasing indefinitely, F reaches a maximum beyond which it cannot go; and, in fact, when P exceeds this maximum value of F, the block will move in the direction of P. In order to move the block with a uniform velocity, it will therefore be necessary to apply a force equal and opposite to the maximum friction force, F.

There are four important ideas (sometimes known as the four laws of friction) associated with the friction force, and these can be demonstrated by careful experimental work.

1 *The friction force, F, is, within limits, proportional to the normal pressure between the surfaces.*

In the case of horizontal surfaces, as in fig.11.1, this normal pressure is equal to the weight of the moving block. Treatment of the inclined surface is covered at a later stage.

This law is true only within the limits indicated in fig.11.2, which shows the relationship between the friction force and the normal pressure. Between the limits indicated, F is taken as proportional to W. When the normal pressure becomes excessive, seizure of the metals in contact is likely to take place. The two metals become 'welded' together.

Hence we can say

$$F = \mu W$$

where μ is the coefficient of friction of the surfaces in contact. The value of μ is found to be constant over a wide range of values of W.

2 *The friction force, F, is independent of the area of contact between the surfaces.*

It is assumed that the area in contact is such that the stress produced over the contact surfaces is not excessive, otherwise penetration of the surfaces would occur, and normal sliding could not take place.

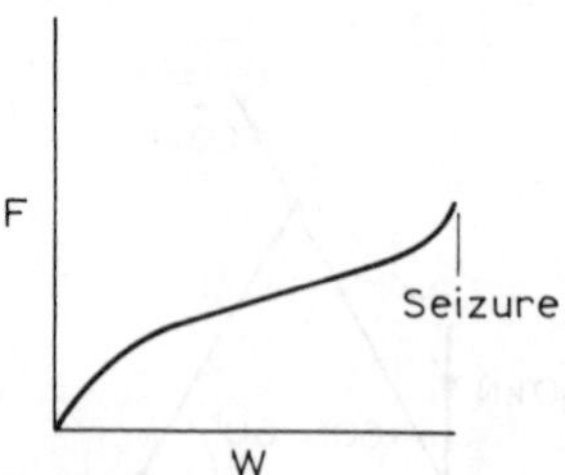

Fig.11.2 Variation of friction force with load. F is proportional to W over a wide range of values. For low and high values of W, however, this relationship is not true.

3 *The friction force, F, is independent of the speed of slipping, or the sliding velocity.*

In fig.11.3, the relationship between μ and the sliding velocity, v, is indicated. The initial frictional force is always rather higher than the force observed when the body is sliding. This gives rise to the idea of 'static' friction and 'kinetic' friction. When the velocity of sliding is relatively high, seizure of the surfaces is likely to take place. You may be aware that the bearings at either the crankshaft of a car or in the connecting-rod are subject to seizure when the car is driven at high speed under load, particularly if the oil pressure is low.

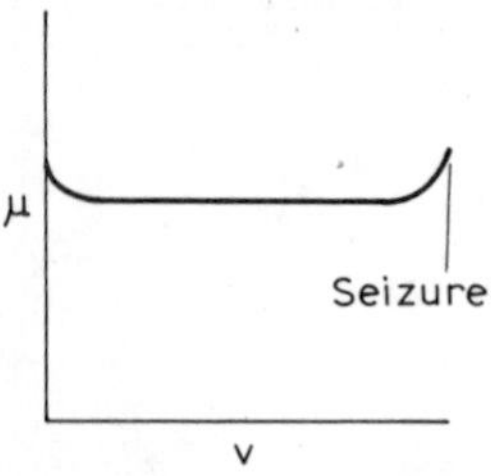

Fig.11.3 Variation of the coefficient of friction with rubbing velocity. The value of μ remains constant over a range of values of the rubbing speed (or sliding velocity), except when v is very small and relatively high.

4 *The friction force, F, depends upon the nature of the surfaces.*

This implies both the type of materials in contact, and the smoothness of the surfaces.

Now refer again to fig.11.1. The forces R and F are both forces which the surface exerts on the block, and can therefore be combined together to form a single reaction. This reaction will no longer be normal to be surface, but inclined backwards

TABLE 1

AVERAGE VALUES OF COEFFICIENT OF FRICTION

Materials	*Coefficient of friction*
bronze on bronze, dry	0·20
bronze on bronze, lubricated .	0·05
leather on steel	0·55
wood on steel	0·50
steel on steel, lubricated . .	0·10

(relative to the direction of motion) through angle ϕ.

$$\tan \phi = \frac{ab}{bc} = \frac{F}{R} = \frac{F}{W} = \mu$$

i.e. For a rough surface, the reaction is inclined backwards through an angle ϕ, such that $\tan \phi = \mu$, the coefficient of friction. The angle ϕ is known as the *angle of friction.*

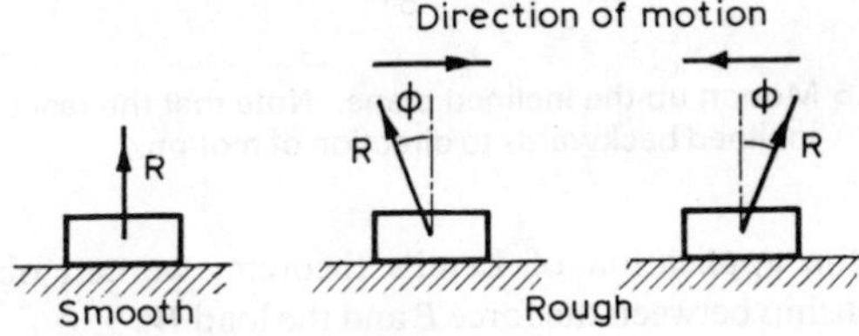

Fig.11.4 Smooth and rough surfaces. For a smooth surface the reaction of the surface is always at right angles to the surface. For a rough surface the reaction is inclined backwards to the direction of motion. The tangent of the angle of inclination is equal to the coefficient of friction of the materials in contact.

Example 11.1 The ends of a link AB are constrained to move in two straight slots at right angles to each other, and in the same plane, as shown in fig.11.5. The sliding block at each end is connected to the rod by means of a pin. A force is applied to the block at A, to overcome a corresponding force at block B. If the resistance at B is 100 N, determine the effort at A when AB makes an angle of (a) 60°, (b) 45°, and (c) 30° with the direction of the motion of A. What is the efficiency of the arrangement for these angles? Take the value of the coefficient of friction at the blocks as 0·2.

Consider the forces at A (fig.11.5):

1 the pull, P, in the direction of motion of A;
2 the tension, T, in rod AB, ultimately overcoming resistance at B;
3 the reaction, R_a, at the block, inclined backwards to the direction of motion of A through an angle ϕ.

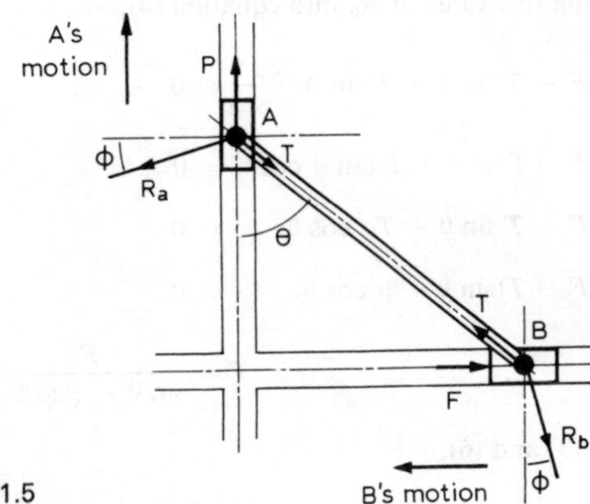

Fig.11.5

Let the inclination of the rod to the direction of A's motion be θ.

Equating vertical components to zero,

$$P - T\cos\theta - R_a \sin\phi = 0 \quad . \quad . \quad . \quad (1)$$

Equating horizontal components to zero,

$$T\sin\theta - R_a\cos\phi = 0 \quad . \quad . \quad . \quad (2)$$

$$R_a = \frac{T\sin\theta}{\cos\phi}$$

Substituting this value of R_a into equation (1),

$$P - T\cos\theta - \frac{T\sin\theta}{\cos\phi}\sin\phi = 0$$

$$P - T\cos\theta - T\tan\phi\sin\theta = 0$$

But $\tan\phi = \mu$

$$P - T\cos\theta - T\mu\sin\theta = 0$$
$$P - T(\cos\theta + \mu\sin\theta) = 0$$

$$T = \frac{P}{\cos\theta + \mu\sin\theta} \quad (3)$$

Consider the forces at B:

1 the resistance, F, opposing the motion of B;
2 tension, T, in rod AB, overcoming this resistance; this force T will always have the same value as the force T at A;
3 the reaction, R_b, at the block, inclined backwards to the direction of motion of B through an angle ϕ.

Equating horizontal components to zero,

$$F - T\sin\theta + R_b\sin\phi = 0 \quad . \quad . \quad . \quad . \quad (4)$$

Equating vertical components to zero,

$$T\cos\theta - R_b\cos\phi = 0 \quad . \quad . \quad . \quad . \quad (5)$$

$$R_b = \frac{T\cos\theta}{\cos\phi}$$

Substituting this value of R_b into equation (4),

$$F - T\sin\theta + T\sin\phi\frac{\cos\theta}{\cos\phi} = 0$$

$$F - T\sin\theta + T\tan\phi\cos\theta = 0$$

$$F - T\sin\theta + T\mu\cos\theta = 0$$

$$F - T(\sin\theta - \mu\cos\theta) = 0$$

$$T = \frac{F}{\sin\theta - \mu\cos\theta} \quad (6)$$

Equating (3) and (6),

$$\frac{P}{\cos\theta + \mu\sin\theta} = T = \frac{F}{\sin\theta - \mu\cos\theta}$$

$$\therefore P = F\frac{\cos\theta + \mu\sin\theta}{\sin\theta - \mu\cos\theta}$$

Dividing numerator and denominator by $\cos\theta$, we have

$$P = F\left(\frac{1 + \mu\tan\theta}{\tan\theta - \mu}\right) \quad . \quad . \quad . \quad . \quad . \quad (7)$$

Substituting $F = 100$ N, $\mu = 0{\cdot}2$, $\theta = 60°$, 45°, and 30°, we have:

$\theta = 60°$ $\quad P = 87{\cdot}8$ N
$\theta = 45°$ $\quad P = 150{\cdot}0$ N
$\theta = 30°$ $\quad P = 296{\cdot}0$ N

The arrangement would be a perfect machine if there were no friction, i.e. if $\mu = 0$.

Let P_i be the ideal effort required to overcome the 100 N resistance, then substituting $\mu = 0$ into equation (7), we have

$$P_i = F\left(\frac{1}{\tan\theta}\right) = F\cot\theta \quad . \quad . \quad . \quad (8)$$

Hence for the corresponding values of the angles, we have:

$\theta = 60°$ $\quad P_i = 57{\cdot}74$ N
$\theta = 45°$ $\quad P_i = 100$ N
$\theta = 30°$ $\quad P_i = 173{\cdot}2$ N

The efficiency of the arrangement is given by $\dfrac{\text{ideal effort}}{\text{actual effort}}$.

$$\theta = 60°, \text{ efficiency} = \frac{57{\cdot}74}{87{\cdot}8} = 0{\cdot}657 \text{ or } 65{\cdot}7\%$$

$$\theta = 45°, \text{ efficiency} = \frac{100}{150} = 0{\cdot}667 \text{ or } 66{\cdot}7\%$$

$$\theta = 30°, \text{ efficiency} = \frac{173{\cdot}2}{296} = 0{\cdot}586 \text{ or } 58{\cdot}6\%$$

Friction and the Inclined Plane—General Case

A block of weight W is being pulled up an inclined plane, inclination angle θ, by a force, P, which is inclined at angle α to the plane (fig.11.6). The reaction, R, is inclined backwards through angle ϕ, as shown.

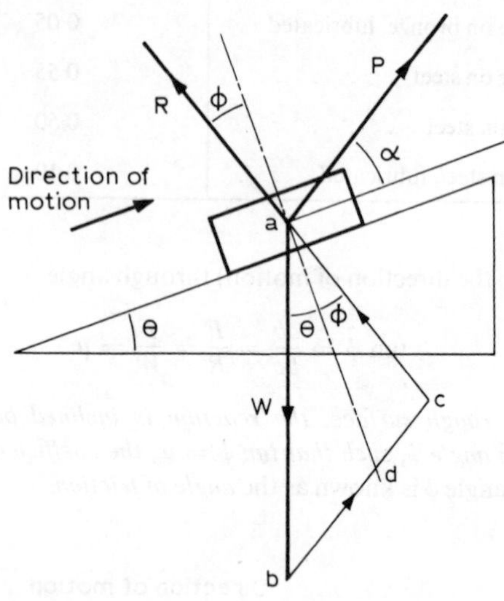

Fig.11.6 Motion up the inclined plane. Note that the reaction R is inclined backwards to direction of motion.

By the application of Lami's theorem, we can obtain a relationship between the force P and the load W.

Angle opposite force P $= 180 - \theta - \phi = 180 - (\theta + \phi)$

Angle opposite reaction $R = 90 + (\theta + \alpha)$

Angle opposite load W $= 90 + \phi - \alpha = 90 - (\alpha - \phi)$

$$\frac{P}{\sin 180 - (\theta + \phi)} = \frac{W}{\sin 90 - (\alpha - \phi)} = \frac{R}{\sin 90 + (\theta + \alpha)}$$

$$\frac{P}{\sin(\theta + \phi)} = \frac{W}{\cos(\alpha - \phi)} = \frac{R}{\cos(\theta + \alpha)}$$

$$\therefore P = \frac{W\sin(\theta + \phi)}{\cos(\alpha - \phi)} \quad . \quad . \quad . \quad . \quad (1)$$

The triangle abc is the vector triangle for the forces acting at a.

Case 1. P is parallel to the plane, i.e. $\alpha = 0$.

$$P = \frac{W\sin(\theta + \phi)}{\cos(0 - \phi)} = \frac{W\sin(\theta + \theta)}{\cos\phi}$$

since $\cos(-\phi) = \cos\phi$.

Expanding the numerator,

$$P = \frac{W(\sin\theta\cos\phi + \sin\phi\cos\theta)}{\cos\phi}$$

$$= W(\sin\theta + \tan\phi\cos\theta)$$
$$= W(\sin\theta + \mu\cos\theta) \quad . \quad . \quad . \quad . \quad . \quad (2)$$

since $\mu = \tan\phi$.

Case 2. P is horizontal, i.e. $\alpha = -\theta$. Notice that the negative sign is used; α was measured in an anticlockwise direction in fig.11.6.

Substituting in equation (1),

$$P = \frac{W\sin(\theta + \phi)}{\cos(-\theta - \phi)} = \frac{W\sin(\theta + \phi)}{\cos -(\theta + \phi)}$$

$$P = W\tan(\theta + \phi) \quad . \quad . \quad . \quad . \quad . \quad . \quad . \quad . \quad (3)$$

since $\cos -(\theta + \phi) = \cos(\theta + \phi)$.

Case 3. Minimum value of P.

$$P = \frac{W\sin(\theta + \phi)}{\cos(\alpha - \phi)}$$

Since $W\sin(\theta + \phi)$ is a constant, i.e. it does not vary with any variation of α, the value of P is minimum when $\cos(\alpha - \phi)$ is maximum; i.e. when $(\alpha - \phi)$ is zero, or when $\alpha = \phi$.

Hence the minimum effort is required when the direction of the pull is inclined at angle ϕ upwards to the plane.

In this case, $P = \dfrac{W\sin(\theta + \phi)}{\cos(\phi - \phi)}$

Minimum $\quad P = W\sin(\theta + \phi) \quad . \quad . \quad . \quad . \quad . \quad . \quad (4)$

Condition for Minimum Effort (Graphical Solution)

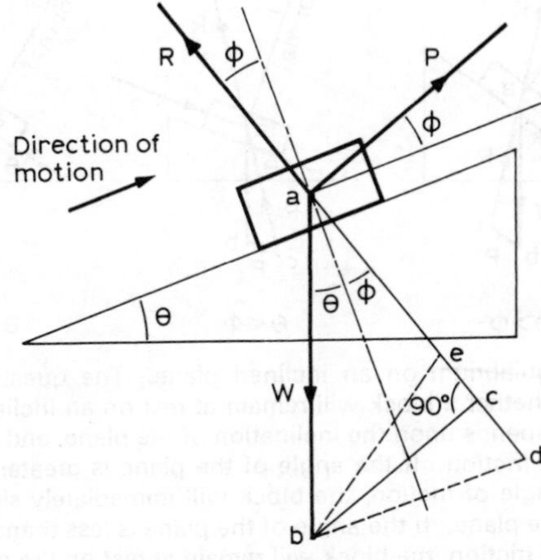

Fig.11.7 Condition for minimum force. Pull P must be inclined at right angles to the reaction R; i.e., pull P must be inclined at angle ϕ, the friction angle, to the plane.

From the force diagram shown in fig.11.7, it will be seen that the magnitude of the effort P, represented by ***bc***, will be dependent upon the direction of the force. The shortest line which can be drawn from b is that which is perpendicular to *ad*. (The dotted lines *bd* and *be* are both longer than *bc*.) This shortest length is $ab\sin(\theta + \phi)$.

Thus the minimum effort will be $W\sin(\theta + \phi)$, and will occur when P is perpendicular to the reaction R, i.e. when P is inclined at angle ϕ to the plane.

Efficiency of the Inclined Plane

The efficiency of the inclined plane can be obtained by comparing the actual effort required to move the load with the ideal effort which would be required if there were no friction present.

$$\text{Efficiency} = \frac{\text{ideal effort}}{\text{actual effort}}$$

In the general case, with effort P inclined at angle α to the plane, we have the relationship

$$\text{actual } P = \frac{W\sin(\theta + \phi)}{\cos(\alpha - \phi)}$$

If there is no friction, $\mu = 0$, and $\phi = 0$ (i.e. no angle of friction):

$$\text{ideal } P = P_i = \frac{W\sin\theta}{\cos\alpha}$$

$$\text{Efficiency} = \frac{\text{ideal effort}}{\text{actual effort}}$$

$$= \frac{W\sin\theta/\cos\alpha}{W\sin(\theta + \phi)/\cos(\alpha - \phi)}$$

$$= \frac{\sin\theta\cos(\alpha - \phi)}{\cos\alpha\sin(\theta + \phi)}$$

$$= \frac{\sin\theta(\cos\alpha\cos\phi + \sin\alpha\sin\phi)}{\cos\alpha(\sin\theta\cos\phi + \sin\phi\cos\theta)}$$

Dividing numerator and denominator by $\sin\theta$, and by $\cos\alpha$,

$$= \frac{\cos\phi + \sin\phi\tan\alpha}{\cos\phi + \sin\phi\cot\theta}$$

Dividing numerator and denominator by $\cos\phi$,

$$\text{efficiency} = \frac{1 + \tan\phi\tan\alpha}{1 + \tan\phi\cot\theta}$$

$$= \frac{1 + \mu\tan\alpha}{1 + \mu\cot\theta}$$

Case 1. When P is parallel to the plane, $\alpha = 0$.

$$\text{Efficiency} = \frac{1}{1 + \mu\cot\theta}$$

Case 2. When P is horizontal, $\alpha = -\theta$.

$$\text{Efficiency} = \frac{1 - \mu \tan \theta}{1 + \mu \cot \theta}$$

Case 3. For the case of minimum effort, i.e. when $\alpha = \phi$.

$$\text{Efficiency} = \frac{1 + \mu \tan \phi}{1 + \mu \cot \theta}$$

But $\tan \phi = \mu$,

$$\therefore \text{efficiency} = \frac{1 + \mu^2}{1 + \mu \cot \theta}$$

It may be useful to notice an alternative treatment in the case of the pull being horizontal. In this case, $P = W \tan (\theta + \phi)$, and therefore, if there is no friction, the ideal effort would be $P_i = W \tan \theta$.

$$\therefore \text{Efficiency} = \frac{\text{ideal effort}}{\text{actual effort}}$$

$$= \frac{W \tan \theta}{W \tan (\theta + \phi)} = \frac{\tan \theta}{\tan (\theta + \phi)}$$

In this form, the efficiency expression has considerable application in screw-thread and worm-gear problems.

Condition	*Efficiency*
P inclined at α to plane . .	$\frac{1 + \mu\tan \alpha}{1 + \mu\cot \theta}$
P parallel to plane	$\frac{1}{1 + \mu\cot \theta}$
P horizontal	$\frac{1 - \mu\tan \theta}{1 + \mu\cot \theta}$
Minimum P	$\frac{1 + \mu^2}{1 + \mu\cot \theta}$

Motion Down the Plane

In considering the motion of the body down the plane, we shall see that there are two distinct problems which arise.

1 The angle of the plane may be so steep that the body has to be held on the plane by a force P opposing motion [fig. 11.8(i)].

2 The angle may be so small that the body has to be pushed down the plane by a force P acting in the direction of motion [fig.11.8(ii)].

We shall consider the first case, and then determine how the results may be applied to the second case. Notice that the direction of the reaction has been changed to the opposite side of the normal, i.e. it is still inclined backwards to the direction of motion.

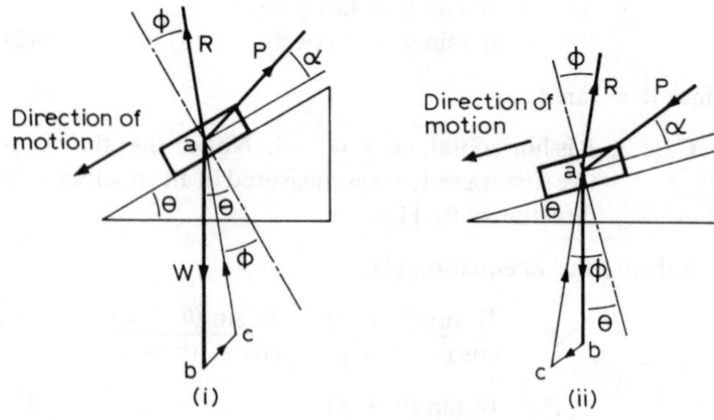

Fig.11.8 Motion down the plane. Case (i) Steep inclination. Direction of P is up the plane, to prevent block accelerating down the plane. Case (ii) Small inclination. Direction of P is down the plane, to make block move with uniform velocity down the plane. Reaction R is inclined backwards to direction of motion in each case.

Angle opposite force $P = 180 - \theta + \phi = 180 - (\theta - \phi)$

Angle opposite reaction $R = 90 + (\theta + \alpha)$

Angle opposite load $W = 90 - \alpha - \phi = 90 - (\alpha + \phi)$

$$\frac{P}{\sin 180 - (\theta - \phi)} = \frac{W}{\sin 90 - (\alpha + \phi)} = \frac{R}{\sin 90 + (\theta + \alpha)}$$

$$\frac{P}{\sin (\theta - \phi)} = \frac{W}{\cos (\alpha + \phi)} = \frac{R}{\cos (\theta + \alpha)}$$

$$P = \frac{W \sin (\theta - \phi)}{\cos (\alpha + \phi)}$$

Notice that P is positive, provided that θ is greater than ϕ.

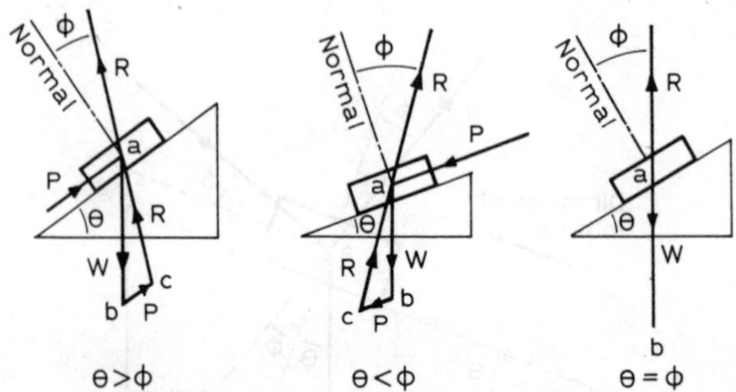

Fig.11.9 Equilibrium on an inclined plane. The question as to whether a block will remain at rest on an inclined plane depends upon the inclination of the plane, and the angle of friction. If the angle of the plane is greater than the angle of friction, the block will immediately slide down the plane. If the angle of the plane is less than the angle of friction, the block will remain at rest on the plane, and would in fact have to be pushed down the plane. The critical case is when the angle of the plane is equal to the angle of friction. This angle is sometimes referred to as the *angle of repose.*

When θ is equal to ϕ, sin $(\theta - \phi)$ is equal to zero, and P is also equal to zero, i.e. the block remains in equilibrium on the plane without the aid of an additional force, P. (In this case, the reaction R is vertical, and in line with W.)

If θ is less than ϕ, sin $(\theta - \phi)$ is negative, and consequently P becomes negative. This means that the direction of P must be changed so that it will have to pull the block down the plane, rather than prevent it from moving down. The three conditions are illustrated in fig.11.9.

Case 1. P is parallel to the plane, i.e. $\alpha = 0$.

$$P = \frac{W \sin(\theta - \phi)}{\cos(0 + \phi)} \quad \frac{W \sin(\theta - \phi)}{\cos \phi}$$

which can be expanded as before, and gives

$$P = W(\sin\theta - \mu \cos\theta)$$

Case 2. P is horizontal, i.e. $\alpha = -\theta$.

$$P = \frac{W \sin(\theta - \phi)}{\cos(-\theta + \phi)} = \frac{W \sin(\theta - \phi)}{\cos(\theta - \phi)}$$

$$= W \tan(\theta - \phi)$$

since $\cos(\theta - \phi) = \cos -(\theta - \phi)$.

Example 11.2 A body of weight 500 N is prevented from sliding down a plane inclined at 20° to the horizontal by the application of a force of 50 N acting upwards and parallel to the plane. Find the coefficient of friction.

If the body is to be pulled up the plane by a force acting at an angle of 30° to the horizontal, find the value of the force, and the efficiency of the lift. IMECHE

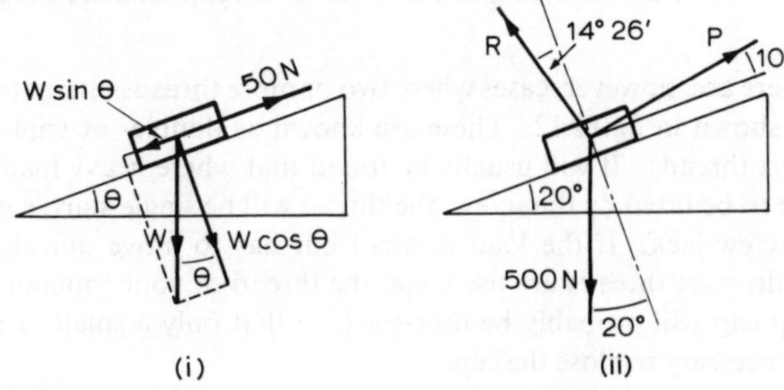

Fig.11.10

1 Component of 500 N down the plane $= W \sin 20°$
$= 500 \times 0{\cdot}3420$
$= 171$ N

Body is prevented from sliding down plane by

(i) the pull of 50 N, and
(ii) the friction force.

∴ Friction force $= 171 - 50 = 121$ N

Component of 500 N perpendicular to plane $= W \cos 20°$
$= 500 \times 0{\cdot}9397$
$= 469{\cdot}8$ N

$$\text{Coefficient of friction} = \frac{\text{friction force}}{\text{normal force}}$$

$$= \frac{121}{469{\cdot}8} = 0{\cdot}26$$

Angle of friction $= \arctan 0{\cdot}26 = 14°26'$

2 Direction of motion is up the plane [fig.11.10(ii)].
Reaction is swung backwards through angle ϕ, or $14°26'$.

Angle opposite load $= 90° - 10° + 14°26'$
$= 94°26'$

Angle opposite pull $P = 180° - 20° - 14°26'$
$= 145°34'$

Applying Lami's theorem,

$$\frac{500}{\sin 94°26'} = \frac{P}{\sin 145°34'}$$

$$P = \frac{500 \sin 145°24'}{\sin 94°26'} = \frac{500 \sin 34°26'}{\sin 85°34'}$$

$$= \frac{500 \times 0{\cdot}5655}{0{\cdot}997}$$

$$= 283{\cdot}6\ \text{N}$$

$$\text{Efficiency of lift} = \frac{\text{ideal effort}}{\text{actual effort}}$$

Ideal effort = effort required if there is no friction
In this case, the reaction is normal to the inclined plane, i.e. $\phi = 0$.

∴ Angle opposite load $= 90 - 10° = 80°$

Angle opposite $P = 180° - 20° = 160°$

Applying Lami's theorem,

$$\frac{500}{\sin 80°} = \frac{P_i}{\sin 160°}$$

$$P_i = \frac{5 \sin 160°}{\sin 80°} = \frac{5 \times 0{\cdot}3420}{0{\cdot}9848}$$

$$= 173{\cdot}7\ \text{N}$$

$$\text{Efficiency} = \frac{\text{ideal effort}}{\text{actual effort}} = \frac{173{\cdot}7}{283{\cdot}6}$$

$= 0{\cdot}6125$, or $61{\cdot}25\%$

i.e. The coefficient of friction is 0·26, the horizontal force required is 283·6 N, and the efficiency of the lift is 61·25%.

Example 11.3 Figure 11.11 shows a wedge arrangement used for lifting loads. The inclination of the wedge is 20°, and the coefficient of friction for all the surfaces in contact is 0·2. Determine the magnitude of the force, F, required to lift a load of 100 N.

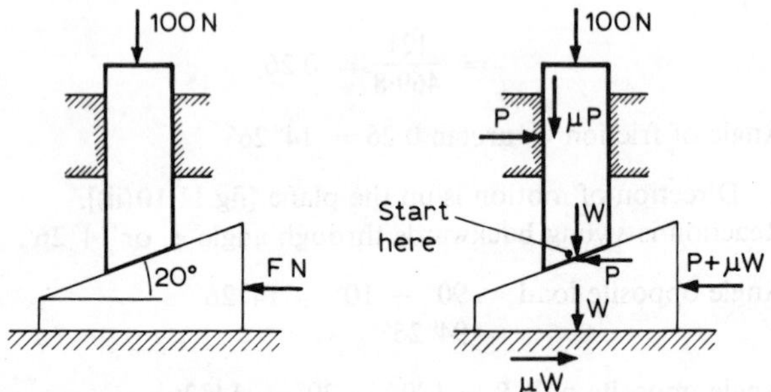

Fig.11.11

The analysis of this problem begins at the area of contact between the wedge and the vertical pillar.

Let the vertical load at this point be W N.

Then the horizontal force required to overcome this load is $P = W \tan(\theta + \phi)$.

An immediate reaction to this force will appear at the left-hand side of the pillar bearing, and will be equal and opposite to P.

In order to move the pillar in the bearing, it will be necessary to overcome bearing friction, in addition to the load of 100 N.

Hence the upward force required will be $(\mu P + 100)$ N; this will be the value of W.

$$W = \mu P + 100$$

Now this force, W, will be transferred through the wedge on to the horizontal floor. The frictional resistance of the floor to movement of the wedge will be μW.

Hence the applied effort, F, will have to overcome this frictional resistance, as well as providing the horizontal force, P.

Thus, $F = \mu W + P$

Hence we have three equations:

$$P = W \tan(\theta + \phi) \quad (1)$$
$$W = \mu P + 100 \quad (2)$$
$$F = \mu W + P \quad (3)$$

Since $\mu = 0{\cdot}2$, $\phi = \arctan 0{\cdot}2 = 11°19'$.

$$\tan(\theta + \phi) = \tan 31°19' = 0{\cdot}6083$$

From (1) $\quad P = 0{\cdot}6083W$

From (2) $\quad W = 0{\cdot}2P + 100$

These two equations give $P = 69{\cdot}4$ N, and $W = 114$ N.

Substituting these in equation (3),

$$F = 0{\cdot}2 \times 114 + 69{\cdot}4$$
$$= 92{\cdot}2 \text{ N}$$

i.e. The required force is 92·2 N.

The student may like to show that the value of F in this problem is equal to $100 \tan(\theta + 2\phi)$.

The Screw-thread

The screw-thread, in whatever form it may be found, is nothing more than an inclined plane which has been wrapped around a cylinder, to form a helical thread. It is important to become familiar with the following terms.

Single- and double-start threads. If the whole of the thread is part of the same helix, it is known as a single-start thread.

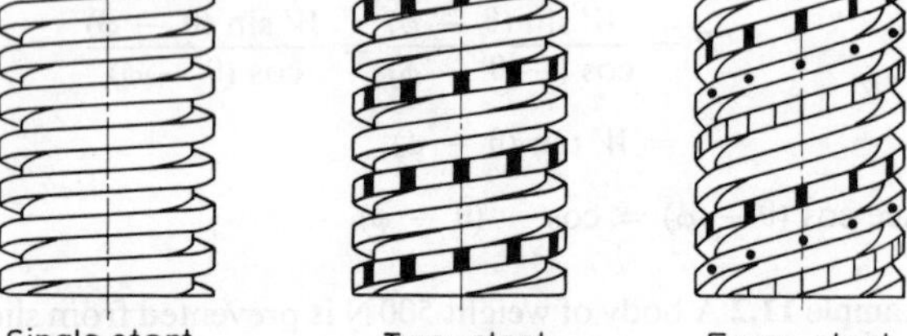

Fig.11.12 Screw-threads. The pitch of the thread is the distance from one thread to the next. The lead of the thread is the axial distance which a nut would move if it were given one full turn. In the diagram, all have the same pitch, but the screw on the right has a lead equal to four times that on the left. Incidentally, since the thread is inclined upwards to the right, it is known as a right-handed thread.

There are, however, cases where two or more threads alternate, as shown in fig.11.12. These are known as double- or triple-start threads. It will usually be found that where heavy loads are to be lifted by the screw, the thread will be single start, e.g. a screw-jack. If the load is small but has to move quickly, multi-start threads are used, e.g. the thread of your fountain-pen cap will probably be four-start, so that only a small turn is necessary to close the cap.

Pitch. The distance from one thread to the next, measured along the axis of the screw.

Lead. The axial distance which the nut will travel along the screw when given one complete turn.

$$\text{Lead} = \text{pitch} \times \text{number of starts}$$

Helix angle. The angle which the thread makes with a plane perpendicular to the axis of the screw. The helix angle of the screw is the same as the angle of inclination of the inclined plane.

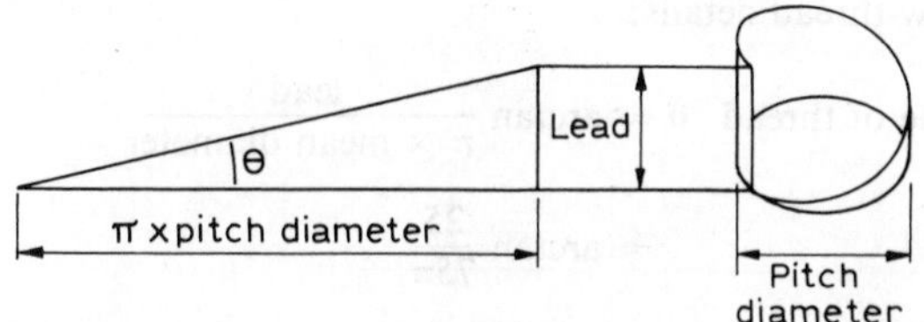

Fig.11.13 The inclined plane and the helix. The helix, which is the basis of the screw-thread, is an inclined plane formed around a cylinder. If the triangle on the left of the diagram were wrapped around a cylinder, it would take up the shape indicated on the right of the diagram.

From fig.11.13 it will be seen that

$$\tan\theta = \frac{\text{lead}}{\pi \times \text{pitch diameter}}$$

We shall here be concerned only with square-thread screws. The action of the screw and nut is identical to that of the inclined plane in which a load is lifted with a horizontal effort.

In all cases of a screw and nut, the nut is perpendicular to the screw. Hence, if the screw is vertical, the nut and the spanner move in the horizontal plane. The horizontal force at the end of the spanner is transferred to the points of contact between the screw and the nut, and still remains horizontal (fig.11.14).

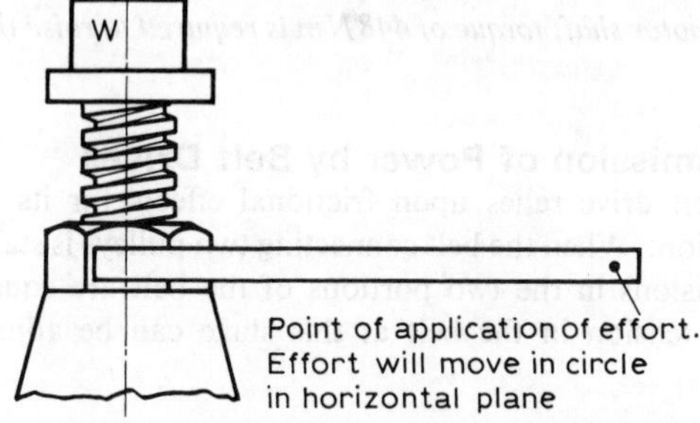

Fig.11.14 The screw-thread. The load W is being lifted by means of a horizontal force applied at the end of a torque arm.

The force, P, required at the radius of the screw, $d/2$, to lift a load W is therefore

$$P = W\tan(\theta + \phi)$$

where θ = helix angle of the thread,
ϕ = angle of friction.

So the torque to be applied to the screw must be

$$\text{force} \times \text{radius} = P \times \frac{d}{2}$$

$$= \frac{Wd}{2}\tan(\theta + \phi)$$

If a force F is applied at the end of a spanner of length l, then the applied torque, Fl, can be equated to that in the above expression.

$$Fl = \frac{Wd}{2}\tan(\theta + \phi)$$

$$F = \frac{Wd}{2l}\tan(\theta + \phi)$$

Example 11.14 Determine the torque necessary to raise a load of 1000 N by a vertical screw having two square threads per centimetre (single start), and a mean diameter of 20 millimetres. The coefficient of friction for the screw and nut is 0·15. What is the efficiency of the screw when lifting the load? NCTEC

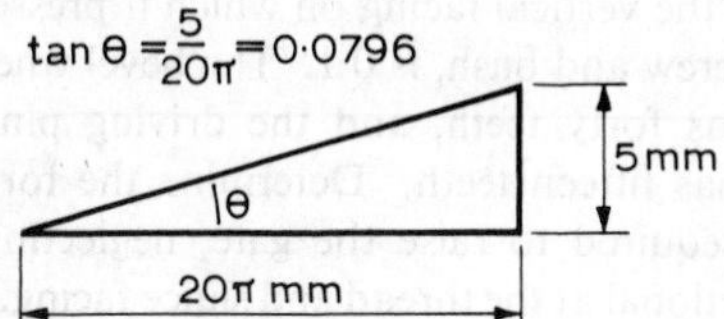

Fig.11.15

Pitch of threads = 5 mm (two threads per cm)

Since screw is single start, lead is equal to pitch.

Lead of screw = 5 mm

$$\tan\theta = \frac{5}{20\pi} = 0{\cdot}0796$$

$$\theta = 4^\circ 33'$$

$$\tan\phi = \mu = 0{\cdot}15$$

$$\phi = 8^\circ 32'$$

Tangential load to lift 1000 N $= 1000\tan(\theta + \phi)$
$= 1000\tan(4^\circ 33' + 8^\circ 32')$
$= 232{\cdot}4\,\text{N}$

This force is applied at radius $= \dfrac{\text{pitch diameter}}{2}$

$= 10\,\text{mm}$

$\therefore$ Torque required $= 232{\cdot}4 \times 10\,\text{N mm}$
$= 2{\cdot}324\,\text{N m}$

Assuming no friction,

tangential load to lift 1000 N $= 1000\tan\theta$
$= 1000\tan 4^\circ 33'$
$= 79{\cdot}7\,\text{N}$

Ideal torque to move load $= 79{\cdot}7 \times 10\,\text{N mm}$
$= 0{\cdot}797\,\text{N m}$

$$\text{Efficiency} = \frac{\text{ideal effort}}{\text{actual effort}}$$

$$= \frac{0{\cdot}797}{2{\cdot}324}$$

$$= 0{\cdot}344 \text{ or } 34{\cdot}4\%$$

i.e. The torque is 2·324 N m and the efficiency 34·4%.

Example 11.5 A bevel-gear drive is used for lifting a sluice gate (fig.11.16). The gate, which has a weight of 30 kN, is subjected to a pressure of 275 kN/m² over a surface 2·4 m in diameter. The vertical screw spindle has a square thread of mean diameter 75 mm, and 25 mm pitch. The screw passes through a bush fixed to the spindle. The coefficient of friction between the sluice and the vertical facing on which it presses, and also between the screw and bush, is 0·1. The bevel wheel keyed to the spindle has forty teeth, and the driving pinion on the motor shaft has fifteen teeth. Determine the torque on the motor shaft required to raise the gate, neglecting all losses other than frictional at the thread and sluice facing.

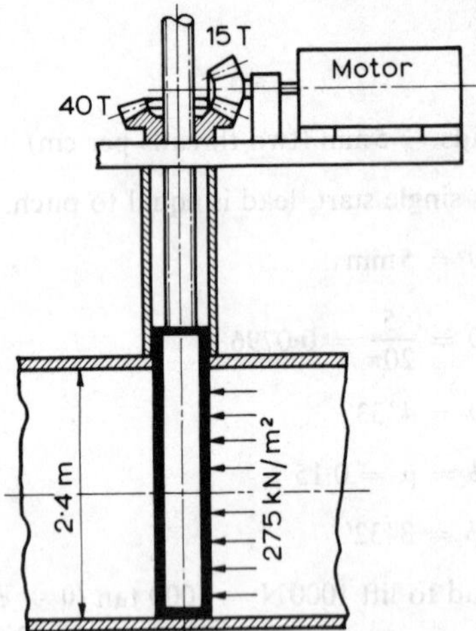

Fig.11.16

$$\text{Area of sluice subject to pressure} = \frac{\pi}{4} \times 2{\cdot}4^2$$

$$= 4{\cdot}5\,\text{m}^2$$

$$\text{Horizontal load on sluice gate} = \text{pressure} \times \text{area}$$
$$= 275 \times 10^3 \times 4{\cdot}5$$
$$= 1240 \times 10^3\,\text{N}$$

$$\text{Friction force at facing} = \mu \times \text{normal load}$$
$$= 0{\cdot}1 \times 1240 \times 10^3$$
$$= 124\,000\,\text{N}$$

$$\text{Weight of gate} = 30\,000\,\text{N}$$

$$\text{Total vertical force to lift gate} = 124\,000 + 30\,000$$
$$= 154\,000\,\text{N}$$

Screw-thread details:

$$\text{Angle of thread } \theta = \arctan \frac{\text{lead}}{\pi \times \text{mean diameter}}$$

$$= \arctan \frac{25}{75\pi}$$

$$\theta = 6°$$

$$\text{Angle of friction } \phi = \arctan \mu$$
$$= \arctan 0{\cdot}1$$
$$\phi = 5°43'$$

Tangential force at screw to overcome 154 000 N

$$= W \tan(\theta + \phi)$$
$$= 154\,000 \tan(6° + 5°43')$$
$$= 154\,000 \tan 11°43'$$
$$= 31\,900\,\text{N}$$

$$\text{Torque required} = \text{load} \times \text{radius}$$

$$= 31\,900 \times \frac{0{\cdot}075}{2}$$

$$= 1196\,\text{N m}$$

$$\text{Torque on motor shaft} = 1196 \times \frac{15}{40}$$

$$= 448\,\text{N m}$$

i.e. A motor shaft torque of 448 N m is required to raise the sluice gate.

Transmission of Power by Belt Drives

The belt drive relies upon frictional effects for its efficient operation. When the belt connecting two pulleys is stationary, the tensions in the two portions of the belt are equal. The actual tension in the belt at this stage can be adjusted by

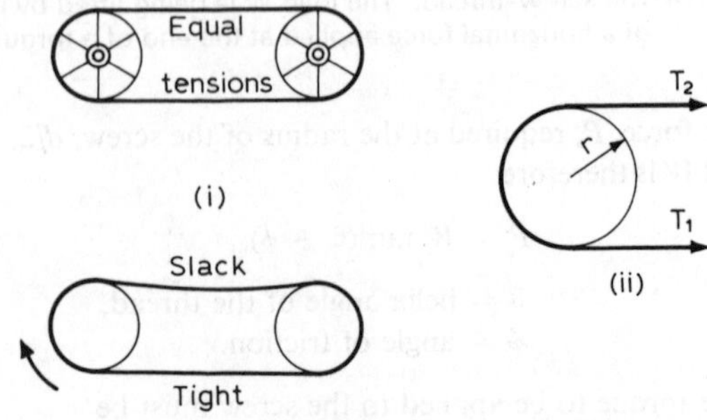

Fig.11.17 Belt drive. The essential characteristic of a belt drive transmitting power is that the tensions on the two sides of the pulley must be different. This is possible due to frictional forces between the pulley and the belt.

various belt-tightening devices. When a torque is applied to the driving pulley, one portion of the belt is stretched, and the other portion becomes slack, giving rise to the characteristic tight and slack sides of the belt drive [fig.11.17(i)]. This difference in tensions is essential for the transmission of the torque. It will be seen from fig.11.17(ii) that the torque transmitted by the pulley is $(T_1 - T_2)r$. Hence, the greater the difference between T_1 and T_2, the greater the torque transmitted by the pulley.

Now the change from T_1 to T_2 is gradual over the portion of the pulley which is in contact with the belt; and, in fact, is possible only as a result of friction between the belt and the pulley. Let us consider in some detail the changes in tension which take place from T_1 to T_2.

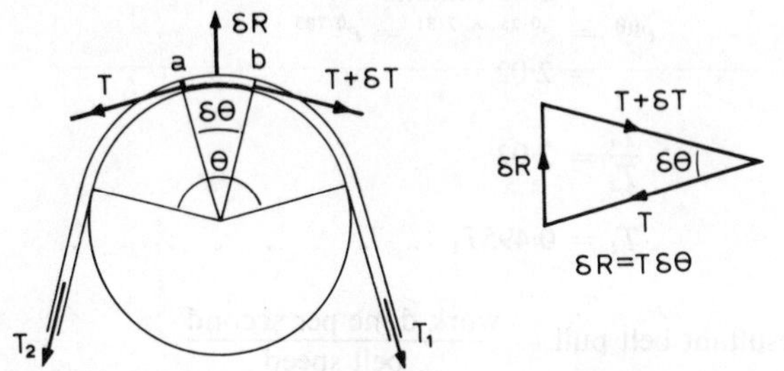

Fig.11.18 Fundamentals of power transmission by belt

Referring to fig.11.18, let T_1 = tension in tight side of belt,
T_2 = tension in slack side of belt,
μ = coefficient of friction, and
θ = angle of contact of belt with pulley.

Consider a small portion, *ab*, in contact with the pulley.

Let the tensions on either side of this portion be T and $T + \delta T$, and let the radial reaction of the pulley on this portion be δR. Now the difference between the two forces at either end of portion *ab* must be due to friction between the belt and the pulley. It follows from the work which we have already done on friction that the maximum value of δT before slipping takes place is

$$\delta T = \mu \delta R \quad . \quad . \quad . \quad . \quad . \quad . \quad (1)$$

From the triangle of forces in fig.11.18, which deals with the three forces acting on the portion *ab*, we see that, if angle $\delta\theta$, subtended by *ab* at the centre of the pulley, is small, we can write

$$\delta R = T\,\delta\theta \quad . \quad . \quad . \quad . \quad . \quad . \quad . \quad (2)$$

(arc = radius × angle in radians)

Note that T and $T + \delta T$ are considered to be nearly equal for small angles.

Substituting this value of δR into equation (1), we have

$$\delta T = \mu T \delta\theta$$

or
$$\frac{\delta T}{T} = \mu \delta\theta$$

As *ab* is made smaller, i.e. as $\delta\theta$ approaches 0, we can write the limiting expression

$$\frac{dT}{T} = \mu d\theta \quad . \quad . \quad . \quad . \quad . \quad . \quad . \quad (3)$$

Integrating both sides between the limits of $T = T_1$ when θ = max. angle θ, and $T = T_2$ when $\theta = 0$,

$$\int_{T_2}^{T_1} \frac{dT}{T} = \mu \int_0^{\theta} d\theta$$

$$\Big[\log_e T\Big]_{T_2}^{T_1} = \mu \Big[\theta\Big]_0^{\theta}$$

$$\log_e T_1 - \log_e T_2 = \mu(\theta - 0)$$

But
$$\log x - \log y = \log (x/y)$$

$$\therefore \log_e \frac{T_1}{T_2} = \mu\theta \quad . \quad . \quad . \quad . \quad . \quad . \quad (4)$$

or, in its more usual form, $\dfrac{T_1}{T_2} = e^{\mu\theta}$

(*Note.* θ is measured in radians.)

For use with common logarithms, equation (4) is sometimes written

$$\log \frac{T_1}{T_2} = 0{\cdot}434\mu\theta$$

Further work in the mechanics of machines will indicate that some slight modification has to be made to this expression when dealing with high-speed belts.

Power Developed by Belt Drive

The resultant driving force acting on the pulley is $T_1 - T_2$. If the belt speed is v m/s, then the work done per second is $(T_1 - T_2)v$ joules, and the power developed is

$$(T_1 - T_2)v \text{ watts} \quad . \quad . \quad . \quad . \quad . \quad (5)$$

But we have just established that

$$T_1/T_2 = e^{\mu\theta}$$

or
$$T_2 = T_1/e^{\mu\theta}$$

Substituting into equation (5), we have

$$\begin{aligned}\text{Power developed} &= (T_1 - T_1/e^{\mu\theta})v \\ &= T_1(1 - 1/e^{\mu\theta})v \\ &= T_1(1 - e^{-\mu\theta})v \text{ watts}\end{aligned}$$

Example 11.6 A belt pulley is 1·2 m in diameter, and rotates at 200 rev/min. The belt, which is 40 mm wide, makes an angle of contact of 150° over the pulley. If the coefficient of friction between the belt and the pulley is 0·3, and the maximum tension in the belt is 40 N/mm width, determine the power which can be transmitted by the belt.

Angle of contact = 150°

$$= \frac{150}{180} \times \pi$$

$$= 2{\cdot}62 \text{ radians}$$

Maximum tension in belt = 40 × 40

= 1600 N. This is T_1.

Tension in slack side, T_2, is given by

$$T_1/T_2 = e^{\mu\theta}$$

$$1600/T_2 = e^{0\cdot3 \times 2\cdot62} = e^{0\cdot786} = 2{\cdot}2$$

$$T_2 = \frac{1600}{2{\cdot}2} = 728\,\text{N}$$

Resultant driving force on pulley = 1600 − 728

= 872 N

Velocity of belt = rim velocity of pulley

= angular velocity of pulley × radius

$$= \frac{200}{60} \times 2\pi \times \frac{1{\cdot}2}{2}$$

$$= 12{\cdot}6\,\text{m/s}$$

Work done per second = force × velocity

= 872 × 12·6

= 11 000 J

i.e. Power transmitted by belt is 11 kW.

Example 11.7 A belt connects two pulleys, 1·2 m and 0·6 m in diameter respectively, and 1·8 m apart. Determine the minimum width of belt required to transmit 7·5 kW, when the belt speed is 12 m/s, and the coefficient of friction between the belt and pulley is 0·25. The maximum tension in the belt is limited to 14 N/mm width of belt. What will be the initial tension in the belts?

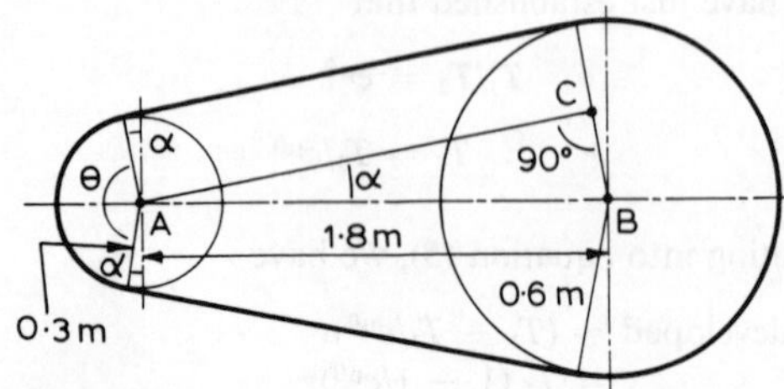

Fig.11.19

Since the angle of lap is a major consideration in determining the power capacity of a belt drive, it follows that the pulley with the smaller angle of lap will be the weak part of the drive. Hence all calculations are based on the smaller pulley.

Angle of lap for small pulley = 180 2α

Angle of lap for large pulley = 180 + 2α

From fig.11.19, it will be seen that

$$\sin\alpha = \frac{CB}{AB} = \frac{0{\cdot}3}{1{\cdot}8}$$

$$\alpha = 9°\,36'$$

Angle of lap, $\theta = 180° - 2 \times 9°\,36'$

$= 160°\,48'$

$= 2{\cdot}81$ radians

$$e^{\mu\theta} = e^{0\cdot25 \times 2\cdot81} = e^{0\cdot703}$$

$$= 2{\cdot}02$$

$$\therefore \frac{T_1}{T_2} = 2{\cdot}02$$

$$T_2 = 0{\cdot}495T_1 \quad \ldots \ldots \ldots \quad (1)$$

$$\text{Resultant belt pull} = \frac{\text{work done per second}}{\text{belt speed}}$$

$$= \frac{7500}{12} = 625\,\text{N}$$

Hence $T_1 - T_2 = 625$

Substituting from (1),

$$T_1 - 0{\cdot}495T_1 = 625$$

$$T_1 = 1240\,\text{N}$$

$$\text{Width of belt} = \frac{1240}{14} = 88{\cdot}5\,\text{mm (say 90 mm)}$$

$$T_2 = 0{\cdot}495 \times 1240 = 615\,\text{N}$$

$$\text{Initial tension in belt} = \frac{1240 + 615}{2}$$

$$= 927{\cdot}5\,\text{N}$$

As the drive commences, the tension in the tight side increases to 1240 N, whilst that in slack side drops to 615 N.

i.e. The minimum width of belt is 90 mm, and the initial belt tension must be 927·5 N.

Exercise 11

1 A block of wood of weight 250 N rests on a plane at 30° to the horizontal. A cord attached to the block, running parallel to the plane, and over a pulley, carries a weight W. If the force of friction opposing the motion is 45 N, what must be the value of W if it is to haul the block a distance of 3 m up the plane in 3 seconds from rest? Find also the tension in the cord. UEI

2 A body just begins to slide down a rough plane inclined at 25°. If the weight of the body is 50 N, find the horizontal force required to haul it up the plane with uniform speed. NCTEC

3 Find the magnitude and direction of the minimum pull required to haul a mass of weight 120 N up a rough plane inclined at 25° to the horizontal. Coefficient of friction 0·2. NCTEC

4 A box rests on a rough table, and is just about to slip when pulled by a string inclined at an angle α to the table. If the coefficient of friction is 0·25, find the tension in the string (a) when $\alpha = 45°$, (b) when $\alpha =$ angle of friction. NCTEC

5 A body of weight 500 N is prevented from sliding down a plane inclined at 20° to the horizontal by the application of a force of 50 N acting upwards and parallel to the plane. Find the coefficient of friction.

If the body is to be pulled up the plane by a force acting at an angle of 30° to the horizontal, find the value of the force, and the efficiency of the lift. IMECHE

6 A body weighing 100 N is drawn up an incline of 30° by the minimum force necessary, the angle of friction being 10°. Find the efficiency of the lift. IMECHE

7 Working from first principles, determine the turning moment necessary to lift a load of 20 kN by means of a vertical single-start screw having a mean thread diameter of 100 mm, and a square thread of 25 mm pitch. The coefficient of friction of the screw is 0·2. What is the efficiency of the screw while the load is being raised?

8 Determine the power which can be transmitted by a belt drive which passes around a pulley 1 m in diameter, making a 120° angle of contact, if the pulley speed is 300 rev/min, the coefficient of friction between the belt and the pulley is 0·4, and the maximum allowable tension in the belt is 445 N.

9 The tensions in the two sides of a belt drive are 500 N and 200 N. The belt pulley is 0·6 m in diameter, and rotates at 100 rev/min. Calculate the power transmitted by the belt drive.

10 (a) A flat belt drives a pulley 600 mm in diameter at 500 rev/min, and the maximum tension on the driving side is three times that on the slack side. Calculate the width of belt required if the drive transmits 20 kW, and the maximum allowable tension in the belt material is 15 N/mm of width.

(b) If the pulley is fixed to a 80 mm in diameter shaft by means of a key 12 mm wide and 80 mm long, calculate the shear stress in the key. NCTEC

11 A belt running on a pulley 300 mm in diameter transmits 350 watts when making 220 rev/min. Calculate the maximum tension in the belt if this is twice the effective tension. UEI

12 A shaft receives 4 kW from a belt driving a pulley 400 mm in diameter keyed to the shaft, the latter revolving at 180 rev/min. Find (a) the greatest tension in the belt, in N, assuming that the tension in the tight side is 2·5 times that in the slack side, and (b) the torque on the shaft, in Nm units. UEI

13 The relation between T_1, the tension on the tight side of a belt, and T_2, the tension on the slack side, is expressed by the formula

$$\log \frac{T_1}{T_2} = 0{\cdot}434\mu\theta$$

where μ is the coefficient of friction between the belt and the surface of the pulley, and θ is the angle (in radians) of lap of the belt on the pulley.

(a) Obtain the relationship between T_1 and T_2 when $\mu = 0{\cdot}3$, and $\theta = 3$ rad. (b) Calculate the power transmitted by a belt 200 mm wide at a linear speed of 5 m/s, the maximum tension in the belt not to exceed 3000 N. UEI

Chapter 12

Stress and Strain

Stress

When a material is subjected to the action of an external force (which infers that an equivalent force acts in the opposite direction, to maintain equilibrium), internal forces are set up in the material. These internal forces are known as *stresses.*

Intensity of Stress

This is defined as the force acting on unit area of cross-section. If every unit area of the section is taking the same load, then the stress is said to be uniform.

Intensity of stress (often abbreviated simply to stress) is expressed as load per unit area.

Types of Stress

There are three fundamental types of stress:

1 tensile stress,
2 compressive stress,
3 shear stress.

Conditions giving rise to these stresses are illustrated in fig. 12.1.

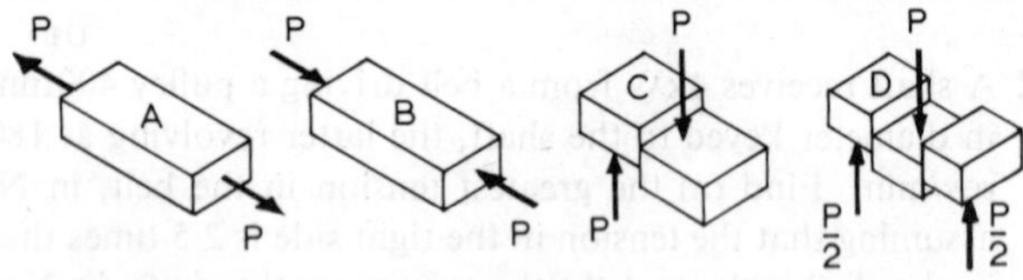

Fig.12.1 The three simple stresses: A is in tension, B is in compression, C and D are in shear.

Tensile stresses (bar A) are produced by forces trying to pull the material apart. The stresses are set up in plane sections of the bar perpendicular to the direction of the force.

Compressive stresses (bar B) are produced by forces trying to compress the bar. Again, these stresses are set up in plane sections of the bar perpendicular to the direction of the force.

Shear stresses (bar C) are produced by equal and opposite parallel forces not in line. The forces tend to make one part of the material slide over the other part. This is the essential characteristic of the shear stress. The stresses are set up on plane sections parallel to the direction of the applied force.

The magnitude of the stress intensity is given as load/area in all cases.

If the design is such that two surfaces are resisting the shearing of the material, then the material is said to be in *double shear*. The pin in the simple coupling joint in fig.12.2 is in double shear. It would tend to fail across two sections.

The intensity of shear stress in this case would be

$$\frac{\text{load}}{2 \times \text{area of cross-section}}$$

In the case of the tensile and compressive stresses, it should be emphasised that the axis of the applied load should coincide with the geometrical axis of the bar of material, otherwise complications will arise due to the bending of the bar. This aspect is dealt with under the heading of 'Direct and bending stresses' in Chapter 15.

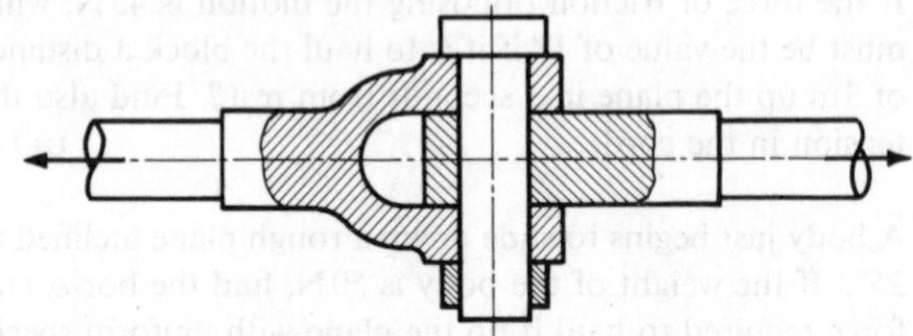

Fig.12.2 Simple coupling for rods. The pin which holds the two rods together is subjected to double shear when the rods are loaded as shown.

Strain

When the load is applied to the material, not only are stresses produced, but there also follows a change of shape of the material. Lengths are increased or decreased. Cross-sections are deformed. This alteration of shape is known as *strain.* There is a type of strain corresponding to each type of stress (fig.12.3).

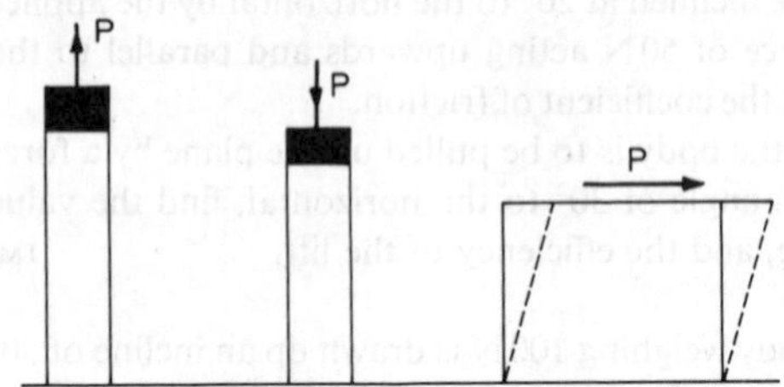

Fig.12.3 The three simple strains. The bar on the left increases its length, being subject to tensile strains. The bar in the centre decreases its length, being subject to compressive strains. The bar on the right is deformed, being subjected to shear strains.

Tensile and Compressive Strain, ε (epsilon)

Let l = original length of the bar,
$l + \delta l$ = length of bar after loading,
δl = extension (negative in case of compression).

$$\text{Strain} = \frac{\text{change in length}}{\text{original length}} = \frac{\delta l}{l}$$

Strain is the ratio of two lengths, and therefore has no dimensions, and therefore no units. It is expressed merely as a number.

Shear Strain, γ (gamma)

A load W applied to the top surface of a rubber block will cause it to deflect as shown in fig.12.4. Immediately W is applied, there is an equal and opposite reaction W at the base

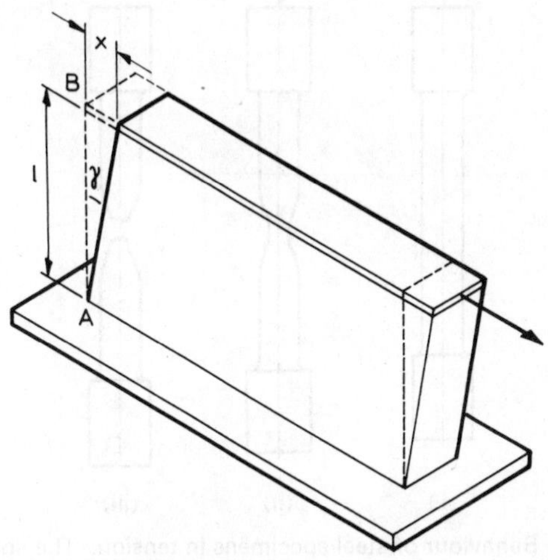

Fig.12.4 Shear strain. The angle γ is a measure of the shear strain.

of the block. These two forces provide the conditions necessary for shear stresses to be established in the material. The distortion of the block is x in a length l.

$$\text{Shear strain} = \frac{x}{AB} = \frac{x}{l} = \gamma \text{ radians}$$

Hence shear strain is a measure of angular displacement of edge AB.

Elasticity

A material is said to be *perfectly elastic* when the strain due to loading disappears when the load is moved, or, alternatively, when the strain at a given load when unloading is equal to the strain at the same load during loading.

Hooke's Law

This fundamental law states that *within the elastic range, the strain (or deformation) produced is directly proportional to the stress producing it*. This law refers to all kinds of stresses.

Tensile and Compressive Stress, σ (sigma)

Stress is proportional to strain, or

$$\text{stress} = \text{constant} \times \text{strain}$$

This constant is known as the *modulus of elasticity*, or *Young's modulus*, and is usually indicated by E.

Let W = applied load (tensile or compressive), in newtons;
a = cross-sectional area, in square metres;
l = length, in metres;
x = extension, in metres;
E = modulus of elasticity, in newtons/square metre.

$$\text{Stress, } \sigma = \frac{W}{a} \text{ N/m}^2$$

$$\text{Strain} = \frac{x}{l} \text{ (note that strain has no units)}$$

$$E = \frac{\text{stress}}{\text{strain}} = \frac{W/a}{x/l}$$

$$\text{i.e. } E = \frac{Wl}{ax} \text{ N/m}^2$$

Shear Stress, τ (tau)

Shear stress is proportional to shear strain:

$$\text{stress} = \text{constant} \times \text{strain}$$

This constant is known as the *modulus of rigidity*, and is indicated by G.

Let τ = shear stress, in newtons/square metre;
γ = shear strain;
G = modulus of rigidity, in newtons/square metre.

Then stress = $G \times$ strain

$$G = \frac{\text{stress}}{\text{strain}} = \frac{\tau}{\gamma}$$

TABLE 2

AVERAGE VALUES OF ELASTIC CONSTANTS E AND G

Material	*Modulus of elasticity* (N/mm^2)	*Modulus of rigidity* (N/mm^2)
steel .	207×10^3	83×10^3
copper . .	83×10^3	39×10^3
brass	69×10^3	37×10^3
wood	$9{\cdot}6 \times 10^3$	$0{\cdot}55 \times 10^3$

Mechanical Properties of Materials

Plasticity. A material is perfectly plastic if no strain disappears when it is relieved of stress. Under very high stresses, a solid will 'flow' in much the same way as a liquid flows. This property is made use of in the squirting of lead pipe, in the pressing of coins, and in forging operations.

Ductility. This refers to that property of the material which allows it to be drawn out by tension to a reduced section, as in wire-drawing. During the wire-drawing process, the material shows a certain degree of elasticity, together with a considerable amount of plasticity.

Brittleness. Lack of ductility.

Malleability. When a material can be beaten or rolled into thin sheets, it is said to be malleable, e.g. gold beaten into leaves.

Tensile Strain of Ductile Materials

Let us analyse the changes which take place when a ductile material is subjected to stresses. For the purpose of this particular analysis, we will think of tensile stresses, although many of the changes indicated will be common to all types of stresses. The variation of stress and strain throughout extension can be plotted on a stress-strain diagram similar to the one shown in fig.12.5.

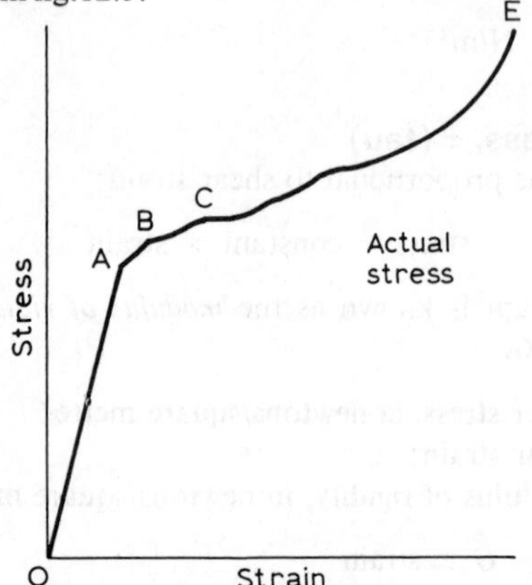

Fig.12.5 Stress-strain diagram for mild steel. The actual stress is plotted against the strain. A is the limit of proportionality. B is the elastic limit, after which the material is no longer elastic. C is the yield point, at which a considerable increase of strain takes place without increase of load. E is the breaking-point.

When the load is applied to the specimen, there is an increase in the stresses set up in the material. These stresses produce corresponding strains within the material. Experimental observations show that, up to the *elastic limit*, the stress is proportional to the strain, and the stress-strain graph consists of a straight line. This portion of the extension is known as the *elastic* extension. After the elastic limit is passed, straining increases more rapidly. Just above the elastic limit, some metals (more particularly soft irons, and low carbon steels) show considerable increase in strain without an appreciable increase in stress. The stress at which the sudden change takes place is known as the *yield point*. Beyond the yield point, stress is no longer directly proportional to the strain. The relationship between stress and strain for ductile extensions depends upon the rate of loading. Just before the greatest load is reached, the material becomes almost perfectly plastic.

During the ductile extension, the area of the cross-section decreases in practically the same proportion as the length increases; in other words, the volume of the specimen remains practically constant. The reduction in area of the cross-section is fairly uniform along the specimen. When the maximum load is reached, a local stretching takes place, and a neck or waist is formed. The local reduction which takes place is such that the loading necessary to break the bar at the neck will be much smaller than the maximum load on the bar before the neck was formed. However, the actual stress at the breaking point is greater than it was before the neck was formed, because of the reduced area of cross-section. The curve shown in fig.12.7 has been obtained by dividing the load by the original cross-sectional area of the specimen. For this reason, some of the later stresses are referred to as *nominal stresses* rather than actual stresses.

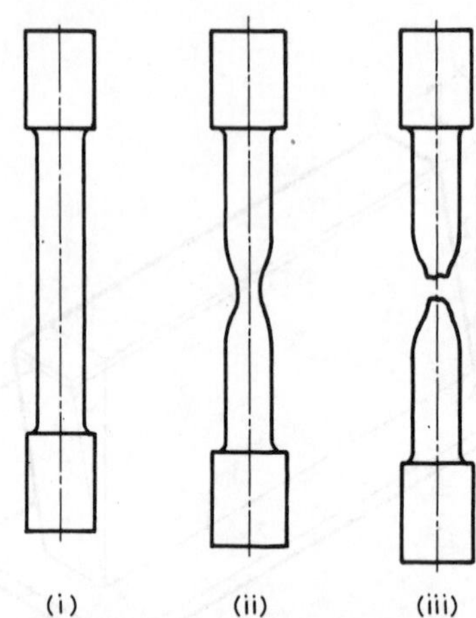

Fig.12.6 Behaviour of steel specimens in tension. The specimen, approximately 200 mm long and 11·28 mm diameter, is subjected to an axial pull. As the load increases, the specimen increases in length, and a 'waist' forms as shown at (ii). This reduction in cross-sectional area is followed by a reduction in the load, but an increase in the actual stress value. Finally, the specimen fractures as shown in (iii).

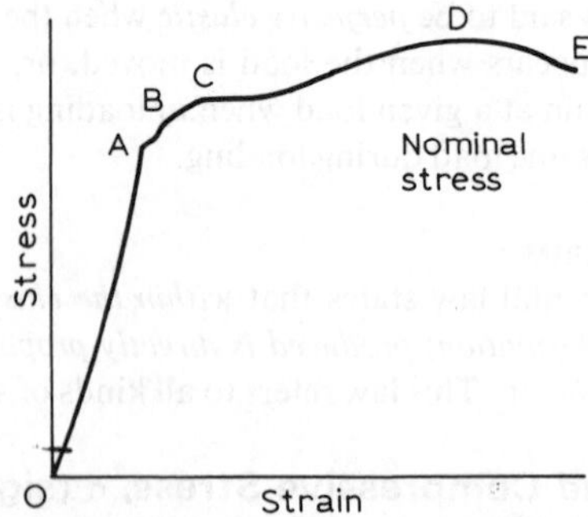

Fig.12.7 Stress-strain diagram for mild steel. This is a nominal-stress diagram, in which the value of the stress is determined by dividing the load by the original cross-sectional area of the specimen. A, B, and C have the same significance as in fig. 12.5. D represents the stress corresponding to the maximum load carried by the specimen. After point D has been passed, the cross-sectional area becomes noticeably smaller, with the result that an increase in stress can be obtained with a reduction of the load. Hence the actual breaking load at E will be less than at D, although the actual stress at E will be greater than that at D.

For wrought iron and steel, the proportionality holds good up to the elastic limit. The elastic limit in tension is the greatest stress to which a material may be subjected without permanent elongation after the stress is removed. The elastic limit cannot always be found from inspection of a stress-strain diagram; e.g. in the case of rolled aluminium, the strain increases faster than the stress, but if the load is removed the strain also disappears. In commercial tests of metals in which definite yield takes place, the yield point is taken as the commercial elastic limit.

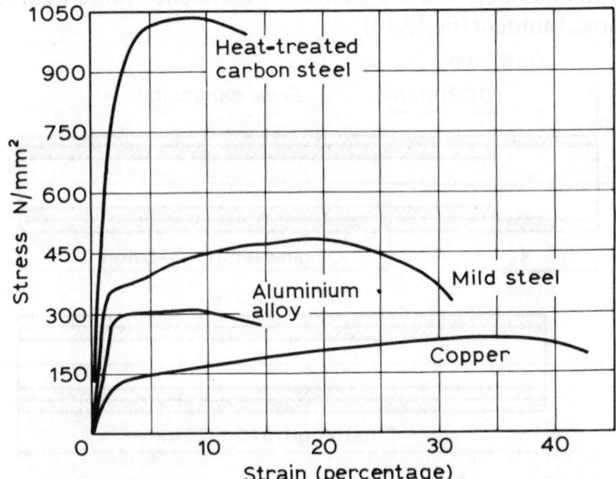

Fig.12.8 Stress-strain diagrams for various materials

Tensile Strength

$$\text{Tensile strength} = \frac{\text{maximum load}}{\text{original area of section}}$$

The tensile strength (formerly known as the ultimate tensile strength or UTS) is of importance in the design of machines and structures. The various parts must not be stressed beyond the allowable working stress, and this must be below the elastic limit for the material. The designer will then ensure that the part remains elastic, i.e. that it returns to its original dimensions on removal of the stress.

Factor of Safety

The load which any member of a machine carries is called the working load, and the stress produced by this load is the 'working' or 'allowable' stress. Obviously the working load must be less than the ultimate breaking load of the member, i.e. the working stress must be less than the tensile strength. It is usual to divide the tensile strength by a suitable factor of safety to get the allowable safe working stress; for example, the tensile strength of a material may be 480 N/mm², or 480 MN/m², but the designer may design the machine so that the maximum stress in the material does not exceed 80 N/mm², or 80 MN/m². There is thus a considerable margin of safety. The stresses and strains to which the bar is subjected should be well within the elastic limit.

$$\text{Factor of safety} = \frac{\text{tensile strength}}{\text{allowable working stress}}$$

The following points affect the factor of safety:

1 the value of the maximum load, and the certainty with which it can be determined beforehand;
2 the nature of the load: whether it is gradually applied or suddenly applied; whether it is a single application (known as 'dead' load), or repeated a number of times per minute (known as 'live' load); whether it is acting in one direction or suddenly reversing direction, i.e. producing alternately tensile and compressive stress in the material;
3 the reliability of the material, and the certainty with which its strength can be stated;
4 The effect of corrosion or wear on the dimensions of the part;
5 Possible errors of workmanship in the manufacture of the component;
6 The consequences of a breakdown.

The value of the factor of safety varies between 3 in the case of steel carrying a dead load, to 20 in the case of timber carrying a shock or suddenly applied load.

Example 12.1 The following observations were taken for the load and extension during a test of a bar of length 250 mm and diameter 22·5 mm.

Load, kN . . .	0	30	60	90	100	105
Extension, mm .	0	0·094	0·19	0·284	0·317	0·333

Load, kN . . .	110	115	118	119	120
Extension, mm .	0·356	0·419	0·53	0·89	1·75

Using the graph, estimate Young's modulus, the elastic limit, and the yield stress. Calculate also the strain energy stored up to the elastic limit. NCTEC

The graph is indicated in fig.12·9.

$$\text{Area of bar} = \frac{\pi}{4} \times 22{\cdot}6^2 = 400\,\text{mm}^2$$

1 Young's modulus

Stress is proportional to strain up to a load of 105 kN, with a corresponding extension of 0·333 mm, which is the elastic limit of the material.

$$\text{Stress at this point} = \frac{\text{load}}{\text{area}} = \frac{105 \times 10^3}{400}$$

$$= 262\,\text{N/mm}^2$$

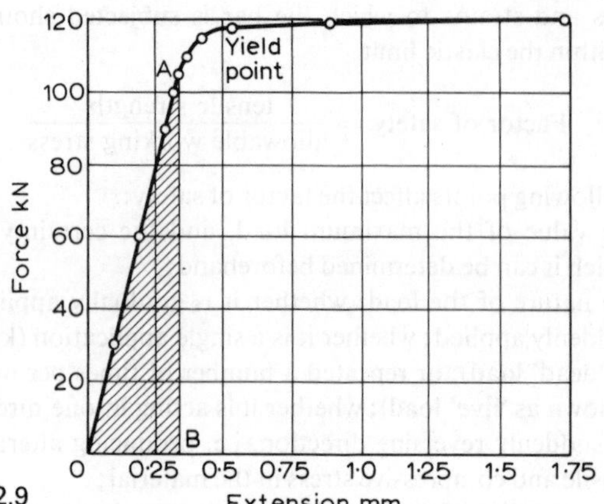

Fig.12.9

$$\text{Strain} = \frac{\text{extension}}{\text{original length}} = \frac{0{\cdot}333}{250}$$

$$= 0{\cdot}001\,33$$

$$\text{Young's modulus, } E = \frac{\text{stress}}{\text{strain}} = \frac{262}{0{\cdot}001\,33}$$

$$= 197 \times 10^3\,\text{N/mm}^2$$

2 Elastic-limit stress = 262 N/mm², as above.

3 Yield-point stress
The yield occurs at 117 kN

$$\text{Yield-point stress} = \frac{117 \times 10^3}{400} = 293\,\text{N/mm}^2$$

4 Strain energy stored up to elastic limit (see page 129)
This is equal to the shaded area shown.

$$\text{Strain energy} = \tfrac{1}{2} \times OB \times BA$$
$$= \tfrac{1}{2} \times 0{\cdot}333 \times 105 \times 10^3$$
$$= 17{\cdot}5 \times 10^3\,\text{N mm, or } 17{\cdot}5\,\text{N m, or } 17{\cdot}5\,\text{joules}$$

i.e. Young's modulus is 197 × 10³ N/mm², the elastic limit stress is 262 N/mm², the yield stress is 293 N/mm², and the strain energy stored up to the elastic limit is 17·5 joules.

Example 12.2 Two tubes, one of copper and one of steel, are of equal length, and rigidly connected together at their ends, so that under all conditions they are of equal length.

The copper tube has internal and external diameters of 100 and 125 mm respectively, whilst the internal and external diameters of the steel tube are 75 and 100 mm respectively. If the original length of the tubes was 375 mm, calculate the stresses set up in them when there is a temperature rise of 22°C.

What is the final length of the tubes?

[$E_{steel} = 207 \times 10^3\,\text{N/mm}^2$, $E_{copper} = 110 \times 10^3\,\text{N/mm}^2$.
Coefficients of expansion per degree Celsius—steel 0·000 012, copper 0·000 019.] UEI

Extension (free) = original length × coefficient of expansion × temperature rise.

If the copper were free, it would extend

$$375 \times 0{\cdot}000\,019 \times 22 = 0{\cdot}157\,\text{mm}$$

If the steel were free, it would extend

$$375 \times 0{\cdot}000\,012 \times 22 = 0{\cdot}099\,\text{mm}$$

Difference in extension = 0·058 mm

Under the constrained condition, the copper will not extend its full amount, and the steel will be stretched more than its normal amount (fig.12.10).

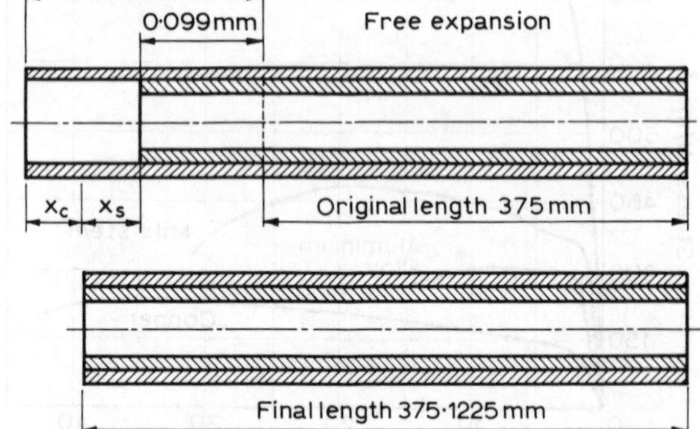

Fig.12.10

Let x_s = extension of steel
x_c = contraction of copper } mm from normal condition

Then $\quad x_s + x_c = 0{\cdot}058 \quad \ldots \quad (1)$

Now $\quad$ strain in copper $= \dfrac{x_c}{375}$

strain in steel $= \dfrac{x_s}{375}$

Note that we have neglected the fact that there has been a slight increase in the length of the tubes. The strains should be $x_c/375{\cdot}157$ and $x_s/375{\cdot}099$. This neglect will not affect the accuracy of the solution.

$$\text{Tensile stress in steel} = \text{strain} \times E_s$$
$$= \frac{x_s}{375} \times 207 \times 10^3$$
$$= 0{\cdot}55 \times 10^3\,x_s\,\text{N/mm}^2$$

$$\text{Tensile load in steel} = \text{stress} \times \text{area}$$
$$= 0{\cdot}55 \times 10^3\,x_s \times \frac{\pi}{4}(100^2 - 75^2)$$
$$= 1{\cdot}89 \times 10^6\,x_s\,\text{N}$$

Compressive stress in copper $=$ strain $\times E_s$

$$= \frac{x_c}{375} \times 110 \times 10^3$$

$$= 0{\cdot}294 \times 10^3\, x_c\,\mathrm{N/mm^2}$$

Compressive load in copper $=$ stress $\times$ area

$$= 0{\cdot}294 \times 10^3\, x_c \times \frac{\pi}{4}(125^2 - 100^2)$$

$$= 1{\cdot}30 \times 10^6\, x_c\,\mathrm{N}$$

But tensile load in steel $=$ compressive load in copper

$$1{\cdot}89 \times 10^6\, x_s = 1{\cdot}3 \times 10^6\, x_c$$

$$x_s = 0{\cdot}686 x_c$$

Substituting in equation (1),

$$0{\cdot}686 x_c + x_c = 0{\cdot}058$$

$$x_c = 0{\cdot}0344$$

$$x_s = 0{\cdot}0235$$

Tensile stress in steel $= 0{\cdot}55 \times 10^3 \times 0{\cdot}0235$

$$= 13\,\mathrm{N/mm^2}$$

Compressive stress in copper $= 0{\cdot}294 \times 10^3 \times 0{\cdot}0344$

$$= 10{\cdot}1\,\mathrm{N/mm^2}$$

i.e. The tensile stress in the steel tube is 13 N/mm², and the compressive stress in the copper is 10·1 N/mm².

The student should note the fundamental difference between this problem, where the loads are equal, and example 12.3, where the strains are equal.

Strain Energy and Resilience

When a spring is stretched, work has to be done; and this work is stored in the spring as strain energy. If the spring is released, it will give up most of this energy stored in it. This principle is used in many cases where the spring is held in a compressed condition by a trigger, and is then released to give a high velocity to a striker.

In precisely the same way, strain energy is stored within a metal bar subjected to strain. Figure 12.11 shows a load-extension graph for a loaded bar. The area under the graph represents the work which has been done in straining the bar, and consequently represents the strain energy stored in the bar.

Let $a =$ cross-sectional area of bar,
$l =$ length of bar,
$V =$ volume of bar $= al$,
$W =$ applied load,
$x =$ extension produced by load,
$\sigma =$ maximum stress in the bar.

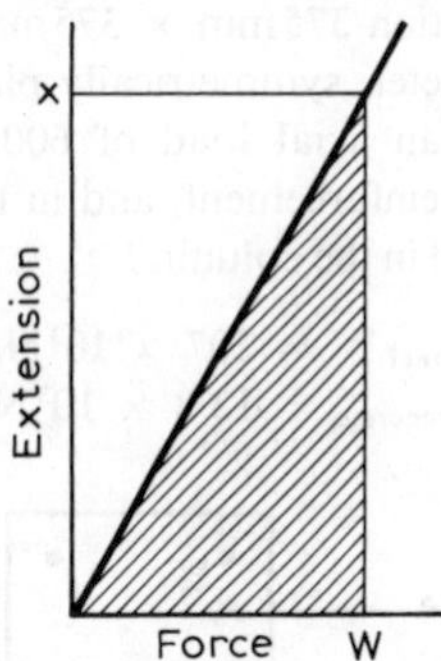

Fig.12.11 Strain energy. The shaded area of the diagram represents the work done in straining a solid or spring. This work is stored in the spring as strain energy, and, provided that the elastic limit has not been exceeded, most of the energy will be given up when the spring is released.

Strain energy $=$ work done by load increasing from 0 to WN

$$= \text{average load} \times \text{distance}$$

$$= \tfrac{1}{2} W.x$$

$$= \tfrac{1}{2}\sigma.a.x \qquad (1)$$

But $\quad x = l \times \text{strain}$

$$x = l \times \frac{\text{stress}}{E}$$

$$x = l \times \frac{\sigma}{E}$$

From (1) we get

strain energy $= \tfrac{1}{2}\sigma a x$

$$= \tfrac{1}{2}\sigma a.\frac{l}{E}$$

$$= \tfrac{1}{2}\sigma^2\frac{la}{E}$$

$$= \frac{\tfrac{1}{2}\sigma^2}{E} \times \text{volume of bar}$$

Strain energy per unit volume of bar

$$= \frac{\tfrac{1}{2}\sigma^2}{E}$$

The amount of strain energy stored in a body is referred to as the *resilience* of the body. It gives some indication of the ability of the body to return to its unstrained condition. The *proof resilience* of a body is the greatest amount of strain energy which can be stored in a body without permanent set taking place; this implies that the body would have to be loaded up to the elastic limit.

Example 12.3 A reinforced-concrete column is 3 m high, and of uniform cross-section 375 mm × 375 mm. It is reinforced by four 25 mm diameter, symmetrically placed steel rods. If the column carries an axial load of 600 kN, determine the stresses in the steel reinforcement, and in the concrete. How much energy is stored in the column?

$$E_{steel} = 207 \times 10^3 \text{ N/mm}^2$$
$$E_{concrete} = 13{\cdot}8 \times 10^3 \text{ N/mm}^2$$

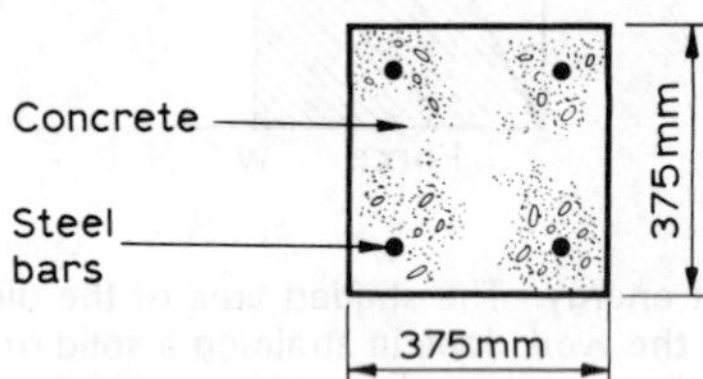

Fig.12.12

$$\text{Total cross-sectional area of rods} = 4 \times \frac{\pi}{4} \times 25^2 = 1960 \text{ mm}^2$$

$$\text{Total cross-sectional area of concrete} = (375 \times 375) - 1960 = 139\,000 \text{ mm}^2$$

Let W_s = load carried by steel, in newtons;

W_c = load carried by concrete, in newtons.

$$\text{Then } W_s + W_c = 600 \times 10^3 \quad (1)$$

$$\text{Stress in steel} = \frac{W_s}{1960} \text{ N/mm}^2$$

$$\text{Stress in concrete} = \frac{W_c}{139 \times 10^3} \text{ N/mm}^2$$

Now $\quad \text{strain} = \dfrac{\text{stress}}{E}$

and the strain of both concrete and steel will be equal, since the compression of the steel is equal to the compression of the concrete.

$$\text{Strain of steel} = \frac{W_s}{1960 \times 207 \times 10^3}$$

$$\text{Strain of concrete} = \frac{W_c}{139 \times 10^3 \times 13{\cdot}8 \times 10^3}$$

$$= \frac{(600 \times 10^3) - W_s}{139 \times 10^3 \times 13{\cdot}8 \times 10^3}$$

from equation (1)

$$\frac{W_s}{1960 \times 207 \times 10^3} = \frac{(600 \times 10^3) - W_s}{139 \times 10^3 \times 13{\cdot}8 \times 10^3}$$

$$W_s = 105 \text{ kN}$$
$$W_c = 600 - 105 = 495 \text{ kN}$$

$$\text{Stress in steel} = \frac{105 \times 10^3}{1960} = 53{\cdot}6 \text{ N/mm}^2$$

$$\text{Stress in concrete} = \frac{495 \times 10^3}{139\,000} = 3{\cdot}56 \text{ N/mm}^2$$

$$\text{Deflection of column under load} = \text{strain} \times l$$

$$= \frac{\text{stress}}{E} \times l$$

$$= \frac{53{\cdot}6 \times 3 \text{ m} \times 10^3}{207 \times 10^3}$$

$$= 0{\cdot}77 \text{ mm}$$

$$\text{Energy stored in column} = \text{work done in compression}$$
$$= \tfrac{1}{2} \times 600 \times 10^3 \times 0{\cdot}77 \times 10^{-3}$$
$$= 231 \text{ J (or N m)}$$

i.e. Stress in steel = 53·6 N/mm², stress in concrete = 3·56 N/mm², and energy stored in column = 231 J.

Example 12.4 A rod of material for which Young's modulus is E has a cross-sectional area a and a length l. Obtain an expression for the strain energy stored in it when elastically stressed by a gradually applied direct load P.

A bolt 500 mm long has a diameter of 125 mm for one half of its length, and of 112·5 mm for the other half. It may, on occasion, be subjected to a maximum tensile force of 1 MN. Determine the total extension of the bolt, and the strain energy in each part. Young's modulus—200 × 10³ N/mm².

IMECHE

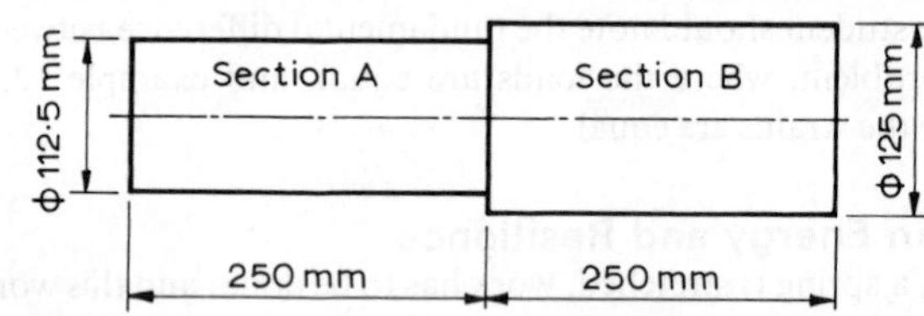

Fig.12.13

Each part of the bolt carries a load of 10^6 N.

Section A.

$$\text{Area of cross-section} = \frac{\pi}{4} \times 112{\cdot}5^2 = 9950 \text{ mm}^2$$

$$\text{Stress in section} = \frac{10^6}{9950} = 100{\cdot}5 \text{ N/mm}^2$$

$$\text{Strain} = \frac{\text{stress}}{E} = \frac{100{\cdot}5}{200 \times 10^3}$$

$$= 0{\cdot}000\,502$$

$$\text{Extension} = \text{strain} \times \text{length}$$

$$= 0{\cdot}000\,502 \times 0{\cdot}25 = 0{\cdot}000\,125\,5 \text{ m}$$

Section B.

Area of cross-section $= \frac{\pi}{4} \times 125^2 = 12\,300\,\text{mm}^2$

Stress in section $= \frac{10^6}{12\,300} = 81{\cdot}3\,\text{N/mm}^2$

Strain $= \frac{\text{stress}}{E} = \frac{81{\cdot}3}{200 \times 10^3}$

$= 0{\cdot}000\,407$

Extension = strain × length

$= 0{\cdot}000\,407 \times 0{\cdot}25 = 0{\cdot}000\,102\,\text{m}$

Total extension $= 0{\cdot}000\,102 + 0{\cdot}000\,125\,5$
$= 0{\cdot}000\,227\,5\,\text{m}$

Strain energy in A $= \frac{1}{2} \times \text{load} \times \text{extension}$
$= \frac{1}{2} \times 10^6 \times 0{\cdot}000\,125\,5$
$= 62{\cdot}7\,\text{J}$

Strain energy in B $= \frac{1}{2} \times \text{load} \times \text{extension}$
$= \frac{1}{2} \times 10^6 \times 0{\cdot}000\,102$
$= 51\,\text{J}$

Alternative solution for strain energy

Strain energy $= \frac{\frac{1}{2}\sigma^2}{E} \times \text{volume}$

For section A, $\sigma = 100{\cdot}5\,\text{N/mm}^2$

Volume $= 9950 \times 250\,\text{mm}^3$

Strain energy $= \frac{1}{2} \times \frac{100{\cdot}5^2 \times 9950 \times 250}{200 \times 10^3}$

$= 62\,700\,\text{N\,mm}$

$= 62{\cdot}7\,\text{J}$ (or N m)

Similarly for Section B.

i.e. The total extension is 0·228 mm, and the strain energy is 62·7 J in A, and 51 J in B.

Stress Due to Falling Weight—Shock Load

Figure 12.14 indicates a bar of metal firmly supported at one end, and carrying a load in the form of a ring. The ring is prevented from falling off the bar by means of a collar rigidly fastened to the bar. If the weight is raised through a height h, and then allowed to fall onto the collar, it will produce the effect of a shock load on the bar. The tensile stresses set up within the bar will be greater than would be the case if the load were gradually applied. In fact, the bar may be quite strong enough to support the steady weight of the ring, but may break if the weight is suddenly applied. We can determine the magnitude of the stresses set up in the bar if we equate the potential energy which the weight has before it is released to the maximum strain energy stored in the bar after the impact.

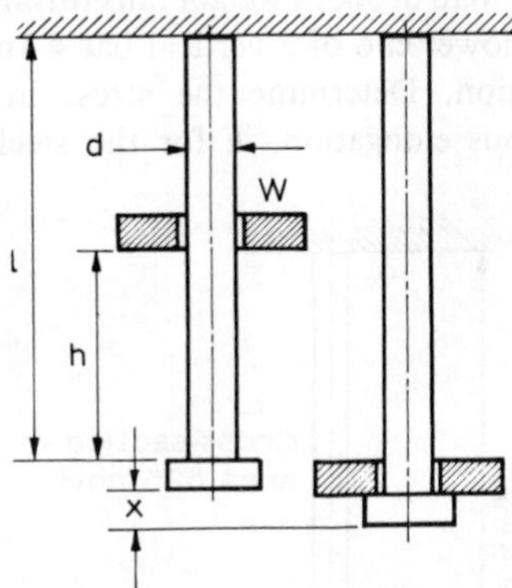

Fig.12.14 Stress due to falling weight. Shock loads are particularly important in engineering design. The diagram shows one of the simplest cases of shock loading.

Let W = weight of ring, in newtons;
A = cross-section area of bar, in square metres;
l = length of bar, in metres;
x = extension produced by load, in metres;
E = Young's modulus of elasticity, in newtons per square metre;
σ = instantaneous stress produced on impact, in newtons per square metre.

Since the weight falls through a total distance $(h + x)$, its potential energy will be $W(h + x)$ joules.

The strain energy stored in the bar when the stress is σ is given by

$$\text{strain energy} = \tfrac{1}{2}\frac{\sigma^2}{E} \times \text{volume of bar}$$

$$= \tfrac{1}{2}\frac{\sigma^2}{E}.Al$$

Equating these two energies, we get

$$\tfrac{1}{2}\frac{\sigma^2}{E}Al = W(h + x)$$

$$\sigma^2 = \frac{2WE(h + x)}{Al}$$

$$\sigma = \sqrt{\frac{2WE(h + x)}{Al}}$$

There are some occasions when the value of x is very small compared with the height, h, through which the load has fallen. In these cases, x can be neglected.

$$\text{Stress produced by falling load (neglecting } x) = \sqrt{\frac{2WEh}{Al}}$$

Example 12.5 A load of 500 N weight falls through 20 mm on to the stop at the lower end of a vertical bar 4·5 m long and 625 mm^2 cross-section. Determine the stress in the bar, and the instantaneous elongation. E for the steel bar = $200 \times 10^3 \text{ N/mm}^2$.

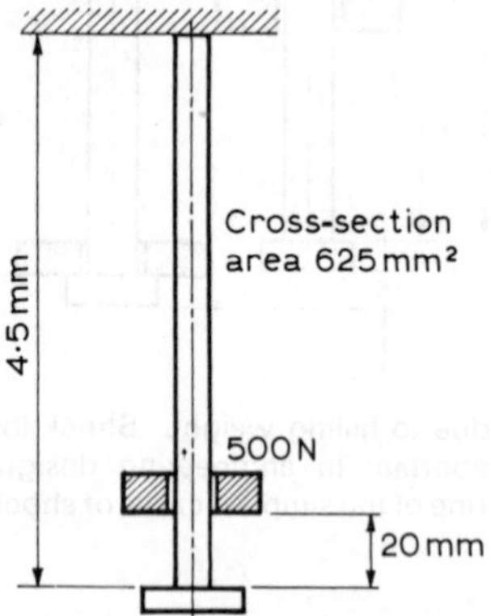

Fig.12.15

Let x metres = the instantaneous elongation produced.

$$\begin{aligned}\text{Potential energy stored in load} &= 500(0{\cdot}020 + x)\text{J}\\ &= \tfrac{1}{2}\text{ load} \times \text{extension}\\ &= \tfrac{1}{2}\text{ stress} \times \text{area} \times \text{extension}\\ &= \tfrac{1}{2}\text{ strain} \times E \times \text{area} \times \text{extension}\\ &= \tfrac{1}{2}\frac{x}{4{\cdot}5} \times 200 \times 10^3 \times 10^6 \times 625 \times 10^{-6} \times x\end{aligned}$$

Equating potential energy to work done,

$$500(0{\cdot}02 + x) = \frac{200 \times 625 \times 10^3 x^2}{2 \times 4{\cdot}5}$$

$$x^2 - 0{\cdot}000\,036x - 0{\cdot}000\,000\,72 = 0$$

$$x = 0{\cdot}000\,87\text{ m}$$
$$\text{or } 0{\cdot}87\text{ mm}$$

$$\text{Stress produced} = \text{strain} \times E$$

$$= \frac{0{\cdot}000\,87}{4{\cdot}5} \times 200 \times 10^3$$

$$= 38{\cdot}7\text{ N/mm}^2$$

i.e. The stress produced in the bar will be 38·7 N/mm², and the elongation 0·87 mm.

Projected Area

Figure 12.16 shows a closed D-shaped vessel which contains a gas under pressure p N/m². The radius of the curved portion can be taken as r metres, and the length of the vessel as h metres. It will be seen that the pressure of the gas in the curved portion of the vessel is at all times normal to (or at

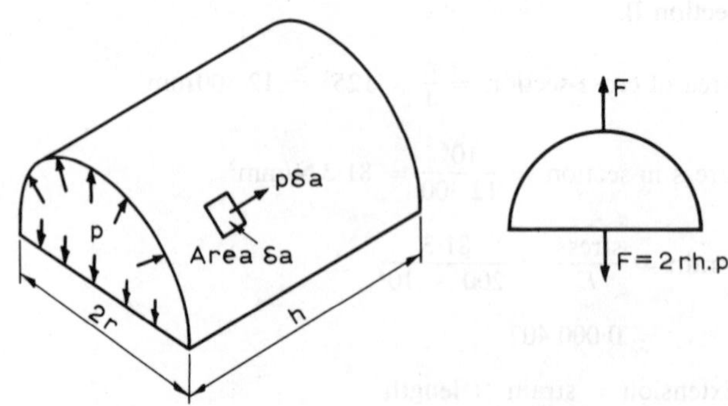

Fig.12.16 Projected area. Upward force on curved portion must equal downward force on plane portion.

right angles to) the curve at all points in fig.12.16. Consequently, the resultant upward force on the vessel can be considered as made up of a number of small forces, each acting normally to the curve and being of magnitude $p\delta a$, where δa is the elementary area of the curved surface. By resolving these forces in the upwards direction, and integrating, it would be possible to obtain the resultant upwards force. But this method may be inconvenient in certain circumstances, and in any case it would never be as convenient as the method which uses the idea of 'projected area'.

The vessel is in equilibrium under the action of the resultant upward force and the resultant downward force. In other words, the resultant upward force must be equal in magnitude to the resultant downward force. This latter force is quite easy to obtain; it is simply the product of the pressure of the gas and the area of the rectangular base, i.e. $p.2rh$. The $2rh$ is the projection into the horizontal plane of the curved surface area. Consequently, we can write

upward force = pressure × projected area of curved surface into plane perpendicular to direction of force.

Example 12.6 A closed cylinder, 1·2 m in diameter and 1·8 m long, is filled with a gas at a pressure of 140 kN/m². What is the force tending to tear the cylinder along a longitudinal section?

The horizontal projected area is $1{\cdot}2 \times 1{\cdot}8 = 2{\cdot}16\text{ m}^2$

$$\begin{aligned}\text{Force} &= \text{pressure} \times \text{projected area}\\ &= 140 \times 10^3 \times 2{\cdot}16\\ &= 302 \times 10^3\text{ N}\end{aligned}$$

i.e. The force tending to tear the cylinder is 302 kN.

In a similar way we can use the idea of projected area to obtain the stress set up over the surface of a curved member of a machine or structure. For example, a shaft, diameter d, supports a bracket, length l, carrying a load F in the direction shown in fig.12.17. The shaft is subjected to a compressive stress on its curved surface.

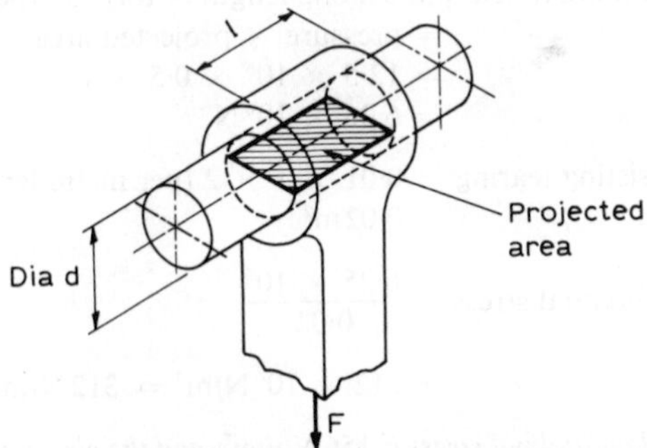

Fig.12.17 Projected area. Bearing or crushing stress on pin, and of course on bearing, is calculated by dividing the load by the projected area shown shaded. This area is equal to diameter × length of bearing.

$$\text{Average compressive stress in shaft} = \frac{\text{load}}{\text{projected area}}$$

The area which is used in determining the stress is the projected area of the curved surface on to a plane perpendicular to the direction of the applied force. This area is shown in fig.12.17.

Stress in Thin Cylinders

A thin cylinder is usually defined as one in which the thickness of the metal is less than one-fiftieth of the diameter of the cylinder. Under these conditions, it is assumed that the stresses set up within the metal are uniform. A Lancashire boiler is one of the classic examples of a thin cylinder. When an internal pressure acts on the inside of the cylinder, two types of stresses are set up within the metal:

1) circumferential or hoop stress, and
2) longitudinal stress.

The effect of these stresses is indicated in fig.12.18. The vessel may fail in one of two ways, depending upon the values of the stresses. If the circumferential stresses become excessive, the metal will tear along a line parallel to the axis of the vessel. If the longitudinal stresses become excessive, the metal may tear along a section perpendicular to the axis. It will be shown that this second type of failure is unlikely unless there is some fault in the metal. Let us examine the two stresses, and determine their effect.

Let p = pressure inside cylinder, in N/m^2;
d = diameter of cylinder, in metres (in the case of a thin cylinder, we can assume that there is no appreciable difference between the inside and outside diameters);
l = length of cylinder, in metres;
t = thickness of metal plate, in metres;
σ_1 = circumferential or hoop stress, in N/m^2;
σ_2 = longitudinal stress, in N/m^2.

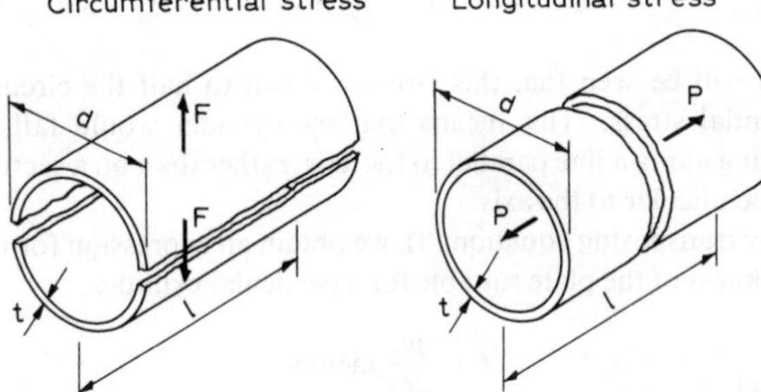

Fig.12.18 Thin cylinders. The left-hand failure is due to excessive stress around the circumference of the cylinder. These stresses are known as *circumferential stresses*. The right-hand failure is due to excessive stress along the length of the cylinder. These stresses are known as *longitudinal stresses.*

1) Circumferential or hoop stress

Referring to fig.12.18, the upward force, F, on the cylinder is equal to pressure × projected area.

$$\text{Upward force, } F = p \times d \times l \quad . \quad . \quad . \quad (1)$$

The area of metal resisting tearing consists of two strips, thickness t and length l, running down the length of the cylinder. The total area resisting tearing is $2tl$.

$$\text{Resistance of plate to tearing} = \text{stress} \times \text{area}$$
$$= \sigma_1 \times 2tl \quad . \quad (2)$$

Equating (1) and (2), we obtain an expression for σ_1:

$$2\sigma_1 tl = pdl$$

$$\sigma_1 = \frac{pd}{2t} \text{N/m}^2 \quad . \quad . \quad . \quad . \quad (3)$$

2) Longitudinal stress

The horizontal force P, shown in fig.12.18 (ii), is produced by the internal pressure acting on the area at the end of the cylinder, and is given by

$$P = p \times \frac{\pi}{4} d^2 \quad . \quad . \quad . \quad . \quad . \quad (4)$$

The area of metal resisting tearing consists of an annulus, diameter d and thickness t. Hence the area resisting tearing is πdt.

$$\text{Resistance of plate to tearing} = \text{stress} \times \text{area}$$
$$= \sigma_2 \times \pi dt \quad . \quad . \quad . \quad . \quad (5)$$

Equating (4) and (5), we obtain an expression for σ_2:

$$\pi dt \sigma_2 = \frac{\pi}{4} d^2 p$$

$$\sigma_2 = \frac{pd}{4t}\text{N/m}^2 \quad . \quad . \quad . \quad . \quad . \quad (6)$$

It will be seen that this stress is equal to half the circumferential stress. This means that the cylinder would fail by tearing along a line parallel to the axis, rather than on a section perpendicular to the axis.

By transposing equation (3), we obtain an expression for the thickness of the plate suitable for a particular cylinder.

$$t = \frac{pd}{2\sigma_1} \text{ metres}$$

There would, of course, be no point in using equation (6) for this thickness, as it would give a value half of that obtained from equation (3).

The strength of the plate at any joining should be sufficient to withstand the force due to internal pressure on the end of the cylinder. Allowance is made for this by dividing the thickness obtained in equation (3) by the efficiency (i.e. the tearing and shearing efficiency) of the joint.

$$\text{Required thickness of plate} = \frac{\text{theoretical thickness}}{\text{efficiency of joint}}$$

$$= \frac{pd}{2\sigma.\eta}$$

where η is the efficiency of the joint, expressed as a decimal.

In this way we make sure that the resistance of the plate to tearing across a joint is adequate. Problems dealing with spherical vessels follow similar solutions to that for thin cylinders, except that there will be longitudinal stresses in all directions. No circumferential stresses can be produced in this arrangement.

Example 12.7 Determine the stresses set up in the shell plate of a torpedo whose diameter is 500mm and thickness 10mm. The internal air pressure is 12·5 MN/m².

Force tending to tear plate around the circumference

$$= \text{pressure} \times \text{area}$$

$$= 12{\cdot}5 \times 10^6 \times \frac{\pi}{4} \times 0{\cdot}5^2$$

$$= 0{\cdot}78 \times 10^6\pi\,\text{N}$$

$$\text{Area resisting tearing} = \pi dt$$

$$= \pi \times 0{\cdot}5 \times 0{\cdot}01$$

$$= 0{\cdot}005\pi\,\text{m}^2$$

$$\text{Longitudinal stress} = \frac{\text{force}}{\text{area}}$$

$$= \frac{0{\cdot}78 \times 10^6\pi}{0{\cdot}005\pi}$$

$$= 156 \times 10^6\,\text{N/m}^2 = 156\,\text{N/mm}^2$$

Force tending to tear plate along length of torpedo (per metre length)

$$= \text{pressure} \times \text{projected area}$$

$$= 12{\cdot}5 \times 10^6 \times 0{\cdot}5 \times 1$$

$$= 6{\cdot}25 \times 10^6\,\text{N}$$

$$\text{Area resisting tearing} = 0{\cdot}01 \times 1 \times 2 \text{ (per metre length)}$$

$$= 0{\cdot}02\,\text{m}^2$$

$$\text{Circumferential stress} = \frac{6{\cdot}25 \times 10^6}{0{\cdot}02}$$

$$= 312 \times 10^6\,\text{N/m}^2 = 312\,\text{N/mm}^2$$

i.e. The longitudinal stress is 156 N/mm², and the circumferential stress is 312 N/mm².

Example 12.8 A cylindrical vessel, 2·4m in diameter, capable of holding a gas at a pressure of 2 MN/m², is to be made from steel plate whose tensile strength is 600 N/mm². Assuming a factor of safety of 4, and a joint efficiency of 70%, determine the minimum thickness of plate required. If you use a formula you must prove it. NCTEC

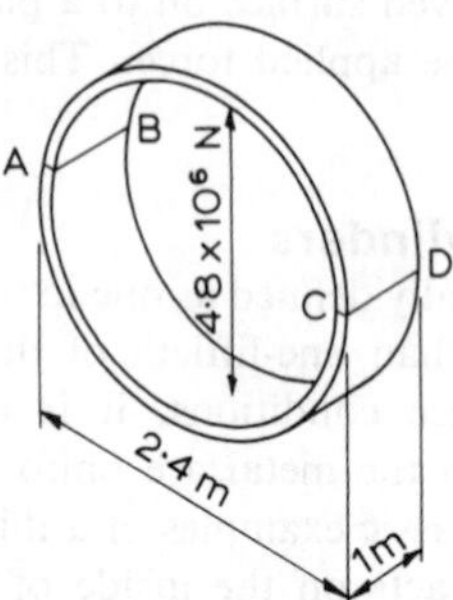

Fig.12.19

The thickness of the required plate is determined by the circumferential stress.

$$\text{Allowable tensile stress} = \frac{\text{tensile strength}}{\text{factor of safety}}$$

$$= \frac{600}{4} = 150\,\text{N/mm}^2$$

Consider a length of cylinder equal to 1 metre, and let tm equal the theoretical thickness of the plate.

Force tending to burst plate along AB and CD

$$= \text{pressure} \times \text{projected area}$$

$$= 2 \times 10^6 \times 2{\cdot}4 \times 1$$

$$= 4{\cdot}8 \times 10^6\,\text{N} \quad . \quad . \quad . \quad . \quad . \quad . \quad (1)$$

Maximum allowable resistance of plate on AB and CD

$$= \text{allowable stress} \times \text{area}$$

$$= 150 \times 10^6 \times 2t \times 1$$

$$= 300 \times 10^6 t\,\text{N} \quad . \quad . \quad . \quad . \quad . \quad (2)$$

Equating (1) and (2),

$$300 \times 10^6 t = 4{\cdot}8 \times 10^6$$
$$t = 0{\cdot}016\,\text{m}$$

$$\text{Actual thickness} = \frac{\text{theoretical thickness}}{\text{efficiency of joint}}$$

$$= \frac{0{\cdot}016}{0{\cdot}7}$$

$$= 0{\cdot}0229\,\text{m}$$

i.e. The minimum thickness of the plate is 22·9 mm, although in practice a plate 25 mm thick would be used.

Example 12.9 A spherical shell, thickness 20 mm, diameter 1 m, is subjected to an internal pressure of 5 MN/m^2. Calculate the stress in the material, and the change in diameter. Take the value of $E = 200 \times 10^3\,N/mm^2$.

Let σ = stress in the material.

Force tending to burst plate along 'equator' of sphere

= pressure × projected area

$$= 5 \times 10^6 \times \frac{\pi}{4} \times 1^2 \quad . \quad . \quad . \quad . \quad (1)$$

Resistance of plate is provided by a section in the form of an annulus.

Area of this section $= \pi Dt$

Resistance of plate = area × stress

$$= \pi Dt \times \sigma$$
$$= \pi \times 1 \times 0{\cdot}02\sigma \quad . \quad . \quad . \quad . \quad (2)$$

Equating (1) and (2),

$$1{\cdot}25 \times 10^6\pi = 0{\cdot}02\sigma\pi$$
$$\sigma = 62{\cdot}5 \times 10^6\,\text{N/m}^2$$
$$= 62{\cdot}5\,\text{N/mm}^2$$

$$\text{Strain} = \frac{\text{stress}}{E}$$

$$= \frac{62{\cdot}5}{200 \times 10^3}$$

$$= 0{\cdot}000\,31$$

Change in diameter = diameter × strain

$$= 1 \times 0{\cdot}000\,31$$
$$= 0{\cdot}000\,31\,\text{m}$$

i.e. The stress is 62·5 N/mm^2, and the change in diameter is 0·31 mm.

Exercise 12

1 Define resilience in connection with a stretched bar.

A vertical bar, 50 mm in diameter and 3 m long, is intended to carry a mass of weight 50 kN at its lower end. The mass is lowered slowly, until the bar takes the whole load. Find the work stored in the bar.

If the mass had been suddenly released when the bar just commenced to take the load, so that the bar took the load suddenly, find the maximum instantaneous stress set up in the material of the bar. ($E = 190 \times 10^3\,N/mm^2$) UEI

2 Describe any testing machine you have used for making a tensile test on a specimen of mild steel. If such a test were made to destruction, sketch a typical load-extension diagram, and state the information you would require in order to find (a) yield-point stress, (b) tensile strength, (c) stress at fracture, (d) percentage elongation, and (e) percentage reduction of area.

Give the approximate values for these items that you would expect for this material UEI

3 Describe, with sketches, any extensometer suitable for the determination of Young's modulus in tension for steel. Explain in detail the procedure you would follow when carrying out the test. UEI

4 Define resilience, dead load, and live load, in connection with a bar subjected to a tensile load.

Derive an expression for resilience for a stretched bar in terms of the volume of the bar, Young's modulus, and the stress produced in the bar.

A load of 20 kN is supported by two 25 mm diameter ropes, each taking half the load. If one rope is cut, find the instantaneous stress produced in the remaining rope, assuming it remains elastic. UEI

5 What is meant by the term 'resilience' in the mechanical sense?

For a given maximum stress, compare the resilience of a bar 0·4 m long, and 30 mm in diameter throughout, with that of a bar of the same length, and 20 mm in diameter for 0·15 m of the length, and 30 mm in diameter for the remainder. UEI

6 Describe fully, with the aid of neat sketches, how you would conduct one of the following experiments (a) to accurately determine the value of g, the gravitational constant, (b) a tensile test on a round specimen, in order to determine Young's modulus, yield point, ultimate stress, and percentage elongation. UEI

7 A tie member in a roof truss has to carry an axial load of 480 kN. The member is a flat bar 15 mm thick, and of constant width. Design and sketch a double-covered butt joint in this member, given that 21 mm diameter rivets are to be used throughout. (Maximum tensile stress 150 N/mm^2, maximum bearing stress 180 N/mm^2, maximum shear stress 90 N/mm^2.) UEI

8 The following observations were taken during a tension test on a specimen of mild steel, diameter 11·3 mm, and gauge length 100 mm.

Load, kN	0	4	8	12	16
Extension, mm	0	0·017	0·039	0·058	0·078
Load, kN	20	24	27·2	28	28·8
Extension, mm	0·097	0·117	0·133	0·149	0·164

Using a graph, estimate Young's modulus, and the stress at the elastic limit. Calculate the resilience at the elastic limit. UEI

9 Define the term 'resilience' and 'proof resilience', and derive an expression for the latter quantity, in terms of tensile stress and E.

A bar of steel 250 mm long, and of 50 mm uniform diameter is subject to a direct tensile stress of 20 N/mm². Another bar of the same material is also 250 mm long, but is 50 mm in diameter for half its length, and 100 mm in diameter for the remainder. It is subjected to an axial pull such that it receives the same amount of elastic strain energy as the first bar. Calculate the stresses in the two parts of the second bar. Neglect any effect of sudden change of section in the distribution of the stress. NCTEC

10 The eye-bolt shown in fig.12.20 has to withstand a tensile load of 80 kN. Find the diameter, d, of the bolt if the tensile stress is not to exceed 90 N/mm². Find also the diameter of the pin assuming that the pin is (a) in shear, and that the shear stress is not to exceed 60 N/mm², (b) supported at A and B, loaded uniformly between these points, and that the bending stress in tension and compression is not to exceed 90 N/mm².

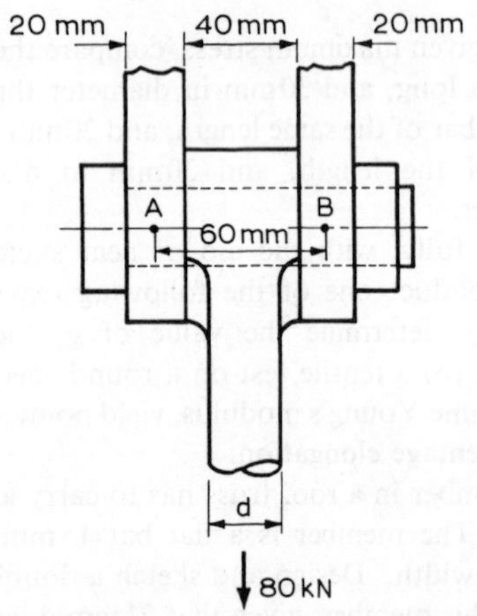

Fig.12.20

If the pin diameter is as calculated from (b), what will be the bearing pressure at the bearing surface? NCTEC

11 A metal bar, 20 mm in diameter and 3·5 m long, has its temperature raised from 15° to 55° C, and the ends are then secured to prevent contraction. If the bar cools to the original temperature, and the total yield of the end fastenings is 0·28 mm, calculate the pull on the bar. $E = 204 \times 10^3$ N/mm². Coefficient of linear expansion = 0·000 012 per degree C. NCTEC

12 In a tensile test on mild steel, explain how the following are determined; give approximate values of each, as shown by any test you have seen, and sketch a load-extension graph showing the positions of (a), (c), and (e): (a) yield point, (b) percentage elongation, (c) maximum load, (d) ultimate strength, and (e) limit of proportionality. NCTEC

13 (a) A short length of steel steam-pipe in a boiler-house is originally fitted in two brackets, to permit a free expansion. Due to faulty fitting, the pipe becomes rigidly locked in the brackets when the temperature rises to 110° C. Find the stress in the pipe due to restricted expansion when the pipe is carrying steam at a temperature of 208° C. The coefficient of linear expansion of the material of the pipe is $1{\cdot}19 \times 10^{-5}$ per °C, and E is 175×10^3 N/mm².

(b) With a test specimen in tension, what is meant by the following terms: elastic limit, yield point, maximum stress, reduction of area per cent?

Give approximate values in each case for any material you know, or have seen tested. NCTEC

14 Derive formulae giving the longitudinal and circumferential stresses in a cylindrical shell under internal pressure.

A compressed air reservoir, 2·4 m in diameter, working pressure 825 kN/m², is to be made from steel having a tensile strength of 465 N/mm². Calculate the thickness of the shell plates, assuming a factor of safety of 5, and the efficiency of the longitudinal joint to be 75% NCTEC

15 Derive formulae for calculating the longitudinal and circumferential stresses in a thin cylindrical shell.

Calculate the thickness of a pipe of 250 mm bore, to carry an internal pressure of 2 MN/m², if the tensile stress in the material is not to exceed 40 N/mm². NCTEC

16 A spherical shell, thickness 12·5 mm, diameter 600 mm, is subjected to an internal pressure of 3·5 MN/m². Calculate the stress in the material, and the change in diameter. Prove any formula you use for the stress. $E = 208 \times 10^3$ N/mm². NCTEC

17 A steel bar, 25 mm in diameter, is tested in tension. The total extension over a length of 200 mm is 136 scale divisions of an extensometer for a pull of 35 kN, the unit of the scale being $\frac{1}{2000}$ mm. Calculate the modulus of elasticity for this material.

On testing to fracture, the specimen broke with a load of 250 kN. A thin, seamless cylinder, 1·5 m mean diameter, is made of this material, and is to withstand an internal pressure of 1 MN/m² gauge. Determine the necessary thickness of the plate required. Assume a factor of safety of 6. ULCI

18 Deduce expressions for the hoop and axial stresses induced in the material of a thin cylindrical shell subjected to an internal pressure.

A cylindrical shell, 2·7 m mean diameter, is constructed of mild-steel plate having a tensile strength of 430 N/mm². It is subjected to an internal pressure of 1·4 MN/m² gauge. Calculate the thickness of the shell plates, assuming a factor of safety of 5, and the efficiency of the longitudinal joint to be 78%. ULCI

19 Deduce expressions for the stresses produced in the longitudinal section (hoop stress) and the transverse section (axial stress) of a thin cylindrical shell subjected to an internal pressure.

A cylindrical shell, 2·1 m mean diameter, is constructed of mild-steel plate having an ultimate tensile stress of 450 N/mm². It is subjected to an internal pressure of 1·75 MN/m² gauge, and the efficiency of the longitudinal joint is 74%. Using a factor of safety of 5, determine the thickness of plate which can be used.

What will be the value of the axial stress in the plate? ULCI

20 A load W falls through a height h before coming to rest on a stop at the lower end of a steel bar, length l, cross-sectional area A. The modulus of elasticity of the material of the rod is E. Obtain an expression for the stress intensity, σ, induced in the rod as a result of the impact, in terms of W, h, l, A, and E. Assume that the extension of the rod is small compared with h.

A vertical bar of mild steel, 25 mm in diameter, and 1·35 m long, has a stop at the lower end. A weight W falls through a distance of 150 mm before coming to rest on the stop. Determine the value of W if the maximum stress produced is not to exceed 80 N/mm². What will be the maximum instantaneous elongation produced in the bar? E for steel $= 208 \times 10^3$ N/mm². ULCI

21 Describe, with a sketch, some form of extensometer suitable for measuring elastic extension in a bar under tension.

Describe carefully how you would make a standard tensile test to destruction on a bar of ductile metal. Give the dimensions of the test piece you would use, and explain clearly what measurements you would make. EMEU

22 Prove that the hoop stress in a thin cylinder subjected to internal pressure is twice the corresponding longitudinal stress. A copper cylinder is 450 mm in internal diameter, and 7·5 mm thick. Calculate the safe operating pressure if the tensile strength of the material is 140 N/mm², and there is to be a factor of safety of 4. EMEU

23 Prove that the resilience of a materia subjected to a uniform direct stress p is equal to $\dfrac{p^2}{2E}$ times the volume of the material.

A steel bar, 350 mm long, is 50 mm in diameter for a length of 250 mm, and 37·5 mm in diameter for the remaining 100 mm. It is subjected to an axial compressive load, which shortens it by 0·25 mm. Calculate the load, and the resilience of the loaded bar. Young's modulus $= 208 \times 10^3$ N/mm². EMEU

24 Define Young's modulus of elasticity, and strain energy.

A tensile test on a mild-steel specimen of diameter 11·3 mm, and gauge length 200 mm, showed that the elastic limit was reached at a load of 40 kN. At this value, the extension on the gauge length was measured as 0·24 mm. The maximum load was 78 kN when the gauge length had increased to 252 mm. From these particulars, evaluate Young's modulus, the elastic limit stress, the percentage elongation, the ultimate stress, and the strain energy at the elastic limit. IMECHE

25 A 20 mm-diameter steel bolt is passed through a brass sleeve of 22 mm internal and 28 mm external diameter. A nut and washer are put on the bolt, and the nut is tightened until the brass sleeve has shortened 0·125 mm.

Neglecting any compression of the washer, determine the extension of the bolt.

(E for brass is 84×10^3 N/mm², E for steel is 208×10^3 N/mm².) ULCI

26 A thin cylindrical pressure vessel is 1 m in diameter. The material is 10 mm thick, and a safe working stress of 50 N/mm² is allowed.

Calculate the safe working internal pressure. State the assumptions made in the formula used.

Show an element of material from the side of the vessel, and indicate the magnitude and direction of the direct stresses acting. ULCI

27 (a) A steel test bar, 25 mm in diameter, and 200 mm gauge length, was subjected to a tensile test. A load of 35 kN produced an extension of 0·066 mm, which is within the limit of proportionality. At fracture, the load was 248 kN, the diameter 17 mm, and the length between gauge points 260 mm.

Determine the modulus of elasticity, the ultimate tensile stress, the percentage elongation, and the percentage reduction of area.

(b) A thin spherical pressure vessel, 1·5 m in diameter, is to be made of this steel, to withstand an internal pressure of 1·4 MN/m². Assuming a factor of safety of 6, determine the minimum thickness of plate.

Derive any formula used. NCTEC

28 Explain the term 'resilience'.

A load of mass 1400 kg is being lowered by a crane at a steady speed of 0·5 m/s. The load is suspended from the crane pulley by means of a steel chain of effective cross-sectional area 625 mm². When the length of chain unwound from the pulley is 7·5 m, the chain suddenly jams on the pulley.

Neglecting the weight of the chain, estimate the stress induced in the chain due to the sudden stoppage. For steel, $E = 208 \times 10^3\,\text{N/mm}^2$. ULCI

29 Derive from first principles an expression for the tensile stress in the material of a thin spherical shell. The shell thickness is small compared with the internal diameter.

A thin spherical shell is 1·5 m in internal diameter, the plate thickness being 5 mm. If the tensile stress in the material of the plate is not to exceed $60 \times 10^3\,\text{N/mm}^2$, what is the maximum allowable internal pressure?

If the efficiency of the riveted joint of the shell is 80 %, by how much must the pressure be reduced? ULCI

Chapter 13

Shearing Forces and Bending Moments

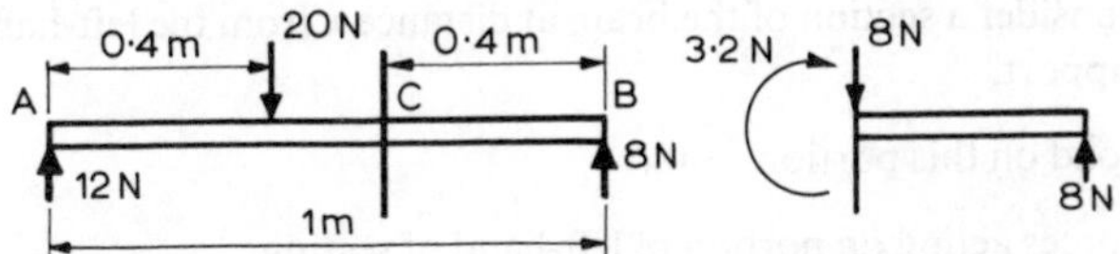

Fig.13.1 Shearing force and bending moment. Right-hand portion, BC, of beam is kept in equilibrium by means of a force, known as a *shearing force,* and a couple, known as a *bending moment,* both acting across the section at C.

Consider the beam shown in fig.13.1; it is in equilibrium under the action of three forces: the load, and the two reactions. In this particular case we are neglecting any weight which the beam may have. Now let us isolate a portion of the beam, such as that bounded by section C and the right-hand support, and analyse the forces and couples which must be acting upon this portion in order to produce equilibrium. Since there is an upward force of 8 N at the reaction, it is necessary that there must be a downward force of 8 N in order that the resultant forces in any direction shall be zero. This downward force can be applied only at the section C. When this is done there is an out-of-balance couple of $8 \times 0{\cdot}4 = 3{\cdot}2$ N m acting in an anticlockwise direction on this portion of the beam. Hence it is necessary to apply a clockwise moment of 3·2 Nm to produce the equilibrium condition which states that the resultant couples must be zero. Again this couple can be applied only at the section C.

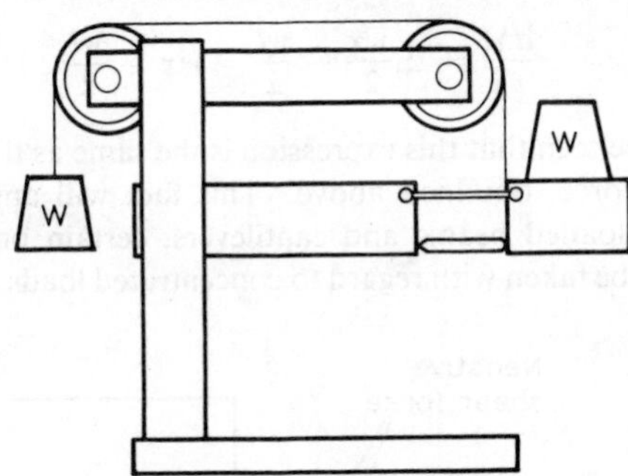

Fig.13.2 Shearing force and bending moment. The cantilever, which is supporting a weight of *W* N at the free end, is broken across a section as shown. In order to maintain equilibrium of the right-hand portion carrying the load it will be necessary

(1) to provide an upward force *W* at the section; this is done by means of the weight *W*, supported by a cord passing over the pulleys;

(2) to provide two connections between the two parts of the cantilever. The upper connection need only be flexible, capable of transmitting a tensile force. The lower connection must be rigid and capable of transmitting a compressive force. These two forces, which are equal and opposite, provide a couple across the section.

The force is known as the *shearing force.*
The couple is known as the *bending moment.*

To keep the portion CB of the beam in equilibrium, it is therefore necessary to apply a force and a couple at the section C. This force is known as a *shearing force*, and the couple is known as a *bending moment*. When the beam is considered as a solid member supporting the load, it will be found that the left-hand portion AC will supply the necessary force and couple across section C to keep CB in equilibrium. Similarly, it will be found that portion CB will provide the necessary force and couple to keep the left-hand portion of the beam AC in equilibrium. If we choose any other section than C we shall find that a different value, and possibly direction, of shearing force and bending moment will be obtained. It is usual to draw a diagram showing the variation of these two quantities along the length of the beam. These diagrams are referred to as *shearing-force* and *bending-moment diagrams.*

Convention of Signs for Shearing Force and Bending Moment

In dealing with shearing force and bending moments, the following convention of signs has been used. Although it must be emphasised that alternative conventions have their advantages and disadvantages, this particular one has been chosen so that the student using it in later work relating to strength of materials will be presented with a positive deflection indicating the deflection which a normal simply supported beam would take.

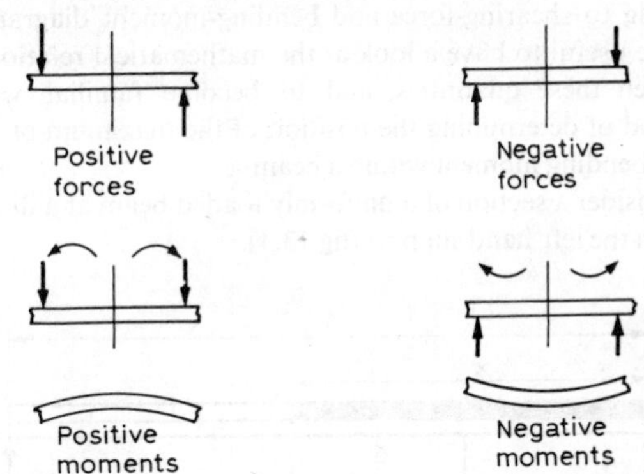

Fig.13.3 Convention for positive and negative forces and moments

Consider any section of the beam, then:

an *upward* force acting on the *right* of the section is *positive*,
a *downward* force acting on the *right* of the section is *negative*,
an *upward* force acting on the *left* of the section is *negative*,
a *downward* force acting on the *left* of the section is *positive*,
a *clockwise* moment on the *right* of the section is *positive*,
an *anticlockwise* moment on the *right* of the section is *negative*,
a *clockwise* moment on the *left* of the section is *negative*,
an *anticlockwise* moment on the *left* of the section is *positive*.

Remember that *the shearing force at any section of the beam is the vertical force which one part of the beam exerts on the other part of the beam, at that section.*

And that *the bending moment at any section of the beam is the couple which one part of the beam exerts on the other part of the beam, at that section.*

Calculation of the Shearing Force at any Section

1 Choose either the right- or the left-hand portion of the beam.
2 Find the algebraic sum of all the forces, including reactions, on the chosen portion of the beam.
3 This algebraic sum of the forces is the required shearing force for that section of the beam.

Calculation of the Bending Moment at any Section

1 Choose either the right- or the left-hand portion of the beam.
2 Find the algebraic sum of the moments of all the forces acting on the chosen portion of the beam.
3 This algebraic sum of the moments is the required bending moment at the given section of the beam.

Mathematical Relationship Between the Shearing Force and the Bending Moment

Before proceeding to work out solutions to typical problems relating to shearing-force and bending-moment diagrams, it will be useful to have a look at the mathematical relationship between these quantities, and to become familiar with a method of determining the position of the maximum or minimum bending moment within a beam.

Consider a section of a uniformly loaded beam at a distance x from the left-hand support (fig.13.4).

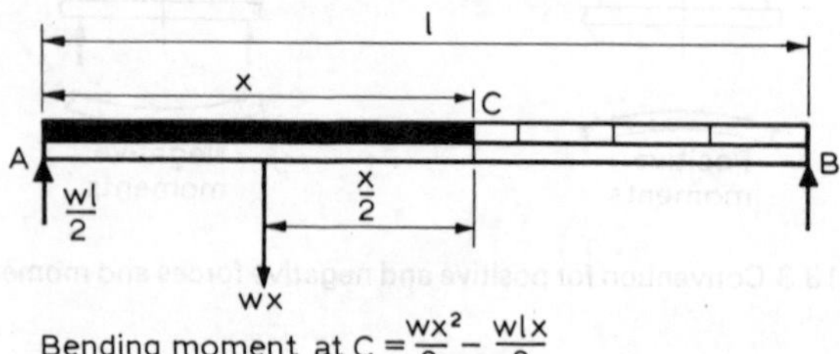

Fig.13.4

Let l = length of beam, in metres;
w = load on beam per metre length, in newtons.

Then wl = total load on beam,

$\frac{wl}{2}$ = reaction at each end.

Consider a section of the beam at distance x from the left-hand support.

Load on this portion $= wx$

Forces acting on portion of left-hand of section:

1 reaction, $\frac{wl}{2}$, upwards (negative),

2 load on section, wx, downwards (positive).

Shearing force at the section, $F = wx - \frac{wl}{2}$

Take moments about the chosen section, and take the load wx to act at the mid-point of the length of the section.

Moment of reaction $= \frac{wl}{2} \times x = \frac{wlx}{2}$ (negative)

(clockwise on the left)

Moment of load $= wx \times \frac{x}{2} = \frac{wx^2}{2}$ (positive)

(anticlockwise on the left)

Bending moment at section, $M = \frac{wx^2}{2} - \frac{wlx}{2}$

Now if we differentiate this expression with respect to x we, have

$$\frac{dM}{dx} = 2.\frac{wx}{2} - \frac{wl}{2} = wx - \frac{wl}{2}$$

It will be seen that this expression is the same as that for the shearing force, obtained above. This fact will apply to all forms of loaded beams and cantilevers, certain precautions having to be taken with regard to concentrated loads.

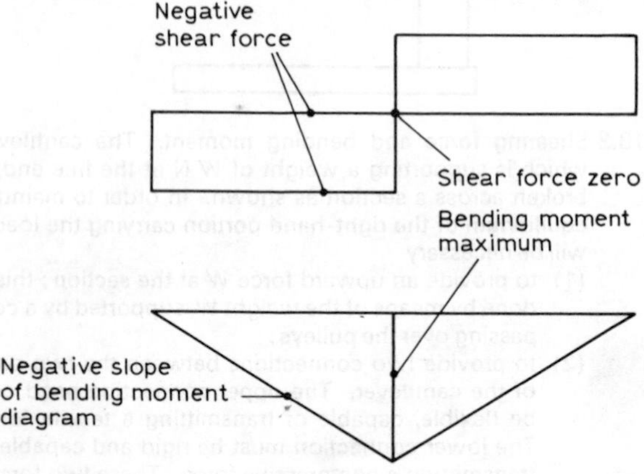

Fig.13.5 Relationship between shearing force and bending moment

From our mathematical work, we know that by differentiating an expression and equating the differential to zero we can determine the maximum or minimum value of the expression. It follows, then, that the maximum or minimum value of the bending moment occurs when the shearing force is zero, since the shearing-force expression is the differential of the bending-moment expression.

1 Shearing-force expression is differential of bending-moment expression.
2 Maximum or minimum bending moment occurs when shearing force is zero.
3 If value of shearing force is positive, then slope of bending-moment diagram is positive, i.e. upward to the right.
If value of shearing force is negative, then slope of bending-moment diagram is negative, i.e. upward to the left.

Alternative Method of Drawing Shearing-force Diagram

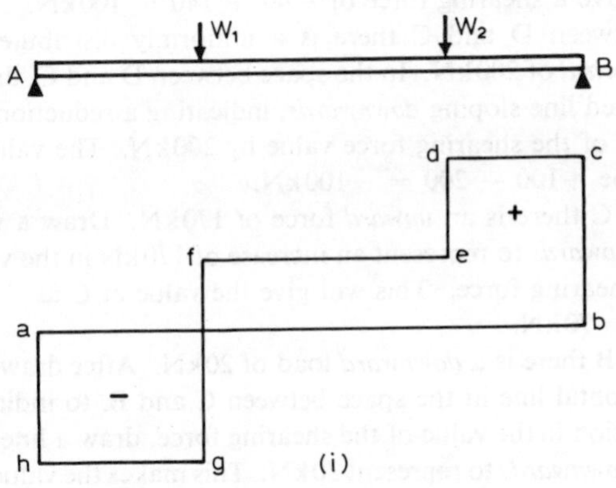

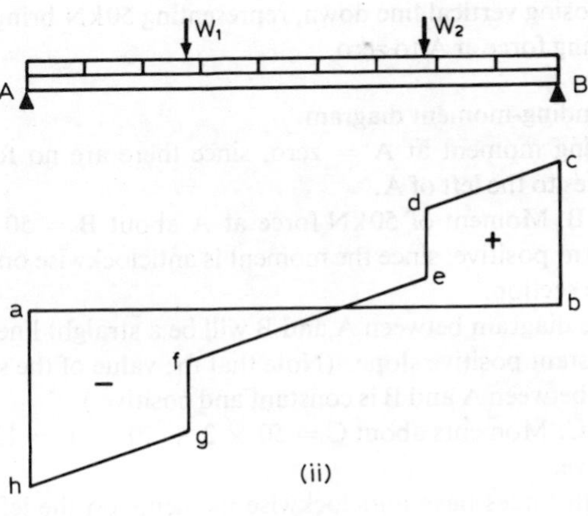

Fig.13.6

(A) Concentrated loads [fig.13.6(i)]

1 Commence at the *right-hand end* of the beam in all cases. Draw the base line *ab* for the shearing-force diagram under the loading diagram.
2 The reaction at B is *upward*, so draw *bc upward* to scale, to represent the reaction at B.
3 Since there is no other force until W_2, draw *cd* horizontal. *d* is in line with W_2.
4 W_2 acts *down*, so draw *de downward* to scale, to represent load W_2.
5 Since there is no other force until W_1, draw *ef* horizontal. *f* is in line with W_1.
6 W_1 acts *down*, so draw *fg downward* to scale to represent load W_1.
7 Since there is no other force until the reaction at A, draw *gh* horizontal.
8 Reaction at A is *upward*, so draw *ha upward* to scale, to represent the reaction at A.
The diagram should now be closed, i.e. *a* should lie on the base line *ab*.

Note. Vertical shearing-force diagram lines are drawn in the direction of the corresponding loads or reactions. If there is no intermediate load, the shearing-force diagram line is horizontal.

(B) Uniformly loaded beam [fig.13.6(ii)]

1 Commence at the *right-hand end* of the beam in all cases. Draw the base line *ab* for the shearing-force diagram under the loading diagram.
2 The reaction at B is *upward*, so draw *bc upward* to scale, to represent the reaction at B.
3 Between B and the load W_2 there is a spread load of, say, w_3; so instead of the line *cd* being horizontal, as in the previous case, the point *d* will be lowered by an amount representing w_3 to scale.
4 W_1 acts *down*, so draw *de downward* to scale, to represent the load W_2.
5 Between W_2 and W_1 there is a spread load of, say, w_2; so the line *ef* slopes down, with the point *f* at a distance below *e* equal to w_2 to scale.
6 W_1 acts *down*, so draw *fg downward* to scale, to represent load W_1.
7 Between W_1 and the reaction at A there is a spread load of, say, w_1 down; so the line *gh* slopes down, with the point *h* at a distance below *g* equal to w_1 to scale.
8 The reaction at A is *upward*, so draw *ha upward* to scale, to represent the reaction at A.
The diagram should now be closed, i.e. *a* should lie on the base line *ab*.

Example 13.1 A beam 10m long rests on two supports placed 5m apart, and overhangs the right-hand support by 3m. It carries a load of 40kN/m run between the supports. In addition, it carries isolated loads of 50kN at the left-hand end, 20 kN at a point 1m from the left-hand end, and 40kN at the right-hand end. Plot the bending moment and shear-force diagrams for the beam, and state where the maximum bending moment occurs. EMEU

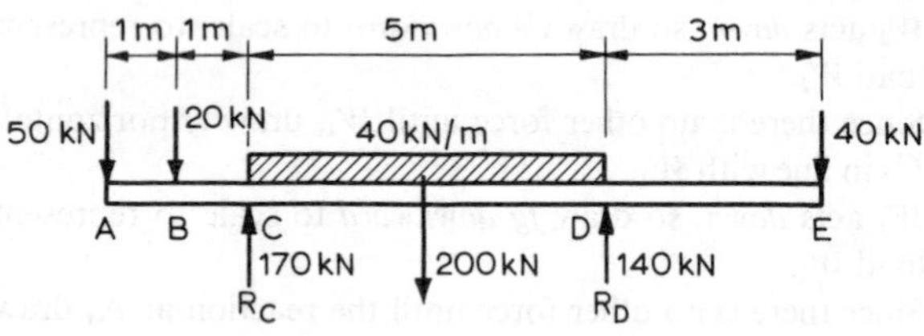

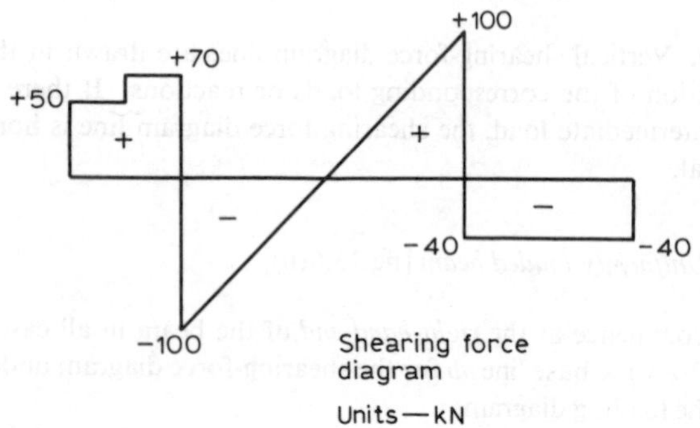

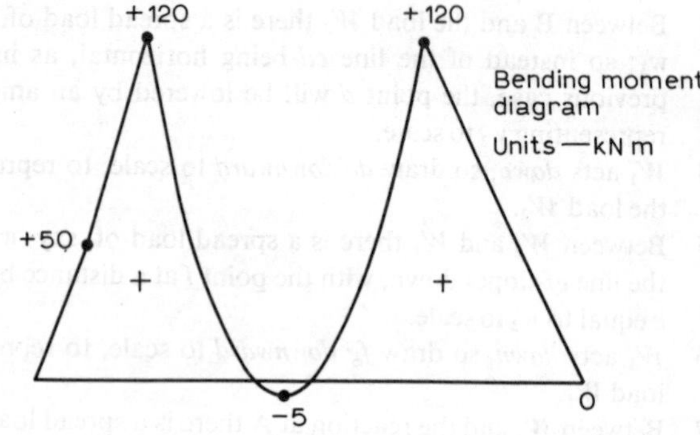

Fig.13.7

1) Draw the loading diagram, with the position of each load drawn to scale.

2) Calculate the reaction at each support.

Support C: take moments about D.

$$5R_C = 200 \times 2{\cdot}5 + 20 \times 6 + 50 \times 7 - 40 \times 3$$
$$= 850$$
$$R_C = 170\text{kN}$$

Support D: take moments about C.

$$5R_D = 200 \times 2{\cdot}5 + 40 \times 8 - 50 \times 2 - 20 \times 1$$
$$= 700$$
$$R_D = 140\text{kN}$$

3) Shearing-force diagram.

Commence with the point E at the right-hand end of the beam, where there is a downward load of 40kN. Draw the vertical line downwards underneath E in the shearing-force diagram, to represent a shearing force of 40kN.

Since there is no other force between E and D, there will be no variation in the shearing force, and the diagram will take the form of a horizontal line, as shown.

At D there is an *upward* force of 140kN. Draw a line vertically *upwards* underneath D to represent this 140kN. This will give a shearing force of $-40 + 140 = 100$kN.

Between D and C there is a uniformly distributed load *downward* of 200kN. In the space between D and C, draw the inclined line sloping *downwards*, indicating a reduction in the value of the shearing force value by 200kN. The value at C will be $+100 - 200 = -100$kN.

At C there is an *upward* force of 170kN. Draw a vertical line *upwards* to represent an increase of 170kN in the value of the shearing force. This will give the value at C as $-100 + 170 = 70$kN.

At B there is a *downward* load of 20kN. After drawing the horizontal line in the space between C and B, to indicate no variation in the value of the shearing force, draw a line vertically *downwards* to represent 20kN. This makes the value of the shearing force at B equal to $70 - 20 = 50$kN.

Finally, there is a *downward* load of 50kN at A. Draw the horizontal line in the space between B and A, and then the closing vertical line down, representing 50kN bringing the shearing force at A to zero.

4) Bending-moment diagram.

Bending moment at A = zero, since there are no forces or couples to the left of A.

At B. Moment of 50kN force at A about B $= 50 \times 1 = 50$kNm positive, since the moment is anticlockwise on the left of the section.

The diagram between A and B will be a straight line having a constant positive slope. (Note that the value of the shearing force between A and B is constant and positive.)

At C. Moments about C $= 50 \times 2 + 20 \times 1 = 120$kNm positive.

Both forces have anticlockwise moments on the left of the section.

At D. Consider the portion of the beam on the right of the section.

Moment about D = 40 × 3 = 120 positive, clockwise on right of section.

Between C and D, the bending-moment diagram will be parabolic in form, and values at any section can be calculated on the lines just indicated.

It will be noticed in this case that the bending moment is minimum at the point where the shearing force is zero. Incidentally, the point of zero shearing force will be seen to be mid-way between C and D. At this point, the bending moment will be (considering the right-hand portion of the beam) $100 \times 1{\cdot}25 + 40 \times 5{\cdot}5 - 140 \times 2{\cdot}5 = -5$kNm.

The maximum bending moment to which the beam is subjected is 120 kNm.

Example 13.2 A horizontal beam ABCDEF is 2·5 m long, and AB = BC = CD = DE = EF = 0·5 m. The ends rest on broad supports, giving uniformly distributed reactions over AB and EF. A concentrated load of 2000 N acts at C, and one of 1000 N at D. In addition, a uniformly distributed load of 6000 N extends over the length CE. Determine the supporting reactions at each end, in N/m, and draw the shearing-force diagram to scale. Obtain the distance from the centre of the beam to the position of maximum bending moment, and calculate the value of this moment.

1) Draw the loading diagram, with the position of each load drawn to scale.

2) Calculate the reaction at each support. Assume that the reaction at either end acts through the mid-point of the supporting length.

Support AB: take moments about mid-point of EF; note that the 6000 N spread load between C and E is taken to act through D, the mid-point of CE.

$$
\begin{aligned}
2R_L &= 6000 \times 0{\cdot}75 + 1000 \times 0{\cdot}75 + 2000 \times 1{\cdot}25 \\
&= 7750 \\
R_L &= 3875\,\text{N}
\end{aligned}
$$

This is spread over a length of 0·5 m, so that the supporting reaction at the right-hand support is 7750 N/m.

Support EF: take moments about mid-point of AB.

$$
\begin{aligned}
2R_R &= 2000 \times 0{\cdot}75 + 6000 \times 1{\cdot}25 + 1000 \times 1{\cdot}25 \\
&= 10\,250 \\
R_R &= 5125\,\text{N}
\end{aligned}
$$

This is equivalent to a spread reaction of 10 250 N/m over AB.

3) Shearing-force diagram.

Commence at the point F at the *right-hand side* of the beam.

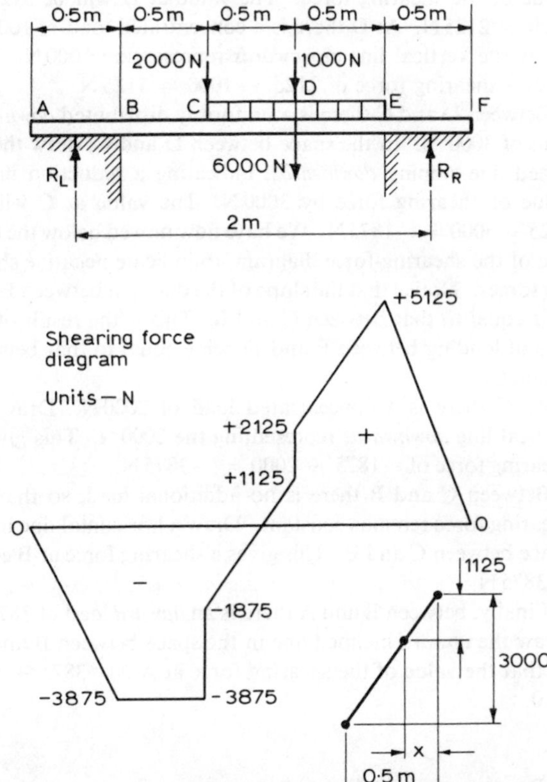

Fig.13.8

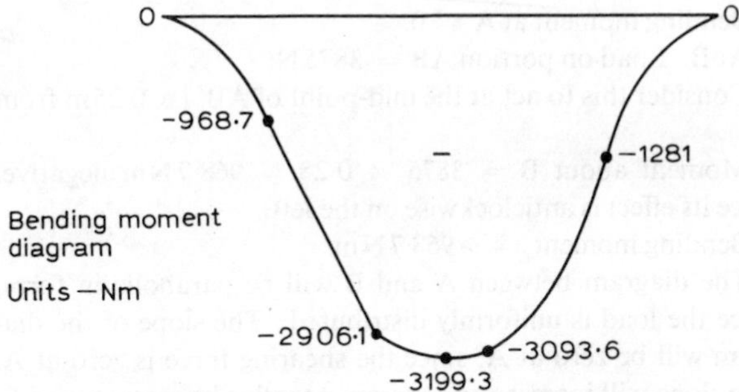

Fig.13.9

Between F and E there is an *upward* load of 5125 N, uniformly distributed. Commencing at the right-hand side of the shearing-force diagram, draw the inclined line *upwards*, so that the value of the shearing force under E is 5125 N. The line is sloping because the shearing force is gradually increasing, the load being uniformly distributed.

Between E and D there is a uniformly distributed *downward* load of 3000 N. In the space between E and D draw the inclined line sloping *downwards*, indicating a reduction of 3000 N in the value of the shearing force. The value at D will be 5125 − 3000 = 2125 N. At D there is a concentrated load of 1000 N. Draw the vertical line *downwards* representing 1000 N. This gives a shearing force of 2125 − 1000 = 1125 N.

Between D and C there is a uniformly distributed *downward* load of 3000 N. In the space between D and C, draw the inclined line sloping *downwards*, indicating a reduction in the value of shearing force by 3000 N. The value at C will be 1125 − 3000 = −1875 N. We have now moved below the base line of the shearing-force diagram, to indicate negative shearing forces. Notice that the slope of the diagram between E and D is equal to that between C and B. This is the result of the rate of loading between E and D being equal to that between D and C.

At C there is a concentrated load of 2000 N. Draw the vertical line *downwards* representing the 2000 N. This gives a shearing force of −1875 − 2000 = −3875 N.

Between C and B there is no additional load, so that the shearing force remains constant. Draw a horizontal line in the space between C and B. This gives a shearing force at B equal to 3875 N.

Finally, between B and A there is an *upward* load of 3875 N. Draw the *upward* inclined line in the space between B and A, so that the value of the shearing force at A is −3875 + 3875 = 0.

4) Bending-moment diagram.
Although the question does not ask for the bending-moment diagram to be drawn, it is included in the solution for the sake of completeness.

Bending moment at A = 0.

At B. Load on portion AB = 3875 N.

Consider this to act at the mid-point of AB, i.e. 0·25 m from B.

Moment about B = 3875 × 0·25 = 968·7 N m negative, since its effect is anticlockwise on the left.

Bending moment = −968·7 N m.

The diagram between A and B will be parabolic in form, since the load is uniformly distributed. The slope of the diagram will be zero at A, since the shearing force is zero at A. The slope will increase and remain negative between A and B, since the shearing force increases and remains negative between these points.

At C. Consider portion ABC.

Moment about C = 3875 × 0·75 = 2906·1 N m negative, again anticlockwise on the left.

At D. Consider right-hand portion of beam DEF (although you would obtain the correct value whichever portion you considered, there is a smaller calculation in this case if you consider the right-hand portion). The load on DE is taken as acting at the mid-point of DE; and that on EF at the mid-point of EF.

$$\begin{aligned}\text{Moments about D} &= -5125 \times 0{\cdot}75 + 3000 \times 0{\cdot}25 \\ &= -3093{\cdot}6\,\text{N m}\end{aligned}$$

Note that the load on DE gives a clockwise moment on the right of the section at D, i.e. a positive moment; whilst that on EF gives an anticlockwise moment on the right of the section at D, i.e. a negative moment.

At E. Load on EF = 5125 N acting at mid-point of EF.

Moment about E = 5125 × 0·25 = 1281·2 N negative, since its effect is anticlockwise on the right of the section at E.

The diagram between C and D, between B and E, and between E and F will also be parabolic, due to the uniformly distributed loads.

5) Maximum bending moment.
This occurs when the shearing force is zero, i.e. between C and D.

The position of this zero force is found by a similar triangle method. The small triangle on the right of the shearing-force diagram is a reproduction of that diagram between C and D. The distance x from D is given by

$$\frac{x}{0{\cdot}5} = \frac{1125}{3000}$$

$$x = 0{\cdot}1875\,\text{m}$$

Taking moments to the right of the section of zero shearing force,

$$\begin{aligned}\text{max. B.M.} &= +\left[(6000 \times 0{\cdot}6875) \times \frac{0{\cdot}6875}{2}\right] \\ &\quad - [5125 \times (0{\cdot}75 + 0{\cdot}1875)] + (1000 \times 0{\cdot}1875) \\ &= -3199{\cdot}3\,\text{N m}\end{aligned}$$

Maximum bending moment is −3199·3 N m at 1·3125 m from A.

Example 13.3 Draw to scale the shearing-force and bending-moment diagrams for the loaded cantilever shown in fig.13.10.

The loading on the cantilever is 2kN/m length, in addition to the concentrated loads. The total continuous load is 10kN, which can be considered to act at the mid-point of the cantilever, i.e. $2\frac{1}{2}$m from the support.

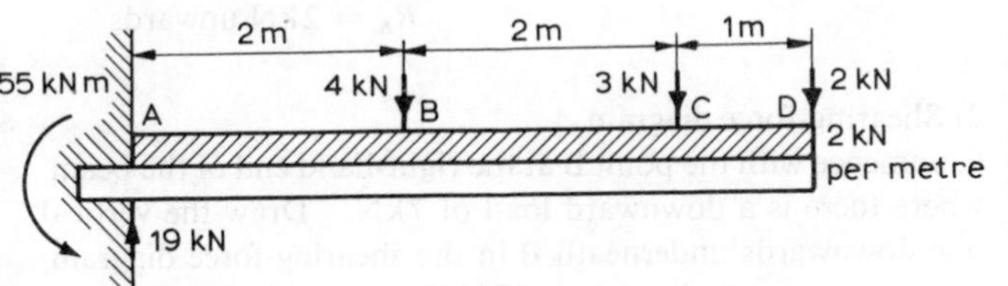

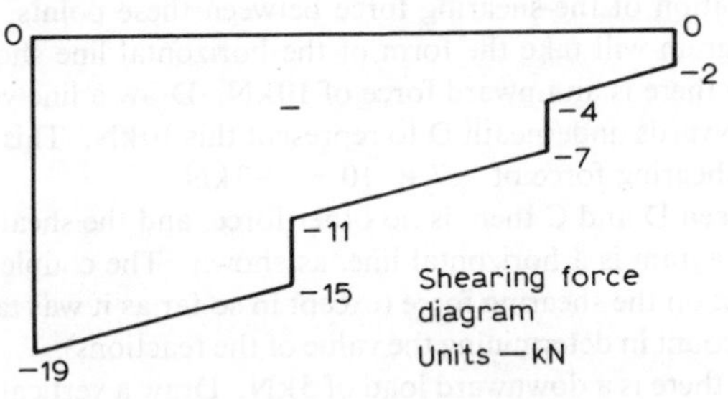

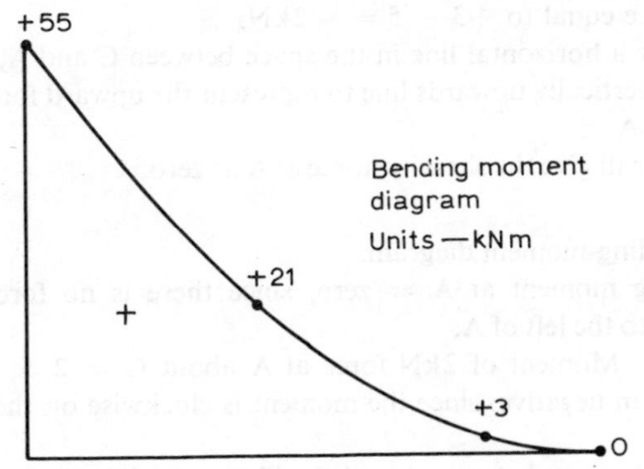

Fig.13.10

Moments about the support give

$$(4 \times 2) + (3 \times 4) + (2 \times 5) + (10 \times 2\tfrac{1}{2})$$

$$= 55\,\text{kN m clockwise}$$

This will have to be balanced by an anticlockwise moment of 55kNm, which is supplied by the support.

In addition, there is a total downwards load of 4 + 3 + 2 + 10 = 19kN. This will be balanced by an upward force of 19 kN at the support.

Hence the support must provide an upward force of 19kN and an anticlockwise moment of 55kNm.

Shearing-force diagram.

Commence at D at the right-hand end of the cantilever, where there is a downward load of 2kN. Draw a vertical line downwards underneath D, to represent a shearing force of 2kN.

Between D and C there is a spread load of 2kN. This will make the shearing force at C equal to −2 − 2 = −4kN. But the diagram will take the form of an inclined line between D and C, since the increase from 2 to 4 is gradual.

At C there is a sudden increase of 3kN. Draw the vertical line downwards underneath C to represent an increase in the shearing force of 3kN. This will give a value of −4 − 3 = −7kN.

Between C and B there is a further gradual increase of 4kN, making the value of the shearing force at B equal to −7 − 4 = −11kN. The diagram takes the form of an inclined line sloping downwards between C and B.

At B there is a downward load of 4kN. Draw the vertical line downwards underneath B to represent an increase of 4kN in the value of the shearing force. Its value is now −11 − 4 = −15kN.

Finally, between B and A there is a spread load of 4kN, so that the shearing force gradually increases from −15 to −15 − 4 = −19kN. The inclined line in the shearing-force diagram indicates this. The upward load of 19kN at the support is represented by the upward vertical line underneath A, which brings the value of the shearing force to zero at A.

Bending-moment diagram.

At A. The support on the left of A provides a bending moment of 55kNm in an anticlockwise direction. Anticlockwise on the left is considered positive; hence the bending moment at A is +55kNm.

At B. Moments of forces on the right of the section at B give

$$(3 \times 2) + (2 \times 3) + (6 \times 1\tfrac{1}{2}) = 21\,\text{kN m}$$

Note that all loads give clockwise moments on the right; hence they are positive. The continuous load of 6kN is assumed to act at the mid-point, i.e. $1\frac{1}{2}$m from B.

At C. Moments of forces on the right of the section give $(2 \times 1) + (2 \times \frac{1}{2}) = 3$kNm. Bending moment at C is +3 kNm.

Since the loading between the concentrated loads is continuous, the bending-moment diagram will be curved. For the purpose of sketching this diagram it is sufficient to indicate the main values just calculated.

If an accurate curve were required it would be necessary to consider other points along the length of the cantilever, and calculate the values of the bending moment at these points.

Example 13.4 A beam AB, 4m long, is supported on rollers at A and on a hinge at B. In addition to the 5 and 10kN loads as shown, there is a couple of magnitude 3kNm acting in an anticlockwise direction at the mid-point of the beam. Draw the shearing-force and bending-moment diagrams for the beam.

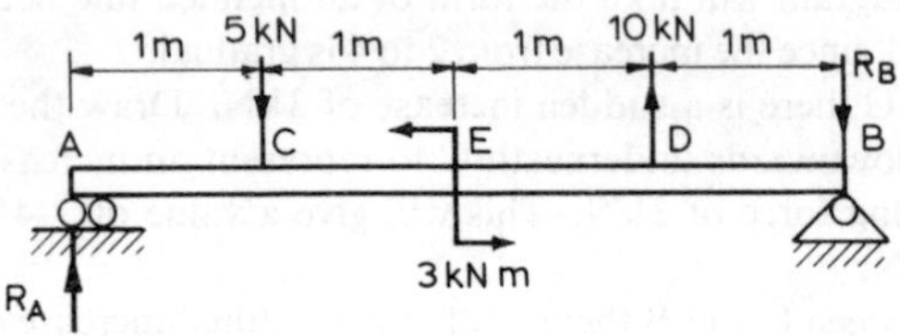

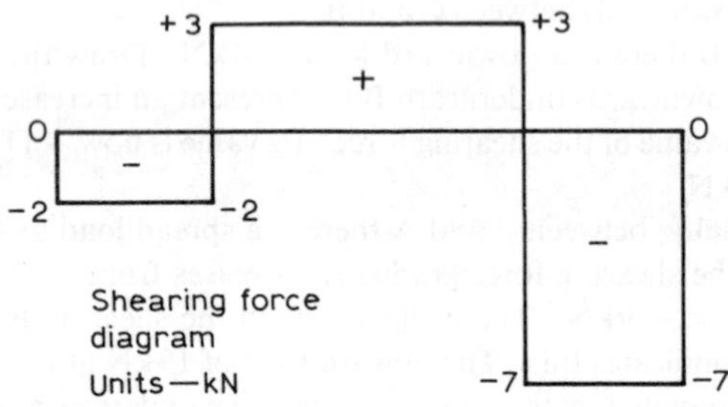

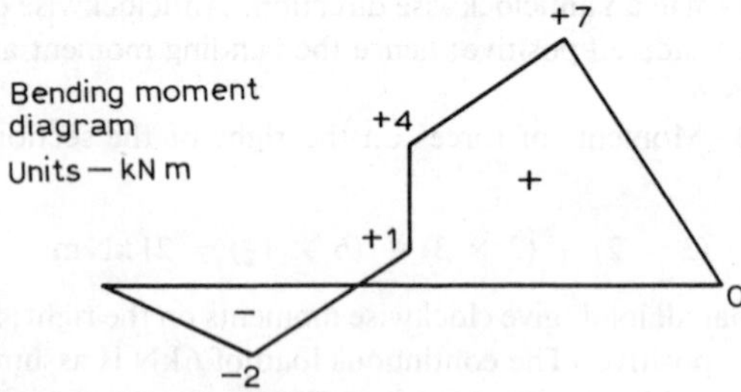

Fig.13.11

1) Calculate the reaction at each support. Since all the loads are vertical, and since the reaction at the rollers must be vertical, it follows that the hinge reaction will also be vertical.

Hinge reaction. Take moments about A, clockwise moments positive.

$$5 \times 1 - 10 \times 3 - 3 + 4R_B = 0$$
$$R_B = 7\text{kN downwards}$$

Note. (i) The -3 in the third part of the above equation is the anticlockwise applied couple at the mid-point. Distance from A is not involved in the effect of this couple.

(ii) It is assumed that the reaction at B would produce a clockwise moment about A, i.e. the force at B would be down. If R_B had been negative, its direction would have had to have been reversed, i.e. upwards.

Roller reaction. Take moments about B, clockwise moments positive.

$$10 \times 1 - 5 \times 3 - 3 + 4R_A = 0$$
$$R_A = 2\text{kN upwards}$$

2) Shearing-force diagram.
Commence with the point B at the right-hand end of the beam, where there is a downward load of 7kN. Draw the vertical line downwards underneath B in the shearing-force diagram, to represent a shearing force of 7kN.

Since there is no other force between B and D, there will be no variation of the shearing force between these points, and the diagram will take the form of the horizontal line shown.

At D there is an upward force of 10kN. Draw a line vertically upwards underneath D to represent this 10kN. This will give a shearing force of $-7 + 10 = +3$kN.

Between D and C there is no other force, and the shearing-force diagram is a horizontal line, as shown. The couple has no effect on the shearing force (except in so far as it was taken into account in determining the value of the reactions).

At C there is a downward load of 5kN. Draw a vertical line downwards underneath C to represent 5kN, making the shearing force equal to $+3 - 5 = -2$kN.

Draw a horizontal line in the space between C and A, and then a vertically upwards line to represent the upward force of 2kN at A.

This will give the shearing force at A as zero.

3) Bending-moment diagram.
Bending moment at A = zero, since there is no force or couple to the left of A.

At C. Moment of 2kN force at A about C = $2 \times 1 = -2$kN m negative, since the moment is clockwise on the left of C.

The diagram between A and C will be a straight line having a constant negative slope. (Note that the value of the shearing force between A and C is constant and negative.)

At E. Moments about E give $5 \times 1 - 2 \times 2 = 1$kNm. The diagram between C and E will be a straight line having a positive slope. Then at E there is an anticlockwise couple of 3kNm. If we consider a section just beyond E, towards D, we see that this couple will be positive (anticlockwise on the left), so that the bending moment at E increases from +1 to +4.

At D. Moment of reaction at B = $7 \times 1 = 7$, clockwise on right. Hence the bending-moment diagram between E and D is a straight line of positive slope (in fact, the same slope as between C and E).

At B. Bending moment is zero. Between D and B the diagram is a straight line with negative slope.

Example 13.5 A uniform rod ABC, 1·2m long, and weighing 150N, is inclined upwards at 45° to the vertical, being supported at A by means of a hinge fastened to a vertical wall, and at B, 0·2m from C, by means of a horizontal cord fastened to the wall (fig.13.12). If a load of 50N is suspended from C, determine the force in the cord.

Draw diagrams showing the variation in shearing force, bending moment, and thrust along the rod.

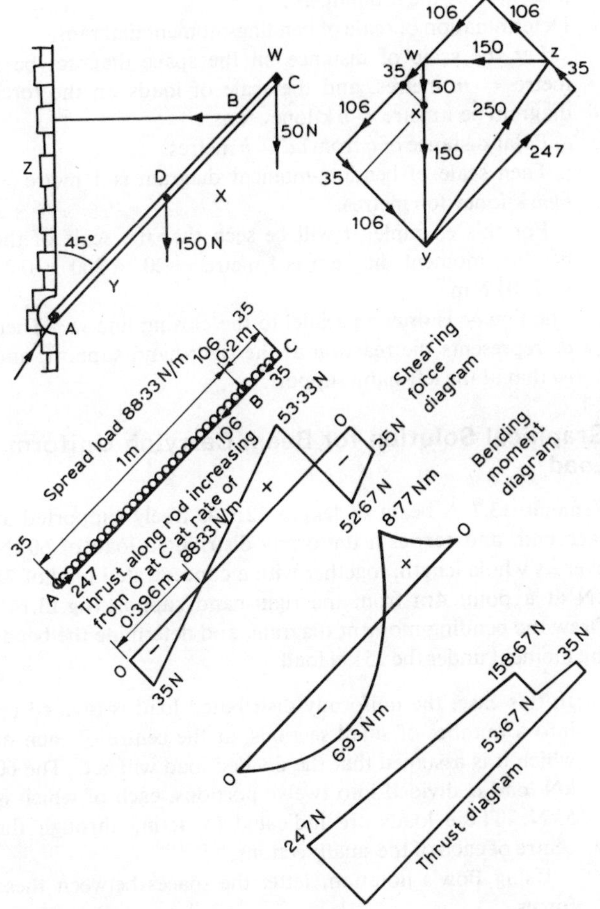

Fig.13.12

1) Determination of force in cord, *T*N.
Taking moments about A.

$$\frac{0{\cdot}6}{\sqrt{2}} \times 150 + \frac{1{\cdot}2}{\sqrt{2}} \times 50 = T \times \frac{1{\cdot}0}{\sqrt{2}}$$

$$T = 150\text{N}$$

2) Letter the spaces, W, X, Y, and Z, using Bow's notation, and draw the force diagram *wxyz*. The closing line *yz* represents the reaction of the hinge at A. Reaction of hinge = 250 N.

3) In order to analyse the shearing forces and bending moments, it is necessary to know the components of the various forces at right angles to the rod. Components along the rod have no effect on the shearing forces and the bending moments; they affect only the thrusts in the rod. The various components are obtained from the force diagram on the left. Their values are indicated on this diagram and also on the skeleton diagram showing forces on the rod immediately below the diagram of the general lay-out. This skeleton diagram is used as the basis of the remaining diagrams.

4) Shearing-force diagram.
Commencing at the right-hand end of the rod, i.e. the upper end, we have a downward force of 35N, and therefore draw the line downwards underneath point C to represent the shearing force of 35N. The remainder of the diagram is drawn in a similar manner to that already indicated in the previous examples.

The shearing force is zero at a point $\dfrac{1{\cdot}0 \times 35}{35 + 53{\cdot}33} = 0{\cdot}396$ m from A.

5) Bending-moment diagram
The bending moment at A is zero. Maximum bending moment at point of zero shearing force is

$$\frac{88{\cdot}35 \times 0{\cdot}396^2}{2} - 35 \times 0{\cdot}396 = 6{\cdot}93\text{Nm}.$$

$$\text{Bending moment at B} = 35 \times 0{\cdot}2 + \frac{88{\cdot}35 \times 0{\cdot}2^2}{2} = 8{\cdot}77\text{Nm}.$$

Note. The forces acting along the rod have been ignored in drawing the shearing-force and bending-moment diagrams.

6) Thrust along the rod.
The component of 35N along the rod causes the rod to be in compression to the extent of 35N between C and B. In addition there is a thrust increasing from 0 at C to 106N at A, i.e. at the rate of 88·33N/m. Hence thrust at B = 35 + (0·2 × 88·33) = 52·67N. At B there is an additional 106N thrust due to tension in the cord; the thrust at B therefore increases to 158·67N. A further increase of 88·33 × 1·0 = 88·33N occurs between B and A, so that the thrust at A is 158·67 + 88·33 = 247N. It will be seen that the component along the rod of the 250N hinge reaction is 247N, which balances the thrust in the rod between B and A.

Note. Since the forces applied to the rod cannot act at a point, but must be spread over a finite area of contact, the change of shearing force and thrust will take place between the two values over that area.

Graphical Solution for Bending-moment Diagrams

A graphical solution of bending-moment problems is often useful, particularly in the more complex loadings, and also in more advanced problems where the deflection of the beam is required. The method of solution is indicated in the two following examples.

Example 13.6 By using the graphical construction, draw the bending-moment diagram for the beam loaded as shown in fig.13.13. What is the scale of the diagram?

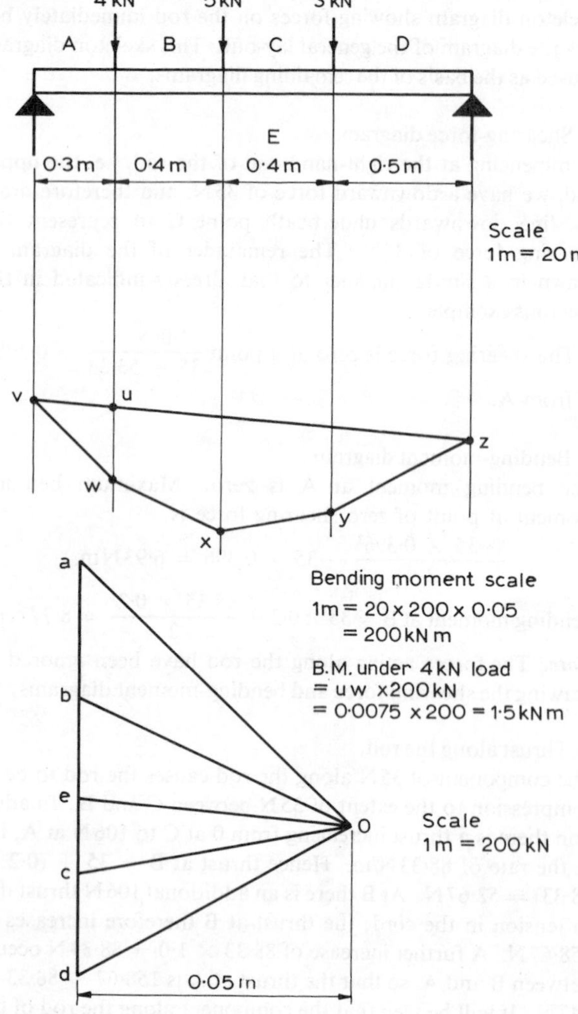

Fig.13.13

The bending-moment diagram is, in effect, the funicular polygon, which we have reviewed already.

1 Letter the spaces using Bow's notation, and draw the force line *abcd*.

2 Choosing any point O, whose horizontal distance from the load line is known, draw the lines *oa*, *ob*, *oc*, and *od*.

3 In space A, draw a line *vw* parallel to *oa*. Note that *v* is any point on the line representing force *EA*. From *w*, draw line *wx* in space B, parallel to *ob*; *xy* in space C is parallel to *oc*; and *yz* in space D is parallel to *od*.

4 Join *vz*, then the completed figure is the bending-moment diagram for the beam. The bending moment for any section is represented by the vertical ordinate of the diagram immediately underneath the particular section. Thus the bending moment underneath the 4 kN load is represented by the ordinate *uw*.

5 Determination of scale of bending-moment diagram.

Let the scale of distance on the space diagram be 1 metre = *m* metres, and the scale of loads on the force diagram be 1 metre = *n* kilonewtons.

Polar distance of *o* from *ad* = *h* metres.

Then scale of bending-moment diagram is 1 metre = *mnh* kilonewton metres.

For this example, it will be seen that the scale of the bending-moment diagram is 1 metre = 20 × 200 × 0·05 = 200 kN m.

6 The line *oe* is drawn parallel to the closing line *vz*. Then *de* represents the reaction at the right-hand support, and *ea* that at the left-hand support.

Graphical Solution for Beam Carrying Uniform Load

Example 13.7 A beam of length 12 m is freely supported at each end, and carries a uniformly distributed load of 60 kN over its whole length, together with a concentrated load of 25 kN at a point 4 m from the right-hand support (fig.13.14). Draw the bending-moment diagram, and determine the bending moment under the 25 kN load.

1 In this case, the uniformly distributed load is divided up into a number of small sections, at the centre of each of which it is assumed that the divided load will act. The 60 kN load is divided into twelve portions, each of which is 5 kN. These loads are indicated as acting through the centre of each of the small sections.

Using Bow's notation, letter the spaces between these forces.

2 Draw the force diagram *a . . . r*. Choose the pole *o* at a known distance from the load line. Join *oa*, *ob . . . or*.

3 Commencing at the point *u*, on the line of the force SA, draw in space A the line *uv* parallel to *oa*. From *v*, draw in space B a line *vw* parallel to *ob*. Continue throughout all the spaces until in space *R* the line *yz* is drawn parallel to *or*.

4 Join *uz*. The enclosed figure is the bending-moment diagram for the loaded beam. It will be noticed that the diagram is in fact made up of a number of straight lines,

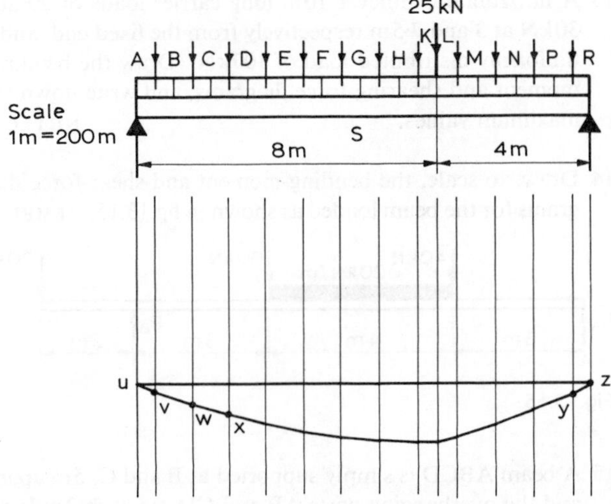

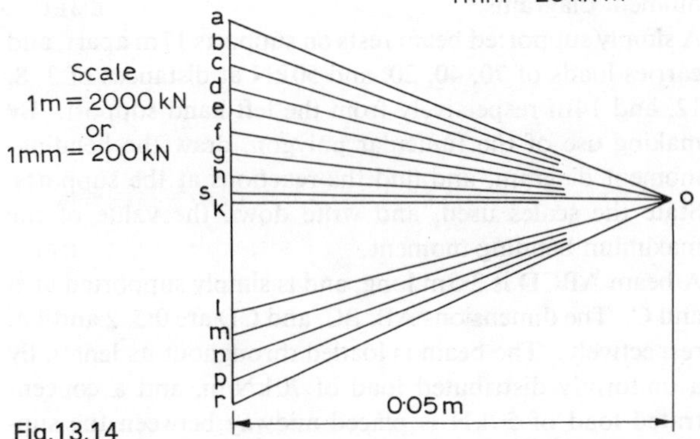

Fig.13.14

which should in fact be parabolic curves. It will be found, however, that the diagram is a very close approximation to the theoretical bending-moment diagram, especially if a large number of sections are taken in the initial division of the uniform load.

5 Scale of bending-moment diagram.

Let the scale of distances on the space diagram be 1 m = *m* m, and the scale of loads on the force diagram be 1 m = *n* kN.

Polar distance of *o* from *ar* = *h* m.

Then scale of bending-moment diagram is 1 m = *mnh* kNm

For this example, the scale will be 1 m = 200 × 2000 × 0·05 = 20 000 kN m. The depth of the bending-moment diagram underneath the 25 kN load is 7·3 mm. Hence the bending moment at this point is 7·3 × 20 = 146 kN m.

6 The line *os* is drawn parallel to the closing line *uz*. Then *rs* represents the reaction at the right-hand support, and *sa* that at the left-hand support.

Exercise 13

1 A horizontal girder ABCD, 20 m long, is hinged at B, and rests on a frictionless roller at C. AB = 4 m, BC = 10 m, and CD = 6 m. A downward vertical concentrated load of 20 kN is applied at A, a uniformly distributed load of 5 kN/m between B and C, and a downward concentrated load of 30 kN, inclined at 60° to the right of the vertical, at D.

Assuming the direction of the reaction at C to be vertical, determine the magnitude of the reaction at C, and the magnitude and direction of the reaction at B.

Sketch the shear-force diagram, and determine the point between the supports where the shear force is zero, and calculate the bending moment at that point.

Also state the maximum bending moment on the beam. ULCI

2 A horizontal beam ABCDEF is simply supported at B and E. A uniformly distributed load of 100 kN/m rests on the beam from A to C, and vertical concentrated loads of 70 and 80 kN are applied at the points D and F. AF = 3 m, AB = 0·6 m, AC = 1·6 m, AD = 2·1 m, and AE = 2·6 m.

Draw, to scales of 1 cm = 50 kN, and 1 cm = 10 kN m, the shearing-force and bending-moment diagrams for the loaded beam.

State the position and magnitude of the maximum bending moment on the beam between the supports. ULCI

3 A uniform shaft, 8 m long and weighing 500 N/m length, is simply supported in bearings placed 1·5 m from each end. A flywheel is keyed to each end of the shaft, the one at the left-hand side weighing 5 kN, and the other 4 kN. Determine the position and magnitude of the maximum bending moment on the portion of the shaft between the supports, when it is stationary.

If the centre of gravity of the left-hand flywheel is 5 mm from the axis of the shaft, determine the maximum loads on the bearings when the shaft rotates at 240 rev/min. ULCI

4 A horizontal beam ABCD, 2·5 m long, is simply supported at points A and C. The beam carries a uniformly distributed load of 2·5 kN/m between A and C, and concentrated loads of 3 and 2 kN at B and D respectively. AC = 2 m, AB = 0·6 m, and CD = 0·5 m.

Sketch the shear-force and bending-moment diagrams for the beam, and determine the position and magnitude of the maximum bending moment on the beam.

5 A horizontal beam AF is 3 m long, and is simply supported at points B and D, 2 m apart, the point B being 0·4 m from the left-hand end A. The beam carries two concentrated loads of 5 and 6 kN at points C and E respectively. AC = 1·4 m, and EF = 0·2 m. From A to C there is a uniformly distributed load of 5 kN/m.

Calculate the shear force and bending moment at the points A, B, C, D, E, and F. Sketch the shear force and bending-moment diagrams for the beam. These diagrams need not be to scale, but the numerical values at the points corresponding to A, B, C, D, E, and F must be given on the diagrams. ULCI

6 A floor having a weight of 5 kN/m² is laid on joists measuring 200 mm by 50 mm, with 3·6 m span between their supports. If the stress in the joist due to bending is 7 N/mm², calculate the distance between the joist centres. NCTEC

7 Draw the shearing-force and bending-moment diagrams for a beam supported on a span of 3 m, carrying a uniformly distributed load of 5 kN, and a central concentrated load of 3 kN. State the maximum values of shearing force and bending moment. NCTEC

8 What is meant by bending moment?

A beam resting on supports 14 m apart carries loads of 40 and 80 kN at 5 and 8 m respectively from the left support. If the beam also carries a uniformly distributed load of 70 kN, draw to scale the bending-moment and shearing-force diagrams, and write down the maximum values. NCTEC

9 A beam resting on supports 15 m apart carries concentrated loads of 30 and 50 kN at 5 and 12 m respectively from the left-hand support, and there is also a uniformly distributed load of 100 kN. Draw to scale the bending-moment and shearing-force diagrams, and write down the maximum values. NCTEC

10 Draw the shearing-force and bending-moment diagrams for a beam 12 m long which is freely supported at the ends, and carries a uniformly distributed load of 60 kN, and a load of 25 kN concentrated at 4 m from the right-hand support. State the scale of the bending-moment diagram. (Scales: 1 cm to 10 kN, 1 cm to 1 m.) (It is intended that this question shall be answered graphically.) NCTEC

11 A uniform beam AD, 10 m long, is symmetrically placed on simple supports at B and C, 7 m apart. The beam carries a load of 300 kN uniformly distributed over its whole length, together with loads of 20 kN at A, 100 kN at D, and 20 kN at E, the mid-point of the beam. Draw, on either graph or drawing paper, the shearing-force and bending-moment diagrams, and mark the value and position of the maximum bending moment. (Scales: 1 cm to 1 m, 1 cm to 25 kN, 1 cm to 50 kNm.) NCTEC

12 A beam ABC, 3 m long, is supported at A and B; AB = 2·4 m. The beam supports a uniformly distributed load of 50 kN/m run, extending from A to D, a distance of 1·8 m, together with a load of 20 kN at C. Using scales of 1 cm to 300 mm, 1 cm to 10 kN, and 1 cm to 5 kNm, draw the shearing-force and bending-moment diagrams for the beam. Clearly mark the value and position of the maximum bending moment. NCTEC

13 A horizontal cantilever 10 m long carries loads of 20 and 30 kN at 3 and 7·5 m respectively from the fixed end, and a uniformly distributed load of 100 kN. Draw the bending-moment and shearing-force diagrams, and write down the maximum values. NCTEC

14 Draw, to scale, the bending-moment and shear-force diagrams for the beam loaded as shown in fig. 13.15. EMEU

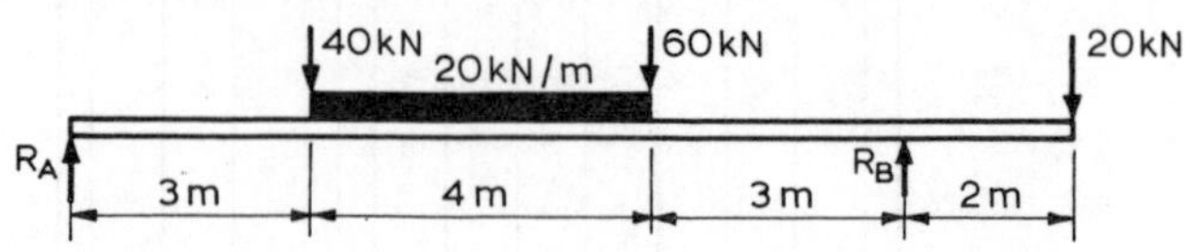

Fig. 13.15

15 A beam ABCD is simply supported at B and C, 5 m apart, and the overhanging parts AB and CD are each 2 m long. The beam carries a uniformly distributed load of 40 kN/m run between A and C, and there is a concentrated load of 90 kN at D. Draw to scale the shearing-force and bending-moment diagrams. EMEU

16 A simply supported beam rests on supports 17 m apart, and carries loads of 70, 40, 20, and 50 kN at distances of 3, 8, 12, and 14 m respectively from the left-hand support. By making use of the funicular polygon, draw the bending-moment diagram, and find the reactions at the supports. State the scales used, and write down the value of the maximum bending moment. UEI

17 A beam ABCD is 3·5 m long, and is simply supported at B and C. The dimensions AB, BC, and CD are 0·5, 2 and 1 m respectively. The beam is loaded throughout its length by a uniformly distributed load of 70 kN/m, and a concentrated load of 50 kN is placed midway between the supports. Draw to scale the shearing-force and bending-moment diagrams for the beam. UEI

18 A beam 15 m long is simply supported at each end. It carries a uniformly distributed load of 14 kN/m run over the left-hand half of the span, together with concentrated loads of 20, 30 and 20 kN situated 2, 3·5, and 7·5 m respectively from the right-hand support,

Draw the bending-moment and shearing-force diagrams for the beam, and determine the maximum bending moment acting on the beam, stating the position where it occurs. UEI

19 A beam of 10 m span, simply supported at its ends, carries a uniformly distributed load of 10 kN/m, and a concentrated load 3 m from one support. The effect of the concentrated load is to double the maximum bending moment caused by the uniformly distributed load alone. Draw the bending-moment and shearing-force diagrams, and determine the value of the concentrated load. UEI

20 A horizontal beam 15 m long, resting on supports at its ends, carries concentrated vertical loads of 70, 90, 50, and 80 kN at distances of 3, 8, 12, and 14 m respectively from the left-hand support. By graphical method only, draw the bending-moment diagram, and find the reactions at the supports. State clearly the different scales, and the value of the maximum bending moment. UEI

21 A small wall crane has a jib, AB, 4·5 m long, of uniform cross-section, and total weight 400 N. It is hinged to the wall at its lower end, A, and is inclined to the vertical at an angle of 30°. A tie rod is pinned to the jib 0·5 m below B, and to the wall 2 m above A. When a load of 2500 N is suspended from B, determine (a) the force in the tie rod, and (b) the thrust, shearing force, and bending moment at the mid-section of the jib. IMECHE

22 A beam ABCD, 12·5 m long, is simply supported at A and at C, 10 m from A. There is a uniformly distributed load of 20 kN/m run between the supports, and concentrated loads of 50 kN at B, 2 m from A, and 20 kN at D. Sketch the shearing-force and bending-moment diagrams approximately to scale, marking thereon the principal values, and state the position and magnitude of the maximum bending moment. IMECHE

23 A beam is 10 m long, and is freely supported at its ends, A and B. The part CB, from the centre of the span to the end B, carries a uniformly distributed load of 20 kN/m. State numerically, and show on a diagram, the forces which are exerted on the portion CB, and show that they satisfy the conditions of equilibrium. The depth of the beam is 0·5 m, and the section is rectangular. IMECHE

24 Draw to scale the shearing-force diagram and the bending-moment diagram for a beam 12 m long, simply supported at its ends, and carrying a uniformly distributed force of 20 kN/m along the entire length.

The distributed force on the left-hand half of the beam is removed, and replaced by a force of equal magnitude concentrated at the mid-length of the left-hand half, i.e. at 3 m from the left-hand end. Draw the diagrams for this case also.

What is the effect on the bending moment of (a) a change in sign of the shearing force, (b) a constant zero shearing force? ULCI

25 A beam is 3 m long, and it carries a uniformly distributed load of 1200 N per metre run. It is supported symmetrically at two points A and B.

Determine the position of the supports for the maximum bending moment in the beam to have its least possible value.

Sketch the shearing-force and the bending-moment diagrams for the beam, inserting the principal values. NCTEC

26 (a) A beam of length l m is simply supported at its ends, and carries a uniformly distributed load of w kN/m over the entire span. In addition, a concentrated load of W kN is situated at the mid-span.

Derive an expression for the maximum bending moment, and state the point at which it occurs.

(b) A horizontal beam ABCDE is simply supported at the left-hand end, A, and at D, which is 12 m from A. AB = 4 m, BC = 4 m, CD = 4 m, and DE = 3 m.

The beam carries a uniformly distributed load of 20 kN/m over the length AB, together with a concentrated load of 40 kN at C. Calculate the values of shear force and bending moment at all the lettered points, and sketch the shear-force and bending-moment diagrams. ULCI

Chapter 14

Centroids and Second Moments of Area

The centroid of an area is the centre or mean position of all the elements of area making up the complete area. When we are considering solids rather than areas, the elements of area become elements of mass, and the centroid is then the centre of gravity.

The position of an irregular figure with respect to the two axes OX and OY is shown in fig.14.1. The position of the centroid is indicated at G.

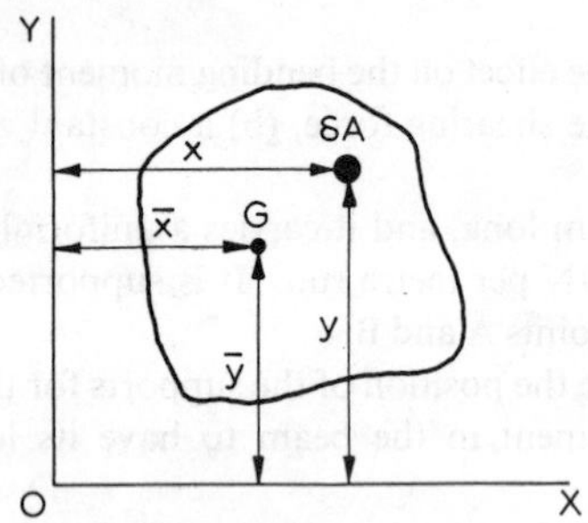

Fig.14.1 Second moment of area

Let A = total area of the figure;
δA = area of small element distance x from OY, and y from OX;
$\bar{x}$ = distance of centroid of figure from OY ($\bar{x}$ is referred to as 'bar x'. and is usually associated with distances to centroids);
$\bar{y}$ = distance of centroid of figure from OX.
The moment of the area δA about OY = $x\delta A$.
The moment of the area δA about OX = $y\delta A$.

Now the position of the centroid is such that the moment about any axis, such as OY, of the whole area concentrated at the centroid must be equal to the sum of the moments, about the same axis, of all the elements of area.

Moment about OY of whole area concentrated at G = $A\bar{x}$ . . (1)

Sum of moments about OY, of elements given = $\Sigma x\delta A$ . . (2)

(The Greek letter Σ (capital sigma) is used as an abbreviation of 'the sum of'. If the value for area δA could be expressed in terms of the distance x, then the integration sign $\int$ could be used in place of Σ.)

Equating (1) and (2), we get

$$\bar{x}A = \Sigma x\delta A$$

$$\bar{x} = \frac{\Sigma x\delta A}{A}$$

Similarly, $$\bar{y} = \frac{\Sigma y\delta A}{A}$$

Important Special Case

If the value of $\bar{x}$ becomes equal to zero, it would mean that the chosen axis OY would actually pass through the centroid of the area (fig.14.2).

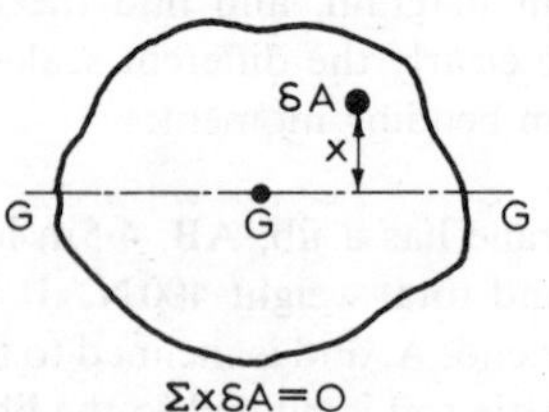

Fig.14.2 Position of centroid

But if $\bar{x} = 0$

then $\frac{\Sigma x\delta A}{A} = 0$

This can only mean that $\Sigma x\delta A = 0$

Conversely, if in any calculation we can show that $\Sigma x\delta A = 0$, then we can conclude that the axis about which the moments have been taken passes through the centroid of the area.

Second Moment of Area

If we multiply the area δA by the distance x from the axis, we obtain the first moment of the area, $x\delta A$, about the axis. If we multiply that product by x again, we obtain the second moment of the area, $x^2\delta A$, about the axis. The second moment of area is denoted by the symbol I, to which are usually attached suffixes indicating the axis about which the second moment has been taken. Referring to fig.14.1, we have

$$I_{OY} = \Sigma x^2\delta A$$

and $$I_{OX} = \Sigma y^2\delta A$$

Simple Case of Second Moment of Area of Rectangle

a) About axis along its base (fig.14.3).

Let b = breadth of the rectangle,
d = depth of the rectangle.

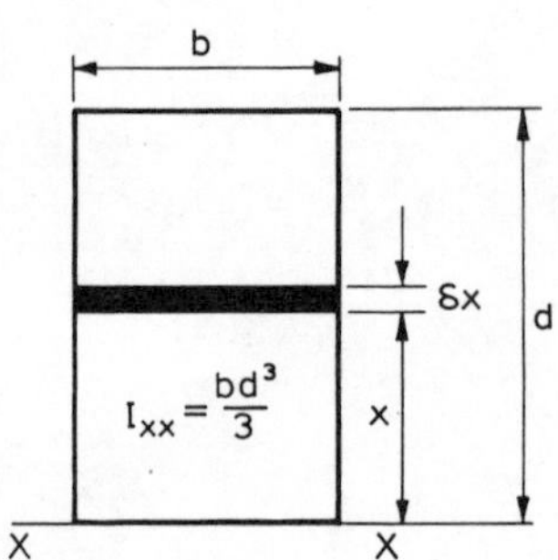

Fig.14.3 Second moment of area of rectangle about base

Consider the small slice thickness δx at distance x from XX.
Area of this slice $= b\delta x$
First moment of area of this slice about XX $= bx\delta x$
Second moment of area of this slice about XX $= bx^2\delta x$
Total second moment of area of rectangle about XX

$$= \int_0^d bx^2 dx$$

(the value of x varies from $x = 0$ to $x = d$)

$$\therefore\ I_{XX} = \left[\frac{bx^3}{3}\right]_0^d = \frac{bd^3}{3}$$

i.e. Second moment of area of rectangle about its base $= \frac{1}{3}bd^3$.

b) I about axis through centroid of rectangle (fig.14.4).

The centroid of the rectangle is the geometrical centre of the area.

Let b = breadth of the rectangle,
d = depth of the rectangle.

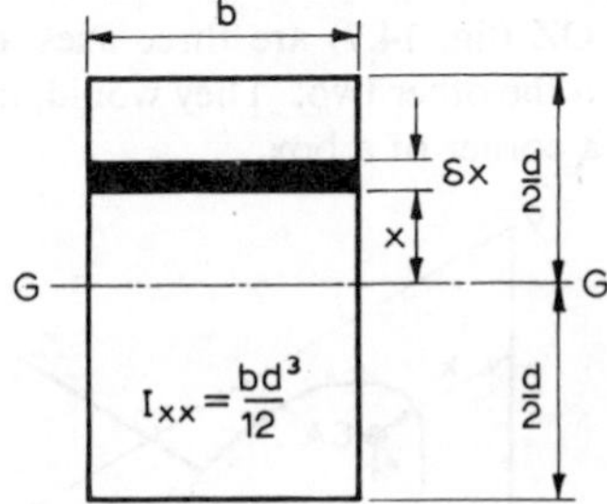

Fig.14.4 Second moment of area of rectangle about axis through centroid

Consider the small slice thickness δx at distance x from axis GG.
Area of this slice $= b\delta x$
Second moment of area of this slice about GG $= bx^2\delta x$

Total second moment of area of rectangle about GG

$$= \int_{-d/2}^{+d/2} bx^2 dx$$

(In this case the value of x varies from $+d/2$ above GG to $-d/2$ below GG.)

$$\therefore\ I_{GG} = \left[\frac{bx^3}{3}\right]_{-d/2}^{+d/2}$$

$$= \tfrac{1}{3}\left[b\left(\frac{d}{2}\right)^3 - b\left(-\frac{d}{2}\right)^3\right]$$

$$= \tfrac{1}{3}\left[\frac{bd^3}{8} + \frac{bd^3}{8}\right]$$

$$= \frac{1}{12}bd^3$$

i.e. Second moment of area of rectangle about axis through centroid, parallel to the base, is $\frac{1}{12}bd^3$.

Units of Second Moment of Area

In general, the units of length with which we are concerned are metres. This means that the units of the second moment of area will be in metres^4.

It will be well to mention a point here which often causes confusion. In problems of dynamics we have to obtain the moment of inertia of solid bodies; the mathematical processes used in finding this are identical to those which we have just used. For example, the moment of inertia of a mass M at distance r from an axis is defined as Mr^2 about that axis. In this case the units are kilogram metre^2. Due to the similarity in the type of expressions, there is often considerable loose thinking in connection with the subject; we often hear of 'moment of inertia of a section', and sometimes see kg m^2 units mentioned when m^4 should be used. A plane section having no mass cannot have any inertia, and consequently cannot have any moment of inertia. Perhaps we might summarise the position as follows.

Subject	*Name*	*Expression*	*Units*
dynamics mechanics of machines	moment of inertia	Mr^2	kg m^2
statics strength of materials	second moment of area	$\frac{bd^3}{12}$	m^4

Important Theorems Involving Second Moments of Area

(a) Theorem of parallel axes

We have already seen that the second moment of area of a rectangle about an axis through the centroid is different from that about an axis coinciding with its base. These two axes are parallel. We shall often be required to know the value of the second moment of area of a section about any number of axes parallel to the one through the centroid. The theorem of parallel axes is a convenient means of obtaining the value of the second moment of area about any axis, if we know the corresponding value about a parallel axis through the centroid.

The axis GG passes through the centroid of the section shown in fig.14.5. The area of this section is A, and its second moment of area about GG is I_{GG}.

We require to know the second moment of area of the section about XX, which is parallel to GG, and at distance h from GG.

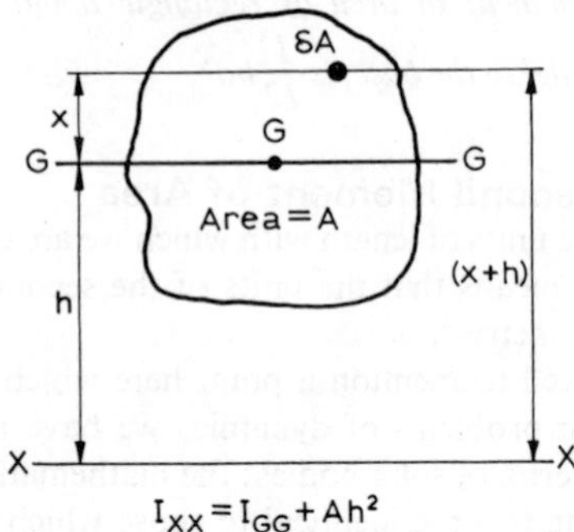

Fig.14.5 Theorem of parallel axes

Consider the small element of area δA, distance x from GG. The element is at a distance $(x + h)$ from XX.
Second moment of area of δA about XX $= (x + h)^2\delta A$
Second moment of area of whole section about XX,

$$I_{XX} = \Sigma(x + h)^2\delta A$$
$$= \Sigma(x^2 + h^2 + 2xh)\delta A$$
$$= \Sigma x^2\delta A + h^2\Sigma\delta A + 2h\Sigma x\delta A$$

(Notice that constants such as 2 and h have been brought outside the summation sign Σ).

Now

$\Sigma x^2\delta A$ is equal to the second moment of area of the section about GG, or I_{GG}.

$\Sigma\delta A$ is equal to the sum of all the small areas, which of course is equal to the total area, A, of the section.

$\Sigma x\delta A$ is equal to the sum of the first moments of area about an axis through the centroid. We have already seen that this is always equal to zero.

Substituting these values in the above expression, we have

$$I_{XX} = \Sigma x^2\delta A + h^2\Sigma\delta A + 2h\Sigma x\delta A$$
$$= I_{GG} + h^2A + 2.h.0$$
$$I_{XX} = I_{GG} + Ah^2$$

In words, *the second moment of area of any section, about an axis parallel to any other axis passing through the centroid of the section, is equal to the second moment of area of the section about the axis passing through the centroid, plus the product of the area of the section and the distance between the axes squared.*

This theorem can be used to obtain the second moment of area of a rectangle about its base (fig.14.6).

The distance between the axes is $d/2$.

Area of the section $= bd$

Second moment of area about axis GG $= \frac{1}{12}bd^3$

$$I_{XX} = I_{GG} + Ah^2$$

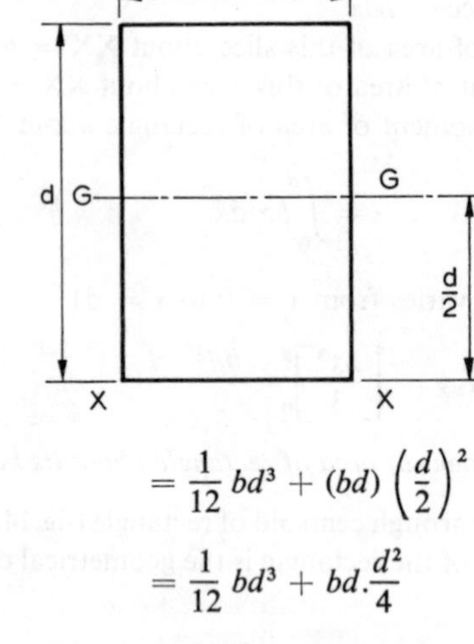

Fig.14.6

$$= \frac{1}{12}bd^3 + (bd)\left(\frac{d}{2}\right)^2$$

$$= \frac{1}{12}bd^3 + bd.\frac{d^2}{4}$$

$$= \tfrac{1}{3}bd^3$$

(b) Theorem of mutually perpendicular axes

OX, OY, and OZ (fig. 14.7) are three axes, each one being perpendicular to the other two. They would, in fact, form the three edges of a corner of a box.

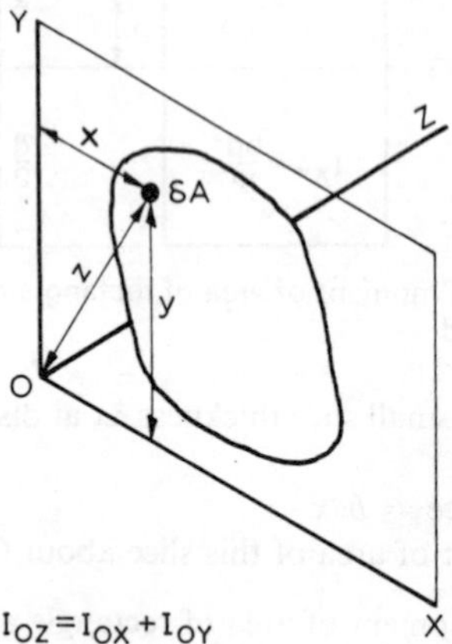

Fig.14.7 Theorem of three axes

In the vertical plane bounded by axes OX and OY is a section containing an element of area δA. This element is distance –

y from OX
x from OY,
z from OZ.

Second moment of area of the element about OZ

$$= z^2\delta A$$
$$= (x^2 + y^2)\delta A$$
$$= x^2\delta A + y^2\delta A$$

which is equal to the sum of the second moments of area of the element about OY and OX. Consequently, if we carry out the summation of the expressions such as $x^2\delta A$, we shall obtain the relationship

$$I_{OZ} = I_{OY} + I_{OX}$$

In words, *the second moment of area of any section, about an axis perpendicular to two perpendicular axes in the plane of the section, is equal to the sum of the second moments of area of the section about these two axes.*

The second moment of area about an axis through the centroid, perpendicular to the section, is known as the *polar* second moment of area.

Notice very carefully that *the two second moments of area which are added together are those about the axes in the plane of the section.*

As an example of the use of this theorem, we can obtain the polar second moment of area of a square.

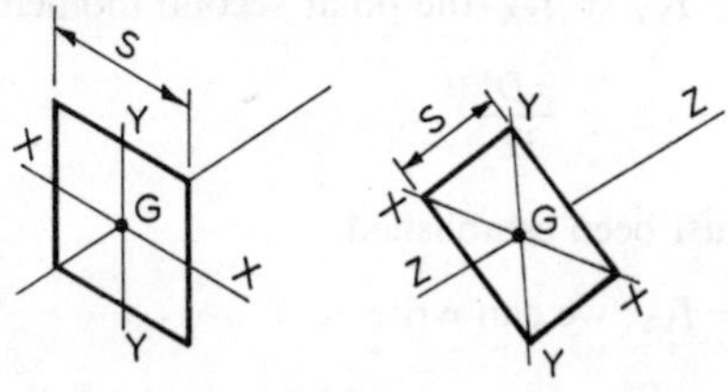

Fig.14.8 Polar second moment of area of square section

Let S = side of the square (fig.14.8).

$$I_{ZZ} = I_{XX} + I_{YY}$$

$$\text{but } I_{XX} = I_{YY} = \frac{1}{12}\,S.S^3 = \frac{S^4}{12}$$

$$\therefore\ I_{ZZ} = \frac{S^4}{12} + \frac{S^4}{12} = \frac{S^4}{6}$$

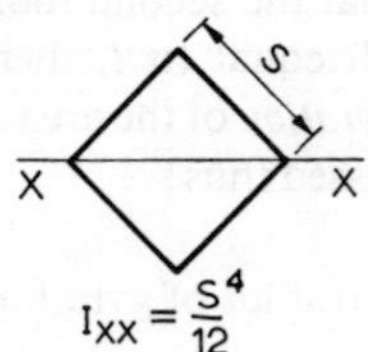

Fig.14.9 Second moment of area of square about diagonal

If the square is turned through 45° (fig.14.9), so that the diagonals fall on the axes XX and YY, we can say that since I_{XX} is the second moment of area about one diagonal, and I_{YY} that about the other, then

$$I_{XX} + I_{YY} = I_{ZZ} = \frac{S^4}{6}$$

but $$I_{XX} = I_{YY}$$

$$\therefore\ I_{XX} = \tfrac{1}{2}\frac{S^4}{6} = \frac{S^4}{12}$$

so that the second moment of area of a square, side S, about its diagonal is equal to $S^4/12$.

Removing the lower half of the square, we can claim that the second moment of area of a right-angled isosceles triangular area about its hypotenuse base is equal to $\frac{1}{2} \times S^4/12 = S^4/24$.

Using the parallel axis theorem, we can now find the second moment of this particular section about an axis parallel to the base, passing through its centroid (fig.14.10).

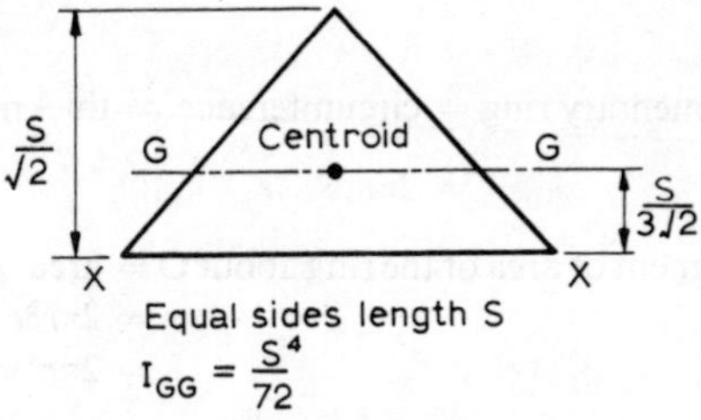

Fig.14.10 Second moment of area of isosceles right-angled triangle

$$\text{Height of the triangle} = \frac{S}{\sqrt{2}}$$

$$\text{Distance from base to centroid} = \tfrac{1}{3}\text{ height}$$

$$= \tfrac{1}{3}\frac{S}{\sqrt{2}}$$

$$\text{Area of triangle} = \frac{S^2}{2}$$

$$\therefore\ I_{GG} = I_{XX} - Ah^2$$

(*Note.* Negative sign when going back to the axis through the centroid.)

$$\text{i.e. } I_{GG} = \frac{S^4}{24} - \frac{S^2}{2}\left(\frac{S}{3\sqrt{2}}\right)^2$$

$$= \frac{S^4}{24} - \frac{S^4}{36}$$

$$I_{GG} = \frac{S^4}{72}$$

Polar Second Moment of Area of Circular Area

We might take the more general case of an annular area, that is the area contained between two concentric circles of radius R_1 (outer) and R_2 (inner).

Note. It is usual to use the symbol J for the polar second moment of area of a circular area.

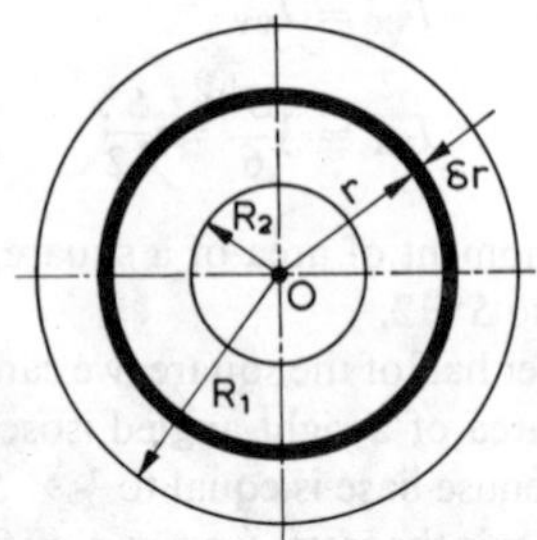

Fig.14.11 Polar second moment of area of annulus

Consider an elementary ring, thickness δr, at a distance r from the polar axis, the end view of which appears as O in fig.14.11.

Area of elementary ring = circumference × thickness

$$= 2\pi r \times \delta r$$

Second moment of area of the ring about O = area × distance²

$$= 2\pi r\delta r \times r^2$$
$$= 2\pi r^3\delta r$$

Total second moment of area of annulus about O (r varies from R_2 to R_1) $= \int_{R_2}^{R_1} 2\pi r^3 \mathrm{d}r$

$$= 2\pi\left[\frac{r^4}{4}\right]_{R_2}^{R_1}$$

$$= 2\pi\left[\frac{R_1^4 - R_2^4}{4}\right]$$

$$J = \frac{\pi}{2}(R_1^4 - R_2^4)$$

Since $R_1 = D_1/2$ and $R_2 = D_2/2$, we have by substitution

$$J = \frac{\pi}{2}\left(\frac{D_1^4}{16} - \frac{D_2^4}{16}\right)$$

$$= \frac{\pi}{32}(D_1^4 - D_2^4)$$

In the case of a circular area, $D_2 = 0$.

Hence polar second moment of area of a circular area is equal to $\pi D^4/32$, where D is the diameter of the circle.

Second Moment of Circular Area about a Diameter

It will be obvious from fig.14.12 that a unique property of the circular area is that its second moment of area about any diameter will have the same value.

In particular, I_{XX} will equal I_{YY}, where XX and YY are two diameters at right angles.

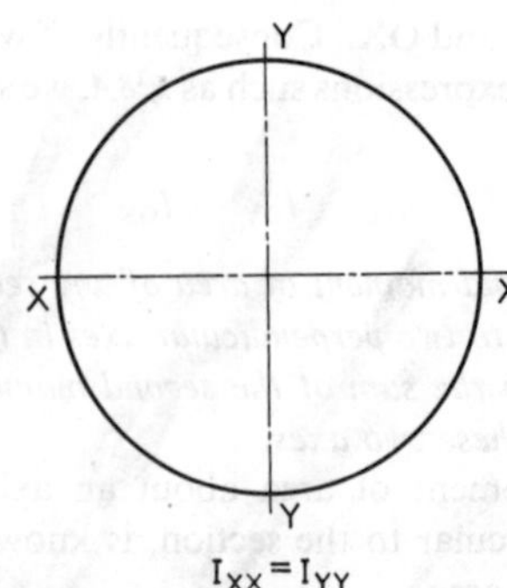

Fig.14.12 Second moment of area of circular disc about a diameter
Since the section is symmetrical about each axis, the second moments of area about each of the perpendicular axes are equal.

But $I_{XX} + I_{YY} = I_{ZZ}$ (the polar second moment of area)

$$= \frac{\pi D^4}{32}$$

which has just been established.

Since $I_{XX} = I_{YY}$, we can write

$$I_{XX} + I_{XX} = \frac{\pi D^4}{32}$$

$$I_{XX} = \frac{\pi D^4}{64}$$

Hence the second moment of area of a circular area about a diameter is equal to $\pi D^4/64$, where D is the diameter of the circle.

Radius of Gyration (k)

If any sectional area, A, whose second moment of area about an axis is I, could be concentrated at one spot, distance k from the axis (fig.14.13), so that the second moment of area of the concentrated spot is still equal to I, then the distance k is defined as the *radius of gyration* of the area about the axis. The relationship can be expressed thus:

$$I = \text{area} \times (\text{radius of gyration about the axis})^2$$
$$= Ak^2$$

Hence radius of gyration about axis

$$= \sqrt{\frac{\text{second moment of area about axis}}{\text{area}}}$$

Applying this expression to a rectangular area, breadth b, depth d, we have

second moment of area about axis through centroid $= \dfrac{bd^3}{12}$

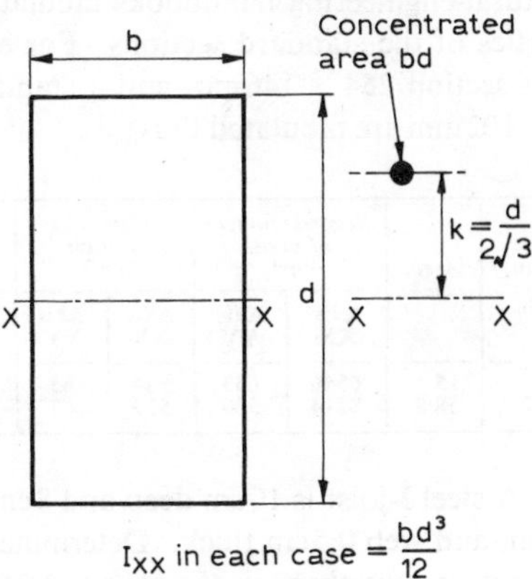

Fig.14.13 Radius of gyration

Area of section $= bd$

Radius of gyration about axis through centroid $= \sqrt{\dfrac{bd^3/12}{bd}}$

$$= \sqrt{\frac{d^2}{12}}$$

$$= \frac{d}{2\sqrt{3}} = 0{\cdot}289d$$

Similarly for a circular area:

polar second moment of area $= \dfrac{\pi D^4}{32}$

Area of section $= \dfrac{\pi D^2}{4}$

Radius of gyration about polar axis $= \sqrt{\dfrac{\pi D^4/32}{\pi D^2/4}}$

$$= \sqrt{\frac{D^2}{8}}$$

$$= \frac{D}{2\sqrt{2}} \text{ or } \frac{R}{\sqrt{2}}$$

$$= 0{\cdot}353D$$

The parallel-axis theorem will also apply to radii of gyration.

Since $I_{GG} = Ak^2{}_{GG}$
and $I_{XX} = Ak^2{}_{XX}$
we can substitute in the equation

$$I_{XX} = I_{GG} + Ah^2$$

and obtain $Ak^2{}_{XX} = Ak^2{}_{GG} + Ah^2$

$$k^2{}_{XX} = k^2{}_{GG} + h^2$$

where h is the distance between the axes.

Section Modulus (Z)

The idea of section modulus is often used in problems relating to the strength of materials.

Section modulus

$$= \frac{\text{second moment of area}}{\text{maximum distance of any part of the section from the axis}}$$

Take, for example, the rectangular area, breadth b and depth d. The second moment of area about an axis through the centroid is $bd^3/12$. The maximum distance of any part of the section from the axis will be $d/2$.

Hence section modulus for rectangular section is

$$\frac{bd^3/12}{d/2} = \frac{bd^2}{6}$$

Similarly for the circular area. Take the case of the polar second moment of area $= \pi D^4/32$. Maximum distance of any part of area from polar axis is $D/2$.

Hence section modulus about polar axis is

$$\frac{\pi D^4/32}{D/2} = \frac{\pi D^3}{16}$$

Two points may be mentioned in connection with the section modulus.

1 The section modulus is normally expressed only about axes through the centroid (including polar axes).

2 For asymmetrical sections, we shall find two section moduli for any axis. This is due to the fact that there is one maximum distance for that part of the area above the axis, and there is another for parts below the axis (fig.14.14),

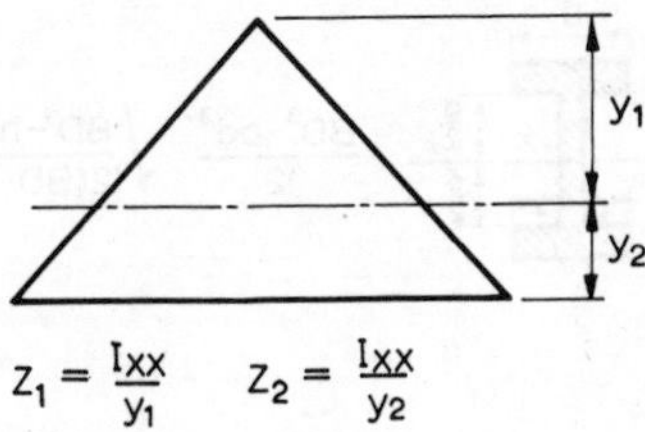

Fig.14.14 Section modulus. Unsymmetrical figures often have two values of section modulus about any one axis, due to the two different values of y.

Units for Section Modulus

Since the dimensions of the various sections are usually expressed in metres, the normal unit for section modulus is metre³.

The properties which we have just been considering are tabulated for certain sectional areas in fig.14.15.

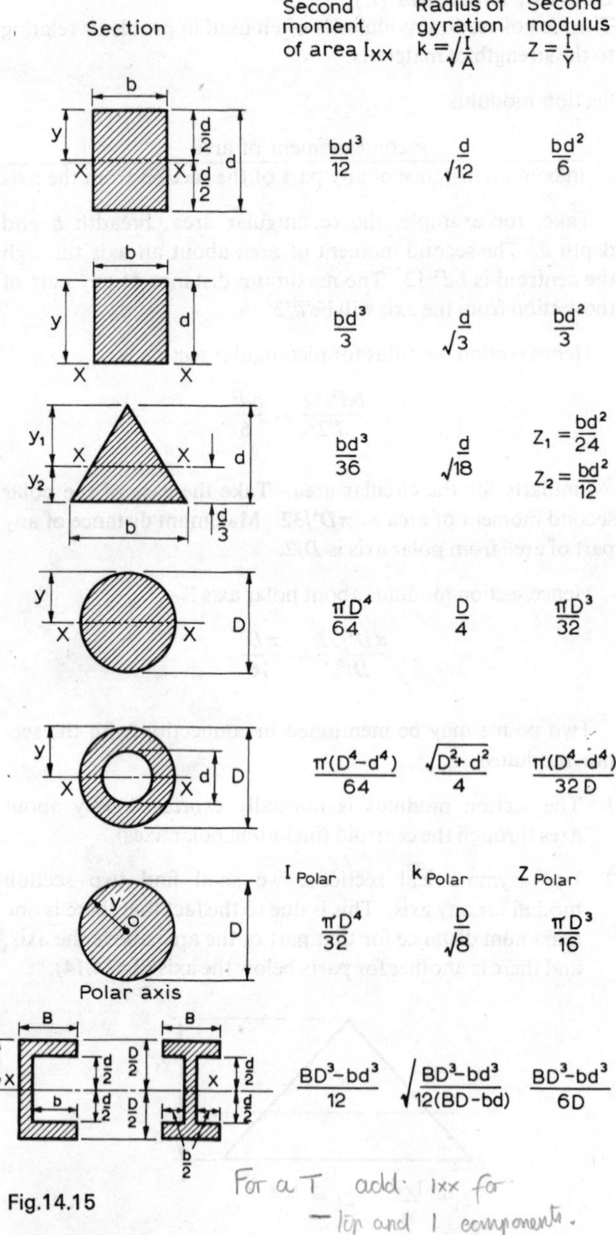

Fig.14.15

Use of Tables

The actual cross-sectional shapes of angle irons, channels, and joints are somewhat modified from the square-cornered, rectangular sections which we have been considering. For reasons of design and production, square internal corners are replaced by rounded fillets, and the flanges are tapered and rounded off at the ends. All this means that it is not quite so easy to determine the various values of the second moment of area, radius of gyration, and section moduli. Many of the sections have to be analysed by graphical methods. For this reason, structural-engineering handbooks tabulate the values of the properties of the standard sections. For example, the standard joist section 254 × 146mm and a standard channel section 305 × 102mm are tabulated thus:

Size, b × d mm	*Mass per m, kg*	*Area, cm²*	*Second moment of area cm⁴*		*Moduli of section cm³*		*Radius of gyration cm*	
			Axis XX	Axis YY	Axis XX	Axis YY	Axis XX	Axis YY
254 × 146	43	15	6546	633	504	85	11	3·4
305 × 102	46·2	58·8	8214	500	539	67	11·8	2·9

Example 14.1 A steel I-joist is 10cm deep and 8cm wide, with flanges 0·75cm, and web 0·5cm thick. Determine the following values about an axis through the centroid of the section parallel to the flanges: (a) the second moment of area of the section, (b) the radius of gyration, and (c) the section modulus.

In the case of an I-joist having equal flanges at the top and bottom, it is convenient to consider the section as consisting of a rectangular area from which two smaller rectangular sections have been removed. Since the section is symmetrical about two axes, its centroid will be at the intersection of the two axes (fig.14.16).

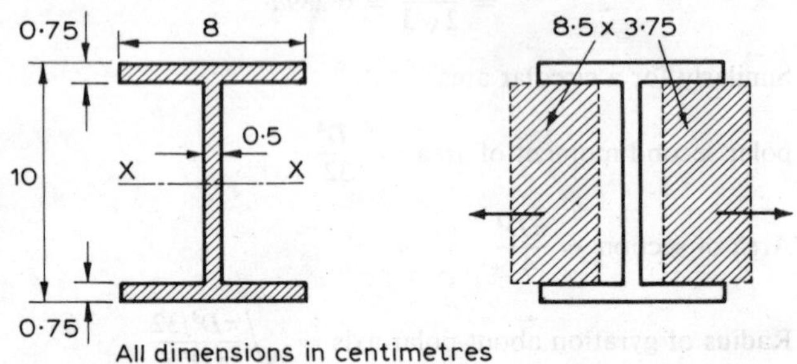

Fig.14.16

(a) Second moment of area

The larger rectangle is 8cm wide and 10cm deep. Hence, for this rectangle.

$$I_{XX} = \frac{bd^3}{12} = \frac{8 \times 10^3}{12} = 666{\cdot}7\,\text{cm}^4$$

The two smaller rectangles are 3·75cm wide, and 8·5cm deep. Hence, for each rectangle.

$$I_{XX} = \frac{bd^3}{12} = \frac{3{\cdot}75 \times 8{\cdot}5^3}{12} = 191{\cdot}5\,\text{cm}^4$$

Applying these results to the complete I-section, we have

$$I_{XX} = 666{\cdot}7 - (2 \times 191{\cdot}5)\,\text{cm}^4$$
$$= 283{\cdot}7\,\text{cm}^4$$

(b) Radius of gyration

Area of section = total area − 2 × area of removed rectangles
= (10 × 8) − 2(3·75 × 8·5)
= 16·26 cm²

$$k^2 = \frac{I}{A} = \frac{283{\cdot}7}{16{\cdot}25} = 17{\cdot}46$$

$$k = 4{\cdot}18\,\text{cm}$$

(c) Section modulus

$$\text{Section modulus, } Z = \frac{I}{y}$$

In this case $y = 5\,\text{cm}$

$$Z = \frac{283{\cdot}7\,\text{cm}^3}{5}$$

$$= 56{\cdot}74\,\text{cm}^3$$

i.e. The second moment of area = 283·7 cm⁴, the radius of gyration = 4·18 cm, and the section modulus = 56·74 cm³, all about axis through centroid parallel to flange.

Example 14.2 A steel joist is 10 cm deep, and 8 cm wide, with flanges 0·75 cm, and web 0·5 cm thick [fig.14.17(i)]. Determine the following values about an axis through the centroid of the section parallel to the web: (a) the second moment of area of the section, (b) the radius of gyration, and (c) the section modulus.

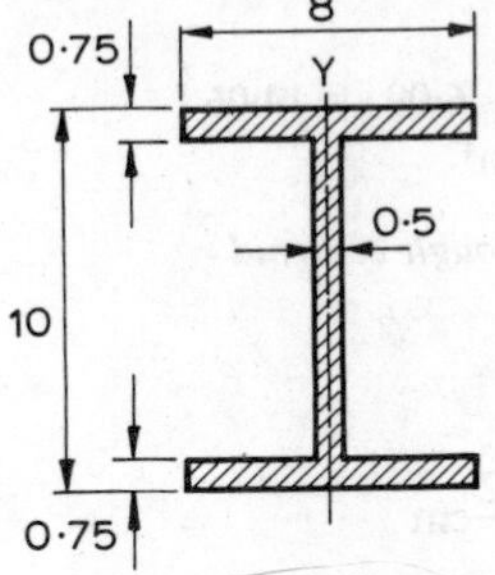

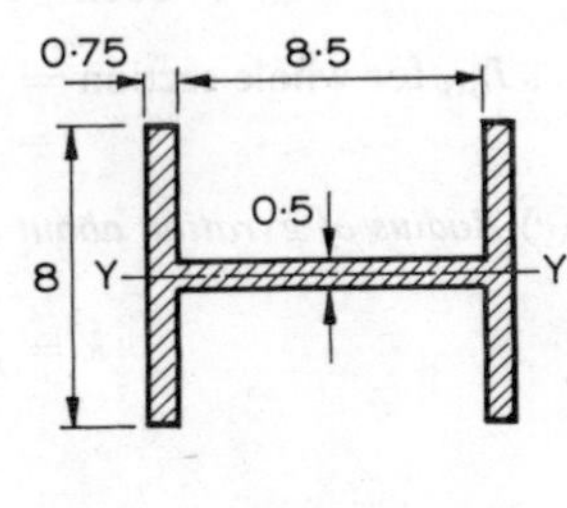

All dimensions in centimetres

Fig.14.17 (i) (ii)

This is the same section as that used in the previous problem, but the basic axis is now at right angles to that used in the previous case. In dealing with this example, we shall have to consider the section divided into three rectangles:

A − 8 cm deep, and 0·75 cm wide;
B − 0·5 cm deep, and 8·5 cm wide;
C − 8 cm deep, and 0·75 cm wide.

Notice that the width of the rectangle is taken parallel to the axis YY, which in this case passes through the centroid of each of the rectangles. The section has been turned through 90° in fig.14.17(ii), to give us the more familiar horizontal axis. The student should try to become equally conversant with vertical axes.

(a) Second moment of area

I for the whole section will be the sum of the I's for the three rectangles.

$$I_{YY} \text{ for } A = \frac{bd^3}{12} = \frac{0{\cdot}75 \times 8^3}{12} = 32{\cdot}0\,\text{cm}^4$$

$$I_{YY} \text{ for } B = \frac{bd^3}{12} = \frac{8{\cdot}5 \times 0{\cdot}5^3}{12} = 0{\cdot}089\,\text{cm}^4$$

$$I_{YY} \text{ for } C = \frac{bd^3}{12} = \frac{0{\cdot}75 \times 8^3}{12} = 32{\cdot}0\,\text{cm}^4$$

$$\text{Total } I \text{ for the section} = 64{\cdot}089\,\text{cm}^4$$

(b) Radius of gyration

Area of the section is (8 × 1·5) + (8·5 × 0·5) = 16·25 cm²

$$k^2 = \frac{I}{A} = \frac{64{\cdot}09}{16{\cdot}25} = 3{\cdot}95$$

$$k = 1{\cdot}98\,\text{cm}$$

(c) Section modulus

$$Z \text{ for the section} = \frac{I}{y}$$

In this case y is equal to $\frac{8}{2} = 4\,\text{cm}$

$$Z = \frac{64{\cdot}09}{4} = 16{\cdot}02\,\text{cm}^3$$

i.e. The second moment of area = 64·09 cm⁴, the radius of gyration = 1·98 cm, and the section modulus = 16·02 cm³, all about axis through centroid parallel to web.

Maximum and Minimum Values of Second Moment of Area

From examples 14.1 and 14.2 we have obtained the following values for the same section:

$$I_{XX} = 283{\cdot}7\,\text{cm}^4,\ k_{XX} = 4{\cdot}18\,\text{cm},\ Z_{XX} = 56{\cdot}74\,\text{cm}^3$$
$$I_{YY} = 64{\cdot}09\,\text{cm}^4,\ k_{YY} = 1{\cdot}98\,\text{cm},\ Z_{YY} = 16{\cdot}02\,\text{cm}^3$$

We might have calculated the value of any of these expressions for any other axis passing through the centroid of the section. We should certainly have found the work much more difficult for any of the inclined axes. Without attempting any proof, it can be stated that the value of, say, the second moment of area about any of the other axes will lie between the values given in the above table. This means that the values expressed above are the maximum and minimum values for the section. This fact will be found to be of great importance in further work in either strength of materials or theory of structures.

Example 14.3 Details are given in fig.14.18 of the section of a steel girder.

Determine (a) the position of the centroid of the section, (b) the second moment of area of the section about a horizontal axis through the centroid, (c) the radius of gyration about this axis, and (d) the section moduli about this axis.

In a section of this type it is convenient to divide the area into three rectangular areas A, B, and C.

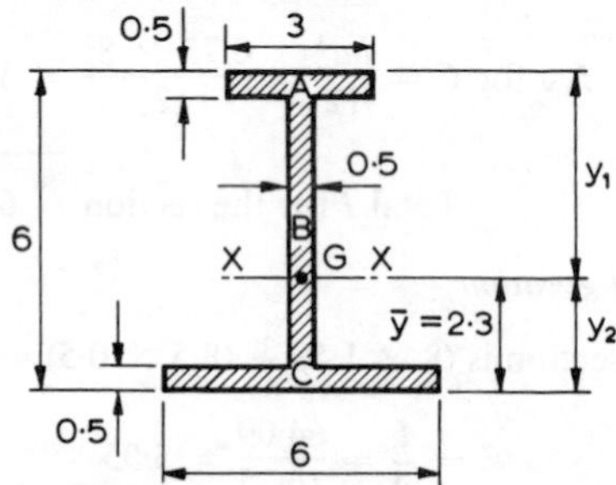

Fig.14.18 All dimensions in centimetres

Part	Area (cm²)	Distance of centroid from base (cm)	Moment about base (cm³)
A	3 × 0·5 = 1·5	5·75	1·5 × 5·75 = 8·625
B	5 × 0·5 = 2·5	3·00	2·5 × 3·00 = 7·50
C	6 × 0·5 = 3·0	0·25	3·0 × 0·25 = 0·75
	Total area = 7·0		Sum of moments about base = 16·875

(a) Distance, $\bar{y}$, of the centroid from the base

$$\bar{y} = \frac{\text{sum of moments about base}}{\text{total area}} = \frac{16{\cdot}875}{7} = 2{\cdot}41\,\text{cm}$$

(b) Second moment of area

In determining the second moment of area, we shall consider each rectangle in turn, obtain its second moment of area about the horizontal axis through its centroid, and then, by means of the parallel axis theorem, obtain the value of I about a horizontal axis through the centroid of the whole area.

Rectangle A, area 1·5 cm²

I_{GG} about axis through its centroid

$$= \frac{bd^3}{12} = \frac{3 \times 0{\cdot}5^3}{12} = 0{\cdot}031\,\text{cm}^4$$

Distance from centroid of A to centroid of whole area

$$= 5{\cdot}75 - 2{\cdot}41 = 3{\cdot}34\,\text{cm}$$

I about axis through centroid of whole area

$$= I_{GG} + Ah^2$$
$$= 0{\cdot}031 + (1{\cdot}5 \times 3{\cdot}34^2)\,\text{cm}^4$$
$$= 16{\cdot}77\,\text{cm}^4$$

Rectangle B, area 2·5 cm²

I_{GG} about axis through centroid

$$= \frac{bd^3}{12} = \frac{0{\cdot}5 \times 5^3}{12} = 5{\cdot}21\,\text{cm}^4$$

Distance from centroid of B to centroid of whole area

$$= 3{\cdot}00 - 2{\cdot}41 = 0{\cdot}59\,\text{cm}$$

I about axis through centroid of whole area

$$= I_{GG} + Ah^2$$
$$= 5{\cdot}21 + (2{\cdot}5 \times 0{\cdot}59^2)\,\text{cm}^4$$
$$= 6{\cdot}09\,\text{cm}^4$$

Rectangle C, area 3 cm²

I_{GG} about axis through centroid

$$= \frac{bd^3}{12} = \frac{6 \times 0{\cdot}5^3}{12} = 0{\cdot}0625\,\text{cm}^4$$

Distance from centroid of B to centroid of whole area

$$= 2{\cdot}41 - 0{\cdot}25 = 2{\cdot}16\,\text{cm}$$

I about axis through centroid of whole area

$$= I_{GG} + Ah^2$$
$$= 0{\cdot}0625 + (3 \times 2{\cdot}16^2)$$
$$= 14{\cdot}06\,\text{cm}^4$$

$\therefore I_{GG}$ for whole section $= 16{\cdot}77 + 6{\cdot}09 + 14{\cdot}06$
$= 36{\cdot}92\,\text{cm}^4$

(c) Radius of gyration about axis through centroid

$$k = \sqrt{\frac{I_{GG}}{A}}$$
$$= \sqrt{\frac{36{\cdot}92}{7}}\,\text{cm}$$
$$k = 2{\cdot}30\,\text{cm}$$

(d) Section moduli

For this section, there will be two section moduli with respect to the horizontal axis through the centroid, since there are two different values of y.

Distance to the top edge $y_1 = 6 - 2{\cdot}41 = 3{\cdot}59\,\text{cm}$

Distance to the bottom edge $y_2 = 2{\cdot}41\,\text{cm}$

$$Z_1 = \frac{I}{y_1} = \frac{36{\cdot}92}{3{\cdot}59} = 10{\cdot}28\,\text{cm}^3$$

$$Z_2 = \frac{I}{y_2} = \frac{36{\cdot}92}{2{\cdot}41} = 15{\cdot}32\,\text{cm}^3$$

i.e. The second moment of area, I_{GG} = 36·92 cm⁴, the radius of gyration, k_{GG} = 2·30 cm, and the section modulus, Z_1 = 10·28 cm³, and Z_2 = 15·32 cm³.

Example 14.4 A fabricated girder system consists of two plates 12 cm × 7·5 mm, and two channels 12 cm × 4 cm, set 4 cm apart, as shown in fig.14.19. The following are the properties of the 12 cm × 4 cm channel section.

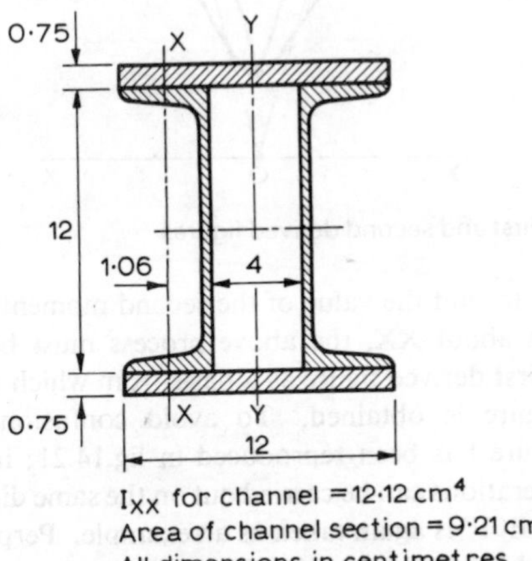

Fig.14.19

Determine the value of the second moment of area, and the radius of gyration about a vertical axis through the centroid of the whole section.

The details supplied are typical of those to be found in structural handbooks relating to the accepted standard sections.

Since the whole section is symmetrical, the centroid will lie on the intersection of the two axes of symmetry.

Consider first the channels. Taking them separately, we have

$$I_{XX} = 12{\cdot}12\,\text{cm}^4$$
$$I_{YY} = I_{XX} + Ah^2$$
$$= 12{\cdot}12 + (9{\cdot}21 \times 3{\cdot}06^2)\,\text{cm}^4$$
$$= 98{\cdot}34\,\text{cm}^4$$

Combined I for both channels $= 2 \times 98{\cdot}34\,\text{cm}^4$
$= 196{\cdot}68\,\text{cm}^4$

Considering each plate separately, we notice that the axis YY passes through the centroid of the area of each plate. For this axis, $b = 0{\cdot}75$ cm, and $d = 12$ cm.

$$I_{YY} = \frac{bd^3}{12}$$
$$= \frac{0{\cdot}75 \times 12^3}{12}\,\text{cm}^4$$
$$= 108\,\text{cm}^4$$

Combined I for both plates $= 2 \times 108\,\text{cm}^4$
$= 216\,\text{cm}^4$

I for whole section about vertical axis through centroid
$= 196{\cdot}68 + 216$
$= 412{\cdot}68\,\text{cm}^4$

Radius of gyration about axis YY
Area of two channels $= 2 + 9{\cdot}21 = 18{\cdot}42\,\text{cm}^2$
Area of two plates $= 2 \times 12 \times 0{\cdot}75 = 18{\cdot}0\,\text{cm}^2$
Total area of section $= 36{\cdot}42\,\text{cm}^2$
Second moment of area $= 402{\cdot}44\,\text{cm}^4$

$$k = \sqrt{\frac{I}{A}} = \sqrt{\frac{412{\cdot}68}{36{\cdot}42}}$$
$$= 3{\cdot}37\,\text{cm}$$

Radius of gyration about YY = 3·37 cm.

Graphical Solution

The position of the centroid of a section and its second moment of area about an axis passing through the centroid are often required for a complicated or irregular section. It is possible to obtain the required information by graphical methods.

An irregular section is shown in fig.14.20. It is required to determine the position of the centroid, and also the value of the second moment of area of the section about the axis XX. The following method is used.

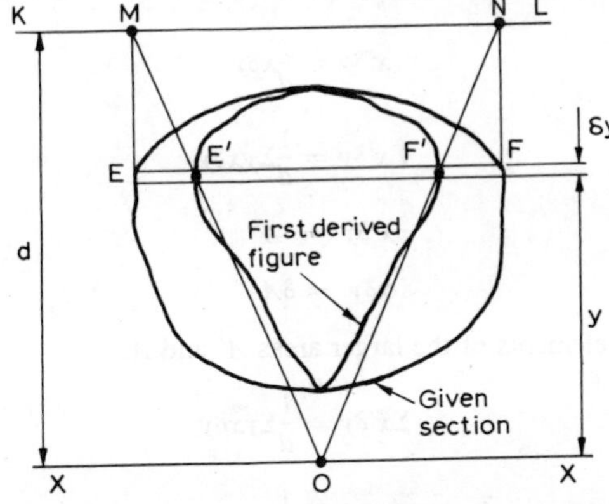

Fig.14.20 Graphical method of determining position of centroid, and second moment of area

1 Draw a line KL parallel to the given axis XX, at a known distance from XX. Choose a point O on the axis XX.
2 Draw any line EF, parallel to XX, cutting the boundary of the given section in E and F.
3 Drop a perpendicular from E and F on to KL, meeting KL in M and N.
4 Join M and N to O, and let MO cut EF in E′, and NO cut EF in F′.

5 Repeat this construction with a number of lines similar to EF, each parallel to XX, and obtain a corresponding number of points such as E′ and F′.
6 Join the points such as E′ and F′ together, to form an enclosed figure. This figure is known as the *first derived figure*.
7 Obtain the area enclosed by the first derived figure. This can be done by counting squares, by any of the accepted rules, such as Simpson's Rule, or with the planimeter.

Let A = area of original section,
A' = area of first derived figure,
d = distance between axis XX and line KL,
y = distance of EF from XX,
δy = width of strip at EF,
$\bar{y}$ = distance to centroid from XX,
x = length of EF,
x' = length of E′ F′.

Then $\bar{y} = \dfrac{A'd}{A}$

Proof MN = x

$$E'F' = \frac{MN}{d} \times y$$

$$x' = \frac{x}{d} \times y \quad . \quad . \quad . \quad . \quad . \quad (1)$$

Multiplying both sides by δy,

$$x'\delta y = \frac{y}{d} x \delta y$$

$$\Sigma x'\delta y = \frac{1}{d}\Sigma y x \delta y$$

But $x'\delta y = \delta A'$

and $x\delta y = \delta A$

being elements of the larger areas A' and A.

$$\Sigma x'\delta y = \frac{1}{d}\Sigma y x \delta y$$

$$\therefore \Sigma \delta A' = \frac{1}{d}\Sigma y \delta A \quad . \quad . \quad (2)$$

Now $\Sigma\delta A' = A'$

and $\Sigma y\delta A$ = first moment of area of section about XX

$= A\bar{y}$

$$\therefore A' = \frac{1}{d}A\bar{y}$$

$$\bar{y} = \frac{A'd}{A} \quad . \quad . \quad . \quad . \quad . \quad . \quad (3)$$

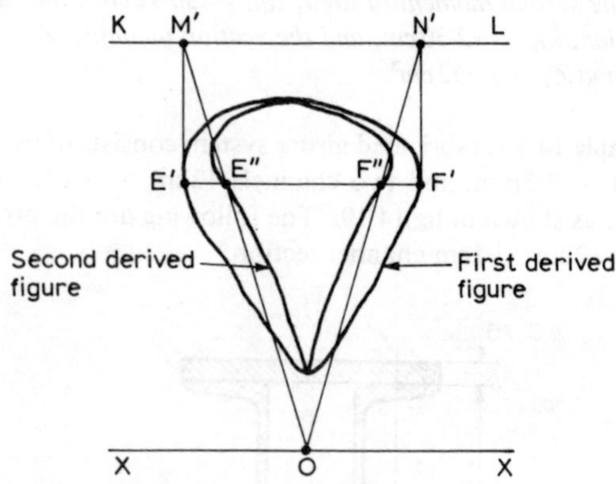

Fig.14.21 First and second derived figures

In order to find the value of the second moment of area of the section about XX, the above process must be repeated using the first derived figure as a basis from which the second derived figure is obtained. To avoid confusion, the first derived figure has been reproduced in fig.14.21; in practice, the two operations can be carried out on the same diagram.

The line E′ F′ is again taken as an example. Perpendiculars from E′ and F′ cut KL in M′ and N′. Joining M′ and N′ to O, the original line E′ F′ is cut at points E″ and F″. More lines similar and parallel to E′ F′ produce more points corresponding to E″ and F″. Joining these points together, the second derived figure is obtained.

$$E''F'' = \frac{M'N'y}{d} = \frac{E'F'}{d}y$$

$$= \frac{x'y}{d}$$

But $x' = \dfrac{x}{d}y$, from equation (1)

$$\therefore E''F'' = x'' = \frac{xy^2}{d^2}$$

Multiplying by δy,

$$x''\delta y = \frac{y^2 x \delta y}{d^2}$$

$$\Sigma x''\delta y = \frac{1}{d^2}\Sigma y^2 x \delta y$$

$$\Sigma\delta A'' = \frac{1}{d^2}\Sigma y^2 \delta A$$

$$A'' = \frac{1}{d^2}I_{XX}$$

since $\Sigma y^2\delta A$ is equal to the second moment of area about XX.

$$\therefore I_{XX} = A''d^2$$

The value of the second moment of area about an axis through the centroid can be found using the parallel-axis theorem.

Summarising, we have

distance to centroid from given axis

$$= \frac{\text{area of first derived figure}}{\text{area of section}} \times d$$

second moment of area about given axis

$$= \text{area of second derived figure} \times d^2$$

Example 14.5 Determine the position of the centroid of a semi-circular area of 3 cm radius, and the value of the second moment of area of the section about an axis through the centroid parallel to the base (fig.14.22).

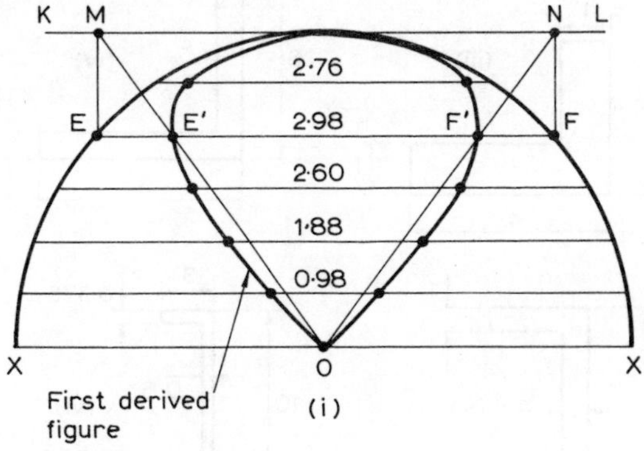

All dimensions in centimetres

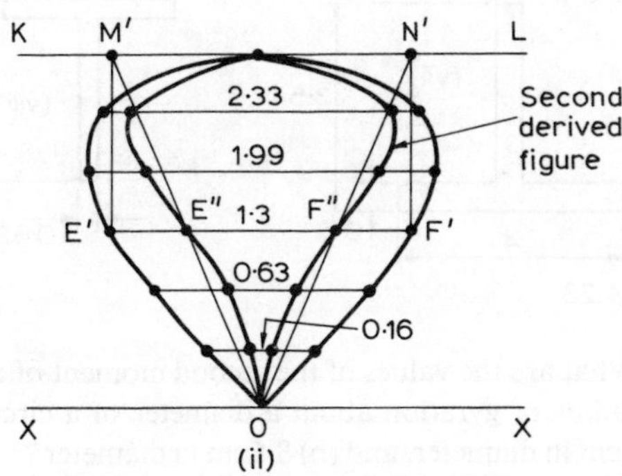

Fig.14.22

Position of centroid.

1 It will be convenient to use the base of the section as the axis XX, and the mid-point of this base diameter as the point O.

2 The line KL can be drawn parallel to XX, tangential to the semicircle. The distance d between KL and XX will therefore be 3 cm.

3 Draw a number of equally spaced lines parallel to the base XX.

4 One of the lines cuts the semicircle in E and F. From E, drop a perpendicular on to KE, cutting it at M. Similarly, N is the foot of the perpendicular from F on to KL.

5 Join M and N to O, and let MO cut EF in E′, and NO cut EF in F′.

6 Repeat this construction for the other parallel lines, and obtain a number of points corresponding to E′ and F′.

7 Join these points, and obtain the first derived figure. Determine the area of this figure. The length of the lines such as E′ F′ have been measured, and indicated on the diagram in fig.14.22(i). Using Simpson's Rule for seven ordinates, we have their value as follows.

Ordinate . .	1	2	3	4	5	6	7
Length . . .	0	0·98	1·88	2·6	2·98	2·76	0

Distance between ordinates is 0·5 cm.

First and last	Odd	Even
0	1·88	0·98
0	2·98	2·6
		2·76
0	4·86	6·34
	2	4
	9·72	25·36

$$\text{Area } A' = \frac{0{\cdot}5}{3}(0 + 9{\cdot}72 + 25{\cdot}36)$$

$$= 5{\cdot}84\,\text{cm}^2$$

$$\text{Area of section, } A = \tfrac{1}{2}\pi r^2 = \tfrac{1}{2}\pi 3^2 = 14{\cdot}15\,\text{cm}^2$$

$$\therefore \bar{y} = \frac{A'd}{A} = \frac{5{\cdot}84 \times 3}{14{\cdot}15} = 1{\cdot}24\,\text{cm}$$

Second moment of area.

1 The above process is repeated, using the first derived figure as the basis, and obtaining from it the second derived figure, as in fig.14.22 (ii). For convenience, the first derived figure has been reproduced in fig.14.22(ii), although in practice all the work could be done on the original diagram, fig.14.22(i).

Points such as E″ and F″, obtained from E′ and F′ as above, are joined together to form the second derived figure.

2 The ordinates of this figure are measured, and indicated on the diagram. Their values are:

Ordinate . . .	1	2	3	4	5	6	7
Length . . .	0	0·16	0·63	1·3	1·99	2·33	0

Distance between the ordinates is 0·5 cm. Applying Simpson's Rule to obtain area A'' we have:

First and last	Odd	Even
0	0·63	0·16
		1·3
0	1·99	2·33
0	2·62	3·79
	2	4
	5·24	15·16

$$\text{Area } A'' = \frac{0{\cdot}5}{3}(0 + 5{\cdot}24 + 15{\cdot}16)$$

$$= 3{\cdot}4\,\text{cm}^2$$

Second moment of area about XX $= 3{\cdot}4 \times 3^2$
$= 30{\cdot}6\,\text{cm}^4$

Second moment of area about GG $= I_{XX} - A\bar{y}^2$
$= 30{\cdot}6 - 14{\cdot}15 \times 1{\cdot}24^2$
$= 30{\cdot}6 - 21{\cdot}7$
$= 8{\cdot}9\,\text{cm}^4$

i.e. The centroid is 1·24 cm from base, and the second moment of area about axis through centroid = 8·9 cm⁴.

Exercise 14

1–8 For each of the given sections in fig.14·23, determine the following values about the horizontal axis XX, and the vertical axis YY, through the centroid of the section: (a) the second moment of area, (b) the radius of gyration, and (c) the least section modulus for each axis.

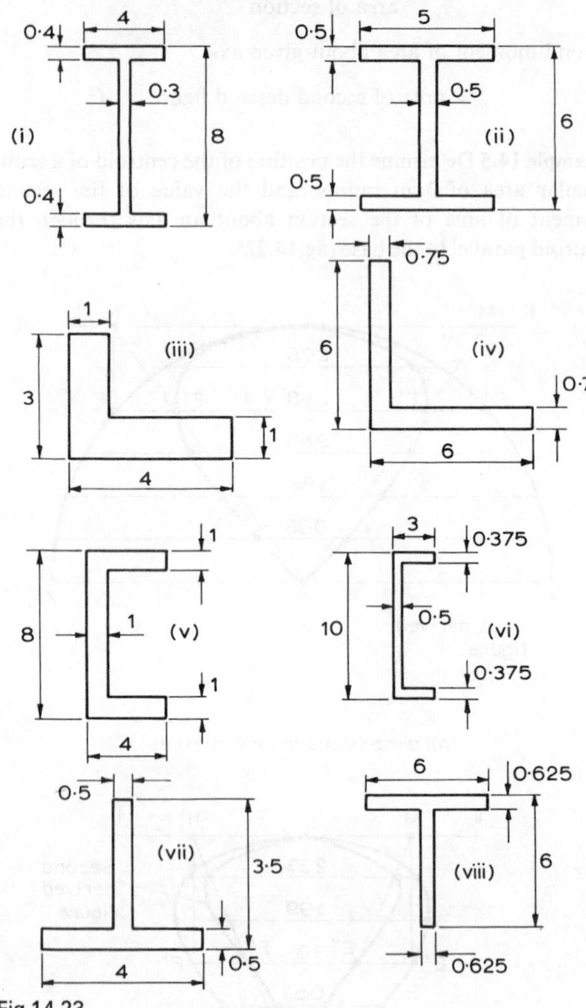

Fig.14.23

9 What are the values of the second moment of area, and the radius of gyration about a diameter of a circular area (a) 3 cm in diameter, and (b) 8·5 cm in diameter?

10 What are the values of the polar second moment of area, and the polar section modulus of a circular area (a) 4 cm in diameter, and (b) 10 cm in diameter?

11 An annular section has an outside diameter of 5 cm, and an inside diameter of 3 cm. Determine its polar second moment of area, and the polar section modulus of the section.

12 An annular section has an outside diameter of 8 cm, and an inside diameter of 4 cm. Determine its polar second moment of area, and the polar radius of gyration. What would be the diameter of a circular area whose polar section modulus is equal to that of the annulus? What would be the polar second moment of area of this circular area?

13 Show that, for a semicircular area of diameter d, the second moment of area about its diameter is approximately $0{\cdot}025d^4$, whilst its value about a parallel axis through the centroid is approximately $0{\cdot}007d^4$.

14 A column consists of two plates, 10 cm × 0·75 cm, and two channels, 8 cm × 3 cm, set 4 cm apart. The following are the properties of the 8 cm × 3 cm channel section: $I_{XX} = 3{\cdot}578\,\text{cm}^4$, area of section $= 4{\cdot}694\,\text{cm}^2$, axis YY from back of channel $= 0{\cdot}834$ cm. Determine the values about an axis through the centroid of the whole area, parallel to XX, of the second moment of area, and the radius of gyration.

15 A cast-iron bracket has a cross-section of **I**-form, with unequal flanges. The total depth of the section is 14 cm, and the metal is 2 cm thick throughout. The top flange is 10 cm wide, and the bottom is 6 cm wide. Calculate the position of the centroid of the section, and the second moment of area about an axis through the centroid parallel to the flanges.

16 Draw the curve $y = 3 \sin (\pi x/6)$ for values of x from 0 to 12 cm. By graphical methods, determine the position of the centroid of the area enclosed by the curve and the x-axis. Determine the value of the second moment of area about a horizontal axis through the centroid.

17 Determine by graphical methods the position of the centroid of a quadrant of a circle 8 cm in radius. What is the value of the second moment of area of the quadrant about a horizontal axis through the centroid, parallel to the horizontal base?

Chapter 15

Beams and Bending

When a beam is subjected to bending, we have seen that at each section of the beam there is a bending moment and a shearing force, and that these vary in intensity from section to section along the beam. These bending moments produce stresses in the beam. In fig.15.1 (i) we have the representation of an unloaded horizontal beam, whilst fig.15.1 (ii) shows the same beam heavily loaded. It will be seen that the underside of the beam is being stretched; this means that parts of this underside of the beam will be subjected to tensile stresses. (Whenever a material is stretched, the stresses set up within it are tensile stresses.) If the tensile stress set up is greater than the tensile strength of the material, cracks will be noticed in the underside of the beam, and failure of the beam will result.

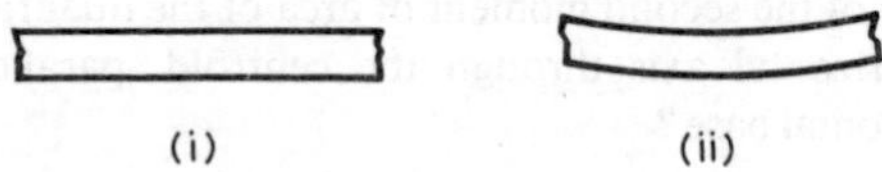

Fig.15.1 Unloaded and loaded beam

Meanwhile the upper side of the beam is being compressed, and compressive stresses are consequently set up on this part of the beam.

If a piece of tissue paper is glued to the side of a rubber beam, and the rubber is then bent, it will be seen that the portion of the paper below the central axis of the beam is torn, whilst that portion above the central axis is crinkled.

Again, place two similar pieces of wood together, end to end, with a layer of glue between them. Before the glue has set hard, try to bend the wood so that the pieces are forced apart at the joining. You will see that the glue fibres are stretched across the gap, which is widest at the underside. If you were to pull the pieces of wood apart along their axis, then the gluey fibres would all be equal in length, since the pieces of wood would remain the same distance apart (fig.15.2). When the pieces are bent, the fibres at the lowest section are stretched the farthest, suggesting that the stresses at this section are the greatest. Of course, this is not quite a true analogy to what exists in a beam subjected to bending, since we do not get the picture of the compressed fibres.

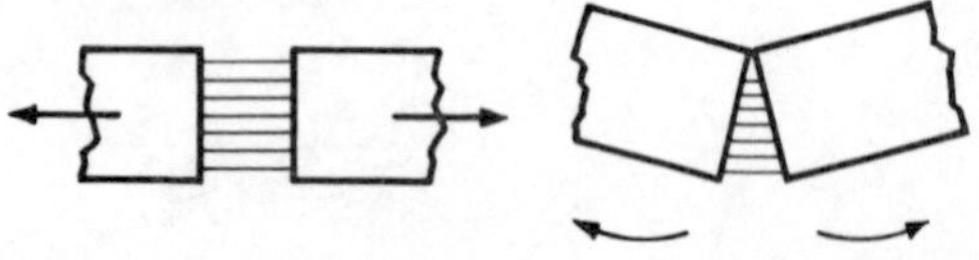

Fig.15.2 Comparison between tensile and bending stresses. The two portions of a block of wood have been lightly glued together. The portions on the left are then pulled apart so that each fibre is equally stretched. This is similar to the action of tensile stresses. In the case of the two blocks on the right, they are moved in the directions shown. The lower fibres are stretched much more than the upper ones. This is similar to the action of bending stresses.

Consider now a beam which is bent so that the underside is in tension, and the upperside is in compression. It follows that there must be some part of the beam which is under neither tension nor compression. In other words, there must be a part of the beam which remains in the same condition as it was before it was bent.

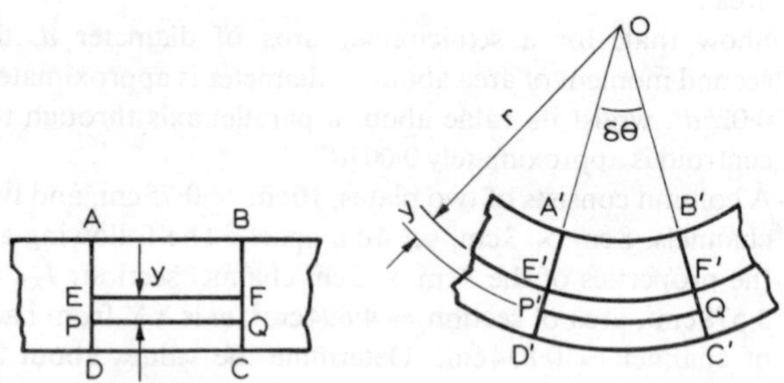

Fig.15.3 Relationship between stress and the distance of the section from the neutral axis

In fig.15.3, ABCD is a rectangle marked on the unbent beam, whilst A′B′C′D′ is the resultant shape of the area after bending. The length CD has increased to C′D′, indicating tension; and the length AB has decreased to A′B′, indicating compression. Consequently, there will be some part EF which will remain the same length after bending. This part is known as the *neutral axis* of the beam. Its position will be determined later; for the time being, let us mark it on the diagram approximately half-way between AB and DC. The final position of EF is indicated as E′F′, such that EF is equal to E′F′.

If the distance between section AD and BC is sufficiently small, we can assume that A′B′ is the arc of a circle subtending an angle $\delta\theta$ at its centre O, which is the point of intersection of D′A′ and C′B′ produced. The radius of this circle measured to section E′F′ is r.

Let us consider what happens to any general section, such as PQ, at a distance y from EF, which after bending becomes P′Q′.

The length of P′Q′ is given by the relationship

$$\frac{E'F'}{OE'} = \frac{P'Q'}{OP'} = \delta\theta \text{ in radians}$$

$$\therefore P'Q' = E'F' . \frac{OP'}{OE'}$$

$$= E'F' \frac{(r + y)}{r}$$

$$= EF \frac{(r + y)}{r}, \text{ since } E'F' = EF$$

$$= \frac{PQ\,(r + y)}{r}, \text{ since } EF = PQ$$

$$\therefore \frac{P'Q'}{PQ} = \left(\frac{r+y}{r}\right)$$

$$= 1 + \frac{y}{r} \quad . \quad . \quad . \quad . \quad . \quad (1)$$

The strain produced on section PQ will be given by

$$\text{strain} = \frac{\text{change in length of PQ}}{\text{PQ}}$$

$$= \frac{P'Q' - PQ}{PQ}$$

$$= \frac{P'Q'}{PQ} - 1$$

$$= 1 + \frac{y}{r} - 1, \text{ from (1) above}$$

$$\therefore \text{strain} = \frac{y}{r}$$

This means that the strain at any section is proportional to the distance, y, of the section from the neutral axis. This agrees with our previous conclusion.

Let σ = the intensity of stress on layer P′Q′.

Then, within the elastic limit, since stress is proportional to strain, we have

$$\text{stress} = E \times \text{strain}$$

$$\sigma = y\frac{E}{r} \quad . \quad . \quad . \quad . \quad . \quad . \quad . \quad (2)$$

or

$$\frac{\sigma}{y} = \frac{E}{r} \quad . \quad . \quad . \quad . \quad . \quad . \quad . \quad (3)$$

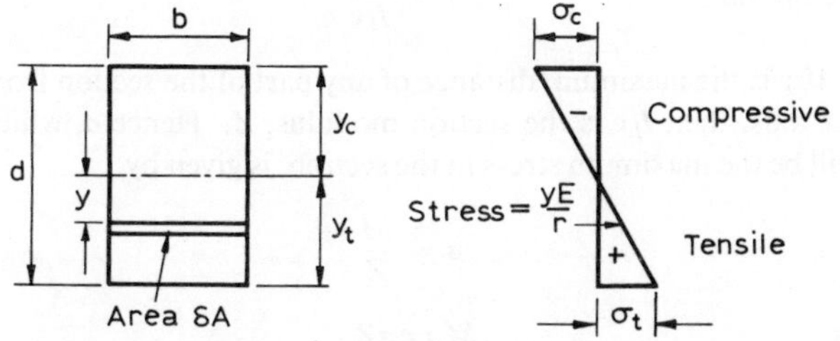

Fig.15.4 Stress variation across section

From equation (2), we see that the stress in any layer is directly proportional to the distance of that layer from the neutral axis.

Let σ_t = intensity of tensile stress at outside fibre,
σ_c = intensity of compressive stress at outside fibre,
y_t = distance from neutral axis to outside fibre under tension,
y_c = distance from neutral axis to outside fibre under compression.

From equation (3), we have

$$\frac{\sigma}{y} = \frac{E}{r} = \frac{\sigma_t}{y_t} = \frac{\sigma_c}{y_c}$$

Position of the Neutral Axis

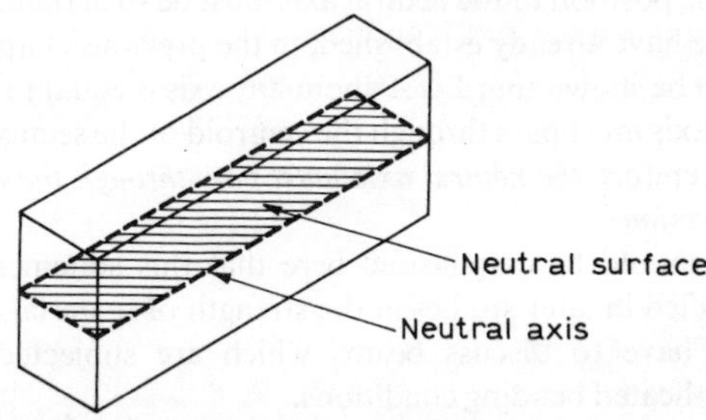

Fig.15.5 Neutral surface and neutral axis

Those parts of the beam which remain unstressed when the beam is bent make up a plane surface or area which might be defined as the neutral surface. The end view of this surface is a straight line, which is referred to as the neutral axis (fig.15.5). Throughout bending, it is subjected neither to tensile nor compressive stresses.

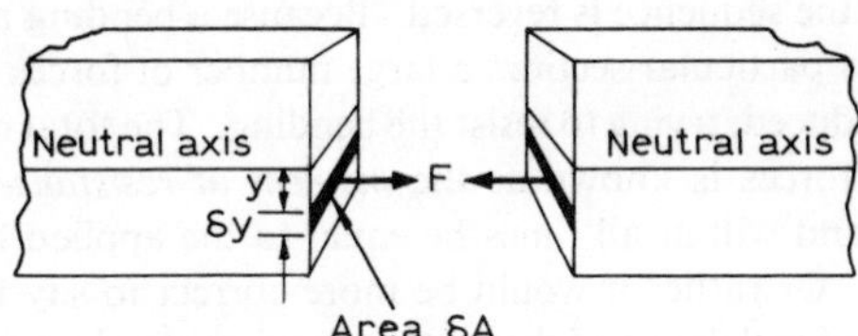

Fig.15.6 Moment of resistance of section

Figure 15.6 shows a beam under conditions of bending. In order to investigate what is happening in the various vertical sections of the beam, let us imagine that two portions of the beam are separated on a vertical section. The approximate position of the neutral axis is shown on the diagram. Consider a small area δA of the section, at a distance y from the neutral axis. This area is shown black in fig.15.6. Now this portion of the beam is under a tensile stress of magnitude yE/r. We can think of this stress as being produced by a force F acting on the area. The magnitude of F will be given by

$$F = \text{stress} \times \text{area}$$

$$F = y\frac{E}{r} \times \delta A$$

The sum of all such forces would be given by $\frac{E}{r}\Sigma y\delta A$. But this sum must equal zero, since any vertical section of a normally loaded beam will be in equilibrium; in other words, referring to the particular diagram which we are discussing, there will be no resultant horizontal force across the vertical section considered.

Hence $$\frac{E}{r}\Sigma y\delta A = 0$$

or, the position of the neutral axis must be such that $\Sigma y\delta A = 0$.

We have already established, in the previous chapter, that if it can be shown that $\Sigma y\delta A$ about any axis is equal to zero, then that axis must pass through the centroid of the section.

Therefore *the neutral axis must pass through the centroid of the section.*

It should be emphasised here that this statement may be modified in later studies in the strength of materials, when we may have to discuss beams which are subjected to more complicated bending conditions.

Moment of Resistance

Referring again to fig.15.6, we see that the force F acting on the elementary area has a moment about the neutral axis of magnitude Fy. A similar moment will be produced by all the forces on all the small areas. In fact, if we take the sum of all these moments, we shall be able to equate this to the moment at that particular section due to the bending of the beam; in other words, to the bending moment at that section. Of course, in practice, the sequence is reversed. Because a bending moment exists at a particular section, a large number of forces such as F are produced, trying to resist the bending. The total moment of these forces is known as the *moment of resistance* of the section, and will at all times be equal to the applied bending moment. Or rather it would be more correct to say that the moment of resistance of the section continues to increase with an increasing bending moment until a maximum value of the moment of resistance is reached. In trying to keep up with further increases in the bending moment, the stresses set up in the beam exceed the elastic limit of the material, and the beam fails; the applied bending moment has exceeded the maximum value of the moment of resistance which the section can exert. It is part of the work of designers to ensure that the section and material of the beam are adequate to enable the maximum moment of resistance offered by the beam to be greater than the maximum bending moment to which it will be subjected. Now you will understand the reason for spending time in determining the value and position of the maximum bending moment.

Moment of force F on strip, about neutral axis

$$= Fy$$

$$= y\frac{E}{r}\delta A . y$$

$$= \frac{E}{r}y^2\delta A$$

Total moment about neutral axis of all similar forces, or moment of resistance of section $= \frac{E}{r}\Sigma y^2\delta A$

But $\Sigma y^2\delta A$ is equal to I, the second moment of area of the section about the neutral axis, or about an axis through the centroid of the section.

$$M = \frac{E}{r}I$$

or $$\frac{M}{I} = \frac{E}{r}$$

We have seen that stress $\sigma = \frac{E}{r}y$

or $$\frac{\sigma}{y} = \frac{E}{r}$$

Hence $$\frac{M}{I} = \frac{\sigma}{y} = \frac{E}{r}$$

These equations are of fundamental importance in strength of material problems. They show the relationship between:

1 applied bending moment, M;
2 dimensions of the section, I and y;
3 radius of curvature of the subsequent bending, r; and
4 elasticity of the material of the beam, E.

By making a suitable choice of equation, it is possible to obtain the required information when certain facts are given.

Taking the pair of expressions,

$$\frac{M}{I} = \frac{\sigma}{y}$$

we obtain $$\sigma = \frac{M}{I/y}$$

If y is the maximum distance of any part of the section from the axis, then I/y is the section modulus, Z. Hence σ, which will be the maximum stress in the section, is given by

$$\sigma = \frac{M}{Z}$$

or $$M = \sigma Z$$

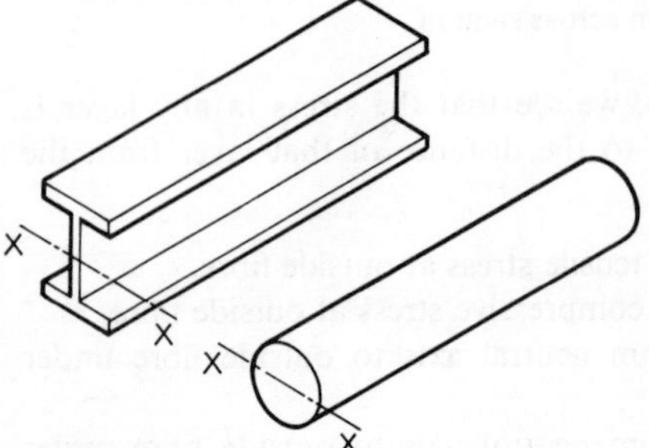

Fig.15.7 Comparison between beam and shaft in bending

In words, *the moment of resistance of a section is equal to the maximum allowable stress, multiplied by the modulus of the section.* This will give an idea of the maximum permissible bending moment which the beam will carry at a given section.

Example 15.1 A rectangular beam, 20 cm deep by 10 cm wide, is subjected to a maximum bending moment of 360 kN m. What is the maximum stress in the beam? If the value of E for the material is 208×10^3 N/mm², determine the radius of curvature for that portion of the beam where the bending moment is 360 kN m.

The stress in the beam is given by the equation

$$\frac{M}{I} = \frac{\sigma}{y}$$

$$M = \text{bending moment} = 360\,000\,\text{N m}$$

$$I = \frac{bd^3}{12} = \frac{10 \times 20^3}{12} = \frac{2 \times 10^4}{3}\,\text{cm}^4$$

y = distance from neutral axis to extreme edge of section

$$= \frac{20}{2} = 10\,\text{cm}$$

Then $\sigma = \dfrac{My}{I}$

$$= \frac{360\,000 \times 0{\cdot}1 \times 3 \times 10^8}{2 \times 10^4}\,\text{N/m}^2$$

$$= 540\,\text{N/mm}^2$$

Alternatively, we could use the relationship

$$\sigma = \frac{M}{Z}$$

where Z is the section modulus.

$$Z = \frac{I}{y} = \frac{2 \times 10^4}{3 \times 10} = \frac{2 \times 10^3}{3}\,\text{cm}^3$$

Stress $\sigma = \dfrac{M}{Z} = \dfrac{360\,000 \times 3 \times 10^6}{2 \times 10^3}\,\text{N/m}^2$

$$= 540\,\text{N/mm}^2$$

Radius of curvature

$$\frac{M}{I} = \frac{E}{r}$$

$$\therefore r = \frac{EI}{M}$$

$$= \frac{208 \times 10^9 \times 2 \times 10^4}{360\,000 \times 3 \times 10^8}$$

$$= 38{\cdot}5\,\text{m}$$

i.e. The maximum stress in beam is 540 N/mm², and the radius of curvature of the beam at this point is 38·5 m.

Example 15.2 A rectangular section beam, 30 cm × 12·5 cm section, is strained so that the maximum stress at the centre of the span is 15 N/mm². If the value of E is 15×10^3 N/mm², determine the value of the radius of curvature at the centre.

$$\frac{M}{I} = \frac{\sigma}{y} = \frac{E}{r}$$

In this example,

$$\sigma = 15 \times 10^6\,\text{N/m}^2$$

$$y = \frac{30}{2} = 15\,\text{cm}$$

$$= 0{\cdot}15\,\text{m}$$

$$E = 15 \times 10^9\,\text{N/m}^2$$

$$\therefore \frac{15 \times 10^6}{0{\cdot}15} = \frac{15 \times 10^9}{r}$$

$$r = \frac{15 \times 10^9 \times 0{\cdot}15}{15 \times 10^6}$$

$$= 150\,\text{m}$$

i.e. At the centre of the span, the radius of curvature of the beam is 150 m.

Example 15.3 A strip of steel, 25 mm wide and 3 mm thick, is bent around a circular drum 2 m in diameter. Calculate the maximum stress due to bending, if E is 208×10^3 N/mm².

$$\frac{M}{I} = \frac{\sigma}{y} = \frac{E}{r}$$

In this case $E = 208 \times 10^9$ N/m²
$r = 1{\cdot}0015$, measured to the neutral axis
$y = 1{\cdot}5$ mm, i.e. $0{\cdot}0015$ m

$$\frac{\sigma}{0{\cdot}0015} = \frac{208 \times 10^9}{1{\cdot}0015}$$

$$\sigma = 312 \times 10^6\,\text{N/m}^2 = 312\,\text{N/mm}^2$$

i.e. The maximum stress set up in the steel is 312 N/mm². This stress would be tensile at the outer surface, and compressive at the inner surface in contact with the drum.

Example 15.4 State what is meant by the moment of resistance of a beam, and obtain the relation $\dfrac{\sigma}{y} = \dfrac{M}{I}$ for the case of a beam subjected to a bending moment of M.

If the second moment of area of a symmetrical section of a beam about the neutral axis is $1{\cdot}2 \times 10^5$ cm⁴, and its depth is

60 cm, find the longest span over which, when simply supported, the beam could carry a uniformly distributed load of 40 kN/m run without the stress due to bending exceeding 120 N/mm². UEI

$$I = 1{\cdot}2 \times 10^5\,\text{cm}^4$$
$$d = 60\,\text{cm}$$

Section modulus of this section $= \dfrac{I}{y}$

For a symmetrical section, with the centroid in the centre of the section, the value of y will be $d/2$, in this case 30 cm.

$$Z = \frac{I}{y} = \frac{1{\cdot}2 \times 10^5}{30} = 4 \times 10^3\,\text{cm}^3$$

Moment of resistance = stress × section modulus

$$= \frac{120 \times 10^6 \times 4 \times 10^3}{10^6}$$

$$= 480\,000\,\text{N m}$$

Thus the maximum bending moment which the beam can safely carry is 480 kN m.

For a simply supported beam, the maximum bending moment occurs at the mid-point and is equal to $wl^2/8$, where w is the load per unit length, and l is the span of the beam.

$$\therefore \frac{wl^2}{8} = 480\,000$$

$$40\,000\,\frac{l^2}{8} = 480\,000$$

$$l^2 = 96$$
$$l = 9{\cdot}8\,\text{m}$$

i.e. The longest span for a simply supported beam under the above conditions would be 9·8 m.

Example 15.5 Establish the formula $\dfrac{\sigma}{y} = \dfrac{M}{I}$ for a beam subjected to simple bending. Determine the maximum uniformly distributed load a simply supported timber beam, 40 cm deep by 25 cm broad, can carry over a span of 3 m, if the maximum permissible bending stress is 2 N/mm². UEI

I for rectangular section $= \dfrac{bd^3}{12} = \dfrac{25 \times 40^3}{12}\,\text{cm}^4$

$$= 133\,000\,\text{cm}^4$$

Distance from neutral axis to extreme fibre $= \dfrac{d}{2} = \dfrac{40}{2} = 20\,\text{cm}$

Section modulus, $Z = \dfrac{I}{y} = \dfrac{133\,000}{20} = 6650\,\text{cm}^3$

Moment of resistance for section = stress × Z

$$= 2 \times 10^6 \times \frac{6650}{10^6}$$

$$= 13\,300\,\text{N m}$$

This will be the value of the maximum bending moment to which the beam may be subjected. Maximum bending moment for a simply supported beam is $wl^2/8$ at the centre of the beam (w is the load per unit length and l is the span.)

$$\therefore \frac{wl^2}{8} = 13\,300$$

$$\frac{w \times 3^2}{8} = 13\,300$$

$$w = \frac{8 \times 13\,300}{9}$$

$$= 11\,800\,\text{N/m run}$$

i.e. The maximum load which the beam can carry is 11 800 N/m run, or a total load of 35 400 N evenly distributed over the 3 m span.

Example 15.6 A cantilever consists of a steel tube having an outside diameter of 100 mm, an inside diameter of 75 mm, and a length of 2·4 m. Find the total uniformly distributed load if the maximum stress due to bending is 75 N/mm². NCTEC

For bending, we require the second moment of area about a diameter.

$$I_{XX} = \frac{\pi}{64}(D^4 - d^4)$$

$$= \frac{\pi}{64}(10^4 - 7{\cdot}5^4)$$

$$= 336\,\text{cm}^4$$

$$y = \frac{10}{2} = 5\,\text{cm}$$

Section modulus $\quad Z = \dfrac{I}{y} = \dfrac{336}{5} = 67{\cdot}2\,\text{cm}^3$

Maximum bending moment = section modulus × stress

$$= \frac{67{\cdot}2 \times 75 \times 10^6}{10^6}$$

$$= 5050\,\text{N m}$$

Let W N = distributed load

Maximum bending moment occurs at fixing, and equals $Wl/2$.

$$\frac{2{\cdot}4W}{2} = 5050$$

$$W = 4200\,\text{N}$$

i.e. The total uniformly distributed load which the cantilever can support is 4200 N.

Direct and Bending Stresses

Figure 15.8 (i) is a bird's-eye view of a square column carrying a load W applied along the vertical axis through the centroid of the horizontal section. The material in the column is considered to be subjected to a uniform compressive stress whose magnitude is equal to $\frac{\text{load}}{\text{area of section}}$. This stress is referred to as the *direct stress*.

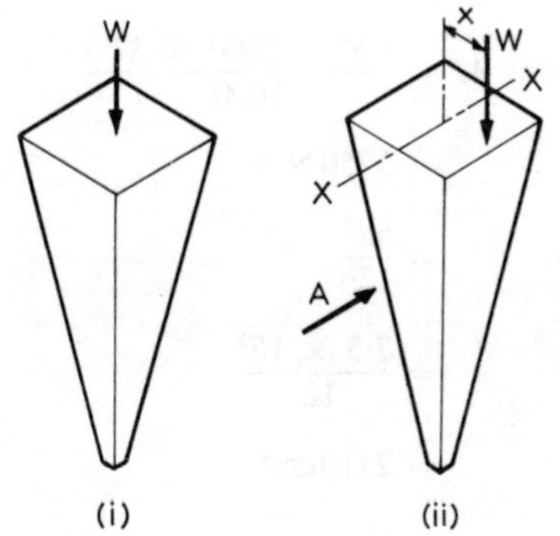

Fig.15.8 Offset loading

If the point of application of the load is displaced by a distance x from the axis, as indicated in fig.15.8 (ii), the stresses in the material are altered considerably. Looking in the direction of the arrow A, before the load is applied, we should see the column as in fig.15.9 (i); whilst fig.15.9 (ii) gives an indication of the form it would take after the load is applied. One side, AB, of the column would be in tension, and the other side, CD, would be in compression. In fact, the column would be under conditions rather similar to a beam subjected to bending. But in addition to these bending stresses there would still be the direct stresses which we have just mentioned.

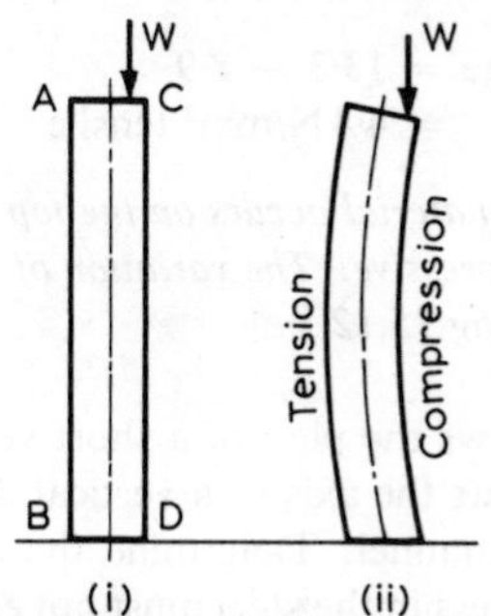

Fig.15.9 Effect of offset loading

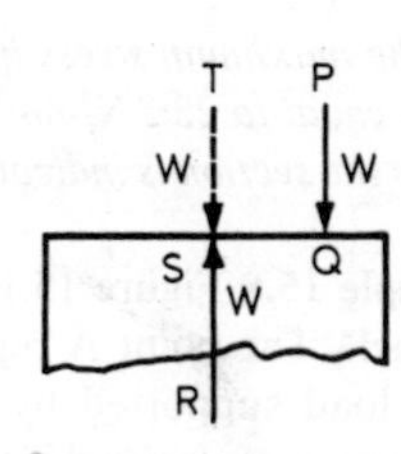

Fig.15.10

In order that we may study the effect more closely, let us refer to fig.15.10, where the load W is indicated by PQ. Along the vertical axis through the centroid, two equal and opposite forces, RS and TS, are shown. The magnitude of both forces is W. Their introduction obviously makes no difference to the loading of the column, since they cancel each other out. If, however, we consider the upward force RS, shown as a full black line, as being linked with the load W, shown as PQ, also a full black line, we can say that these two equal and opposite forces form a couple; in fact, a clockwise couple. This will leave us with a force TS, acting along the vertical axis through the centroid. Thus the original offset force PQ is equivalent to:

1 an equal force TS, magnitude W, along the axis through the centroid, producing a direct stress (compressive in this case); and

2 a couple, magnitude Wx, which is bending the beam, and producing both tensile and compressive stresses.

Let W = applied load,

x = distance from load to centroid of section,

A = cross-sectional area of section,

I_{XX} = second moment of area of section about axis through centroid, perpendicular to axis through point of application of load and centroid [XX in fig.15.8 (ii)],

y_c = distance from axis XX to extreme point in section under compressive stress,

y_t = distance from axis XX to extreme point in section under tensile stress,

σ_c = compressive stress due to bending,

σ_t = tensile stress due to bending,

σ_d = direct stress, either tensile or compressive.

$$\text{Direct stress } \sigma_d = \frac{W}{A}$$

Bending stresses. These are produced by the couple or bending moment $Wx = M$.

$$\frac{M}{I} = \frac{\sigma_c}{y_c} = \frac{\sigma_t}{y_t}$$

$$\text{Compressive stress } \sigma_c = \frac{My_c}{I} = \frac{Wxy_c}{I_{XX}}$$

$$\text{Tensile stress } \sigma_t = \frac{My_t}{I} = \frac{Wxy_t}{I_{XX}}$$

$$\text{Total compressive stress} = \sigma_c + \sigma_d$$

$$= \frac{Wxy_c}{I_{XX}} + \frac{W}{A}$$

$$\text{Total tensile stress} = \sigma_t - \sigma_d$$

$$= \frac{Wxy_t}{I_{XX}} - \frac{W}{A}$$

If the direction of W were reversed, σ_d would be a tensile stress. The resultant compressive stress would be $\sigma_c - \sigma_d$, and the resultant tensile stress $\sigma_t + \sigma_d$.

A diagram showing the variation of stress across the section is shown in fig.15.11.

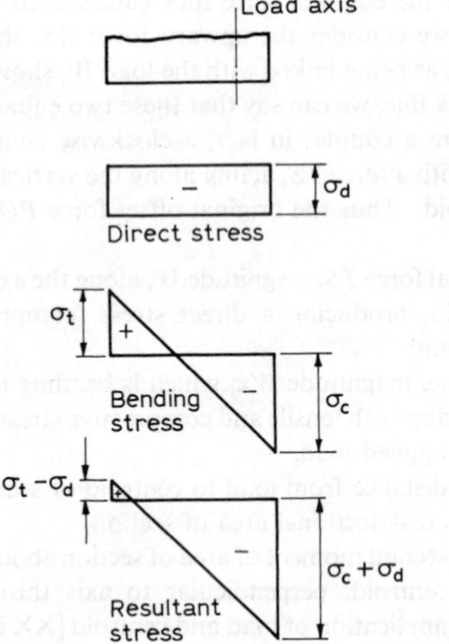

Fig.15.11 Stress variation due to direct and bending stresses

From this diagram we see that the tensile stresses are small compared with the compressive stresses. In fact, it will be obvious that, under certain conditions in which the value of the direct stress exceeds the value of the tensile stress due to bending, the resultant stress in the section will be entirely compressive. This fact is the basis of all masonry and concrete constructions. These materials are very suitable to withstand compressive loads, but are completely inadequate to deal with tensile stresses. Consequently, designers have to arrange the dimensions of the structure to make sure that no tensile stresses occur on any cross-section.

It will also be obvious from fig.15.11 that the position of no stress is very near to one edge of the section, and not along an axis through the centroid. For this reason, it was emphasised, when dealing with centroids and neutral axes, that the neutral axis, or axis on which there was no stress, passed through the centroid of the section only when dealing with cases of simple bending.

Example 15.7 A bar of rectangular section, 150mm × 75mm, carries an offset load of 100kN, shown in fig.15.12. The distance from the axis of the load to the centre of the bar is 37·5 mm. Determine the maximum tensile and compressive stresses in the material, and draw a diagram indicating the variation of the stress.

Direct stress $\sigma_d = \dfrac{100 \times 10^3}{150 \times 75 \times 10^{-6}} = 8{\cdot}9\,\text{Nmm}^2$ compressive

Bending stress $\dfrac{M}{I} = \dfrac{\sigma}{y}$

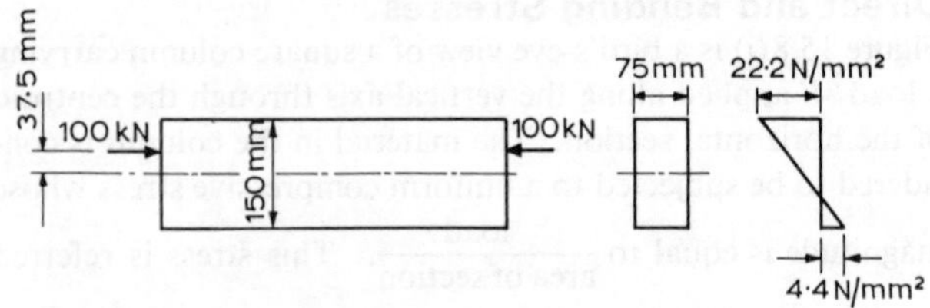

Fig.15.12

$$\text{Bending moment } M = \frac{100 \times 1000 \times 37{\cdot}5}{1000}$$

$$= 3750\,\text{Nm}$$

$$I_{XX} \text{ for section} = \frac{bd^3}{12}$$

$$= \frac{7{\cdot}5 \times 15^3}{12}$$

$$= 2110\,\text{cm}^4$$

$$y = \frac{d}{2} = 7{\cdot}5\,\text{cm}$$

$$\sigma = \frac{My}{I_{XX}} = \frac{3750 \times 7{\cdot}5 \times 10^6}{2110}$$

$$= 13{\cdot}3\,\text{N/mm}^2$$

Compressive stress on top edge due to bending moment

$$= 13{\cdot}3\,\text{N/mm}^2$$

Tensile stress on bottom edge due to bending moment

$$= 13{\cdot}3\,\text{N/mm}^2$$

Resultant stress on top edge $= 13{\cdot}3 + 8{\cdot}9$
$= 22{\cdot}2\,\text{N/mm}^2$ compressive

Resultant stress on bottom edge $= 13{\cdot}3 - 8{\cdot}9$
$= 4{\cdot}4\,\text{N/mm}^2$ tensile

i.e. The maximum stress in the material occurs on the top edge, and is equal to 22·2 N/mm² compressive. The variation of stress across the section is indicated in fig.15.12.

Example 15.8 Figure 15.13 shows the plan of a short vertical channel. The point A represents the axis of a vertical downward load supported by the channel. Determine the maximum value of the load if the stress in the steel must not exceed 50 N/mm². NCTEC

Due to the position of the load axis, the edge XX will be subjected to tensile stresses, and the edge YY will be in compression. In addition, the direct stress over the area will be compressive. Hence the resultant stress will be increased along YY, and will be decreased along XX. Consequently, edge

YY will have the maximum stress, which must not exceed $50\,N/mm^2$.

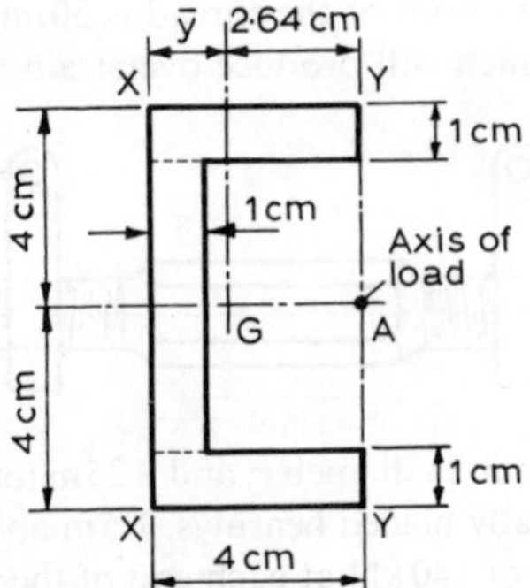

Fig.15.13

Determination of position of centroid of section

Area of section $= (4 \times 1) + (4 \times 1) + (6 \times 1) = 14\,cm^2$

Taking moments about XX of the three rectangles indicated, and equating to the total moment,

$$14\bar{y} = (4 \times 1 \times 2) + (4 \times 1 \times 2) + (6 \times 1 \times \tfrac{1}{2})$$
$$= 19$$
$$\bar{y} = 1{\cdot}36\,cm$$

Load is offset from G by $4 - 1{\cdot}36 = 2{\cdot}64\,cm$.

Second moment of area about XX. Again considering the second moment of area of the three rectangles in turn,

$$\text{Total } I_{XX} = \tfrac{1}{3}(1 \times 4^3) + \tfrac{1}{3}(1 \times 4^3) + \tfrac{1}{3}(6 \times 1^3)$$
$$= 44{\cdot}66\,cm^4$$
$$I_{GG} = I_{XX} - A\bar{y}^2 \text{ (note negative sign)}$$
$$= 44{\cdot}66 - 14 \times 1{\cdot}36^2$$
$$= 18{\cdot}66\,cm^4$$

Let W = applied load in newtons

$$\sigma_d = \text{direct stress} = \frac{\text{load}}{\text{area}} = \frac{W \times 10^4}{14}\,N/m^2$$
$$= 715\,W\,N/m^2$$

Bending stress is given by $\dfrac{M}{I} = \dfrac{\sigma}{y}$

$$\sigma_c = \frac{My}{I}$$

$$\text{Bending moment} = \frac{W \times 2{\cdot}64}{100}\,Nm$$

$y = 2{\cdot}64\,cm$ to YY edge, where stress will be maximum

$$\sigma_c = \frac{2{\cdot}64\,W \times 2{\cdot}64}{100 \times 100} \times \frac{10^8}{18{\cdot}66}$$
$$= 3740\,W\,N/m^2$$

Total compressive stress on YY

$$= \sigma_d + \sigma_c$$
$$= (715 + 3740)W$$
$$= 4455\,W$$

This must not exceed $50\,N/mm^2$.

$$4455W = 50 \times 10^6$$
$$W = 11\,250\,N$$

i.e. The maximum load which the column can support is 11 250 N.

Exercise 15

1 Obtain an expression giving the approximate moment of resistance of a beam of I-section. If such a beam is 4 cm wide by 8 cm deep, and the flanges are 5 mm thick, find the moment of resistance for a maximum stress due to bending of $50\,N/mm^2$.

What are the values of I and r in your calculation if

$$\frac{\sigma}{y} = \frac{M}{I} = \frac{E}{r}?$$

$(E = 208 \times 10^3\,N/mm^2.)$ NCTEC

2 Derive the expression $\dfrac{y}{\sigma} = \dfrac{r}{E}$, stating your assumptions clearly.

Find the stress due to bending in steel wire 3 mm in diameter wound on a drum 3·6 m in diameter. $E = 190 \times 10^3\,N/mm^2$. NCTEC

3 A timber beam of 4·5 m span is to carry a uniformly distributed load of 22 kN/m. If the beam section is rectangular, having a depth equal to twice the width, and the maximum stress due to bending $8\,N/mm^2$, find the dimensions of the section. NCTEC

4 A round bar, 125 mm in diameter, is to be used as a beam. Find the maximum allowable bending moment, if the stress due to bending is limited to $17{\cdot}5\,N/mm^2$. Calculate also the radius of curvature at the point of maximum bending moment if $E = 200 \times 10^3\,N/mm^2$. NCTEC

5 A steel bar has a rectangular section, 200 mm by 50 mm. If the bar is used as a beam, compare the relative strengths in resisting bending moment when it is (a) laid flat, and (b) laid on its smaller edge.

If, when laid flat, the bar rests on supports 1·8 m apart, find the uniformly distributed load to give a maximum stress due to bending of $75\,N/mm^2$. NCTEC

6 A rolled-steel girder is of I-section measuring 200 mm by 500 mm, with web 12·5 mm, and flanges 25 mm thick. It has a span of 6 m, and is freely supported at its ends. It carries a load of 500 kN, uniformly distributed over the entire span. Determine the greatest tensile stress set up in the girder, taking into account the strength of the web in resisting bending. NCTEC

7 A short column of solid rectangular section, 150 mm × 75 mm, carries a vertical load whose line of thrust is on the centre line parallel to the longer sides, and distant 125 mm from the centre line parallel to the shorter sides. Find the magnitude of the load for a maximum tensile stress of 30 N/mm^2, and calculate the value of the maximum compressive stress. NCTEC

8 A beam is made up of two 200 mm × 100 mm timber joists, between which a 150 mm × 50 mm joist is placed symmetrically; the three are bolted securely together, with the 200 mm and 150 mm edges vertical. If this beam is supported at the ends, calculate the maximum central load if the stress is limited to 7·75 N/mm^2, and the span is 2·4 m. The timber has a density of 800 kg/m^3. NCTEC

9 A cantilever of rectangular section is uniformly loaded along its length of 2·4 m at 1500 N/m run. If the material is wood, 75 mm wide, find the depth at the position of maximum bending moment for a maximum stress due to bending of 4 N/mm^2. Derive any formula used for calculating the maximum bending moment, and sketch the bending-moment diagram. NCTEC

10 A short brick pier is 1 m square, and carries a direct axial load of 100 kN. A bracket is secured to the side of the column, to carry a load at a point 1·25 m from the centre of the column. Determine the maximum load which may be carried by the bracket, so that the brickwork is just not in tension. NCTEC

11 A symmetrical beam AB, l m long, is supported in a simple manner at two points, C and D, each x m from the ends of the beam. Two loads, each of W kN, are concentrated at A and B. Sketch the shearing-force diagram and bending-moment diagram, and dimension them when $W = 2$, $l = 10$, and $x = 2$. Comment on the shape of the bending-moment diagram between the supports, and the shape of the loaded beam between the supports.

If the beam is 20 cm deep, and the maximum stress due to bending is 125 N/mm^2, calculate the radius of curvature at the point D. Young's modulus, E, is 200×10^3 N/mm^2. NCTEC

12 A steel tube, 8 mm bore, with walls 0·08 mm thick, is fully charged with mercury (density 13 600 kg/m^3), and forms part of some physical apparatus. In use, the tube, which is 500 mm long, is supported symmetrically and horizontally on supports 450 mm apart. What is the maximum stress in the tube due to bending? Neglect the weight of the tube. ***Note.*** The second moment of area, I, of a plane circular area, diameter D, about a diameter, is given by $I = \pi D^4/64$. NCTEC

13 The elastic limit of the material of the coupling screw shown in fig.15.14 is 280 N/mm^2 If the diameter of the screw at the bottom of the thread is 50 mm, find the least value of T which will produce overstrain. NCTEC

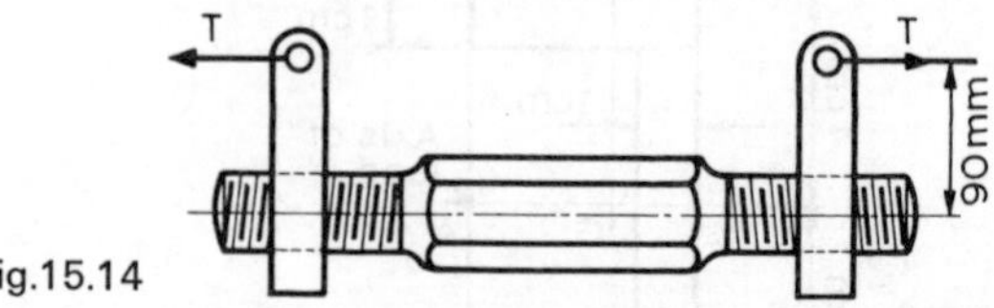

Fig.15.14

14 An axle, 175 mm in diameter, and 2·25 m long, is supported in symmetrically placed bearings, 1·5 m apart. There is an upward load of 140 kN at each end of the axle. Draw the shearing-force and bending-moment diagrams for the axle. Determine the maximum bending stress in the axle, and the radius of curvature. Young's modulus for steel = 208×10^3 N/mm^2. NCTEC

15 The T-section shown in fig.15.15 (i) is used as a beam, with the 100 mm flange underneath. Determine the position of the neutral axis, and the second moment of area of the section about this axis.

If the maximum allowable bending stress in the material is 90 N/mm^2, and the T-bar is placed on supports 2·4 m apart, what is the greatest uniform load, in kN/m, that can be placed on the beam between the supports? Neglect the weight of the beam. Show on a diagram the variation of stress over the section, due to bending. NCTEC

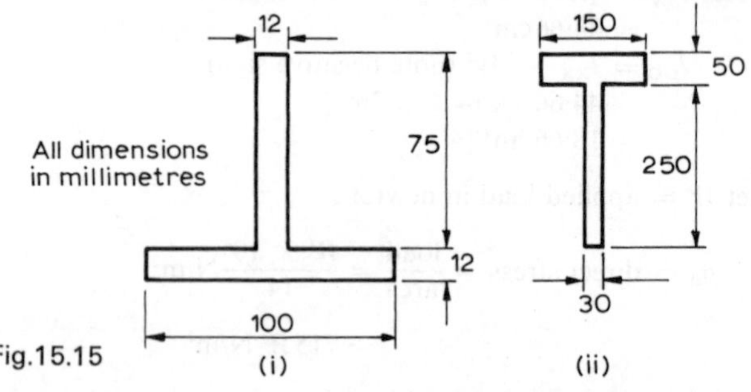

Fig.15.15

16 A beam is 2·4 m long, and is simply supported at its ends. It carries a uniformly distributed load of 100 kN/m run over the whole length. Plot the bending-stress diagram for the section at the mid-point of the beam if it has the dimensions shown in fig.15.15 (ii). State the maximum value of bending stress in the flange and in the web. EMEU

17 A beam of T-section is used as a cantilever, with the flange uppermost. The flange is 150 mm wide and 25 mm deep, and the web is 20 mm wide and 150 mm deep, whilst the cantilever is 2·4 m long. Determine the maximum permissible load which may be suspended from the free end of the cantilever if the limiting stresses in tension and compression are 90 and 150 N/mm^2. EMEU

18 A beam is simply supported over a span of 2·4 m, and it carries, in addition to a central load of 100 kN, a uniformly distributed load of 18 kN/m run over the whole span. Calculate the maximum tensile and compressive bending stresses in the beam, the dimensions of which are as follows: top flange 100 mm wide by 25 mm deep, web 40 mm wide by 250 mm deep, bottom flange 250 mm wide by 50 mm deep. EMEU

19 Prove that the neutral axis of a beam subjected to simple bending passes through the centre of gravity of the section.

A beam of T-section, 160 mm deep, second moment of area of section 800 cm^4, and span 3 m, is supported freely at its ends. It carries a uniformly distributed load of 8 kN/m. Find the maximum tensile and compressive stresses, and show, with the aid of a diagram, the distribution of stress across a section of the beam.

The neutral axis of the section is 55 mm from the outer edge of the flange. UEI

20 Prove the relation $\frac{\sigma}{y} = \frac{E}{r}$ in connection with simple bending. State clearly the assumptions made.

A steel strip of a rectangular section 1 mm thick is to be wound on a drum. Find the least diameter of the drum so that the stress due to bending shall not exceed 125 N/mm^2. ($E = 200 \times 10^3$ N/mm^2.)

21 Determine the maximum bending moment which a circular bar of 50 mm diameter can carry, if the maximum bending stress is not to exceed 150 N/mm^2. Establish from first principles any theory of bending formula you employ. UEI

22 A floor, which is required to carry a load of 10 kN/m^2, is supported by wooden joists, 250 mm deep and 100 mm wide in cross-section. If the effective span of the joists is 4·5 m, and the stress due to bending is not to exceed 7 N/mm^2, determine the distance between the joists, centre to centre. Obtain, from first principles, the expression used for the bending moment on the joists. UEI

23 Establish the formula $\frac{\sigma}{y} = \frac{M}{I}$ for a beam subjected to simple bending.

Determine the maximum uniformly distributed load a simply supported timber beam, 375 mm deep $\times$ 250 mm broad, can carry over a span of 3 m, if the maximum permissible bending stress is 2 N/mm^2. UEI

24 A horizontal lever 1·2 m long is made of steel bar of rectangular cross-section. The depth of the section is twice the breadth. A vertical force of 1 kN is applied at one end, whilst the other end is held rigid. The shorter edge is horizontal. Determine the minimum dimensions of the cross-section of the bar if the tensile strength of the steel is 450 N/mm^2, and a factor of safety of 6 is used for the bending stress produced.

If the modulus of elasticity of the material of the bar is 200×10^3 N/mm^2, determine the radius of curvature to which the loaded bar will bend at the section just outside the support. ULCI

25 A wooden beam has a cross-section 75 mm wide $\times$ 125 mm deep. The 75 mm edge is horizontal. Calculate the maximum bending stress induced in the section when the beam is simply supported on a span of 2·4 m, and is loaded with two concentrated loads of 400 N and 700 N at points 0·9 and 1·8 m respectively from the left-hand end. Neglect the weight of the beam. ULCI

26 Show that, in connection with the theory of bending of beams, $\frac{\sigma}{y} = \frac{M}{I}$.

A steel bar, of rectangular section 25 mm wide and 1·5 m long, is laid symmetrically on two knife-edges at the same level, 0·75 m apart, with the 25 mm edge horizontal. A load of 45 N is hung at each end, and the modulus of elasticity of the material is 200×10^3 N/mm^2. Determine (a) the minimum thickness of the bar if the maximum stress due to bending is not to exceed 75 N/mm^2, and (b) the radius of curvature of that portion of the bar between the knife-edges. ULCI

27 A beam is bent to the form of a circular arc of radius r. Establish an expression for the stress, σ, produced in the material at a point distant y from the neutral axis of the cross-section, in terms of r, y, and the modulus of elasticity, E, of the material. State the assumptions made. A length of solid, circular-section bar is to be bent into the arc of a circle 2·7 m in diameter, but must be capable of recovering its straight form. Determine the maximum diameter for the cross-section of the bar if the elastic-limit stress is 230 N/mm^2, and $E = 200 \times 10^3$ N/mm^2. What will be the maximum bending moment exerted by the bar in the bent form? ULCI

28 A cast-iron bracket subject to bending has a cross-section of **I**-form, with unequal flanges. The total depth of the section is 350 mm, and the metal is 50 mm thick throughout. The top flange is 250 mm wide, and the bottom is 150 mm. Calculate the position of the neutral axis, and the second moment of area of the section about this axis, and determine the maximum bending moment that should be imposed on this section if the tensile stress in the top flange is not to exceed 17 N/mm^2. What is then the value of the compressive stress in the bottom flange? IMECHE

29 A timber beam, 6 m long, and of rectangular section 175 mm deep by 100 mm broad, carries a uniformly distributed load of 7·5 kN/m run over the whole length. It overhangs its supports by 1·25 m at each end. You are required to (a) sketch the forms of the shearing-force and bending-moment diagrams, (b) show that the bending moments at a support and at the centre are opposite in kind, but numerically equal, and (c) evaluate the maximum bending stress.

IMECHE

30 State the assumptions made in the theory of simple elastic bending.

A rolled steel joist of **I**-section has flanges 125 mm wide, and is 200 mm deep overall. The flanges are 25 mm thick, and the web is 12·5 mm thick. If the joist, which is 3 m long, is simply supported at the ends, and carries a single concentrated load of 40 kN at a point 0·9 m from one end, determine the maximum stress due to bending in the material of the beam. Also, calculate the radius of curvature to which the beam is bent at the mid-span. The 125 mm edge of the beam is horizontal.

For steel, $E = 200 \times 10^3\,\text{N/mm}^2$. ULCI

Chapter 16

Torsion of Shafts

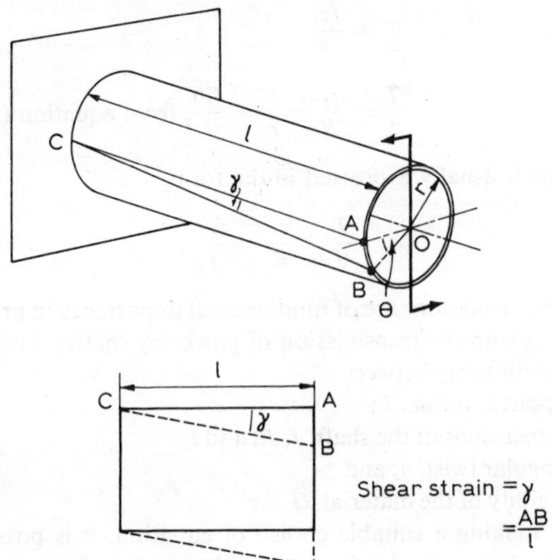

Fig.16.1 Torsion of thin tube

Figure 16.1 represents a thin, hollow shaft of radius r, and length l, fixed at one end, and subjected to a couple applied in the plane of the cross-section at O. In this case, we produce pure torsion, and correspondingly pure shear stresses. A radius such as OA will twist into position OB, such that the angle of twist in a length l is θ rad. Hence a straight line CA becomes CB, which is really part of a helix; but, the angle of twist being small, the line CB is regarded as a straight line. The distance AB can be considered either as part of the circle, centre O, or as part of a circle, centre C, radius CA. Using the expression arc = radius × angle in radians, we can express the length of AB in two ways:

$$AB = OA \times \theta = r\theta$$

or

$$AB = CA \times \gamma = l\gamma$$

Equate these two expressions and we have:

$$l\gamma = r\theta$$

$$\gamma = \frac{r\theta}{l} \quad \ldots\ldots \quad (1)$$

Now this angle can be taken as a measure of the shear strain in the shaft. The smaller diagram in fig.16.1 is a reminder of the way in which we have previously defined shear strain.

But $\dfrac{\text{shear stress}}{\text{shear strain}}$ is equal to the modulus of rigidity (G).

Let τ = the shear stress at radius r.

$$\frac{\tau}{\gamma} = G$$

$$\gamma = \frac{\tau}{G}$$

Substituting this into equation (1),

$$\frac{\tau}{G} = \frac{r\theta}{l}$$

$$\frac{\tau}{r} = \frac{G\theta}{l} \quad \ldots\ldots \quad (2)$$

or

$$\text{stress, } \tau = \frac{G\theta}{l}.r \quad \ldots\ldots \quad (3)$$

or

$$\text{angle of twist, } \theta = \frac{l\tau}{Gr} \quad \ldots\ldots \quad (4)$$

Thus the shear stress at radius r is directly proportional to the radius. Now a solid shaft can be considered as being made up of an infinite number of concentric tubes; the shear stress on each will be proportional to the radius of the tube. The maximum stress will be at the maximum radius. Thus, for a shaft of diameter D, the maximum stress will be

$$\tau = \frac{G\theta r}{l} \text{ or } \frac{G\theta D}{2l}$$

Moment of Resistance of a Circular Cross-section

Consider a hollow circular shaft, outer radius R_1, inner radius R_2. Due to the shear stresses set up, every cross-section will offer a resisting moment equal and opposite to the applied twisting moment. This is much the same as the way in which the various sections of the beam offer a moment of resistance to the applied bending moment. In the case of the shaft, it is necessary that the designer designs a shaft of sufficient diameter to enable its moment of resistance to be greater than any applied torque to which it is likely to be subjected.

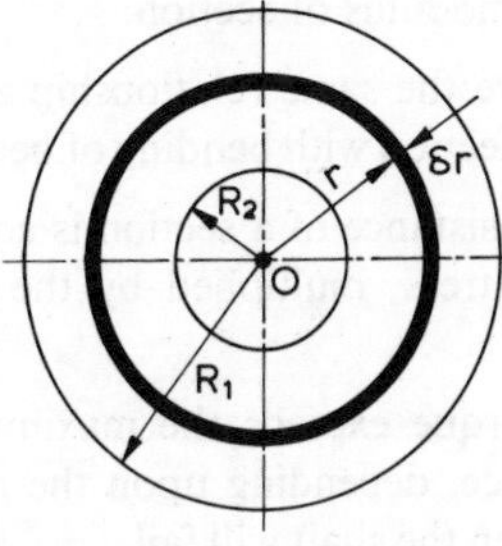

Fig.16.2 Moment of resistance of annular section

Let τ_1 = maximum shear stress at outer surface, radius R_1.

Consider an elementary tube, radius r, of width δr.

Let τ = shear stress in this element.

Then $\tau = \tau_1 \dfrac{r}{R_1}$, since $\dfrac{\text{stress}}{\text{radius}}$ = constant.

Force on element = stress × area

$$= \tau_1 \frac{r}{R_1} \times 2\pi r \delta r$$

$$= \frac{2\pi r^2 \delta r \tau_1}{R_1}$$

Moment of force about centre

$$= \frac{2\pi\tau_1}{R_1} r^2 \delta r \times r = \frac{2\pi\tau_1}{R_1} r^3 \delta r$$

Total moment of all such forces $= \dfrac{2\pi\tau_1}{R_1}\displaystyle\int_{R_2}^{R_1} r^3 dr$

$$= \frac{2\pi\tau_1}{R_1}\left[\frac{r^4}{4}\right]_{R_2}^{R_1}$$

$$= \frac{\pi\tau_1}{2R_1}(R_1^4 - R_2^4)$$

Substituting $D_1 = 2R_1$, and $D_2 = 2R_2$,

$$\text{moment of resistance} = \frac{\pi\tau_1}{16}\left(\frac{D_1^4 - D_2^4}{D_1}\right) \quad . \quad . \quad . \quad . \quad (5)$$

This can be written as

$$\text{moment of resistance} = \frac{\pi}{32}\frac{(D_1^4 - D_2^4)\tau_1}{D_1/2}$$

But $\pi(D_1^4 - D_2^4)/32$ is the polar second moment of area, J, of a circular annulus section; and $D_1/2$ is the distance from the axis to the extreme part of the section.

$$\therefore \text{ Moment of resistance} = \frac{J}{R_1}\tau_1 \quad . \quad . \quad . \quad . \quad . \quad . \quad (6)$$

$$= Z_P \tau_1$$

where Z_P = polar modulus of section.

In words, we have the same relationship as the one which we obtained in connection with bending of beams, viz.

the moment of resistance of a section is equal to the maximum allowable stress, multiplied by the modulus of the section.

If the applied torque exceeds the maximum value of the moment of resistance, depending upon the maximum allowable shear stress, then the shaft will fail.

Conversely to all this, we can obtain the value of the stress set up in the shaft when a given torque, or twisting moment, is applied.

Let T = applied torque,
τ_1 = maximum shear stress produced by this torque,
R = outer radius of shaft.

Then from equation (6), since the moment of resistance is equal and opposite to the applied torque, we have

$$T = \frac{J\tau_1}{R}$$

$$\frac{T}{J} = \frac{\tau_1}{R} = \frac{\tau}{r} = \frac{G\theta}{l}, \text{ from equation (2)}$$

This is usually expressed in the form

$$\frac{T}{J} = \frac{\tau_1}{R} = \frac{G\theta}{l}$$

These equations are of fundamental importance in problems dealing with the transmission of power by shafts. They show the relationship between:

1 applied torque, T;
2 dimensions of the shaft, J, R, and l;
3 angular twist, θ; and
4 rigidity of the material, G.

By making a suitable choice of equation, it is possible to obtain the required information when certain facts are given.

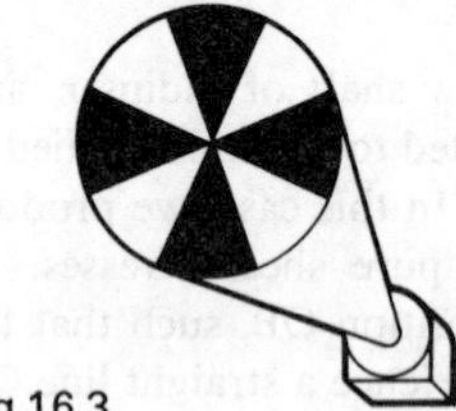

For shafts transmitting power, use polar values $J = \dfrac{\pi D^4}{32}$

Fig.16.3

Example 16.1 A rule often used in shaft design states that the angle of twist shall not exceed 1° on a length equal to 20 diameters. What stress in the material does this imply if the modulus of rigidity is equal to 80 × 10³ N/mm²?

$$\frac{T}{J} = \frac{\tau}{r} = \frac{G\theta}{l}$$

Let D = diameter of shaft.

Then $l = 20D$

$$\theta = 1° = \frac{2\pi}{360} = 0{\cdot}0174 \text{ rad}$$

$$G = 80 \times 10^9$$

$$r = D/2$$

$$\therefore \frac{\tau}{D/2} = \frac{80 \times 10^9 \times 0{\cdot}0174}{20D}$$

$$\tau = \frac{80 \times 10^9 \times 0{\cdot}0174 \times D}{20D \times 2}$$

$$= 34{\cdot}8 \text{ N/mm}^2$$

i.e. If a steel shaft ($G = 80 \times 10^3$ N/mm²) is designed to have an angle of twist of 1° in a length of 20 diameters, the maximum shear stress in the steel will be 34·8 N/mm².

Example 16.2 Determine the maximum allowable power which can be transmitted by a 150mm diameter shaft running at 240 rev/min, when the permissible shear stress is 55N/mm². The shaft has a coupling on it, having six bolts on a 260mm diameter pitch circle. Determine the diameter of the bolts if the maximum shear stress in the bolts must not exceed 100N/mm².

NCTEC

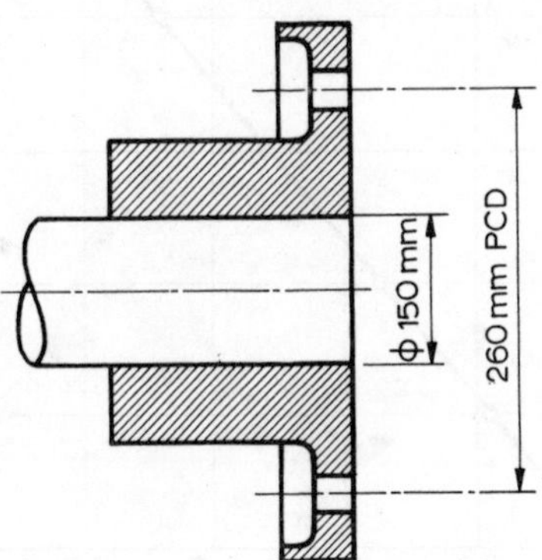

Fig.16.4

$$\frac{T}{J} = \frac{\tau}{r}$$

$$\tau = 55 \times 10^6 \text{N/m}^2$$

$$J = \frac{\pi D^4}{32} = \frac{\pi}{32} \times 0{\cdot}15^4 = 0{\cdot}000\,05\text{m}^4$$

$$r = \frac{0{\cdot}15}{2} = 0{\cdot}075$$

$$\text{Then } \frac{T}{0{\cdot}000\,05} = \frac{55 \times 10^6}{0{\cdot}075}$$

$$T = \frac{55 \times 10^6 \times 0{\cdot}000\,05}{0{\cdot}075}$$

$$= 36{\cdot}5 \times 10^3 \text{Nm}$$

$$\text{Power} = 36{\cdot}5 \times 10^3 \frac{240}{60} \times 2\pi$$

$$= 920 \times 10^3 \text{ watts}$$

$$= 920\text{kW}$$

$$\text{Tangential load at pitch line} = \frac{\text{torque}}{\text{pitch radius}}$$

$$= \frac{36{\cdot}5 \times 10^3}{0{\cdot}13}$$

$$= 280 \times 10^3 \text{N}$$

$$\text{Load carried per bolt} = \frac{280 \times 10^3}{6}$$

$$= 46{\cdot}7 \times 10^3 \text{N}$$

But load = stress × area,

$$\therefore \text{ required area} = \frac{\text{load}}{\text{stress}} = \frac{46{\cdot}7 \times 10^3}{100 \times 10^6}$$

$$= 4{\cdot}67 \times 10^{-4}\text{m}^2 = 467\text{mm}^2$$

$$\therefore \frac{\pi d^2}{4} = 467$$

$$\text{Bolt diameter} = \sqrt{\left(\frac{4 \times 467}{\pi}\right)} \text{ mm}$$

$$= 24{\cdot}5\text{mm, say } 25\text{mm.}$$

i.e. The maximum allowable power transmitted by the shaft is 920kW, and the required diameter of the coupling bolts is 24·5 mm (say 25mm).

Alternative Solution

The value of the torque which is being transmitted by the shaft can easily be obtained using the expression

$$T = \frac{\pi D^3 \tau}{16}$$

This is a very common expression, and is often used in connection with shaft design.

$$T = \frac{\pi}{16} \times 0{\cdot}15^3 \times 55 \times 10^6$$

$$= 36{\cdot}5 \times 10^3 \text{Nm}$$

The remainder of the solution would follow as above.

Example 16.3 An extension of a light drive is effected by attaching a tube, 2·4m long, 30mm in internal diameter, 36 mm in external diameter, to the end of a solid spindle 30mm in diameter. If the drive sets up a maximum shear stress of 30N/mm² in the spindle, calculate the maximum shear stress in the tube, and the angle of twist in the 2·4m length. (Modulus of rigidity = 80 × 10³N/mm².)

IMECHE

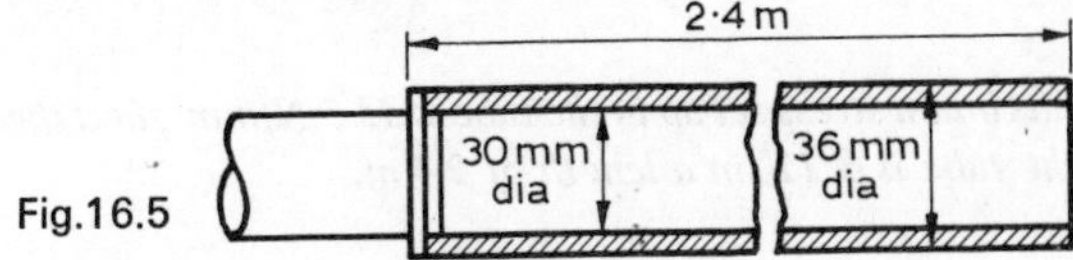

Fig.16.5

In this case, the torque transmitted by the spindle is equal to that transmitted by the tube.

Let τ_s = maximum stress in spindle,
τ_t = maximum stress in tube,
Z_s = section modulus for spindle,
Z_t = section modulus for tube,
T = torque transmitted.

$$\tau_s Z_s = \tau_t Z_t$$

$$\therefore \tau_t = \tau_s \frac{Z_s}{Z_t}$$

For the tube $Z_t = \frac{\pi}{16}\left(\frac{D_1^4 - D_2^4}{D_1}\right)$

$$= \frac{\pi}{16}\left(\frac{3{\cdot}6^4 - 3{\cdot}0^4}{3{\cdot}6}\right) \text{cm}^3$$

$$= 4{\cdot}75\,\text{cm}^3$$

For the spindle $Z_S = \frac{\pi}{16} D_2^3$

$$= \frac{\pi}{16} \times 3{\cdot}0^3\,\text{cm}^3$$

$$= 5{\cdot}3\,\text{cm}^3$$

Then, since $\tau_s = 30 \times 10^6\,\text{N/m}^2$

$$\tau_t = \tau_s . \frac{Z_s}{Z_t} = \frac{30 \times 10^6 \times 5{\cdot}3}{4{\cdot}75}$$

$$= 33{\cdot}5 \times 10^6\,\text{N/m}^2$$

Fundamental equation for torsion $\frac{T}{J} = \frac{\tau_s}{r} = \frac{G\theta}{l}$

$$\tau_s = 33{\cdot}5 \times 10^6\,\text{N/m}^2$$
$$r = 1{\cdot}8\,\text{cm} = 0{\cdot}018\,\text{m}$$
$$G = 80 \times 10^9\,\text{N/m}^2$$
$$l = 2{\cdot}4\,\text{m}$$

$$\therefore \frac{33{\cdot}5 \times 10^6}{0{\cdot}018} = \frac{80 \times 10^9 \times \theta}{2{\cdot}4}$$

$$\theta = \frac{33{\cdot}5 \times 10^6 \times 2{\cdot}4}{0{\cdot}018 \times 80 \times 10^9}$$

$$= 0{\cdot}056 \text{ radians}$$

$$= \frac{0{\cdot}056 \times 360}{2\pi} \text{ degrees}$$

$$= 3{\cdot}2^\circ$$

i.e. The maximum stress set up in the tube is 33·5 N/mm², and the twist in the tube is 3°11′ in a length of 2·4 m.

Example 16.4 A steel bar, 25 mm in diameter, was tested in torsion, and the following values of the twist, in degrees, corresponding to the given torques, in newton metres, were obtained on a gauge length of 200 mm.

Torque, Nm . . .	0	50	100	150	200	250	300
Twist, deg. . . .	0	0·19	0·37	0·54	0·72	0·91	1·08

Plot a graph of torque against angle of twist, and from it determine the modulus of rigidity of the material.

Also determine the maximum shear stress in the material when the torque is 275 Nm. ULCI

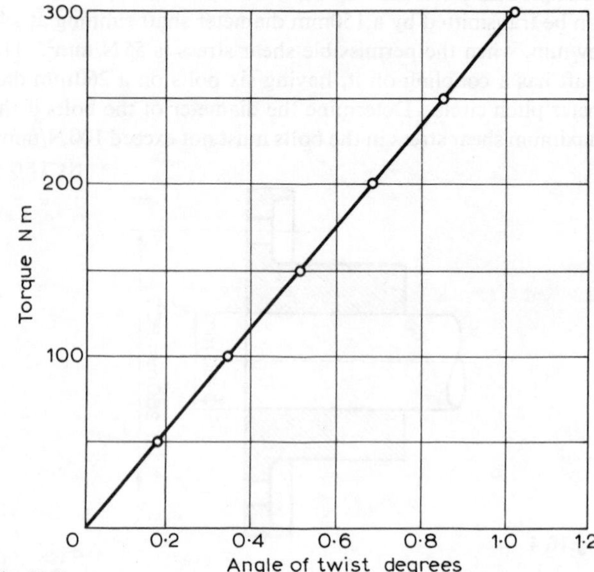

Fig.16.6

For torsion, we require the polar second moment of area

$$J = \frac{\pi}{32} D^4$$

$$= \frac{\pi}{32} \times 2{\cdot}5^4 = 3{\cdot}84\,\text{cm}^4$$

$$\frac{T}{J} = \frac{G\theta}{l}$$

$\therefore$ Modulus of rigidity $G = \frac{Tl}{J\theta} = \frac{T}{\theta} \times \frac{l}{J}$

On the graph (fig.16.6) a straight line has been drawn, approximating to the points.

The slope of this line gives T/θ and equals 250/0·91, with θ in degrees. Converting into radians, for use in the above expression, we have

$$\frac{T}{\theta} = \frac{250}{0{\cdot}91} \times \frac{180}{\pi} = 15\,800$$

Now $G = \frac{T}{\theta} \times \frac{l}{J}$

$$= \frac{15\,800 \times 0{\cdot}2}{3{\cdot}84 \times 10^{-8}}$$

$$= 820 \times 10^8\,\text{N/m}^2$$
$$= 82 \times 10^3\,\text{N/mm}^2$$

Shear stress: $\frac{T}{J} = \frac{\tau}{r}$

$$T = 275\,\text{Nm}$$
$$\tau = \text{shear stress at radius } r$$
$$J = 3{\cdot}84\,\text{cm}^4$$

$$r = \text{maximum radius} = 1{\cdot}25\,\text{cm}$$

$$\tau = \frac{Tr}{J} = \frac{275 \times 1{\cdot}25 \times 10^{-2}}{3{\cdot}84 \times 10^{-8}}$$

$$= 89{\cdot}5 \times 10^{6}\,\text{N/m}^2 \text{ or } 89{\cdot}5\,\text{N/mm}^2$$

i.e. The modulus of rigidity is 82 × 10^3 N/mm² and maximum shear stress in the material is 89·5 N/mm².

Example 16.5 Determine suitable values for the external and internal diameters (D and d) for a hollow shaft to transmit 750 kW at 50 rev/min, given that the angle of twist must not exceed 1° in a length of $20D$. Assume that $d = 0{\cdot}6D$, and the modulus of rigidity for the steel is $85 \times 10^3\,\text{N/mm}^2$. NCTEC

$$\text{Torque transmitted} = \frac{\text{power (watts)}}{\text{speed (rad/s)}}$$

$$= \frac{750 \times 1000 \times 60}{50 \times 2\pi}$$

$$= 143\,000\,\text{Nm}$$

$$\text{Now } \frac{T}{J} = \frac{\tau}{r} = \frac{G\theta}{l}$$

$$T = 143\,000\,\text{Nm}$$

$$G = 85 \times 10^9\,\text{N/m}^2$$

$$\theta = 1^\circ = \frac{2\pi}{360}\text{ radians}$$

$$l = 20D$$

$$J = \frac{\pi}{32}(D^4 - d^4)$$

Substituting these values in the main equation, we have

$$\frac{143\,000}{J} = \frac{85 \times 10^9}{20D} \times \frac{2\pi}{360}$$

$$J = \frac{143\,000 \times 360 \times 20D}{85 \times 10^9 \times 2\pi}$$

$$= 1{\cdot}93 \times 10^{-3}D$$

$$\frac{\pi}{32}(D^4 - d^4) = 1{\cdot}93 \times 10^{-3}D$$

$$\frac{\pi}{32}(D^4 - 0{\cdot}6^4D^4) = 1{\cdot}93 \times 10^{-3}D$$

$$\frac{\pi}{32}(1 - 0{\cdot}13)\,D^4 = 1{\cdot}93 \times 10^{-3}D$$

$$0{\cdot}0855D^4 = 1{\cdot}93 \times 10^{-3}D$$

$$D^3 = \frac{1{\cdot}93 \times 10^{-3}}{0{\cdot}0855} = 22{\cdot}50 \times 10^{-3}$$

$$D = 0{\cdot}283\,\text{m}$$

$$d = 0{\cdot}6 \times 0{\cdot}283 = 0{\cdot}17\,\text{m}$$

i.e. The theoretical diameters for the shaft are 283 mm external, and 170 mm internal.

Close-coiled Helical Springs

The long, thin rod indicated in fig.16.7 is fixed at one end, and has an arm carrying a load fastened to the other end. The rod is supported so that there is no vertical deflection due to the applied load. Provided that the shear stress in the material remains within the elastic limit, a certain springy condition will be noticed at the end of the arm. The arm will rotate through an angle of twist θ radians, due to the effect of the applied torque WR; and the weight will move through a vertical distance $x = R\theta$, due to torsional deflection only. When the load is removed, the arm will return to its original position.

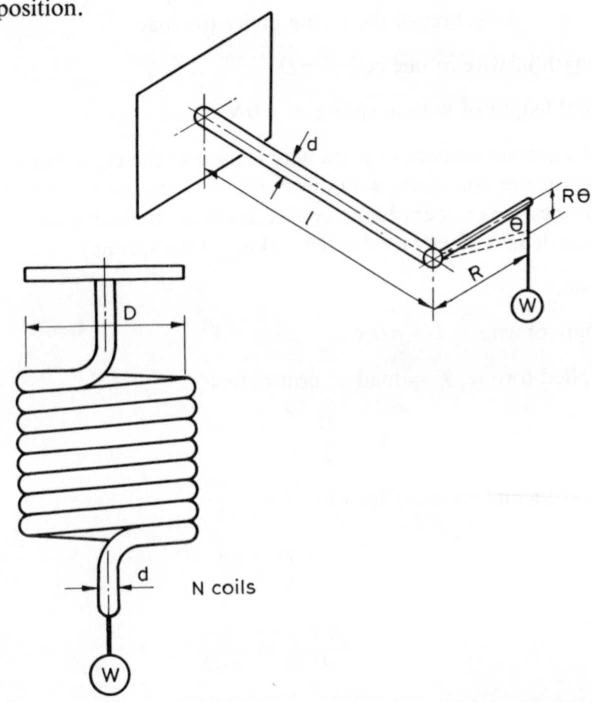

Fig.16.7 The close-coiled helical spring. Basically the action of the close-coiled helical spring is the same as that of the long rod in torsion.

If the rod is wound around a cylinder of diameter $D = 2R$, we have the basis of a close-coiled helical spring. Fundamentally, the long rod and the close-coiled spring are under identical conditions. The end of the spring wire is bent towards the axis of the spring, so that the load W is applied along this axis. Consequently, the wire is subjected throughout its length to a torque $WD/2$, and an angle of twist, θ, is produced. This in turn causes a vertical deflection $\theta D/2$. Incidentally, it is assumed that the plane of each coil of the spring is perpendicular to the axis of the spring, and that the coils remain very close together after the application of the load. If these two conditions are not complied with very closely, it will not be possible to claim that the wire is subjected only to torsion, and that the deflection is due only to twist. Complications due to bending, and to subsequent bending stresses, are added when we consider the open-coiled spring; the type, for example, which you find in the indicator mechanisms in the heat-engine laboratories.

For our purposes we are concerned only with the close-coiled spring.

Let d = diameter of wire in the spring,
D = mean diameter of the spring,
N = number of coils,
W = applied load,
G = modulus of rigidity of the material,
x = deflection of the spring under the load.

Length of wire in one coil $= \pi D$

Total length of wire in spring $= \pi DN$

(A certain amount of extra wire is used at the ends, but we need not be concerned with this at this present stage. Empirical rules are in operation to enable designers to determine the actual length of wire used in the making of the spring.)

Then,

length of wire, $l = \pi DN$

applied torque, T = load × arm radius

$$= W \times \frac{D}{2}$$

Polar second moment for wire, $J = \frac{\pi d^4}{32}$

$$\frac{T}{J} = \frac{G\theta}{l}$$

$$\frac{WD/2}{\pi d^4/32} = \frac{G\theta}{\pi DN}$$

$$\theta = \frac{16WD^2N}{Gd^4}$$

The deflection of the spring, $x = \frac{D}{2}\theta$

$$= \frac{D}{2} \cdot \frac{16WD^2N}{Gd^4}$$

$$\text{Deflection} = \frac{8WD^3N}{Gd^4}$$

The 'stiffness' of a spring is defined as the load required to produce unit deflection. If, for example, a load of 20 newtons produces a deflection of 100 millimetres, then 200 newtons would produce a deflection of 1 metre. Consequently the stiffness of the spring is expressed as 200 newtons per metre.

$$\text{Stiffness} = \frac{\text{load}}{\text{deflection}}$$

$$= \frac{W}{8WD^3N/Gd^4}$$

$$\text{Stiffness} = \frac{Gd^4}{8D^3N}$$

The maximum shear stress set up in the spring, under load, occurs around the outer surface of the wire. Its value is given by the equation

$$\frac{T}{J} = \frac{\tau_s}{r}$$

Note that r = radius of the wire $= d/2$.

Substituting the previously obtained expression into this equation, we have

$$\frac{WD/2}{\pi d^4/32} = \frac{\tau_s}{d/2}$$

$$\text{Maximum shear stress } \tau_s = \frac{16WD}{2\pi d^3} = \frac{8WD}{\pi d^3}$$

Note. All the above expressions apply equally well to springs in tension or compression, provided the coils remain reasonably close.

Example 16.6 A closely coiled helical spring is made from a piece of steel wire 1·5 m long (exclusive of amount required for end connections), and 3 mm in diameter. The mean diameter of the coils is 75 mm. When the spring is subjected to an axial load of 10 N, find (a) the shear stress set up in the wire, and (b) the deflection at the bottom of the helix, if the modulus of rigidity of the material is 80 × 10³ N/mm². UEI

Basic equation:

$$\frac{T}{J} = \frac{\tau_s}{r} = \frac{G\theta}{l}$$

$$T = \text{applied torque} = W \times \frac{D}{2}$$

$$= \frac{10 \times 0{\cdot}075}{2} = 0{\cdot}375 \text{ Nm}$$

$$J = \text{polar second moment} = \frac{\pi}{32} \times 0{\cdot}003^4 \text{ m}^4$$

$$= 7{\cdot}9 \times 10^{-12} \text{ m}^4$$

$$r = \frac{\text{diameter of wire}}{2} = \frac{0{\cdot}003}{2} = 0{\cdot}0015 \text{ m}$$

$$G = 80 \times 10^9 \text{ N/m}^2$$

$$l = 1{\cdot}5 \text{ m}$$

$$x = \text{deflection or extension of spring} = \frac{D}{2} \times \theta$$

$$\theta = \frac{2x}{D} = \frac{2x}{0.075} = 26.7x$$

(a) Shear stress
Using the first pair of equations,

$$\frac{T}{J} = \frac{\tau_s}{r}$$

$$\frac{0.375}{7.9 \times 10^{-12}} = \frac{\tau_s}{0.0015}$$

$$\tau_s = \frac{0.375 \times 0.0015}{7.9 \times 10^{-12}}$$

$$= 71.4 \times 10^6 \text{ N/m}^2$$

(b) Deflection of spring
Using first and last expression

$$\frac{T}{J} = \frac{G\theta}{l}$$

(In this way we avoid making use of the stress value just obtained. By this means, any error made in calculating the stress does not affect the second part of the solution.)

$$\frac{0.375}{7.9 \times 10^{-12}} = \frac{80 \times 10^9 \times 26.7x}{1.5}$$

$$\text{Deflection } x = \frac{1.5 \times 0.375}{7.9 \times 10^{-12} \times 80 \times 10^9 \times 26.7} \text{ m}$$

$$= 0.033 \text{ m or } 33 \text{ mm}$$

i.e. Under the given load, the spring will extend 33 mm, and the wire will be subjected to a maximum shear stress of 71·4 N/mm².

Exercise 16

1 Calculate the power transmitted by a solid shaft 22 mm in diameter when running at 2500 rev/min, if the maximum shear stress in the shaft must not exceed 90 N/mm².

2 Calculate a suitable diameter for a solid shaft to transmit 200 kW when running at 180 rev/min, if the maximum shear stress must not exceed 85 N/mm².

3 At what speed must a shaft 80 mm in diameter rotate to transmit 125 kW when the maximum allowable shear stress is 60 N/mm²?

4 Using the rule that a shaft must not twist more than 1° in a length equal to 20 times the diameter, calculate the diameter of a shaft required to transmit 150 kW at 300 rev/min. (Modulus of rigidity = 80 × 10³ N/mm².)

5 A hollow steel shaft has to transmit 6750 kW at 120 rev/min. The maximum twisting moment exceeds the mean by 25%. If the maximum shear stress is not to exceed 50 N/mm², and the internal diameter of the shaft is 0·6 × external diameter, determine the internal and external diameters of the shaft.

6 The following observations were taken from a test on a shaft when transmitting power:

material of shaft . .	mild steel ($G = 80 \times 10^3$ N/mm²)
diameter of shaft . .	75 mm
length under test . .	15 m
total angle of twist .	20°
speed of rotation . .	280 rev/min

Calculate (a) the maximum stress in the shaft, (b) the maximum torque transmitted, and (c) the power transmitted.

7 Calculate the twist, in degrees, of a solid shaft, 300 mm in diameter and 6 m long, when transmitting 1600 kW at 75 rev/min. (Modulus of rigidity = 80 × 10³ N/mm².) NCTEC

8 A solid shaft is made of steel having a modulus of rigidity of 80 × 10³ N/mm². The shaft transmits 4000 kW at 300 rev/min when the angle of twist on a 6 m length of shaft is 2°. What is the diameter of the shaft? NCTEC

9 State the advantages of hollow as compared with solid shafts.

A solid shaft, 350 mm in diameter, transmits 3750 kW at 180 rev/min. Calculate the maximum shear stress. NCTEC

10 The internal diameter of a hollow shaft is 0·75 times the external diameter. Compare the torque which can be carried with that for a solid shaft of the same weight and material, and having the same maximum stress. NCTEC

11 In order to effect a saving in weight, a solid steel shaft is replaced by a hollow shaft of the same diameter, but manufactured from a higher-quality steel which permits the maximum shear stress to be 40% greater. Taking the shafts to have the same strength in torsion, find the ratio of the diameters of the hollow shaft. NCTEC

12 Calculate the modulus of rigidity of the material of a hollow shaft having an outside diameter of 42 mm, and an inside diameter of 24 mm, if a torque of 450 N m causes an angle of twist of 0·53° on a 300 mm length of the shaft. NCTEC

13 The table gives values of the torque, T, and the corresponding angles of twist, α, as observed during a test of a duralumin bar in a simple torsion-testing machine. The specimen was 12·5 mm in diameter, and the angle was read over a gauge length of 0·75 m. Determine the modulus of rigidity of the material.

T, N m .	0	0·75	1·5	2·25	3·0	3·75
α, degrees .	0	0·7	1·5	2·2	3·0	3·4
T, N m .	4·5	5·25	6·0	6·75	7·5	8·25
α, degrees .	4·0	4·7	5·4	5·8	6·3	7·1

NCTEC

14 Calculate the diameter of a hollow circular shaft to transmit 4000 kW at 400 rev/min, if the outer diameter is twice the inner, and the angle of twist must not exceed 9° in a length of 30 m. (The modulus of rigidity of the material is 80×10^3 N/mm².) NCTEC

15 A solid steel shaft is transmitting 200 kW at 160 rev/min. Calculate the diameter of the shaft if the maximum shear stress is 90 N/mm² under these conditions. This shaft is now replaced by a hollow shaft of the same outside diameter, length, and material. Calculate the inner diameter of the new shaft if the angle of twist is now 50% greater than in the case of the solid shaft for the same working conditions. EMEU

16 When a hollow propeller shaft transmits 325 kW at 210 rev/min, it twists 2° on a length of 1·2 m. Calculate the external diameter if the inner diameter of the shaft is 75 mm. Calculate the maximum shear stress under the above conditions. (Modulus of rigidity = 80×10^3 N/mm².) EMEU

17 When under load, a 75 mm diameter solid steel shaft twists through an angle of 8° over a length of 6 m. If the modulus of rigidity of the steel is 80×10^3 N/mm², determine the applied twisting moment, and the maximum shearing stress in the shaft.

If the shaft rotates at 150 rev/min, determine the power being transmitted. UEI

18 A torque of 55 000 Nm is to be transmitted by a hollow shaft of internal diameter half the external diameter. If the maximum shear stress is not to exceed 75 N/mm², calculate the outside diameter of the shaft.

What would be the angle of twist in degrees over a length of 3 m for the shaft under the above torque? (Modulus of rigidity is 80×10^3 N/mm².) UEI

19 (a) Prove the relation $\frac{T}{J} = \frac{\tau}{r}$ in connection with simple torsion. State the assumptions made.

(b) Given a close-coiled helical spring, show how you would determine the value of G for the material of which the spring is made. Write down the approximate value you would expect to obtain for the material of such a spring. UEI

20 Starting with the relation $\frac{T}{J} = \frac{G\theta}{l}$, obtain an expression for the deflection of the free end of a closely coiled helical spring carrying an axial load W.

Such a spring is made from 12·5 mm diameter steel wire, and its ten coils have a mean diameter of 250 mm. Find (a) the deflection of the free end, and (b) the shear stress produced in the wire when the spring carries an axial load of 175 N. ($G = 80 \times 10^3$ N/mm².) UEI

21 A solid circular shaft is to be replaced by a hollow circular shaft of similar material, having an internal diameter three-quarter times the external diameter.

Find their relative weights if the shafts have the same torsional strengths. UEI

22 The table gives the values of the load, W, and the corresponding angle of twist, θ, as observed during a torsion test on a mild steel bar. The diameter of the specimen was 25 mm, and the angle was read over a gauge length of 125 mm.

Determine, by the aid of a graph, the modulus of rigidity for the material. The length of the load lever of the testing machine was 435 mm.

W, newtons .	0	50	100	150	200	250
θ, degrees .	0	0·048	0·094	0·141	0·189	0·236
W, newtons .		300	350	400	450	500
θ, degrees .		0·285	0·330	0·383	0·430	0·487

UEI

23 When under load, a 100 mm diameter solid steel shaft twists through an angle of 10° over a length of 7·5 m. If the modulus of rigidity for steel is 80×10^3 N/mm², determine the applied twisting moment, and the maximum shearing stress in the shaft.

If the shaft rotates at 200 rev/min, determine the power being transmitted.

24 A hollow steel shaft, of 100 mm external and 62·5 mm internal diameter, when transmitting power is observed to twist through an angle of 1·8° over a length of 3 m. The modulus of rigidity of the steel is 85×10^3 N/mm².

Determine (a) the maximum shear stress induced in the material by the torque transmitted, and (b) the power transmitted by the shaft when it is revolving at 180 rev/min. ULCI

25 A solid shaft transmits 90 kW, and rotates at a speed of 150 rev/min. The maximum shear stress in the material of the shaft is not to exceed 55 N/mm², and the modulus of rigidity of the material is 80×10^3 N/mm². Determine the necessary minimum diameter for the shaft.

What will be the angle of twist, in degrees, of this shaft over a length of 3 m? ULCI

26 A solid shaft of diameter d, and a hollow shaft of the same material, with an internal diameter d, and an external diameter of $D = 1{\cdot}25d$, have to transmit the same torque. Show that the ratio of the maximum shear stresses is nearly 1·15.

A solid steel shaft, 100 mm in diameter and 1 m long, is to be coupled to a hollow shaft of internal diameter 100 mm and external diameter 125 mm. The length, l, of the hollow shaft is to be such that, when a torque of 13 500 Nm is transmitted, the total angle of twist shall not be less than 0·035 radian. Determine the least possible value for l. (Modulus of rigidity = 80×10^3 N/mm².) IMECHE

27 In a standard experiment to determine the modulus of rigidity of the material of a wire, a body of known moment of inertia I is attached to the end of the vertically suspended

wire, and the system is set oscillating torsionally. The periodic time in such a case is given by $2\pi\sqrt{(I/c)}$, where c is the torsional stiffness of the wire (torque per radian of twist).

In a particular case, the wire was 1 m long, and its diameter was 0·9 mm. The mass attached had a moment of inertia about the vertical axis of the wire of 0·004 kg m^2. The periodic time of small torsional oscillations was observed to be 5·5 seconds. Determine the torsional stiffness of the wire, and hence deduce the modulus of rigidity of the material. IMECHE

28 Find the external diameter of a hollow steel shaft to transmit 3 MW at 200 rev/min, if the internal diameter is 0·75 of the external, and the maximum shear stress due to torsion is not to exceed 55 N/mm^2. If the modulus of rigidity of the steel is 80×10^3 N/mm^2, find the elastic twist of the shaft in a length of 3·6 m when stressed to the maximum allowed intensity. IMECHE

29 During the conversion of a ship's propelling machinery, it is decided to replace an existing 250 mm diameter solid steel propeller shaft, transmitting 950 kW at 80 rev/min, by a hollow steel shaft, the internal diameter of which is to be one-half of its external diameter. The hollow shaft is to be capable of transmitting 1500 kW at 80 rev/min, with the same maximum shear stress as for the solid shaft. Calculate this maximum shear stress, and use the value obtained to determine the dimensions of the hollow shaft. NCTEC

30 Show from first principles that, when a circular shaft is subjected to pure torsion, the shear stress induced is proportional to the radius.

A hollow steel shaft, having an external diameter twice the internal diameter, is to transmit 2500 kW at a speed of 400 rev/min. If the angle of twist is not to exceed 1° on a length equivalent to 16 times the external diameter, and the maximum torque exceeds the mean value by 25%, calculate the maximum shear stress induced in the material due to torsion, and the internal and external diameters of the shaft.

Modulus of rigidity, $G = 80 \times 10^3$ N/mm^2. ULCI

Chapter 17

Pressure of Liquids

We shall now be concerned with the pressure of liquids on immersed surfaces such as the sides of tanks, or lock gates, or sluice gates for controlling the flow of water into a hydraulic turbine plant. The solution to problems of this type is dependent upon three experimentally established facts relating to the pressure of liquids.

1 The pressure exerted by a liquid is always perpendicular to the surface of the containing vessel.
2 The pressure of a liquid inside a closed vessel is constant throughout the vessel. (This statement assumes that we are neglecting the variation of pressure which there will be with the depth of liquid in the vessel; in any case, this may be small compared with the pressure applied by external forces.)
3 The pressure exerted by the liquid is dependent upon the *head* of the liquid, or the vertical distance from the point considered to the surface of the liquid.

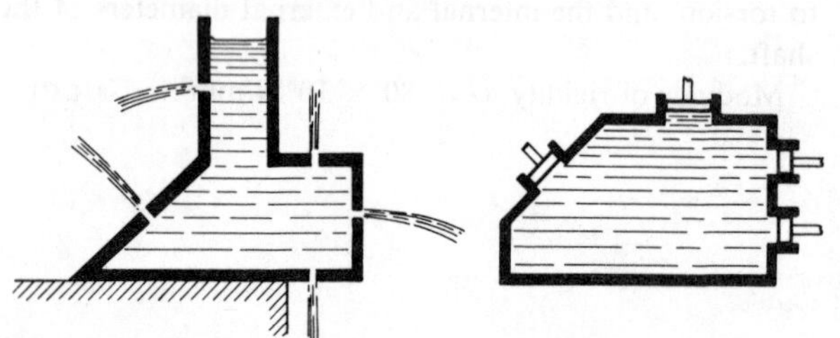

Fig.17.1 Pressure of a liquid. The vessel on the left illustrates the principle that the pressure exerted by a liquid is always perpendicular to the side of the enclosing vessel. The closed vessel on the right indicates that the pressure of liquid in a closed vessel is the same for all points in the liquid (neglecting any variations which there may be due to the depth of the liquid in the vessel). Hence the pressure produced in the liquid by one of the pistons is immediately transferred to all the other pistons.

Points 1 and 2 require experimental verification, and fig.17.1 indicates two of the ways in which this can be partially obtained. We must look more closely, however, at the reason for, and the implication behind, the statement 3, regarding pressure exerted by the liquid. In this connection, it might be well to state that there is a certain amount of loose thinking associated with the word 'pressure'. In all other engineering connections, we understand pressure to be 'load or force per unit area'. Coming to the subject of hydraulics (or hydrostatics, as this branch of hydraulics is often named), we find that the pressure exerted by a liquid on a plane surface can mean the total force exerted by the liquid on the surface. Indeed, since the pressure in N/m² may well vary over a surface under certain conditions, the actual pressure over the surface could not be stated. Consequently the term 'intensity of pressure' is often used in hydraulics, to convey the idea of force per unit area.

Pressure at Any Depth in a Liquid

Consider a vertical cylinder of liquid, of height h, and of cross-sectional area δA (fig.17.2).

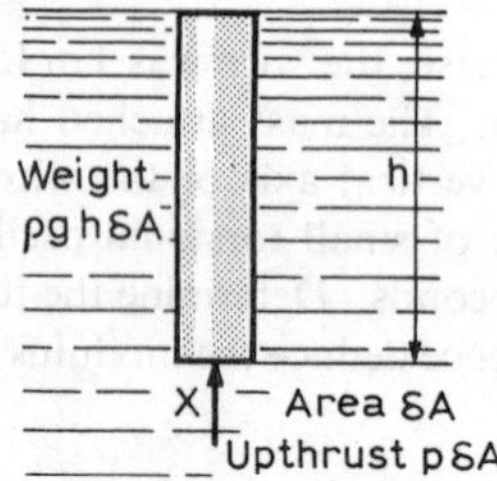

Fig.17.2 Pressure of liquid at any depth. The pressure of the liquid is dependent upon the density of the liquid, and upon the depth of the considered point below the free surface of the liquid.

Let ρ = the mass of the liquid per unit volume (i.e. the density of the liquid)
Weight of cylinder of liquid $= \rho g h \delta A$
Let p = the pressure at the point X.
Upthrust at bottom of cylinder = pressure × area

$$= p\delta A$$

Equating the upthrust on the base to the weight of the cylinder,

$$p\delta A = \rho g h \delta A$$

$$h = \frac{p}{\rho g}$$

If h is in metres, and ρ is in kg/m², then the pressure p is in N/m². In questions dealing with water, the value of ρ will be 1000 kg/m³ for fresh water, and about 1030 kg/m³ for sea-water. For all other liquids the value of ρ will be 1000 × specific gravity, kg/m³.

If we have a column of water 1 m high, the pressure exerted by that column is

$$\begin{aligned} p &= \rho g h \\ &= 1000 \times 9{\cdot}81 \times 1 \\ &= 9810\,\text{N/m}^2 \end{aligned}$$

Hence 1 m of water is equivalent to a pressure of 9810 N/m².

Consequently, at a depth of 10 m below the free surface level of water, the pressure will be 10 × 9810 or 98 100 N/m² or 0·981 bar.

Conversely, we can consider the height of a column of water which will produce a pressure of one bar.

$$h = \frac{p}{\rho g}$$

$$= \frac{10^5}{9810} = 10{\cdot}3\,\text{m}$$

Hence 1 bar is equivalent to a head of 10·3 m of water.

Force on an Immersed Plane Surface when the Immersed Plate is Parallel to the Free Surface

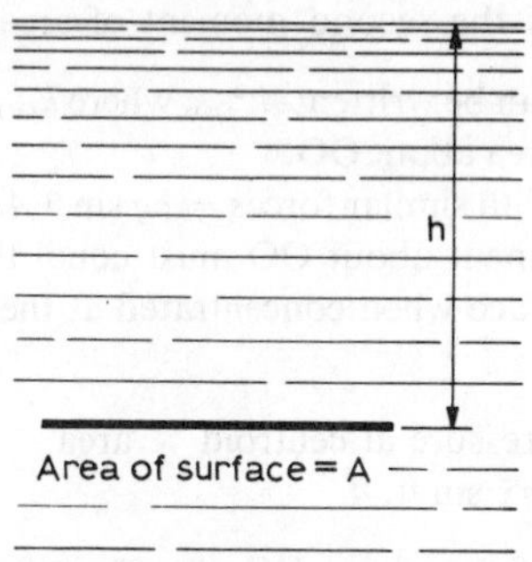

Fig.17.3 Force on plane surface parallel to free surface of liquid

Let h = depth of immersion in m,
A = area of surface in, m²;
ρ = mass of liquid per unit volume, in kg/m³, i.e. density of liquid;
p = pressure, in N/m².

Note that this pressure will be uniform over the whole area, since every point on the surface is at the same depth below the free surface of the liquid (fig. 17.3).

$$p = \rho g h$$

$$\begin{aligned}\text{Force on surface} &= \text{area} \times \text{intensity of pressure}\\ &= A \times \rho g h\\ &= A\rho g h\,\text{N}\end{aligned}$$

Example 17.1 A rectangular tank, whose base measures 6 m by 4 m, contains water to a depth of 3 m. What is the pressure at the base, and what is the force exerted by the water on the base?

$$\begin{aligned}\text{Pressure} &= \rho g h\\ &= 1000 \times 9{\cdot}81 \times 3\\ &= 29\,430\,\text{N/m}^2\\ \text{or} \quad &= 0{\cdot}2943\ \text{bar}\end{aligned}$$

$$\begin{aligned}\text{Area of base} &= 6 \times 4\\ &= 24\,\text{m}^2\end{aligned}$$

$$\begin{aligned}\text{Force on base} &= \text{area} \times \text{pressure}\\ &= 24 \times 29\,430\\ &= 705\,000\,\text{N}\end{aligned}$$

i.e. Pressure on base is 29·4 kN/m², total force on base is 705 kN.

Notice that the volume of water in the tank is 6 × 4 × 3 = 72 m³, and that the weight of this water is 72 × 9810 = 705 000 N. It seems reasonable to accept the fact that the base is supporting the whole weight of this water, and that consequently the force on the base will be 705 000 N. If, however,

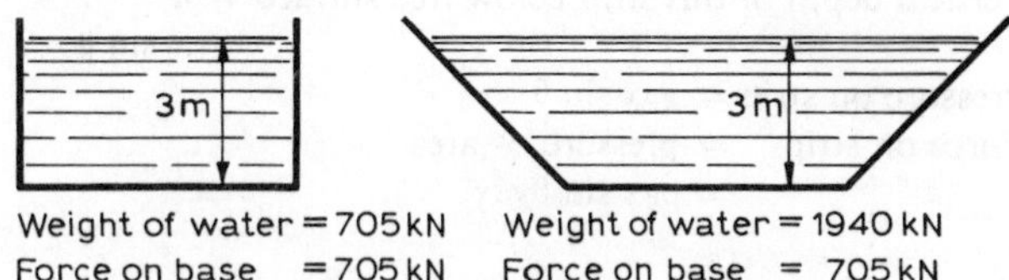

Fig.17.4 Pressure due to head of liquid. Each vessel contains the same depth of water. Each has the same area of base. The force on the base of each is the same, although the vessel on the right contains nearly three times as much water as that on the left.

we refer to fig.17.4, we have represented there two tanks: one with dimensions as given in the example just reviewed; whilst the other tank has the same area of base, but has sloping sides. If all the sides slope at an angle of 45°, the vessel will contain 198 m³ of water weighing 1940 kN when the depth is 3 m. This is nearly three times as much water as the first tank contained. Yet the force on the base of each tank will be the same. The force is dependent upon the depth of water, and the area of the base. These two factors are the same in each tank. The sides of the larger tank are taking a certain proportion of the weight of the contained water. This accounts for the difference between the force on the base and the weight of the water.

Force on an Immersed Inclined Plane Surface

In this very general case, we shall consider the immersed surface as being of irregular area, and inclined at angle θ to the free surface of the liquid (fig.17.5). The area of the surface and the position of its centroid, G, are both known. The line OO is the intersection of the surface, produced if necessary, and the free surface of the liquid.

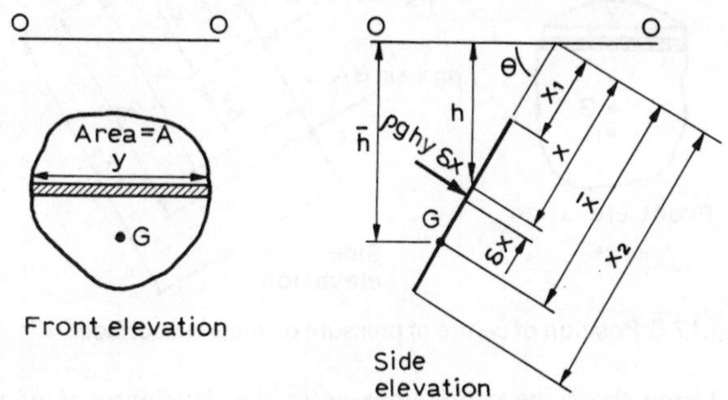

Fig.17.5 Force on inclined surface

Let A = area of immersed surface,
$\bar{x}$ = distance of centroid of immersed area from OO,
$\bar{h}$ = vertical distance of centroid below free surface,
ρ = mass of liquid per unit volume, i.e. density of liquid.

Consider the force on a narrow strip of length y, width δx, parallel to OO, and at distance x from OO.

Vertical depth of this strip below free surface $= h$
$= x \sin \theta$

Pressure on strip $= g\rho x \sin \theta$
Force on strip $=$ pressure $\times$ area
$= \rho g x \sin \theta y \delta x$

$$\text{Force on immersed area} = \sum_{x_1}^{x_2} \rho g x \sin\theta y \delta x$$
$$= \rho g \sin \theta \sum_{x_1}^{x_2} xy\delta x$$

But the expression $\sum_{x_1}^{x_2} xy\delta x$ is the first moment of area of the immersed surface about OO, since $y\delta x$ is the area of the strip at distance x from OO. Consequently we can substitute $A\bar{x}$ for $\sum_{x_1}^{x_2} xy\delta x$ in the above expression.

Force on immersed area $= \rho g \sin \theta \, A\bar{x}$
$= \rho g \bar{x} \sin \theta \, A$
$= \rho g \bar{h} A$, since $\bar{x} \sin \theta = \bar{h}$.

But $\rho g \bar{h}$ is the pressure of the liquid at a depth $\bar{h}$, hence we can write
force on immersed area = pressure at centroid of area × area

Centre of Pressure

The centre of pressure of a surface immersed in a liquid is that point in the surface at which the whole of the force due to the liquid can be considered to act. It is indicated in fig.17.6 as C. Its distance from the free surface of the liquid, measured along the surface area, is shown as $\bar{X}$.

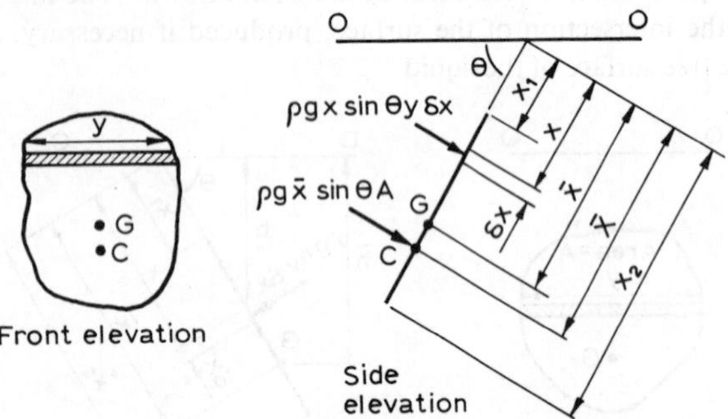

Fig.17.6 Position of centre of pressure on inclined surface

Using the same expressions as in the development of the expression for the force on the immersed area, and considering the same narrow strip length y, width δx, parallel to OO, and at distance x from OO, we have

Pressure on strip $= \rho g x \sin \theta$
Force on strip $= \rho g x \sin \theta y \delta x$
Moment of force on strip $=$ force $\times$ distance
$= \rho g x \sin \theta y \delta x . x$
$= \rho g \sin \theta \, x^2 y \delta x$

Total moment of all similar forces $= \rho g \sin \theta \sum_{x_1}^{x_2} x^2 y \delta x$

But $\sum_{x_1}^{x_2} x^2 y \delta x$ is the second moment of area of the surface about OO, and can be written Ak^2_{OO}, where k_{OO} is the radius of gyration of the area about OO.

Total moment of all similar forces $= \rho g \sin \theta \, Ak^2_{OO}$. (1)

This total moment about OO must equal that of the total force on the surface when concentrated at the centre of pressure.

Total force $=$ pressure at centroid $\times$ area
$= \rho g \bar{x} \sin \theta . A$

Moment of this force about OO $= \rho g \bar{x} \sin \theta \, A\bar{X}$ . . (2)

Equating (1) and (2), we have

$$\rho g \bar{x} \sin \theta \, A\bar{X} = \rho g \sin \theta \, Ak^2_{OO}$$
$$\bar{X} = \frac{k^2_{OO}}{\bar{x}}$$

But we have seen from the work which we did on centroids that, if k_{GG} is the radius of gyration about an axis GG through the centroid of the area, and k_{OO} is the radius of gyration about any other axis, parallel to GG, and at distance $\bar{x}$ from it, then

$$k^2_{OO} = k^2_{GG} + \bar{x}^2$$

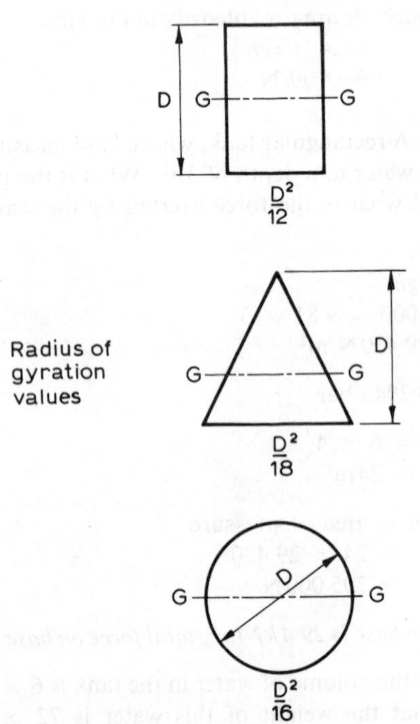

Fig.17.7 Value of radius of gyration. Under each section is indicated the value of k^2 about an axis through the centroid.

Now the distance GC $= \bar{X} - \bar{x}$

$$= \frac{k^2_{GG} + \bar{x}^2}{\bar{x}} - \bar{x}$$

$$= \frac{k^2_{GG}}{\bar{x}}$$

In words, *the centre of pressure is always below the centroid of area by a distance equal to*

$$\frac{\textit{(radius of gyration about centroid)}^2}{\textit{distance to centroid from free surface}}.$$

This is a particularly useful way to obtain the position of the centre of pressure.

As a reminder of the values of k_{GG} for some of the more common areas, the diagram (fig.17.7) is presented. It may be useful at this stage to refer to the work which has been done on centroids of areas in Chapter 14.

Special Case of Vertical Rectangular Area

In the very common case of a vertical rectangular area immersed in a liquid, it would be advisable to know the simple expression relating to the centre of pressure (fig.17.8).

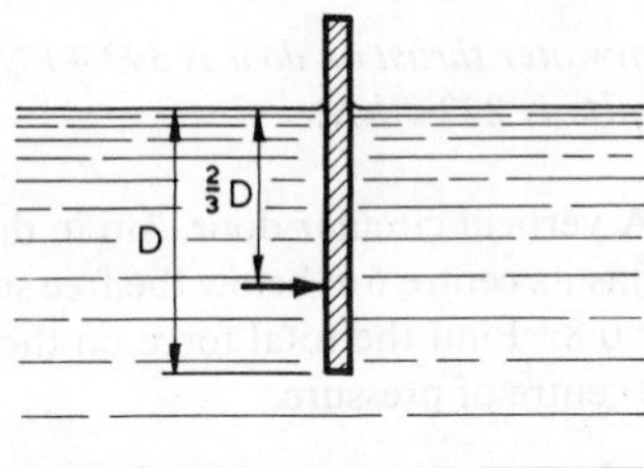

Fig.17.8 Position of centre of pressure for rectangular surface. Centre of pressure for rectangular area is at two-thirds of depth of immersion.

If D is the depth of immersion, then the depth to the centroid of the immersed area will be $D/2$. The value of the square of the radius of gyration, k^2_{GG}, about an axis through the centroid is $D^2/12$.

Hence the centre of pressure is $\frac{k^2_{GG}}{\bar{x}}$ below the centroid

or $\frac{D^2/12}{D/2} = \frac{D}{6}$ below the centroid

which is $\frac{D}{2} + \frac{D}{6} = \frac{2D}{3}$ below the free surface of the liquid

This is a very important expression, which might well be memorised. *The centre of pressure of an immersed vertical rectangular section is at a point ⅔ of the depth of the section below the free surface of the liquid.*

Example 17.2 A tank with vertical sides is square in plan, the sides being 6 m long. It contains water to a depth of 7 m. Taking the density of water as 1000 kg/m³, determine (a) the total free force on each side of the tank, (b) from first principles, the height above the base of the centre of pressure of each side of the tank, and (c) the pressure on the base of the tank, above the atmospheric pressure. ULCI

a) Area of immersed section $= 6 \times 7 = 42\,\text{m}^2$

Depth to centroid $= \frac{7}{2} = 3{\cdot}5\,\text{m}$

Pressure at centroid $= 9810 \times 3{\cdot}5$
$= 34\,400\,\text{N/m}^2$

Total force on side = area × pressure at centroid
$= 42 \times 34\,400$

Total force on side of tank = 1445000 N, or 1·445 MN.

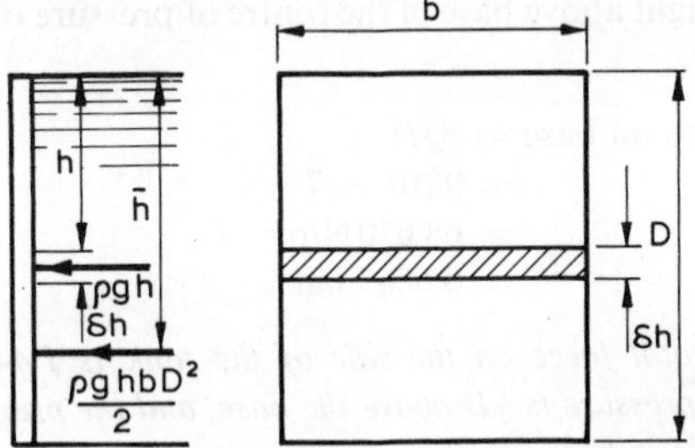

Fig.17.9

b) Consider the rectangular area shown in fig.17.9, on which is an elementary strip, width δh, at depth h below the free surface.

Pressure on strip $= \rho gh$

Area of strip $= b\delta h$

Force on strip $= \rho gh . b\delta h$
$= \rho gbh\delta h$ . . . . (1)

$$\text{Total force on area} = \int_0^D \rho gbh dh$$

$$= \rho gb \left[\frac{h^2}{2}\right]_0^D$$

$$= \rho gb \frac{D^2}{2} \quad \text{. . . . . . . (2)}$$

Let $\bar{h}$ be the distance to the centre of pressure from the free surface.

Moment of total force about free surface

$$= \frac{\rho gbD^2}{2} . \bar{h} \quad \text{. . . . . . . (3)}$$

Moment of force on strip about free surface [from (1)]

$$= \rho gbh\delta h \times h$$
$$= \rho gbh^2\delta h$$

Total moment of all such forces $= \int_0^D \rho gbh^2 dh$

$$= \rho gb\left[\frac{h^3}{3}\right]_0^D$$

$$= \frac{\rho gbD^3}{3}$$

This must equal the expression given in equation (3).

Hence $\frac{\rho gbD^2}{2}\bar{h} = \frac{\rho gbD^3}{3}$

$$\bar{h} = \tfrac{2}{3}D$$

Alternatively, the centre of pressure is $\frac{1}{3}$ D from the base. Hence height above base of the centre of pressure of side is 7/3 or $2\frac{1}{3}$ m.

c) Pressure on base $= \rho gD$

$$= 9810 \times 7$$
$$= 68\,670\,\text{N/m}^2$$
$$= 0{\cdot}6867 \text{ bar}$$

i.e. The total force on the side of the tank is 1·445 MN, the centre of pressure is $\frac{1}{3}D$ above the base, and the pressure on the base is 0·6876 bar.

Example 17.3 Define centre of pressure, and establish the formula for the depth to the centre of pressure of a submerged vertical rectangular surface.

A rectangular door, 4 m deep by 2 m wide, covers an opening in the vertical side of a tank. The top edge is 3 m below the surface of the water in the tank, and is hinged to the tank wall. The lower edge is bolted to the wall. Calculate the resultant water thrust on the door, and the force acting on the bolts.

IMECHE

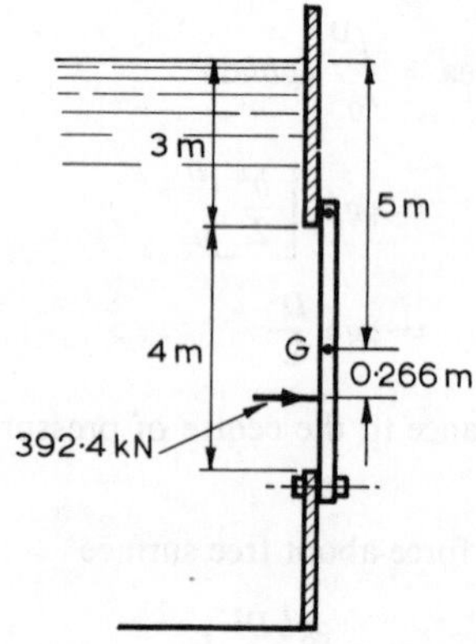

Fig.17.10

Centroid of door is $3 + \frac{4}{2} = 5$ m below free surface.

Pressure at centroid $= 9810 \times 5$

$$= 49\,050\,\text{N/m}^2$$

Force on door = pressure at centroid × area

$$= 49\,050 \times 4 \times 2$$
$$= 392\,400$$
$$= 392{\cdot}4\,\text{kN}$$

Position of centre of pressure

This is $\frac{k^2_{GG}}{\bar{x}}$ below centroid.

$$k^2_{GG} = \frac{D^2}{12} = \frac{4^2}{12} = 1{\cdot}33\,\text{m}^2$$

$$\bar{x} = 5\,\text{m}$$

$$\frac{k^2_{GG}}{\bar{x}} = \frac{1{\cdot}33}{5} = 0{\cdot}266\,\text{m below centroid}$$

or $2 + 0{\cdot}266 = 2{\cdot}266$ m below hinge position

Take moments about the hinge, and let F be the force on the bolts.

$$F \times 4 = 392\,400 \times 2{\cdot}266$$
$$F = 222\,294\ \text{N}$$

i.e. The resultant water thrust on door is 392·4 kN, and the force acting on the bolts is 222·3 kN.

Example 17.4 A vertical circular door, 3 m in diameter, in the side of a tank has its centre 6 m below the free surface of oil of specific gravity 0·8. Find the total force on the area, and the position of the centre of pressure.

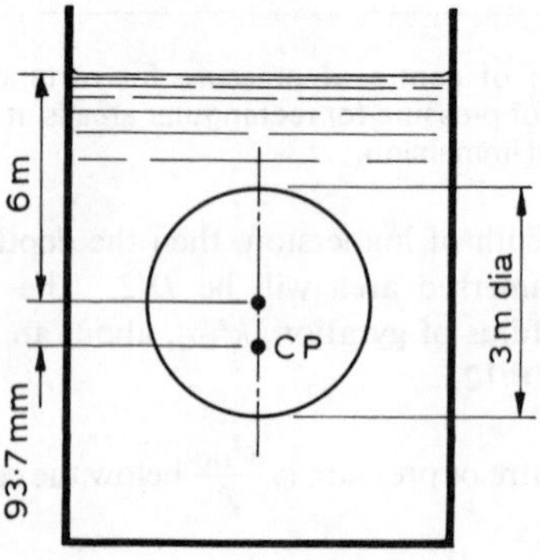

Fig.17.11

Density of oil $\rho = 1000 \times 0{\cdot}8$

$$= 800\,\text{kg/m}^3$$

Centroid of area is 6 m below oil surface.

Pressure at centroid $= \rho g\bar{x}$

$$= 800 \times 9{\cdot}81 \times 6$$
$$= 47\,100\,\text{N/m}^2$$

Total force on area = pressure at centroid × area

$$= 47\,100 \times \frac{\pi}{4} \times 3^2\text{N}$$

$$= 334\,000\text{N}$$

Centre of pressure is $k^2_{GG}/\bar{x}$ below centroid.

$$k^2_{GG} \text{ for circular area} = \frac{D^2}{16}$$

$$= \frac{3^2}{16} = 0{\cdot}562\text{m}^2$$

$$\frac{k^2_{GG}}{\bar{x}} = \frac{0{\cdot}562}{6} = 0{\cdot}0937\text{m, or } 93{\cdot}7\text{mm below centroid.}$$

i.e. The total force on the area is 334 kN, and the centre of pressure is 6·094 m below the oil surface.

Archimedes' Principle

There are two forces acting on a body floating in a liquid:

1 the gravitational force acting through the centre of gravity, i.e. the weight of the body;

2 the upthrust of the liquid, sometimes called the force of buoyancy, or simply 'buoyancy'. This second force acts through a point known as the centre of buoyancy.

If these two forces are equal, the body will float; if the weight of the body is greater than the buoyancy, then the body will sink.

Consider a cylinder of length l, cross-sectional area A, floating in a liquid whose density is ρ. The cylinder, whose density is d, is immersed to a depth of h (fig.17.12).

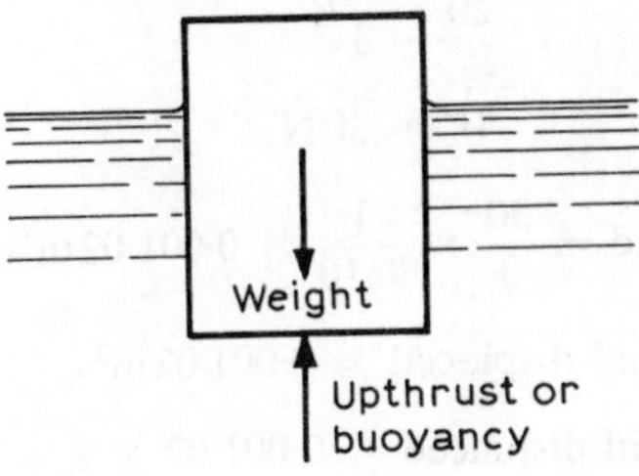

Fig.17.12 Archimedes' principle. Upthrust of liquid must be equal to weight of solid.

Weight of cylinder = volume × density × gravitational acceleration

$= Aldg$

Pressure at base of cylinder = density × depth below surface × gravitational constant

$= \rho gh$

Upthrust of liquid = area of base × pressure

$= A\rho gh$

But $A\rho gh$, which can be rewritten $Ah \times \rho g$, is equal to the volume of the solid actually immersed in the liquid, multiplied by the weight of unit volume of the liquid which occupied the space now taken up with the immersed solid, i.e. the weight of the liquid which has been displaced.

Hence if a body is floating we can say:

weight of body = upthrust of liquid
= weight of liquid displaced by the immersed solid,

and hence
mass of body = mass of liquid displaced by the immersed solid.

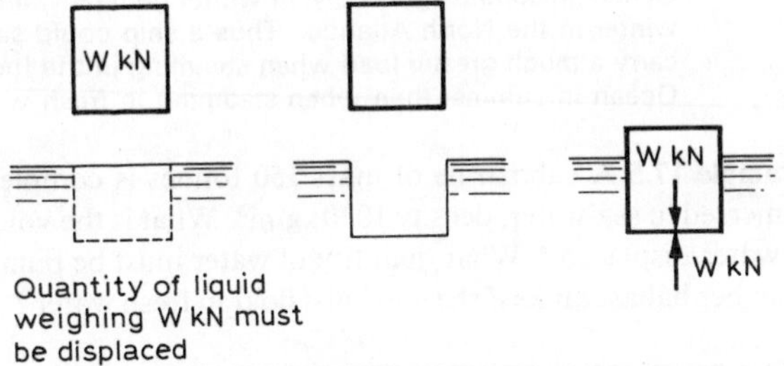

Fig.17.13 Archimedes' principle. Solid will displace an amount of liquid of weight equal to the weight of the solid.

This relationship is known as Archimedes' Principle. Archimedes was the first to realise the connection existing between the quantity of displaced liquid and the weight of the immersed solid.

Thus any solid body, on immersion in a liquid, will continue to sink to a depth such that the weight of liquid displaced is equal to its own weight. The body will then float.

Incidentally, it is usual to speak of the displacement of a ship as so many tonnes. This is simply another way of indicating the mass of the vessel; it suggests that the vessel will displace a certain quantity of water. From what we have just seen, it follows that this mass of displaced water is equal to the mass of the vessel.

Since the density of sea-water is greater than that of fresh water (1030 kg/m³, as compared with 1000 kg/m³), there is a variation in the depth of immersion or 'draught' of the vessel as it moves from a fresh-water canal into sea-water. The vessel may lift as much as 250 mm as it enters the sea-water area.

As a help to the ultimate safety of ships, a mark is painted on the side of a vessel to indicate the level of the water-line. This mark is known as the Plimsoll line, named after a Bristol politician whose concern with the number of tragedies at sea due to overloaded boats led him to devote considerable energies to securing the safety of sailors at sea. The Plimsoll line, or load line, indicates the water-line level for a number of conditions due to the variation of water density. We have noted the variation of density between sea-water and fresh water; there is a similar variation between sea-water density in summer and in winter, and between its density in the North Atlantic and in the Indian Oceans.

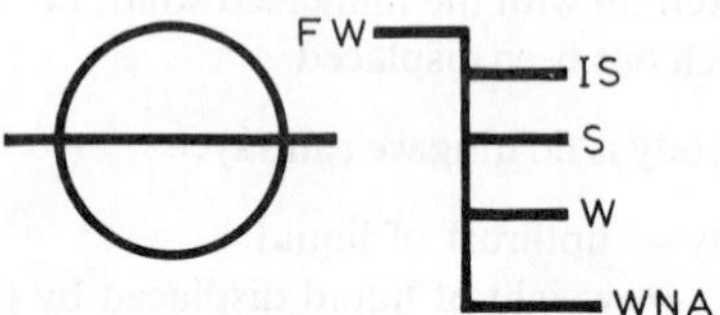

Fig.17.14 Plimsoll line. The safety mark on the side of a ship. The marks indicate the safe depth of water in which a ship should float in fresh water, in summer in the Indian Ocean, in summer generally, in winter generally, and in winter in the North Atlantic. Thus a ship could safely carry a much greater load when steaming in the Indian Ocean in summer than when steaming in fresh water.

Example 17.5 A submarine of mass 150 tonnes is completely immersed in sea-water, density $1030\,kg/m^3$. What is the volume of water displaced? What quantity of water must be pumped from her ballast tanks if she must just float in fresh water?

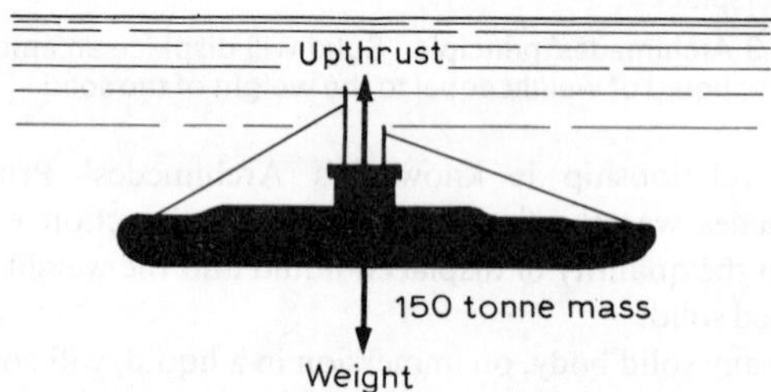

Fig.17.15 Equilibrium of submarine. The upthrust must always equal the weight of the submarine. The upthrust cannot be altered once the submarine is under the water (apart from any change due to variation of density of water). Modifications can be made to the weight of the vessel by taking in or pumping out water to or from the tanks. Thus the submarine could take in water and sink farther down, or it could 'blow out' the tanks, reduce its weight, and surface.

Mass of sea-water displaced = 150 tonnes, since submarine is completely immersed.

$$\text{Volume of water displaced} = \frac{150 \times 1000}{1030}$$

$$= 146\,m^3$$

This quantity of fresh water has a mass of 146 tonnes.

Hence the submarine must reduce its mass to 146 tonnes by pumping out (150 − 146) i.e. 4 tonnes of water from the ballast tanks.

Example 17.6 A solid, whose specific gravity is 3, weighs 20 N in water, and 25 N in a liquid. Calculate the weight of the solid in air, and the specific gravity of the liquid.

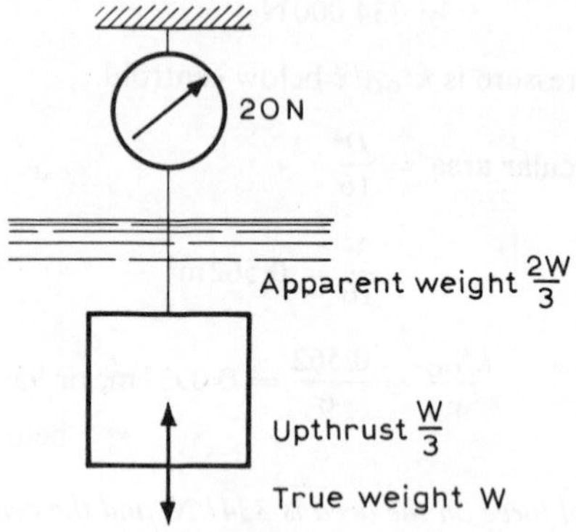

Fig.17.16

Let W = weight of solid in air,
s = specific gravity of the liquid.

Since the weight of the solid is 3 times that of an equal volume of water,

$$\text{weight of water displaced} = \frac{W}{3}\,N$$

$$\text{Upthrust on solid} = \frac{W}{3}\,N$$

$$\text{Resultant force on solid} = W - \frac{W}{3} = \frac{2}{3}W\,N$$

This will be equal to 20 N.

$$20 = \frac{2}{3}W$$

$$W = 30\,N$$

$$\text{Volume of solid} = \frac{30}{3} \times \frac{1}{9810} = 0{\cdot}001\,02\,m^3$$

$$\text{Volume of liquid displaced} = 0{\cdot}001\,02\,m^3$$

$$\text{Weight of liquid displaced} = 0{\cdot}001\,02 \times s \times 9810 = 10s\,N$$

$$\text{Upthrust on solid} = 10s\,N$$

$$\text{Resultant force on solid} = 30 - 10s\,N$$

This will be equal to 25 N.

$$30 - 10s = 25$$
$$10s = 5$$
$$s = 0{\cdot}5$$

i.e. The weight of the solid in air is 30 N, and the specific gravity of the liquid is 0·5.

Example 17.7 A wooden cube of side 200 mm, and whose specific gravity is 0·75, is immersed in water, and floats with its upper face horizontal. What will be the depth of the immersion? What quantity of aluminium, whose specific gravity is 2·8, must be attached to (a) the upper face, (b) the lower face, so that the block will just be completely immersed? In the second case, the aluminium will also be immersed.

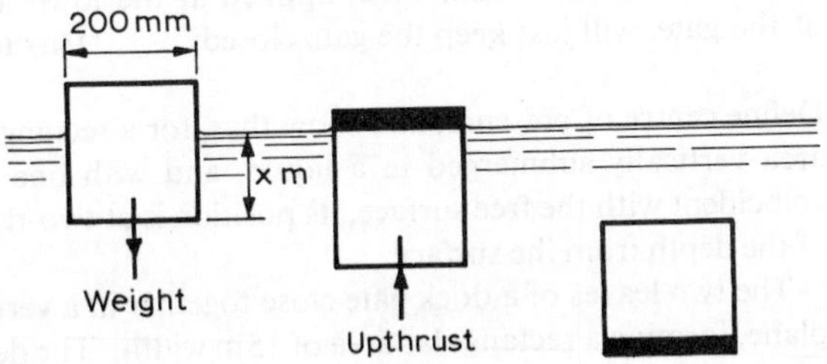

Fig.17.17

Let x = depth of cube under water.

$$\text{Density of material} = 0{\cdot}75 \times 1000 = 750\,\text{kg/m}^3$$

$$\text{Mass of cube} = \text{volume} \times \text{density} = 0{\cdot}2^3 \times 750 = 6\,\text{kg}$$

$$\text{Volume of water displaced} = 0{\cdot}2 \times 0{\cdot}2 \times x = 0{\cdot}04x\,\text{m}^3$$

$$\text{Mass of water displaced} = 0{\cdot}04x \times 1000 = 40x\,\text{kg}$$

This must be equal to the mass of the cube.

$$40x = 6$$
$$x = 0{\cdot}15\,\text{m}$$

i.e. The cube floats with an immersion of 150 mm.

Note. It is left to the student to verify that this immersion is in fact depth × specific gravity, i.e. 200 × 0·75 = 150 mm.

a) If the aluminium is placed on top of the cube, the aluminium will not be immersed.

Mass of water displaced by complete immersion of cube

$$= 0{\cdot}2^3 \times 1000 = 8\,\text{kg}$$

$$\text{Mass of cube} + \text{mass of aluminium} = 8\,\text{kg}$$

$$\therefore \text{Mass of aluminium} = 8 - 6 = 2\,\text{kg}$$

b) If the aluminium is placed under the cube, both cube and aluminium will be immersed.

Let M = mass of aluminium.

$$\text{Volume of aluminium} = \frac{M}{1000 \times 2{\cdot}8}\,\text{m}^3$$

$$\text{Total volume immersed} = \text{cube} + \text{aluminium} = 0{\cdot}2^3 + \frac{M}{2800}$$

$$\text{Mass of water displaced} = 1000\left[0{\cdot}2^3 + \frac{M}{2800}\right]$$

This must equal the mass of the cube plus aluminium.

$$\therefore 1000\left[0{\cdot}2^3 + \frac{M}{2800}\right] = 6 + M$$

$$8 + \frac{M}{2{\cdot}8} = 6 + M$$

$$M = 3{\cdot}1\,\text{kg}$$

Hence, if aluminium is placed on top of the cube, its mass must be 2 kg; whilst its mass would be 3·1 kg if placed underneath the cube.

Exercise 17

1 A wooden cube, whose side is 250 mm long, has a specific gravity of 0·7. It is floating in water with its upper face horizontal. Determine the height of the cube appearing above the water.

2 A submarine of mass 100 tonnes is completely submerged in sea-water of density 1030 kg/m³. What is the volume of displaced water? What weight of water must be pumped from her ballast tanks if she must just float in fresh water?

3 A ship, of mass 5000 tonnes, is observed to sink 375 mm in sea-water when loaded with 500 tonnes of cargo. Assuming that the sides of the ship near to the water line are vertical, and that the density of sea-water is 1030 kg/m³, determine the cross-sectional area of the ship at the water line. How far will the ship sink when passing from sea-water to fresh water, density 1000 kg/m³?

4 A wooden cube of side 10 cm, and specific gravity 0·8, is floating in water with its upper face horizontal. (a) What depth of the cube is immersed? (b) What weight of aluminium (specific gravity 2·8) must be attached: (i) to the upper face, (ii) to the lower face, so that the block will just be completely immersed? EMEU

5 State Archimedes' Principle.

A solid of specific gravity 2·5 weighs 16·8 N in water, and 20 N in a certain liquid. Calculate the weight of the solid in air, and the specific gravity of the liquid. EMEU

6 A concrete reservoir dam has a vertical face on the water side, and dimensions as shown in fig.17.18. The top water level reaches 4 m below the crest of the dam. Find the magnitude of the resultant thrust on the base, and where its line of action cuts the base when (a) the reservoir is empty, and (b) the reservoir is full. (Take the density of the concrete to be 2400 kg/m³.)

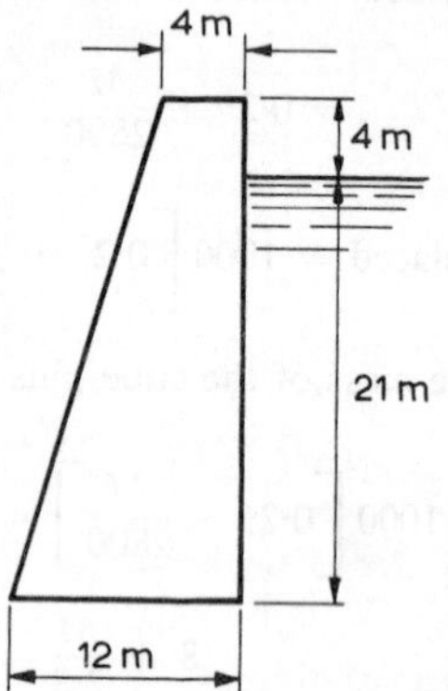

Fig.17.18

7 A fresh-water tank has a rectangular door 6 m high and 4 m wide in a vertical side. The long sides of the door are vertical. The door has a horizontal hinge in the top short side. Find the horizontal pull, perpendicular to the door and through the lower horizontal side, to keep the door closed when the water level is 2 m above the hinge. IMECHE

8 A dam bounding one end of a reservoir is in the form of an isosceles trapezoid, 100 m along the top, which is at water level, and 60 m along the bottom. The dam is 30 m high. Find by integration the total thrust on the dam.

Also find at what depth the pressure will be equal to the mean pressure over the face of the dam. IMECHE

9 The outlet in the side of a vertical rectangular tank is closed by a square gate, with one side parallel to the water surface in the tank. The gate, sides a m, is hinged on its upper edge, whilst the level of the water in the tank is a m above this edge. Taking ρ as the density of the water, find by integration (a) the thrust on the gate, (b) the moment of the thrust on the gate about the hinges. Also determine (c) the position of the centre of pressure of the gate, and (d) the least force which, when applied at the lower edge of the gate, will just keep the gate closed. IMECHE

10 Define centre of pressure, and show that, for a rectangular area vertically submerged in a liquid, and with one side coincident with the free surface, its position is at two-thirds of the depth from the surface.

The two leaves of a dock gate close together in a vertical plane, forming a rectangular area of 15 m width. The depth of water may vary between 15 and 25 m. The gate is held closed against the thrust by two horizontal beams, fixed at positions 4 and 13 m above the bottom. Determine the change in load on each beam when the depth of water reduces from the high limit to the low. IMECHE

11 A vertical-sided tank is rectangular in form, and contains equal masses of oil and water to a total depth of 5 m, the specific gravity of the oil being 0·78. Calculate (a) the depth of water, and (b) the total force per metre length of side. UEI

12 An aperture in a vertical wall of a water tank is closed by a circular plate, 2 m in diameter. This is held in position by three stops, one at each end of the horizontal diameter, and one at the lowest point.

Calculate the reactions at these points when the water surface is 1·5 m above the centre of the plate. ULCI

Chapter 18

Flow of Water

Steady and Turbulent Flow

When we speak of a steady motion with regard to fluids, we have in mind the idea that all the particles of the fluid which are passing through any fixed point do so with the same velocity, i.e. they travel in the same direction with the same speed. This means that in steady motion the particles are travelling in lines, or 'filaments', which are straight or curved. Osborne Reynolds did some pioneer work associated with the steady or 'streamlined' flow of liquids. His name will always be linked with a piece of apparatus, shown diagrammatically in fig.18.1, which demonstrated the conditions of streamline and turbulent flow.

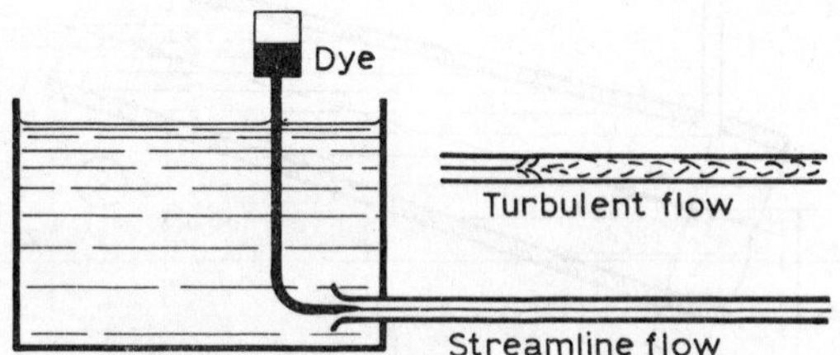

Fig.18.1 Osborne Reynolds' experiment. When the flow of water is low, and conditions are known as *streamline flow*, the filament of dye remains steady. As the velocity of flow is increased, conditions are reached when streamline flow ceases, and gives place to turbulent flow, the dye mixes with the flowing water, as in the upper diagram.

A thin filament of coloured liquid is introduced into a quantity of water flowing through a smooth glass tube. When the velocity of water in the tube is low, it will be seen that the coloured liquid travels in a straight line, and appears to be quite separated from the water in the tube. If the velocity of the water is gradually increased, a state will be reached when the coloured filament at some distance from the jet will break up, and mix with the surrounding water. This change takes place at the critical velocity of flow.

For velocities below the critical value, the flow is streamline.

For velocities above the critical value the motion is turbulent, accompanied by whirling action, or 'eddies'. The value of the critical velocity will depend, among other things, on the temperature of the water, which in turn affects a property known as its viscosity. (At normal temperatures, treacle is a very viscous, slow-moving liquid, but it flows readily at high temperatures.)

Energy Stored in Water

Before looking more closely at the factors affecting the flow of water, it may be well to consider the three types of energy which may be stored in water. These are illustrated in fig.18.2.

(1) *Potential energy*

This is the energy stored in water by reason of its position. The cistern of the normal household hot-water-supply system is

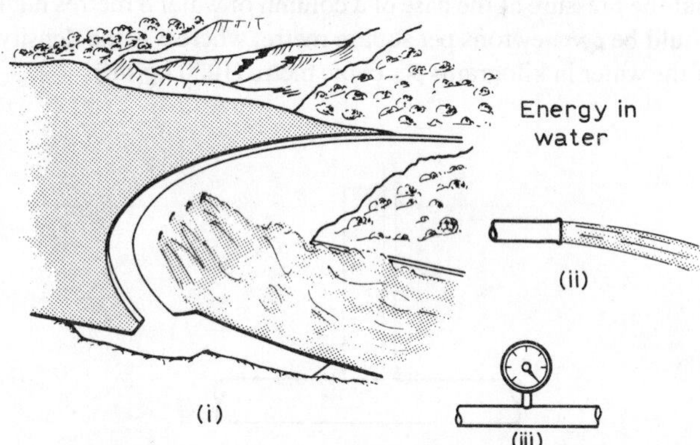

Fig.18.2 The three basic types of energy associated with hydraulics:
(i) potential energy due to position,
(ii) kinetic energy due to velocity,
(iii) pressure energy due to increased pressure in closed pipe.

usually in one of the upstairs rooms. The water filling the cistern has potential energy, due to its height above the boiler. This energy is capable of maintaining an adequate flow of water through the hot-water system.

On a much vaster scale, there are cases of water stored in lakes and reservoirs, or of water flowing in rivers, or over waterfalls. In these examples, considerable quantities of water are at a high level relative to their surroundings.

Let z = the height from any datum line to the point under consideration, in m;
M = mass of water at this level, in kg.

Then Mgz newton metres, i.e. joules, is the potential energy stored in the water in relation to the datum line. It is usual to express these energies in terms of a mass of water of 1 kg, so that the potential energy of the water would be given as gz joules/kg.

(2) *Kinetic energy*

Water in motion possesses kinetic energy, or energy of motion.

Let v = velocity of flow, in m/s;
M = mass of water flowing, in kg.
Then $\frac{1}{2}Mv^2$ = kinetic energy of the water, in joules.

Referring this to the flow of 1 kg of water, we have the kinetic energy of the water per kg given as $v^2/2$ joules per kg.

(3) *Pressure energy*

Water in an enclosed pipe under pressure possesses pressure energy. If a union were made in such a pipe, as shown in fig. 18.3, and another pipe, known as a piezometer, were inserted at right angles to the original pipe, then water would rise in the piezometer to a steady height of h metres. We have seen that the pressure at the base of a column of water h metres high would be ρgh newtons per square metre, where ρ is the density of the water in kilograms per cubic metre (1000 kg/m³).

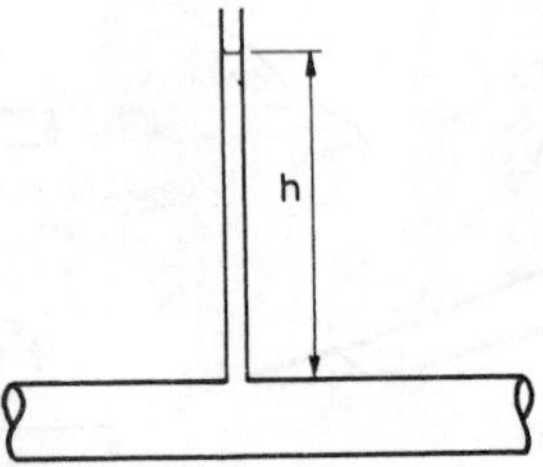

Fig.18.3 Pressure energy. The piezometer tube inserted in the pipeline allows the liquid to rise to a height h. This gives an indication of the pressure of the liquid, and is the basis of the manometer.

Hence, if p = pressure of water, in N/m²,
h = height of water in piezometer, in m,
ρ = density of water, in kg/m³,

then $p = \rho gh$

or $h = \frac{p}{\rho g}$ metres

and pressure energy $= gh$

$= \frac{p}{\rho}$ joules/kg

In certain problems, it is convenient to work in terms of this height h, in which case it is called the 'head' of water.

Total Energy of Water

In general, water in motion possesses all three types of energy, and since these have all been expressed in joules, it is possible to add them together, to obtain the total energy of water.

Total energy of water per kg flow

$$= \frac{p}{\rho} + \frac{v^2}{2} + gz$$

pressure energy per kg + kinetic energy per kg + potential energy per kg

Bernoulli's Law

In any hydraulic scheme, there is a continual variation of conditions of flow. A pipe-line may change in diameter; it may increase in diameter, for example, with a consequent reduction in the velocity of the water, and a corresponding reduction in kinetic energy. Or the pipe-line may be laid over hilly country; the water may travel up an incline, with a consequent increase in potential head. Although variation of individual energies is continually taking place, there is a definite relationship between them, a relationship expressed in Bernoulli's Law. This is simply a law applying to hydraulics a principle which we have met before, namely the principle of the conservation of energy. We are assuming that we are dealing with an incompressible fluid, and not a gas.

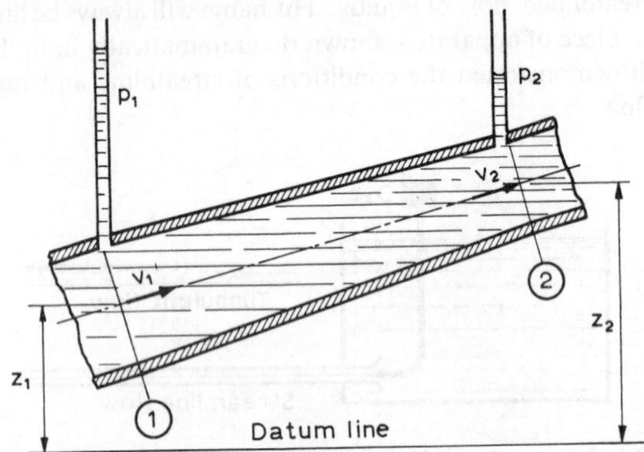

Fig.18.4 Bernoulli's law. Total energy at section 1 is equal to total energy at section 2, neglecting frictional losses.

Bernoulli's law states that, assuming there is no loss due to friction or any other cause, the total energy of the water will remain constant, i.e. the value of $\frac{p}{\rho} + \frac{v^2}{2} + gz$ will be a constant value. If p_1, v_1, and z_1 refer to the pressure, velocity, and position of the water at any section 1 of the pipe-line; and p_2, v_2, and z_2 the corresponding values at any other section 2, then

$$\frac{p_1}{\rho} + \frac{v_1^2}{2} + gz_1 = \frac{p_2}{\rho} + \frac{v_2^2}{2} + gz_2$$

Taking any losses into account, the relationship becomes

$$\frac{p_1}{\rho} + \frac{v_1^2}{2} + gz_1 = \frac{p_2}{\rho} + \frac{v_2^2}{2} + gz_2 + \text{losses}$$

The following examples will give an indication of the use of Bernoulli's law.

Example 18.1 A horizontal pipe-line increases uniformly from 75 mm diameter to 150 mm diameter in the direction of the flow of water. When 85 litres of water is flowing per second, a pressure gauge at the 75 mm diameter section reads 2 bar. What would be the reading of the gauge at the 150 mm section, neglecting any losses?

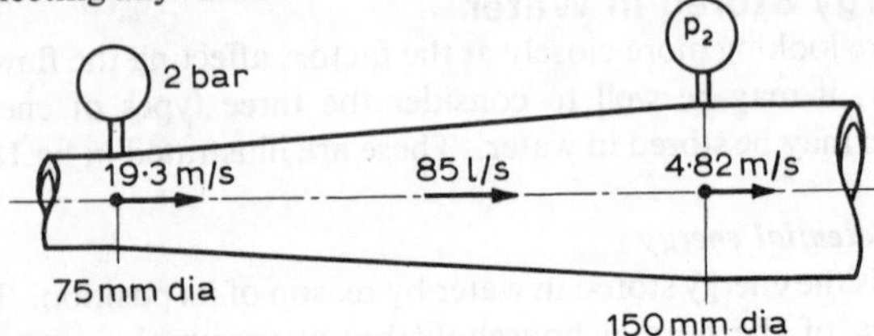

Fig.18.5

Let the required gauge reading be p_2 bar.

Velocity of water at 75 mm diameter section

$$= \frac{\text{volume}}{\text{pipe area}}$$

$$= \frac{0{\cdot}085}{0{\cdot}075^2 \times \pi/4}$$

$$= 19{\cdot}3\,\text{m/s}$$

Velocity of water at 150 mm diameter section

$$= 19{\cdot}3 \times \left(\frac{0{\cdot}075}{0{\cdot}15}\right)^2$$

$$= 4{\cdot}82\,\text{m/s}$$

(***Note.*** Velocity is inversely proportional to diameter².)

Using Bernoulli's law, and indicating the 75 mm diameter portion by section 1, and the 150 mm diameter portion by section 2, we have

$$\frac{p_1}{\rho} + \frac{v_1^2}{2} + gz_1 = \frac{p_2}{\rho} + \frac{v_2^2}{2} + gz_2$$

Since the pipe is horizontal, z_1 and z_2 are equal, and can be cancelled from the equation.

$$\frac{2 \times 10^5}{1000} + \frac{19{\cdot}3^2}{2} = \frac{p_2 \times 10^5}{1000} + \frac{4{\cdot}82^2}{2}$$

$$\therefore p_2 = \frac{200}{100} + \frac{19{\cdot}3^2 - 4{\cdot}82^2}{200}$$

$$= 3{\cdot}74 \text{ bar}$$

i.e. Gauge at 150 mm section reads 3·74 bar.

Example 18.2 If the pipe in the previous example were vertical, with the 75 mm diameter section below the 150 mm diameter section, and the flow upwards, determine the reading of the 150 mm diameter section pressure gauge if this is 6 m above the 75 mm diameter section pressure gauge.

In this case we can consider the datum line passing through the lower gauge, so that $z_1 = 0$ and $z_2 = 6$ m.

Using Bernoulli's law, and taking the same values as in the previous example, we have

$$\frac{p_1}{\rho} + \frac{v_1^2}{2} + gz_1 = \frac{p_2}{\rho} + \frac{v_2^2}{2} + gz_2$$

$$\frac{2 \times 10^5}{1000} + \frac{19{\cdot}3^2}{2} + 0 = \frac{p_2 \times 10^5}{1000} + \frac{4{\cdot}82^2}{2} + 9{\cdot}81 \times 6$$

$$2 + \frac{19{\cdot}3^2}{200} = p_2 + \frac{4{\cdot}82^2}{200} + \frac{9{\cdot}81 \times 6}{100}$$

$$\therefore p_2 = 3{\cdot}15 \text{ bar}$$

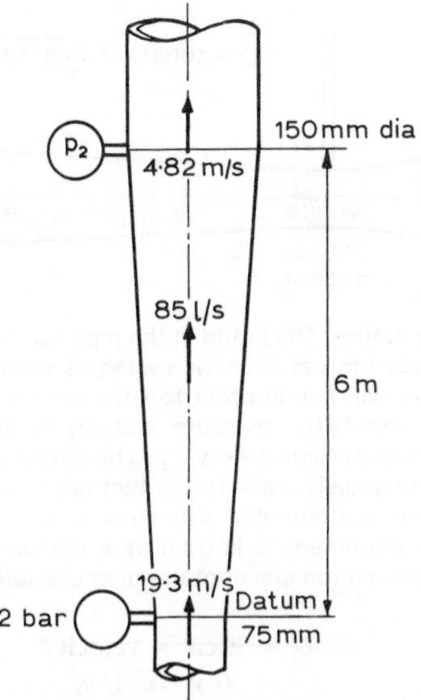

Fig.18.6

The pressure is lower in this case, because the water has increased its potential head by 6 m.
i.e. Gauge at 150 mm section reads 3·15 bar.

Venturi Meter

The Venturi meter affords a very convenient method of measuring the quantity of liquid flowing through a pipe-line. The bore of the pipe is reduced to a small diameter, known as the 'throat' of the meter, and then gradually increased back to its original size. As the water passes through the restricted throat, its velocity, and consequently its kinetic energy, is increased. Since the total energy of the liquid remains constant (we are assuming that there are no losses), it follows that the pressure energy will decrease. Normally these meters are placed in horizontal pipe-lines, so that there is no change in potential energy. The decrease in pressure energy can be measured by means of a manometer, and thus it is possible to determine the velocity of a liquid in the pipe, and so obtain the quantity of liquid flowing.

The convergent and divergent portions of the meter are suitably arranged to minimise any losses due to turbulence.

Let A_i = cross-sectional area of pipe at inlet,
A_t = cross-sectional area of throat,
v_i = velocity of liquid in pipe,
v_t = velocity of liquid in throat,
p_i = pressure of liquid in pipe,
p_t = pressure of liquid in throat,
Q = quantity of liquid flowing,
ρ = density of liquid.

All the above units involve metres.

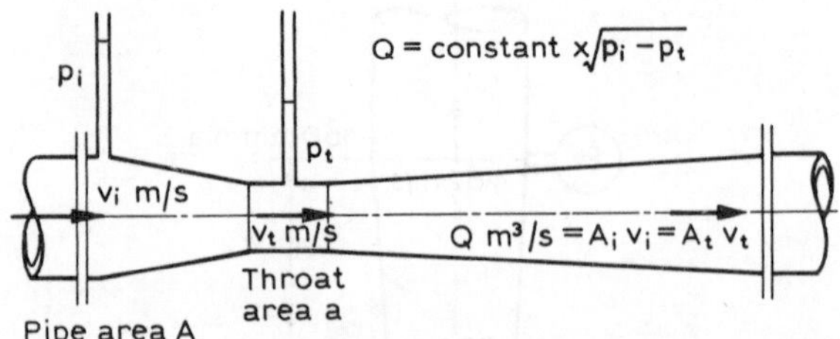

Fig.18.7 Venturi meter. The liquid in the pipe has to flow through a restricted throat, thus increasing its velocity. Hence its pressure will fall, in order to keep the total energy constant. This fall in pressure, suitably measured, enables the quantity of liquid flowing to be determined. Connections are usually made to the two tubes, which, for convenience, are mounted side by side on a vertical board. This arrangement is known as a *manometer*. In most cases the manometer contains mercury, rather than water.

$$Q = \text{area} \times \text{velocity}$$
$$= A_i\, v_i = A_t\, v_t$$

$$\therefore v_t = \frac{A_i}{A_t} v_i \quad . \quad . \quad . \quad . \quad . \quad . \quad (1)$$

Applying Bernoulli's theorem to pipe and throat,

$$\frac{p_i}{\rho} + \frac{v_i^2}{2} = \frac{p_t}{\rho} + \frac{v_t^2}{2}$$

$$\therefore \frac{v_t^2 - v_i^2}{2} = \frac{p_i - p_t}{\rho}$$

Substituting from (1),

$$\frac{(A_i/A_t)^2 v_i^2 - v_i^2}{2} = \frac{p_i - p_t}{\rho}$$

$$\frac{v_i^2}{2}\left(\frac{A_i^2}{A_t^2} - 1\right) = \frac{p_i - p_t}{\rho}$$

$$v_i^2 = \frac{2(p_i - p_t)}{\rho[(A_i/A_t)^2 - 1]}$$

$$= \frac{2A_t^2\,(p_i - p_t)}{\rho(A_i^2 - A_t^2)}$$

$$v_i = A_t \sqrt{\frac{2(p_i - p_t)}{\rho(A_i^2 - A_t^2)}}$$

$$Q = Av$$

$$\therefore Q = A_i A_t \sqrt{\frac{2(p_i - p_t)}{\rho(A_i^2 - A_t^2)}} \quad (2)$$

In a Venturi meter it is frequently convenient to measure the pressure difference by connecting a manometer between the throat and the inlet (fig.18.8). A manometer consists of two vertical glass tubes, one connected to the inlet and the other to the throat, with a scale mounted between them as in fig.18.8.

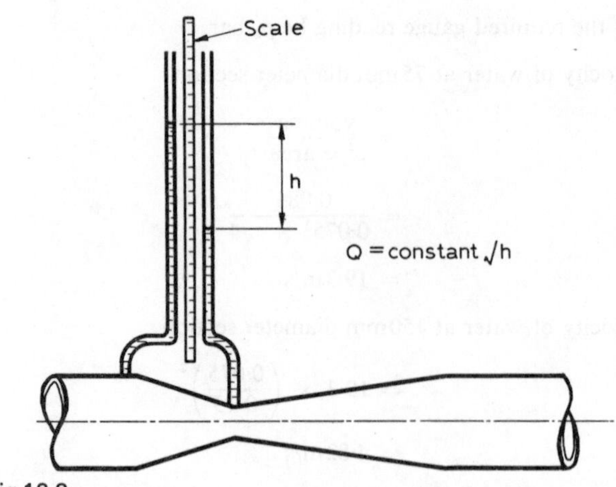

Fig.18.8

Since the pressure at inlet is greater than at the throat, the liquid in the inlet tube will stand higher than in the throat tube. If the difference in level is h metres, then

$$h = \frac{(p_i - p_t)}{\rho g}$$

Note. That h is the difference in head between inlet and throat. The rate of flow of liquid is then given by

$$Q = A_i A_t \sqrt{\frac{2gh}{A_i^2 - A_t^2}}$$

Since A_i, A_t, and g are all constants, it follows that

$$\text{quantity of liquid flowing} = \text{constant} \times \sqrt{h}$$

When this constant is known, it is a very easy matter to convert the manometer reading, h, into quantity of liquid flowing.

Equation 2 gives the quantity of liquid flowing on the assumptions stated. It is usual to multiply this by a meter coefficient to allow for losses.

$$\text{Actual quantity} = Q \times \text{meter coefficient}$$

Example 18.3 A Venturi meter has an inlet of 150 mm, and a throat of 75 mm diameter. What will be the manometer reading in metres between the inlet and the throat if the water passing through the meter is 40 litres per second? UEI

$$40 \text{ l/s} = 0{\cdot}04 \text{ m}^3\text{/s}$$

$$\text{Area of inlet} = \frac{\pi}{4} \times 0{\cdot}15^2$$
$$= 0{\cdot}0177 \text{ m}^2$$

$$\text{Area of throat} = \frac{\pi}{4} \times 0{\cdot}075^2$$
$$= 0{\cdot}0044 \text{ m}^2$$

$$\text{Velocity at inlet} = \frac{0\cdot04}{0\cdot0177} = 2\cdot26\,\text{m/s}$$

$$\text{Velocity at throat} = \frac{0\cdot04}{0\cdot0044} = 9\cdot04\,\text{m/s}$$

Let p_i = pressure at inlet,
p_t = pressure at throat.

Then, applying Bernoulli's theorem,

$$\frac{p_i}{\rho} + \frac{2\cdot26^2}{2} = \frac{p_t}{\rho} + \frac{9\cdot04^2}{2}$$

$$\frac{p_i - p_t}{\rho g} = \frac{9\cdot04^2 - 2\cdot26^2}{2 \times 9\cdot81}$$

$$= 3\cdot9\,\text{m}$$

i.e. The difference in head, in metres of water, between inlet and throat is 3·9 m.

Use of Mercury in Manometer Tubes

It will obviously not be very convenient to deal with large differences of head of water, such as might be expected under conditions just given. To avoid this, it is usual to use mercury in the manometer, since mercury is much heavier than water.

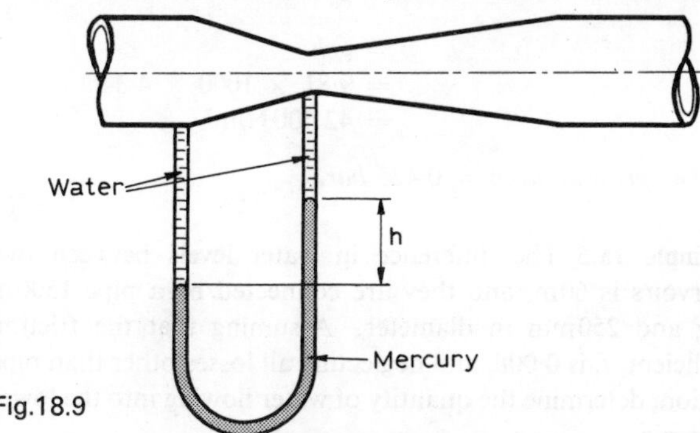

Fig.18.9

Such an arrangement is shown in fig.18.9, where the U-tube manometer, containing mercury, is connected across the Venturi meter. The difference in pressure between inlet and throat is now the equivalent of a column of mercury of height h in the right-hand limb, minus the equivalent of a column of water of height h in the left-hand limb. Thus, the height h for the mercury manometer is reduced, compared with that in a water manometer, in the ratio

$$\frac{\text{specific gravity of water}}{\text{specific gravity of mercury} - \text{specific gravity of water}}$$

$$= \frac{1}{13\cdot6 - 1} = \frac{1}{12\cdot6}$$

Consequently the difference in pressure between the inlet and throat of the Venturi could be indicated by a column of mercury 3·9/12·6 or 0·310 metres high.

In dealing with problems involving mercury manometers, you should first determine the manometer reading for water, and then convert to a corresponding reading for mercury, in the manner just outlined.

Effect of Friction: D'Arcy's Formula

One of the main causes of losses of energy in hydraulic schemes is that due to friction between the containing pipe or channel and the flowing water. In a length of pipe, considered to be level, and of uniform diameter between two sections 1 and 2, it would be necessary to have a greater pressure at 1 than at 2, in order to overcome the frictional resistances of the pipe.

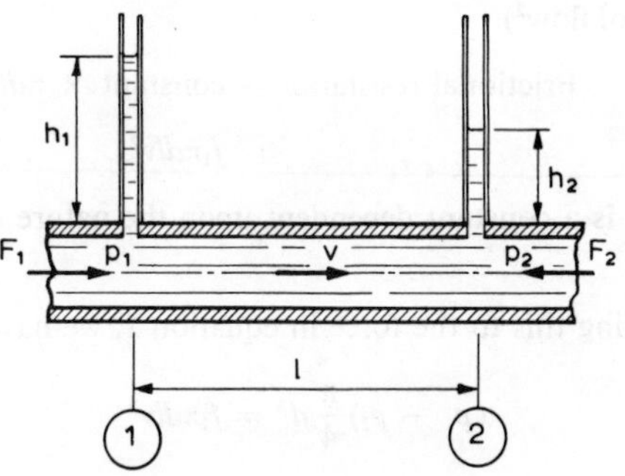

Fig.18.10 Friction in pipes. The resultant difference between the forces F_1 at 1 and F_2 at 2 is required to move the water along the pipe, overcoming friction between the water and the pipe surface.

Let d = the diameter of the pipe, in m;
l = the length of the pipe, in m;
p_1 = pressure at section 1, in N/m²;
p_2 = pressure at section 2, in N/m²;
h_1 = piezometer head at section 1, in m;
h_2 = piezometer head at section 2, in m;
v = velocity of water in m/s;
f and f_1 = frictional coefficients.

Force at 1:

$$F_1 = \text{pressure} \times \text{cross-sectional area of pipe}$$

$$= p_1 \times \frac{\pi}{4} d^2$$

Force at 2:

$$F_2 = p_2 \times \frac{\pi}{4} d^2$$

Resultant force in direction of water flow

$$= F_1 - F_2$$

$$= (p_1 - p_2) \frac{\pi}{4} d_2. \quad . \quad . \quad . \quad (1)$$

This force must just equal the frictional resistance force of the pipe. Experiments on pipes of different diameters and lengths have shown that this resistance force is dependent upon three factors:

1 the nature of the surface of the pipe, rough or smooth;

2 the area of the pipe surface in contact with the water;

3 the square of the velocity of flow—this would be the case for the more common type of pipe flow; if, however, the pipe bore was very small, and the velocity of flow was also small, the flow would be defined as streamlined, and other conditions would apply.

Thus frictional resistance is proportional to (area of contact × velocity of flow²).

$$\text{Frictional resistance} = \text{constant} \times \pi dl \times v^2$$

$$= f_1 \pi dl v^2$$

where f_1 is a constant dependent upon the nature of the pipe surface.

Equating this to the force in equation 1, we have

$$(p_1 - p_2)\frac{\pi}{4}d^2 = f_1 \pi dl v^2$$

$$p_1 - p_2 = \frac{4 f_1 l v^2}{d}$$

By making a slight change in the value of the constant, and using f, where $f = f_1 \frac{2}{\rho}$ (which is still a constant), we obtain

$$p_1 - p_2 = \frac{4f\rho l v^2}{2d}$$

or

$$\frac{p_1 - p_2}{\rho g} = \frac{4flv^2}{2gd}$$

The value of ρ is the density of water (or in fact of any liquid considered) in kg/m³, and g is the usual 9·81 m/s². The need for its introduction may not appear obvious at this stage; it does, however, enable the value of f to be a dimensionless constant. Incidentally, whilst the 4 and the 2 would appear to cancel, they are usually left in this characteristic form.

$(p_1 - p_2)/\rho g$ is equal to $z_1 - z_2$, which is the difference in levels of water in the piezometer tubes, and is actually the value of the head loss due to friction. In this form the expression is known as D'Arcy's formula.

$$\text{Head loss due to friction, } h_f = \frac{4flv^2}{2gd}$$

Typical values for f are
smooth concrete pipes: 0·0015,
rough concrete pipes: 0·0060,
smooth steel pipes: 0·0003.

Example 18.4 Determine the pressure difference, in N/m², between two points 800 m apart in a horizontal pipe-line, 150 mm diameter, discharging water at the rate of 12·5 litres per second. Take the frictional coefficient, f, as being 0·008.

$$12{\cdot}5\ \text{l/s} = 0{\cdot}0125\ \text{m}^3/\text{s}$$

$$\text{Area of pipe} = \frac{\pi}{4} \times 0{\cdot}15^2 = 0{\cdot}0177\ \text{m}^2$$

$$\text{Velocity of water in pipe} = \frac{\text{volume per second}}{\text{area}}$$

$$= \frac{0{\cdot}0125}{0{\cdot}0177}$$

$$= 0{\cdot}707\ \text{m/s}$$

$$\text{Loss of head due to friction} = \frac{4flv^2}{2gd}$$

$$= \frac{4 \times 0{\cdot}008 \times 800 \times 0{\cdot}707^2}{2 \times 9{\cdot}81 \times 0{\cdot}15}$$

$$= 4{\cdot}34\ \text{m}$$

Since $h = \dfrac{p}{\rho g}$

$$p = \rho g h$$
$$= 9{\cdot}81 \times 1000 \times 4{\cdot}34$$
$$= 42\,500\ \text{N/m}^2$$

i.e. The pressure drop = 0·425 *bar.*

Example 18.5 The difference in water levels between two reservoirs is 60 m, and they are connected by a pipe 1500 m long and 250 mm in diameter. Assuming that the friction coefficient, f, is 0·008, and neglecting all losses other than pipe-friction, determine the quantity of water flowing into the lower reservoir.

Neglecting other losses, the difference in head between the two reservoirs is required to overcome the frictional loss in the pipe.

Let v = velocity of water in pipe.

$$\text{Hence } 60 = \frac{4flv^2}{2gd}$$

$$= \frac{4 \times 0{\cdot}008 \times 1500 v^2}{2 \times 9{\cdot}81 \times 0{\cdot}25}$$

$$v^2 = 6{\cdot}14$$
$$v = 2{\cdot}48\ \text{m/s}$$

$$\text{Area of pipe} = \frac{\pi}{4} \times 0{\cdot}25^2$$

$$= 0{\cdot}0492\ \text{m}^2$$

Quantity flowing = area × velocity
= 0·0492 × 2·48
= 0·122 m^3/s

i.e. Quantity flowing = 122 litres per second.

Flow through Orifices

By an orifice we usually understand a small circular opening through which a liquid or gas can flow. If a tank is provided with an orifice near to its base, then the discharge of liquid from the tank through the orifice will depend upon the velocity of flow through the opening, together with the size of the opening. You will probably have noticed that the velocity of flow through an orifice will be much greater when the tank is full than when it is nearly empty. In fact, we shall see that the velocity is very closely connected with the head of liquid above the level of the orifice.

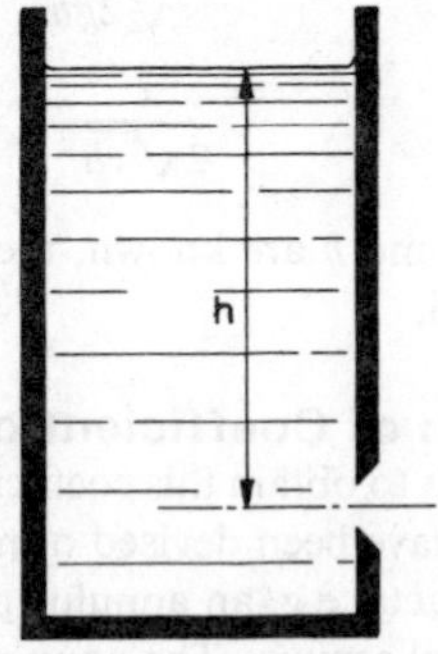

Fig.18.11 Flow through orifice. An orifice is an opening, usually sharp-edged, through which water can flow. The velocity of the water through the orifice in the side of the tank is dependent upon the head of water, *h*. The potential energy of the water at the free surface is converted into kinetic energy at the orifice.

Figure 18.11 shows a tank containing water which is maintained at a constant level by means of an inlet pipe. The level of water is *h* metres above the level of the orifice. With reference to the orifice, water at the free surface possesses potential energy, but, since it is reasonably still, it has no kinetic energy. On the other hand, the water passing through the orifice has no potential energy, but, due to its velocity, it possesses kinetic energy. We have already reviewed a very important principle in connection with energy, which shows that

energy at free surface = energy at orifice

i.e. potential energy at free surface = kinetic energy at orifice

Consider 1 kg of water.
Potential energy at surface = $1 \times h \times g$

$$= gh$$

Kinetic energy at orifice $= \frac{1}{2} \times 1 \times v^2$
where v is velocity of water at orifice.

Equating these two expressions,

$$\frac{v^2}{2} = gh$$

$$v = \sqrt{2gh}\ \text{m/s}$$

In practice, the actual velocity is slightly less than the theoretical velocity given by the above expression. The difference is due mainly to friction losses between the liquid and the containing tank.

$$\text{Coefficient of velocity, } C_v = \frac{\text{actual velocity}}{\text{theoretical velocity}}$$

C_v is approximately 0·94 to 0·99
∴ Actual velocity of water, through the orifice

$$= C_v \sqrt{2gh}\ \text{m/s}$$

Contraction in Area of Jet

If we examine the jet of water, we shall see that at a short distance from the orifice the jet has a minimum diameter. There is a characteristic contraction in jet diameter, and consequently in area of the jet. This contracted diameter is referred to as the *vena contracta*.

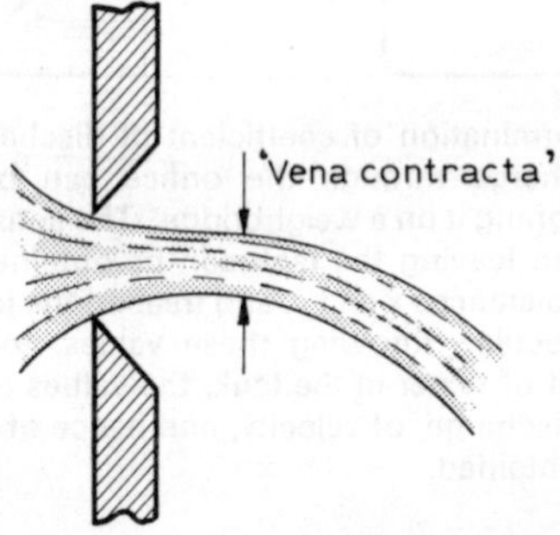

Fig.18.12 Contraction in jet. The cross-sectional area of the jet has a minimum value at a short distance past the orifice. The contracted section is known as the *vena contracta*, and its area is approximately 0·6 times the area of the orifice.

$$\text{Coefficient of contraction, } C_c = \frac{\text{area of vena contracta}}{\text{area of orifice}}$$

Area of vena contract = C_c × area of orifice
Average value of $C_c = 0·66$
Discharge of water in cubic metres per second is given by actual velocity (m/s) × area of vena contracta (m^2).

Discharge = $C_v \sqrt{2gh} \times C_c$ × area of orifice
= $C_v C_c \sqrt{2gh}$ × area of orifice
= $C \sqrt{2gh}$ × area of orifice

where C is the coefficient of discharge, and is equal to the product of C_v and C_c.

Determination of Coefficient of Discharge

The value of the coefficient of discharge, C, can be obtained in a very simple experimental manner. The actual discharge from the tank can be measured by means of a bucket and weighbridge. The weight of water discharged in a given interval of time can be reduced to newtons per second, and then to cubic metres per second.

The theoretical discharge is given by $\sqrt{2gh} \times$ area of orifice; then the coefficient of discharge is given by

$$C = \frac{\text{actual discharge}}{\text{theoretical discharge}}$$

Determination of Coefficient of Velocity

To determine the actual velocity with which the jet leaves the orifice, we measure the vertical distance through which the jet falls in a known horizontal distance (fig.18.13).

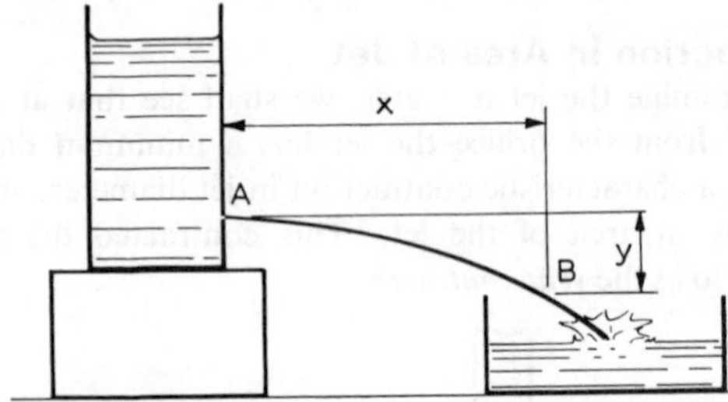

Fig.18.13 Determination of coefficient of discharge. The actual discharge through the orifice can be measured by weighing it on a weighbridge. The actual velocity of the jet on leaving the tank can be obtained by measuring the distances x and y, and treating the jet as a horizontal projectile. Knowing these values, together with the head of water in the tank, the values of the coefficient of discharge, of velocity, and hence of contraction, can be obtained.

Let t seconds be the time the jet takes to move from A to B, v_A m/s be the actual velocity with which the jet leaves the orifice, x and y be the ordinates of the point B, taking A as the origin.

Horizontal motion

Moving with forward velocity v_A, the jet moves a horizontal distance of x m in t seconds.

$$t = \frac{x}{v_A} \text{ seconds}$$

Vertical motion

Starting with zero initial vertical velocity, the jet moves through a vertical distance y in t seconds, with an acceleration g m/s^2. Using the expression $s = ut - \frac{1}{2}gt^2$,

$$s = -y \text{ (negative, since } s \text{ increases downwards)}$$
$$u = 0$$

$$t = \frac{x}{v_A} \text{ from above equation}$$

$$\therefore\ -y = 0 - \tfrac{1}{2}g\left(\frac{x}{v_A}\right)^2$$

$$\therefore\ v_A{}^2 = \frac{gx^2}{2y}$$

Actual velocity $v_A = x\sqrt{\dfrac{g}{2y}}$ m/s

Theoretical velocity $v = \sqrt{2gh}$

$$\text{Coefficient of velocity } C_v = \frac{\text{actual velocity}}{\text{theoretical velocity}}$$
$$= \frac{x\sqrt{g/2y}}{\sqrt{2gh}}$$
$$= \frac{x}{2\sqrt{yh}}$$

Hence, if x, y, and h are known, the coefficient of velocity can be determined.

Determination of Coefficient of Contraction

It is rather difficult to obtain this coefficient by actual measurement. Methods have been devised of measuring the diameter of the vena contracta, e.g. an annulus provided with three- or four-pointed radial screws. The annulus is placed so that the jet passes through it, and the screws are adjusted so that each just touches the jet at the vena contracta. The annulus is then removed, and the diameter of the vena contracta is obtained by measuring the distance between the points of the screws.

A more satisfactory method is to determine the values of the coefficients of discharge and velocity, as indicated above. Then, since coefficient of discharge $= C_c \times C_v$, we can obtain the coefficient of contraction, C_c, from the relationship

$$\text{coefficient of contraction} = \frac{\text{coefficient of discharge}}{\text{coefficient of velocity}}$$

Example 18.6 Determine the quantity of water flowing per hour through a 40 mm diameter orifice in the side of a tank containing a constant head of 6 m of water. The coefficient of discharge for the orifice is 0·6.

$$\text{Area of orifice} = \frac{\pi}{4} \times 0{\cdot}04^2$$
$$= 0{\cdot}001\,27\,\text{m}^2$$

$$\text{Theoretical discharge velocity} = \sqrt{2g \times \text{head}}$$
$$= \sqrt{2g \times 6}$$
$$= 10{\cdot}8\,\text{m/s}$$

Theoretical discharge = area × velocity

$$= 0{\cdot}001\,27 \times 10{\cdot}8$$
$$= 0{\cdot}0137\,\text{m}^3/\text{s}$$

Actual discharge = theoretical discharge × coefficient of discharge

$$= 0{\cdot}0137 \times 0{\cdot}6$$
$$= 0{\cdot}0082\,\text{m}^3/\text{s}$$
$$= 8{\cdot}2\ \text{l/s}$$

i.e. Actual discharge = 8·21/s.

Example 18.7 A jet of water issues from an orifice in a vertical wall. Show how to deduce the velocity of efflux from measurements of a point in the path of the jet relative to the centre of the orifice.

A sharp-edged orifice of 50mm diameter has a coefficient of velocity of 0·97, and a coefficient of contraction of 0·64, and discharges into a pond, the surface of which is 1m below the centre of the orifice. The jet strikes the surface at a horizontal distance of 3·2m from the orifice. Estimate the rate of discharge in litres per second, and the head over the orifice. IMECHE

$$\text{Area of orifice} = \frac{\pi}{4} \times 0{\cdot}05^2$$
$$= 0{\cdot}001\,96\,\text{m}^2$$

$$\text{Area of vena contracta} = 0{\cdot}64 \times 0{\cdot}001\,96$$
$$= 0{\cdot}001\,26\,\text{m}^2$$

Let v_A = actual velocity of jet at the orifice.
Time taken for water to fall 1m starting from rest is given by

$$s = ut - \tfrac{1}{2}gt^2$$
$$u = 0$$
$$s = -1 \text{ (down)}$$
$$\therefore\ -1 = 0 - \tfrac{1}{2}gt^2$$
$$t = 0{\cdot}45 \text{ seconds.}$$

In 0·45 seconds the jet moves forward 3·2m with constant velocity v_A.

$$\therefore\ v_A = \frac{3{\cdot}2}{0{\cdot}45} = 7{\cdot}1\,\text{m/s}$$

Actual discharge = area of vena contract × actual velocity

$$= 0{\cdot}001\,26 \times 7{\cdot}1$$
$$= 0{\cdot}008\,95\,\text{m}^3/\text{s}$$
$$= 8{\cdot}95\,\text{l/s}$$

$$\text{Theoretical velocity} = \frac{\text{actual velocity}}{\text{coefficient of velocity}}$$

$$= \frac{7{\cdot}1}{0{\cdot}97} = 7{\cdot}33\,\text{m/s}$$

Let h = head of water above orifice, in m.

Then $\sqrt{2gh} = 7{\cdot}33$

$$h = 2{\cdot}75\,\text{m}$$

i.e. Head of water above orifice is 2·75m, actual discharge of water is 8·95 litres per second.

Exercise 18

1 A horizontal pipe, 75mm in diameter, conveys water at the rate of 12 l/s between the points A and B, 100m apart. The pressure at A is 2·75 bar absolute. Determine the pressure at B if the frictional coefficient for the pipe is 0·008.

If there is a small hole on top of the pipe at B, determine the height to which the water will rise if the coefficient of velocity for the hole is unity, and the atmospheric pressure is 1 bar. ULCI

2 The difference in height of the water level in two reservoirs is 45m, and they are connected by a pipe 3km long. Determine the diameter of the pipe required to discharge 455 m³/h into the lower reservoir. Assume the frictional coefficient f, to be 0·0075, and neglect all losses other than pipe friction.

Also determine the pressure difference, in N/m², between two points in the pipe both at the same height, but 400m apart. ULCI

3 A horizontal pipe-line, 75mm in diameter, conveys oil of specific gravity 0·9, and is fitted with a Venturi meter having a throat diameter of 25mm. Manometer tubes are led from the entrance and throat of the meter to a U-tube containing mercury (specific gravity 13·57), which records a difference in the mercury levels of 315mm. The coefficient of the meter is 0·98. Determine (a) the pressure difference, in N/m², between the entrance and the throat of the Venturi, and (b) the quantity of oil flowing through the pipe, in litres per second. ULCI

4 Show that the theoretical velocity of discharge of a jet of water from a small orifice is $k\sqrt{h}$, where h is the head of water above the orifice, and k is a constant.

In an experiment to determine the coefficients of contraction, velocity, and discharge of an orifice, the following observations were made:

diameter of orifice = 9·5mm; head of water above the centre of the orifice = 685mm; discharge of water = 57·2 kg in 6 minutes. The jet issues horizontally, and in a horizontal distance of 460mm it falls 82·5mm. Determine the values of the coefficients for this orifice. ULCI

5 Water is supplied to a nozzle, 12·5mm in diameter, at 2·75 bar above the atmospheric pressure. The coefficients of velocity and discharge for the nozzle are both assumed to be unity. Determine the velocity and the mass of water discharged per second from the nozzle.

The jet of water is deflected through 120° by passing over a stationary curved vane. Determine the magnitude and direction of the force on the vane due to the passage of the water over it. ULCI

6 The term 'metres of head' is commonly used in connection with fluids. Explain its meaning, and the quantities to which it may be applied.

A section, AB, of a water pipe-line is 45 m long, and, in order to clear an obstruction, it is laid on a rising incline of 1 in 20. At A, the diameter is 150 mm, the speed of flow is 1·5 m/s, and a gauge records the pressure as 2 bar. At the upper point, B, the diameter is 100 mm, and between A and B there is a frictional loss of energy of 15 J/kg of water. Determine the pressure at B, in metres of head. IMECHE

7 State Bernoulli's Theorem for the steady flow of a liquid, explaining the meaning of the terms, and the units of the quantities given.

Water is in steady motion in a pipe inclined downwards. At the upper end, A, the pipe is 100 mm in diameter, and the pressure, as shown by a gauge there, is 55 kN/m². At B, which is 3 m below A, the diameter is 62·5 mm, and the pressure is 35 kN/m². Assuming there are no losses by friction between the positions, determine the flow in litres per second. IMECHE

8 Define the coefficients of velocity, contraction, and discharge, as used in connection with flow through an orifice.

The flow of water from a sharp-edged orifice of 15·2 mm diameter, under a head of 1·22 m, was measured as 0·568 litres per second. The jet discharged into a tank, the water surface in which was 114 mm below the centre of the orifice, and struck the surface at a horizontal distance of 670 mm from the plane of the orifice. Determine the values of the three coefficients. IMECHE

9 A pipe conveying water rises at one place from a position A to a position B, 3 m above A. At the lower level, the pipe diameter is 300 mm, and the pressure there remains constant at 35 kN/m² gauge, even though the flow quantity may vary. At B, a Venturi throat is formed, so that flow changes may be observed by means of gauge readings there. The maximum flow is at the rate of 190 litres per second, and for this condition the pressure at the throat at B is not to be lower than 35 kN/m² below atmospheric. Determine the minimum throat diameter permissible.

If the flow rate falls by 10% below the maximum, estimate the change in the gauge reading at B. IMECHE

10 Write down the equation relating to energy items at two positions on the path of a flowing fluid, introducing a term, say H m of head, to represent a loss of energy by work against friction between the two positions. Explain briefly the meanings of the various terms in the statement.

A centrifugal pump draws water from a pond 3 m below its own level, and discharges into an open tank 75 m above its own level. The speed of flow in the suction pipe is 1·5 m/s, and the pipe is 150 mm in diameter. The diameter of the delivery pipe is 125 mm. There are friction losses equivalent to 600 mm of head in the suction pipe, and to 13·5 m in the delivery pipe. The efficiency of the pump is 65%. Determine the discharge in litres per second, and the power required to drive the pump. Obtain the values of the pressures in the pipes at the inlet to, and the outlet from, the pump, stating these in kN/m² below and above atmosphere. IMECHE

11 Water is pumped through a pipe AB, in which B is 8·8 m above A. The diameter of the pipe at A is 75 mm, and at B it is 125 mm. The pressure at A is 234 kN/m², and at B 137·5 kN/m², and there is a frictional loss between A and B equivalent to a head of 1·2 m of water. Determine the discharge at B in litres per second, and the loss of power, owing to friction, in watts. UEI

12 State Bernoulli's equation for steady flow in a horizontal path, and deduce therefrom an expression for the flow of water in litres per second through a horizontal Venturi meter of entry and throat areas respectively A_1 and A_2, if the pressure-head difference between these points is H. Explain why this theoretical expression has to be corrected by a coefficient, k, to give actual quantities.

In a test of a horizontal Venturi meter, the flow of water measured over a period of 5 minutes was 7300 litres. The entry and throat areas were 0·0812 and 0·0116 m² respectively, and the difference of pressure was given by a U-tube manometer as 240 mm of water. Determine the value of the coefficient k for this meter. UEI

13 State Bernoulli's Theorem regarding the flow of an incompressible fluid.

The centre line of a pipe 6 m long is at 30° to the horizontal. It tapers from 300 mm in diameter at the lower end to 225 mm in diameter at the upper end. With a flow of 0·127 m³/s, the pipe is running full. The flow is from the lower end to the upper.

Calculate the change in kinetic energy per unit mass of water, and the pressure at the lower end for a pressure of 1 bar at the upper end. Neglect losses. ULCI

14 State Bernoulli's law or theorem.

A horizontal pipe 100 mm in diameter, full of water, has a reduced section 50 mm in diameter forming a Venturi tube. The difference in pressure between the 100 mm and 50 mm portions is measured by a mercury filled U-tube, in which the difference in mercury level is 445 mm. Working from first principles, and neglecting losses due to friction, calculate the velocity of water in the 100 mm portion, and the mass flow in kg/min. NCTEC

15 By reference to the energy equation, justify Bernoulli's Theorem for the flow of an incompressible fluid.

A Venturi meter is to be used to measure the quantity of oil flowing in a horizontal pipe of 62·5 mm bore.

The diameter of the meter at the throat is 25 mm, and the difference of head between the entrance and the throat is measured on a U-tube mercury manometer having oil above the mercury. If the difference in the mercury levels in the two limbs of the U-tube is 500 mm, and assuming a meter discharge coefficient of 0·9, calculate the flow in kilogram per hour.

(Specific gravity of oil = 0·8. Specific gravity of mercury = 13·6.)

Chapter 19

Impact of Jets

When a steady jet of water impinges on a solid surface, there is no rebound of the water, as would be the case if two solid bodies collide. Instead, a thin stream is formed, and this glides along the surface until it reaches the boundary of the plate, which it leaves at approximately a tangent to the surface The solution of problems of this type is dependent upon the work which we have done regarding impact and momentum. In the case which we are considering, there is a continuous sequence of impacts. The momentum which the impinging water has in the direction of its flow is being continually destroyed, the rate of destruction determining the force on the plate.

Flat Plate at Rest (fig.19.1)

Let v = the velocity of the jet, in m/s;
A = cross-sectional area of the jet, in m^2;
ρ = density of water, in kg/m^3.

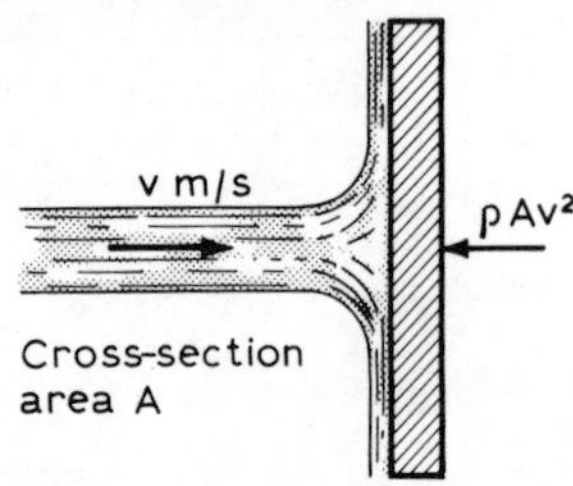

Fig.19.1 Force exerted on a flat plate, at rest, by a jet of liquid

Volume of water striking plate per second = $Av \, m^3$
Mass of water striking plate per second = ρAv kg
Initial momentum of water per second in direction of jet

$$= \text{mass} \times \text{velocity}$$
$$= \rho Av \times v$$

Final momentum of water per second in direction of jet = 0.
Change of momentum of water per second in direction of jet

$$= \rho Av^2.$$

This is the rate of change of momentum, which is equal to the force on the plate.

Force on plate = ρAv^2 newtons.

But if the velocity v is expressed in terms of the head h required to produce such a velocity, we have, since $v = \sqrt{2gh}$,

$$\text{force on plate} = 2\,\rho g A h \text{ newtons.}$$

It is interesting to compare this force with that which would be exerted on the plate if it were to cover an orifice, area A, over which was a static head of water, height h.

Pressure at this depth = ρgh newtons
Force on plate = pressure × area
$= \rho ghA$

which is just half that produced on a plate by a jet whose velocity head is h.

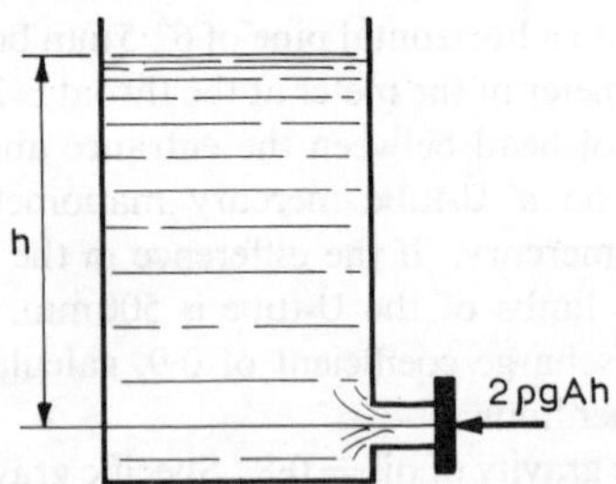

Fig.19.2 Force on plate due to jet flowing through orifice. The force on the plate when held a little in front of the orifice is double that which the plate experiences when covering the orifice opening in the tank.

Example 19.1 A square plate of 300 mm edge is hung so that it can swing about the upper horizontal edge. A horizontal jet, 20 mm in diameter, and having a velocity of 15 m/s, impinges on to the plate 150 mm from the centre line of the jet to the upper edge of the plate (fig.19.3). Determine the horizontal force which must be applied at the lower edge of the plate in order to keep it in a vertical position.

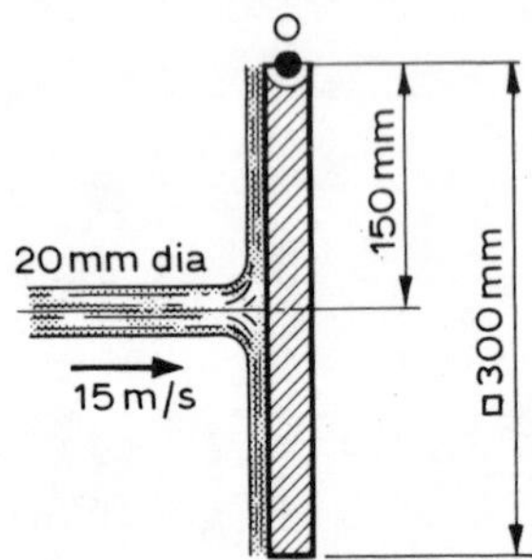

Fig.19.3

Area of jet $= \frac{\pi}{4} \times 0{\cdot}02^2 = \pi \times 10^{-4} m^2$

Volume of water per second $= \pi \times 10^{-4} \times 15$
$= 4{\cdot}71 \times 10^{-3} m^3$

Mass of water per second $= 4{\cdot}71 \times 10^{-3} \times 1000$
$= 4{\cdot}71$ kg/s

Momentum of water per second striking plate $= 4{\cdot}71 \times 15$
$= 70{\cdot}8 \, kg\,m/s^2$

Momentum of water per second (in direction of original motion) after striking plate = 0, since velocity in this direction is 0.

Change in momentum per second $= 70{\cdot}8 - 0$
$= 70{\cdot}8 \, kg\,m/s^2$

∴ Force exerted by jet on plate $= 70{\cdot}8$ N

Take moments about 0.

$$70{\cdot}8 \times 0{\cdot}15 = F \times 0{\cdot}3$$

$$F = 35{\cdot}4\text{N}$$

i.e. The force at the lower edge to keep the plate vertical is 35·4 N.

Impact on Flat Plate Moving in Direction of Jet

Obviously, if the plate is moving away from the jet with the same velocity as the jet, there will be no force exerted by the jet on the plate. The expression for jet force is therefore dependent upon the relative velocity of the plate and jet.

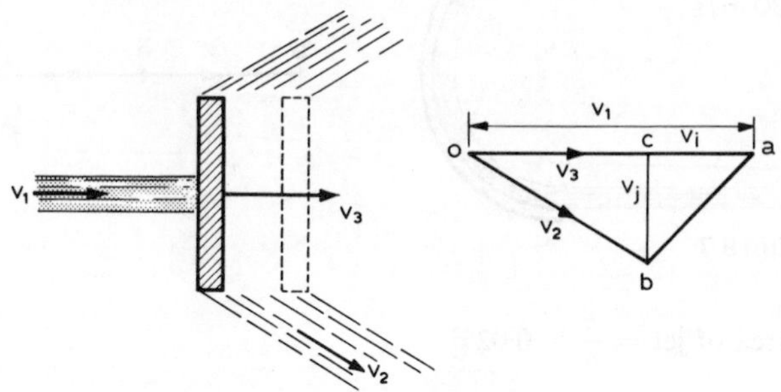

Fig.19.4 Force exerted by jet of liquid on flat plate moving in same direction as jet

Let v_1 = velocity of water before striking plate,
v_2 = velocity of water on leaving plate,
v_3 = velocity of plate,
v_i = velocity of water relative to plate at inlet,
v_j = velocity of water relative to plate at outlet.

These velocities are indicated on the vector triangle.

oa represents the velocity of the water before striking the plate,

oc represents the velocity of the plate,

ca represents the velocity of water relative to the plate at the inlet.

From this we obtain the quantity of water striking the plate per second. Using the same symbols as in the previous paragraph, we have

$$\text{mass of water striking plate per second} = \rho A(v_1 - v_3)$$

Now, relative to the plate, the water is turned through an angle of 90°; and, if we assume that there are no losses due to friction, we can claim that the magnitude of the relative velocity remains unchanged.

Thus vector ***cb*** is drawn equal to ***ca*** in length, but the direction is turned through 90°. Thus vector ***cb*** represents the velocity of water relative to the plate at the outlet.

Vector ***ob***, which is the sum of ***oc*** and ***cb***, will then represent the actual velocity of the water as it leaves the plate, v_2.

Finally, since ***oa*** is the initial velocity of the water, and ***ob*** is the final velocity of the water, ***ab*** will represent the change in velocity.

Change in velocity in direction of motion of plate (component of ***ab***) = ***ac***, which is equal to $v_1 - v_3$.

Change in momentum per second in direction of motion = mass flow per second × change in velocity in direction of motion

$$= \rho A\,(v_1 - v_3) \times ac$$
$$= \rho A\,(v_1 - v_3)^2$$

This rate of change of momentum is equal to the force which causes it.

Hence force exerted by plate on jet, or, alternatively, force exerted by jet on plate in direction of motion, is equal to $\rho A\,(v_1 - v_3)^2$ newtons.

Note. When the jet strikes the plate, the water will cover the surface of the plate. From the vector diagram just drawn, it would appear that, after striking the plate, the water moves in one direction only. This assumption will not affect the result just obtained. The resultant force on the plate will, in fact, be in the direction of motion of the jet.

Example 19.2 Define momentum and enunciate Newton's Second Law of Motion.

A jet of water having a velocity of 100 m/s strikes a flat plate moving in the direction of the jet with a speed of 50 m/s. If the mass of water striking the plate each second is 15 kg, calculate the force exerted on the plate. No water splashes back. NCTEC

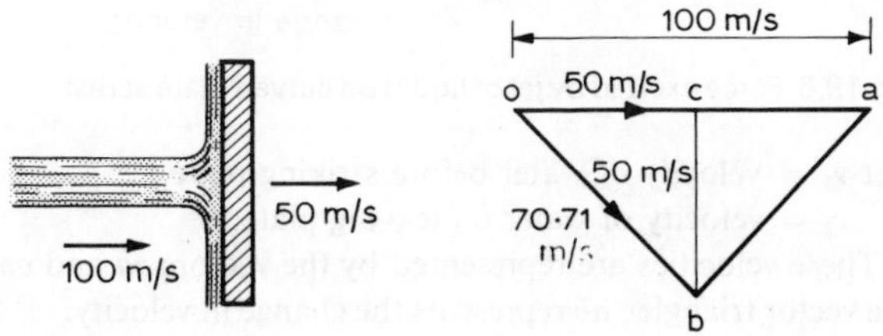

Fig.19.5

See Appendix 3 for Newton's Laws of Motion.

Momentum of water per second striking plate

$$= \text{mass} \times \text{velocity}$$
$$= 15 \times 100$$
$$= 1500\,\text{kg m/s}$$

Velocity of water leaving plate = ***ob***

$$= 70{\cdot}71\,\text{m/s}$$

Component of this velocity in direction of motion = ***oc***

$$= 50\,\text{m/s}$$

Momentum of water per second leaving plate (component in direction of motion) = mass × velocity in direction of motion

$= 15 \times 50$

$= 750\,\text{kgm/s}$

Change of momentum per second in direction of jet's motion

$= 1500 - 750$

$= 750\,\text{kgm/s}$

But force is equal to change of momentum per second.

i.e. Force exerted by water on plate = 750 N.

Note particularly that, in this question, we are told the quantity of water striking the plate per second, and consequently need not calculate the relative velocity of jet to plate.

Impact on Curved Plate at Rest

The water impinges on the curved plate, and is deflected through angle θ, as shown in fig.19.6.

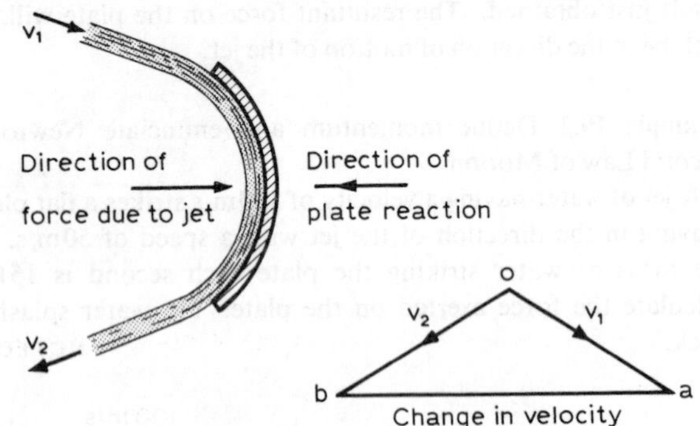

Fig.19.6 Force exerted by jet of liquid on curved plate at rest

Let v_1 = velocity of water before striking plate,
v_2 = velocity of water on leaving plate.

These velocities are represented by the vectors ***oa*** and ***ob*** in the vector triangle. ***ab*** represents the change in velocity.
The mass of water striking the plate per second $= \rho A v_1$

Change in momentum of water per second

$= $ mass per second × change in velocity

$= \rho A v_1 \times \boldsymbol{ab}$

This rate of change of momentum is equal to the force causing it, i.e. equal to the force which the plate exerts on the jet of water, and also to the force which the jet exerts on the plate.

Force on plate $= \rho A v_1 \times \boldsymbol{ab}$

The expressions which have been developed in connection with the forces exerted by jets on plates are the basis of work on hydraulic turbines. The expressions will be further developed, and associated with the work done by the jet on the moving plates, in order that the power and the efficiency of the various hydraulic prime movers can be obtained. But this work must wait until a later stage, when hydraulic machinery is under review.

Example 19.3 A curved plate deflects a jet of water through 180°. Determine the force on the plate if the jet has a diameter of 25 mm, and a velocity of 30 m/s. Assume that there is no friction loss at the surface of the plate.

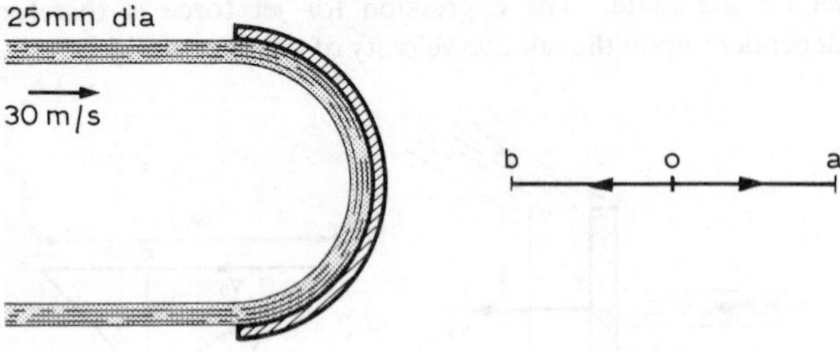

Fig.19.7

$$\text{Area of jet} = \frac{\pi}{4} \times 0{\cdot}025^2$$

$$= 4{\cdot}9 \times 10^{-4}\,\text{m}^2$$

Volume of water striking jet per second = area × velocity

$= 4{\cdot}9 \times 10^{-4} \times 30$

$= 14{\cdot}7 \times 10^{-3}\,\text{m}^3$

Mass of water striking plate per second

$= 14{\cdot}7 \times 10^{-3} \times 1000$

$= 14{\cdot}7\,\text{kg/s}$

Since there is no friction loss, the velocity of water leaving the plate will, in this case, be equal and opposite to the velocity of water striking the plate.

Velocity of water leaving jet = ***ob***

$= -30\,\text{m/s}$

Change in velocity of water = ***oa*** − ***ob***

$= 30 - (-30)$

$= 60\,\text{m/s}$

Change in momentum per second of water

$= $ mass per second × change in velocity

$= 14{\cdot}7 \times 60$

$= 882\,\text{kgm/s}^2$

Hence force on plate due to jet is 882 *N*.

Exercise 19

1 A jet of water 50 mm in diameter, moving with a velocity of 15 m/s, strikes a flat plate at right angles to its direction of motion. Determine the force exerted by the jet on the plate.

2 A square plate of 375 mm side is hung so that it can swing about the upper horizontal edge. A horizontal jet, 20 mm in diameter, and having a velocity of 24 m/s, impinges on to the plate, 100 mm from the centre line of the jet to the lower edge of the plate. Determine the horizontal force which must be applied at the lower edge of the plate in order to keep it in a vertical position.

3 A tank contains water to a height of 3 m. A 50 mm diameter orifice at the base of the tank is covered by a plate. What force will be required to hold the plate against the orifice? If the plate is then moved a short distance away from the tank, so that it receives the full force of the jet flowing through the orifice, determine the force required to hold the plate at right angles to the jet.

4 A jet of water having a velocity of 45 m/s strikes a flat plate moving in the direction of the jet with a velocity of 12 m/s. If the mass of water striking the plate each second is 14 kg, calculate the force exerted on the plate, assuming no splash back of water.

5 A jet of water 12·5 mm in diameter has a velocity of 15 m/s, It strikes a plate moving in the same direction as the jet with a velocity of 3 m/s. Determine the force exerted by the jet on the plate. What will be the force on the plate if the velocity of the plate is increased to 12 m/s?

6 A curved plate deflects a jet of water through 180°. If the impinging jet has a velocity of 15 m/s, and a diameter of 20 mm, determine the force exerted by the jet on the plate.

7 At two points A and B, 3 m apart, in a vertical pipe, the diameters are 25 and 50 mm respectively. The end A is open to the atmosphere; and, when water flows upwards from B to A, the pressure at B is 2·4 bar gauge. Just above the opening A, there is a fixed flat plate, with its surface normal to the axis of the pipe. Neglecting the loss due to pipe friction, and the loss of velocity of the jet between A and the plate, determine (a) the quantity of water flowing in kg/s, and (b) the force exerted on the plate. ULCI

Appendix 1

Approximate Values of Sin θ and Cos θ for Small Values of θ

On a number of occasions, we have to make use of the substitution sin θ = θ (radians), and cos θ = 1, when θ is a small angle. The following tables indicate the justification for, and the limits of, this substitution.

degrees	θ *radians*	sin θ	*Difference between* θ *and* sin θ	*Percentage difference*
0	0·000 00	0·000 000	0·000 00	0·000
1	0·107 45	0·017 45	0·000 00	0·000
2	0·034 91	0·034 90	0·000 01	0·0286
3	0·052 36	0·052 34	0·000 02	0·0382
4	0·069 81	0·069 76	0·000 05	0·0715
5	0·087 27	0·087 16	0·000 11	0·126
6	0·104 72	0·104 53	0·000 19	0·182
7	0·122 17	0·121 87	0·000 30	0·246
8	0·139 63	0·139 17	0·000 46	0·331
9	0·157 08	0·156 43	0·000 65	0·415
10	0·174 53	0·173 65	0·000 88	0·507
11	0·191 99	0·190 81	0·001 18	0·617
12	0·209 44	0·207 91	0·001 53	0·736
13	0·226 89	0·224 95	0·001 94	0·863
14	0·244 35	0·241 92	0·002 43	1·000

For values of θ greater than 14°, the difference between sin θ and θ is greater than 1%.

θ *degrees*	cos θ	*Difference between* cos θ *and* 1	*Percentage difference*
0	1·000 00	0·000 00	0·000
1	0·999 85	0·000 15	0·015
2	0·999 39	0·000 61	0·061
3	0·998 63	0·001 37	0·137
4	0·997 56	0·002 44	0·244
5	0·996 19	0·003 81	0·381
6	0·994 52	0·005 48	0·548
7	0·992 55	0·007 45	0·745
8	0·990 27	0·009 73	0·973
9	0·987 69	0·012 31	1·231

For values of θ greater than 10°, the difference between cos θ and 1 is greater than 1%.

Appendix 2

Methods of Determining Area under Curve

1) *Counting squares.* Count the number of whole squares. If the curve passes through a square, count the square in the total provided that more than half the area of the square is under the curve. If less than half the area is under the square, then neglect the square.

2) *Mid-ordinate method.* Divide the total base into a suitable number of equal parts, and erect ordinates at the mid-point of the base of each strip. Each strip is then considered to have an area equal to the base × mid-ordinate length. Since each strip has the same width of base, the total area is equal to the sum of the mid-ordinates, multiplied by the width of one strip.

3) *Simpson's rule.* Divide the base into an even number of equal parts, and erect ordinates at each point of division. Number the first ordinate 1, the next 2, and so on, finishing with an odd number. The area of the figure is given by
area = width of one strip × sum of first + last ordinate

$$\text{area} = \frac{\text{width of one strip}}{3} \times$$

$$\text{sum of} \begin{bmatrix} \text{first} + \text{last ordinate} \\ 2 \times \text{sum of odd ordinates} \\ 4 \times \text{sum of even ordinates} \end{bmatrix}$$

The first and the last ordinates must not be included in the sum of the odd ordinates.

A rather special application of this rule can be made when the curve under consideration is of reasonably constant form, i.e. when there are no sudden changes in its shape. By taking the first, last, and middle ordinates, Simpson's rule becomes

$$\text{area} = \frac{\text{base}}{6} \times$$

$$[\text{first} + \text{last ordinate} + (4 \times \text{middle ordinate})]$$

4) *Planimeter.* At this stage, the student should make himself familiar with the planimeter. A boundary curve of an area is traced out by a pointer on the instrument, and the enclosed area is recorded on a graduated disc.

Appendix 3

Sir Isaac Newton and the Laws of Motion

Sir Isaac Newton, who was born at Grantham, Lincolnshire, in 1642, and who died in 1727, made extremely far-reaching discoveries relating to the differential calculus, the composition of light, and gravitational attraction, while only a young man of twenty-four. In 1685 he wrote his great work *Philosophiae Naturalis Principia Mathematica*, once described as the supreme feat of the human intellect, in which, amongst many other remarkable investigations relating to the motion of the planets and the comets, to physical mathematics, and to the science of fluid movements, he expounded what are generally referred to as Newton's Laws of Motion. Although the principles behind these laws had been used previously by scientists like Galileo. Newton was the first man to record them in formal shape. He expressed them thus:

1 every body continues in its state of rest, or of uniform motion in a straight line, except in so far as it is compelled by external forces to change that state;

2 change of momentum per unit time is proportional to the applied force, and takes place in the direction of the straight line in which the force acts;

3 to every action there is always an equal and opposite reaction.

In addition to these three laws, there is a fourth, known as Newton's Law of Gravitation which states: *every particle of matter attracts every other particle of matter with a force which varies directly as the product of the masses of the particles, and inversely as the square of the distance between them.*

Appendix 4

Graphical Construction for Centroid of Trapezium

The following graphical construction for the determination of the position of the centroid of a trapezium often proves useful.

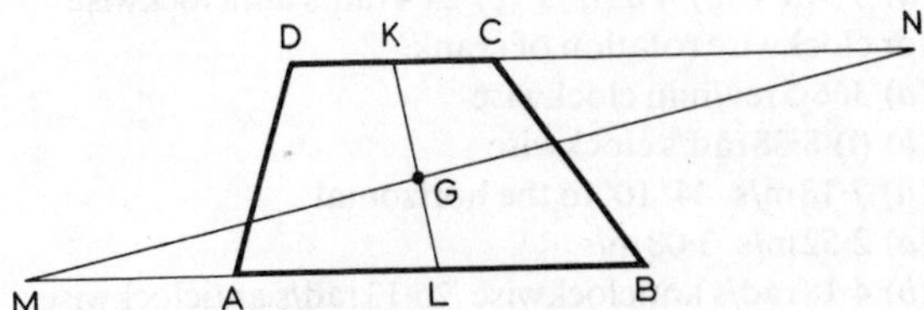

ABCD is the trapezium, with AB and DC the parallel sides.
Produce BA to M, making AM equal to DC.
Produce DC to N, making CN equal to AB.
Join MN.
Join K and L, the mid-points of the parallel sides.
MN and KL intersect at G, the centroid of the trapezium.

Answers

Exercise 1

1 28 units N30°20′E
2 21·2 units due S
3 $21{\cdot}22_{87}^{\circ}$
4 $15{\cdot}64_{81}^{\circ}$
5 185 units N$22\frac{1}{2}$°W
6 $32{\cdot}2_{107}^{\circ}$
7 $6{\cdot}4_{51\cdot3}^{\circ}$
8 (*a*) 765m (*b*) 24·7s (*c*) 122·4m/s (*d*) 6·12s and 18·35s
9 0·275 m/s^2
10 22·36 s
11 256m
12 14m/s 8m/s^2 18m
13 28·2, 22·9, 15 units per second; −102·6, −192·8, −259·8 units per second^2
14 5·31 m 4·66 m/s 1·14 m/s^2
15 13·5m/s 7940m 749m 790m
16 116·6s
17 0·2m/s^2 937·5m from A
18 1·39m/s^2
19 178m
20 0·08 km
21 31·32 m/s 0 m/s

Exercise 2

1 5861m
2 136mm
3 3300m 24·75s
4 (*a*) 1·83s (*b*) 28·5m (*c*) 4·13m
5 16·3 m/s 23°2′ upwards to the horizontal
27·5m/s
56°56′ downwards to the horizontal
6 3100m
7 7·68m/s
8 49·1m/s 23°33′ upwards to the horizontal
9 25·5m/s 66°54′ upwards to the horizontal
10 (*a*) 3·06s (*b*) 79·5m (*c*) 11·5m

Exercise 3

1 64·8km/h N19°8′E
2 1·16h N69°12′W 2·5°h N69°12′E
3 (*a*) 21·26km/h S48°18′E
(*b*) 0·576km 28·2 minutes later
4 4·48km 6minutes
5 v_b = 3m/s due E 1·414rad/s clockwise
6 47·25m/s making 131°35′ with v_a and 86°35′ with AB
7 v_a = 8·66m/s v_c = 4·51m/s 1·25rad/s clockwise
8 1·45hours N7°11′E
0·93hours S7°11′E
9 50·1km/h N33°46′E
10 34·2 km/h S 82° 57′ W
11 1h 47 min N60°22′E
12 (*a*) 11·6m/s (*b*) 12·1m/s 27°30′ to horizontal
(*c*) 37·5rad/s anticlockwise
13 (*a*) N10°33′E (*b*) 16·96km (*c*) 14·6minutes
14 (*a*) 5·3m/s (*b*) 4·82m/s (*c*) 24·4rad/s anticlockwise for clockwise rotation of crank
15 (*a*) 366·5rev/min clockwise
(*b*) (i) 8·38rad/s clockwise
(ii) 7·18m/s 44°10′ to the horizontal
16 (*a*) 2·52m/s 3·08m/s
(*b*) 4·18rad/s anticlockwise 25·13rad/s anticlockwise
(this is vectorial difference of the two angular velocities)
(*c*) 358J (37 + 321) crank assumed clockwise rotation
17 (*a*) 45° (i) 3·18m/s (ii) 3·33m/s (iii) 1·86rad/s anticlockwise 120° (i) 3·11m/s (ii) 3·47m/s 1·32rad/s clockwise, crank assumed clockwise
(b) 676J (49 + 627)
18 (*a*) 14·4km/h N8°42′E (b) 0212h for 1h 5min

Exercise 4

1 27·6s
2 40·84kN
3 586kW
4 59·4m/s N57°22′E
5 780kW
6 8·99kW
7 32·43kN
8 (*a*) 41·3N/tonne (*b*) 61·3N/tonne
9 37kN
10 1014kW 0·047m/s^2
11 47m
12 119m
13 320N 66°30′ to original direction
14 24·5N 16·67kN
15 0·49m/s^2
16 (*a*) 15·5N (*b*) 0·66m/s^2 (*c*) 1·7s (*d*) 2·25J
17 7410N 9810N 11·4kN
18 (*a*) 56·2N/tonne (*b*) 36·2N/tonne
19 141·75kW
20 875kW 175kN
21 0·084m/s^2 800kW
22 518tonnes 14·40kW
23 395m 35·7s 26·67kW 20kW 895kJ
24 (*a*) 343·5kW (*b*) 0·0028m/s^2
25 6655N 717N 46·2m

Exercise 5

1 13·5kgm^2 245mm
2 1·37kgm^2 152mm
3 23·7 kgm^2 275 mm
4 0·54m
5 2·81kgm^2 168mm
6 43N 37·7s
7 124rev/min 5·73 62·5kNm

8 7 min 45 s 1300 revs
9 4950 J 790 Nm
10 107 rev/min
11 14·94 kN 11·75 kNm
12 0·818 m/s² 85 N 89·9 N
13 56·2 revs
14 (*a*) 1·02 rad/s² (*b*) 0·126 m
15 (*a*) 26·7 s (from 120 rev/min) (*b*) 6980 N
16 161 Nm
17 (*a*) 4760 Nm (*b*) 6000 N (*c*) 20·4 kW
18 33·4 kNm
19 4215 N
20 427·5 Nm 2686 J 13·43 kW
21 107 Nm 19·8 kW
22 1125 Nm 0·05
23 0·68 W
24 (*a*) 60 Nm (*b*) 942·6 W
25 (*a*) 30 Nm (*b*) 628·4 W (*c*) 628·4 W
26 1·7 m/s²
27 0·4 m/s² 0·061
28 8·53 m/s² 0·15 4·82 m/s²

Exercise 6

1 3·09 m/s
2 48·5 J
3 73·6 mm
4 2·2 km
5 (*a*) 31·9 kJ (*b*) 3 kNm
6 870 Nm 2·43 MJ 1·83 MJ
7 273 Nm 150 revs
8 226 W 2720 J
9 1·27 MJ 1350 Nm
10 61·5 kgm² 94·95% 13·06 revs
11 110 kgm² 46 Nm
12 440 kg 49·8 Nm
13 5·7 MJ 3770 Nm
14 13·73 J 3·7 rad/s
15 12·04 m/s
16 (*a*) 191 Nm (*b*) 270 kJ
17 94 kJ
18 (*b*) 155 m/s
19 (*a*) 217 rev/min (*b*) 2025
20 (*a*) 2720 J (*b*) ±3·44% 110 kgm²
21 69 N 55·8 N 3·45 kgm² 251 mm 76 J
22 421·5 kN
23 15·25 mm

Exercise 7

1 0·44 m/s west
2 A 6·31 m/s north B 3·7 m/s south. No loss of energy since spheres are perfectly elastic
3 $v_a = 20$ m/s north $v_b = 0$
4 28·3 mm 7·35 kJ
5 0·5 m/s 2·87 kJ 12·75 mm
6 9·6 km/h 53·33 kJ
7 30 kJ
8 (*a*) 4·5 km/h (*b*) 15 kJ
9 10·8 kN s 240 kJ
10 (*a*) 0·5 m/s (*b*) 1·37 kJ (*c*) 12·75 mm
11 0·49 m/s 47·9 m

Exercise 8

1 7·5 m/s² towards centre
2 197 m/s²
3 (*a*) centripetal force 10·6 kN towards shaft
(*b*) centrifugal force 10·6 kN towards block
4 8·75 rev/min
5 0·889 m/s² 0·883 m/s² 53·3 kN 5° 12′
6 7·63 N 19·08 mm
7 108 km/h
8 20·6 m/s
9 72·3 km/h
10 2·42 m/s 0 N 5·44 m/s 13·3 N
11 0·187 m
12 90·4 km/h
13 56·9 km/h
14 0·26 m
15 0·071 m
16 3·07 m
17 0·5
18 0·14 m
19 27·42 N
20 29·32 kN 88·4 kN 580 N/m²
21 10·16 m 51·83 N 1·5 rev/min
22 (*a*) 25·8 kN 52·7 kN (*b*) 41·1 m
23 (*a*) 0·74 m (*b*) 84·3 N
24 (*a*) 36·1 N/mm² (*b*) 9·42 N/mm² (*c*) 9·9
25 1·14 m 41·45 rev/min
26 1·57 m
27 93·7 km/h
28 27·42 N

Exercise 9

1 27·3
2 62·1 mm (based on frequency = 2 Hz)
3 994 mm
4 85·6 kN 74·17 kN 6·56 m/s
5 27·6 mm 0·015 mm
6 (*a*) 0·45 s (*b*) 0·53 m/s
7 0·29 s 0·28 m/s
8 (*a*) 149·6 N 1·57 m/s (*b*) 224·4 N
9 (*a*) 0·6 m/s 0·69 m/s (*b*) 3·63 s
10 1·1 s 2·07 m
11 (*a*) 234 mm (*b*) 121 mm
12 3·33 m/s 7·54 kN

13 0·50s 4·9 m/s² 0·49 m/s
14 (*a*) 1·9 kN/m (*b*) 21·5 mm
15 (*a*) 4·54 m/s (*b*) 11·56 kN
16 (i) 5·18 Hz (ii) 1·63 m/s (iii) 13·24 m/s²
17 1·8 m/s 12·6s
18 (*a*) 1085 N (*b*) 542·5 N (*c*) 5·44 m/s.
19 20·2 mm 3·52 Hz (*b*) 0·39 m/s 4·91 m/s² (*c*) 1·43 J
20 3·14 m/s 4·59 kN
21 (*a*) 0·71 s (*b*) 0·5 m/s
22 0·31 m/s 3·59 m/s²
23 1·5 m 0·262 s

Exercise 10

1 79·3 N at 3·45 m from A 22° 37′ to horizontal
2 *CG* = 26 kN [C] *GH* = 3·8 kN [C] *DH* = 15 kN [C] *AI* = 10 kN [T]
3 (*a*) 27·5 kN (*b*) *AD* = 45 kN [C] *EC* = 26·5 kN [T] *FG* = 10 kN [C]
4 *P* = 59 kN [C] *Q* = 18 kN [T] *R* = 80 kN [T]
5 (*a*) 26 kN (*b*) 35 kN at 80° 20′ to vertical (*c*) *AB* = 55 kN [T] *DC* = 60·8 kN [C]
6 *AB* = 55 kN [C] *BC* = 82·5 kN [T] *CD* = 50 kN [T]
7 *KL* = 75 kN [C] *CL* = 46 kN [T] *LM* = 69 kN [C]
8 *AE* = 150 kN [T] *HG* = 93 kN [C] *GF* = 140 kN [T]
KH = 80 kN [T] *HC* = 24 kN [C] *BK* = 47 kN [C]
FD = 70 kN [C] *AK* = 24 kN [T] *FE* = 162 kN [C]
AG = 70 kN [T] extension = 1·43 mm
9 *AB* = 165 kN [C] *BC* = 125 kN [C] *CD* = 125 kN [C]
DE = 215 kN [C] *AF* = 23·5 kN [T]
BF = 90 kN [C] *CF* = 120 kN [C] *DF* = 200 kN [C]
EF = 305 kN [T]
10 7·8 N at 36° to the vertical passing through A
11 *AB* = 13·8 kN [C] *BC* = 27·6 kN [C]
CD = 41·5 kN [C] *DE* = 32·5 kN [C]
EF = 32·4 kN [C] *FG* = 16·2 kN [T]
GH = 36·8 kN [T] *HJ* = 34·5 kN [T]
JK = 20·7 kN [T] *KL* = 6·93 kN [T]
LA = 13·8 kN [C] *AK* = 13·8 kN [T]
KB = 13·8 kN [C] *BJ* = 13·8 kN [T]
JC = 13·8 kN [C] *CH* = 13·8 kN [T]
HD = 0·92 kN [T] *DG* = 0·92 kN [C]
GE = 3·24 kN [C]
12 Roller 8·65 kN vertical; hinge 23·3 kN at 45° to horizontal
PQ = 15·7 kN [C] *RS* = 13 kN [T] *PR* = 0
13 R_C = 6930 N R_A = 6930 N at 30° to horizontal
DE = 0
14 R_L = 34·4 kN R_R 12·5 kN *y* = 25 kN [C] *x* = 0
15 *AB* = 450 kN [T] *BC* = 300 kN [T]
CD = 150 kN [T] *DE* = 180 kN [C]
EF = 150 kN [C] *FG* = 300 kN [C]
BG = 180 kN [C] *CF* = 180 kN [C]
BF = 100 kN [T] *EC* = 100 kN [T]
16 (*a*) 10 kN (*b*) 11·18 kN at 63° 26′ to vertical
(*c*) *AB* = 3·54 kN [T] *BC* = 3·54 kN [T]
CD = 3·54 kN [C] *DA* = 10·61 kN [T]
BD = 5 kN [C]
17 *P* = 2·8 N *Q* = 12·2 N Resultant = 10·3 N at 83 mm from A at 79° to horizontal
18 *BD* = 26 kN [C] *AC* = 24·6 kN [T] *BC* = 2·9 kN [T]
19 *X* = 554 kN [C] *Y* = 46·2 kN [C] *Z* = 577 kN [T]
20 R_a = 66 kN, 63° 30° to horizontal towards A
R_b = 51 kN
AB = 14 kN [T] *AC* = 23 kN [C] *AD* = 37 kN [C]
BC = 46 kN [C] *CD* = 22 kN [C]
21 Each reaction 2000 N. Working in clockwise direction from 12 o'clock position around:
Left hand load 4650 N [C] 4200 N [T]
Centre load 4250 N [C] 1950 N [T] 1950 N [T] 4250 N [C]
Right-hand load 4200 N [T] 4650 N [C]
Short members 900 N [C]
Member A 2400 N [T]
22 R_a = 63 kN 18° 24′ to horizontal to the left from A.
R_b = 100 kN. Commencing with the top left-hand corner and working across and down:

68 kN [C]	8 kN [C]	41 kN [C]
48 kN [T]	48 kN [C]	41 kN [C]
23 kN [C]	23 kN [T]	3 kN [C]
32 kN [T]	32 kN [C]	78 kN [C]
37 kN [T]		

23 R_X = 473·2 N R_Y = 856 N at 15° 48′ to vertical
AY = 951 N [C] *AB* = 951 N [C] *BC* = 946 N [C]
CX = 946 N [C] *XD* = 820 N [T] *DY* = 708 N [T]
AD = 500 N [C] *BD* = 689 N [C] *CD* = 400 N [C]
24 32·3 kN at 12; to the vertical, cutting lower horizontal 293 mm from left-hand end.
25 *OA* = 6·43 kN *OB* = 6·79 kN *OC* = 2·75 kN
26 7·5 kN [C] 7·5 kN [C] 10·6 kN [T]
15 kN [C] clockwise from left

Exercise 11

1 *W* = 200 N 187 N
2 59·6 N
3 71 N, 36° 19 to horizontal
4 (*a*) 0·283 W (*b*) 0·242 W
5 0·26 284 N 61·1%
6 78·8%
7 284 Nm 28%
8 3·96 kW
9 942·6 W
10 (*a*) 314 mm (*b*) 10 N/mm²
11 204 N
12 (*a*) 1765 N 212 Nm
13 (*a*) 2·46 : 1 (*b*) 8·9 kW

Exercise 12

1 10 J 51 N/mm^2
4 61 N/mm^2
5 29 %
7 225 mm 9 rivets
8 208 × 10^3 N/mm^2 212 N/mm^2 1·08 J
9 6·33 N/mm^2 25·3 N/mm^2
10 33·7 mm (*a*) 29·1 mm (*b*) 40·7 mm 49 N/mm^2
11 20 kN
13 201 N/mm^2
14 14·2 mm
15 6·25 mm
16 42 N/mm^2 0·12 mm
17 210 × 10^3 N/mm^2 0·88 mm
18 28·2 mm
19 27·2 mm 45 N/mm^2
20 68 N 0·52 mm
22 1·17 N/mm^2
23 238 kN 29·8 J
24 208 × 10^3 N/mm^2 250 N/mm^2 26 % 425 N/mm^2 3 J
25 0·038 mm
26 1 N/mm^2
27 (*a*) 216 × 10^3 N/mm^2 505 N/mm^2 30 % 54 % (*b*) 6·25 mm
28 342 N/mm^2
29 0·8 N/mm^2 Reduced by 0·16 N/mm^2 to 0·64 N/mm^2

Exercise 13

1 $R_C = 4{\cdot}1$ kN $R_B = 5{\cdot}1$ kN at 30° 33′ left of vertical
5·5 m from B 2·06 kN m max B.M. = 9 kN m
2 855 mm from B 18·5 kN m
3 4·6 m from L.H. end 5·66 kN m 2·1 kN L.H. bearing
480 N R.H. bearing
4 3·27 kN m 0·6 m from A
5 S.F. at A, B, C, D, E, and F = 0 B.M.$_A$ = 0
B.M.$_B$ = 0·4 kN m B.M.$_C$ = 2·35 kN m B.M.$_D$ = 2·4 kN m
B.M.$_E$ = B.M.$_F$ = 0
6 305 mm
7 4 kN 4·125 kN m
8 95 kN 480 kN m
9 100 kN 337·5 kN m
11 183·75 kN m at C
12 26·27 kN m 1·025 m from A
13 150 kN 785 kN m
14 290 kN m max B.M.
16 86·5 kN 93·5 kN
18 346 kN m at 7·03 m from L.H. support
19 69 kN
20 R_R 113·3 kN R_L 176·7 kN 557 kN m
21 (*a*) 3765 N (*b*) 59·55 N 270 N 155 N m
22 280·6 kN m 4·25 m from A
25 1·76 m apart
26 S.F. A 80 kN B 0 kN C 40 kN D 40 kN E 0 kN
B.M. A 0 kN m B 100 kN m C 160 kN m D 0 kN m *E* 0 kN m

Exercise 14

	I_{XX} cm^4	I_{YY} cm^4	k_{XX} cm	k_{YY} cm	Z_{XX} cm^3	Z_{YY} cm^4
1	55·7	14·28	3·22	0·89	13·92	2·14
2	43·1	10·47	2·4	1·18	14·37	4·19
3	4	8·5	0·82	1·19	2	3·4
4	28·12	28·12	1·83	1·83	6·66	6·66
5	116·7	18·88	2·89	1·16	29·17	7·14
6	85	4·15	3·52	0·77	17	1·77
7	3·79	2·7	1·04	0·88	1·52	1·35
8	24·17	11·36	1·84	1·26	5·66	3·79

9 (*a*) 3·97 cm^4 0·75 cm (*b*) 256 cm^4 2·13 cm
10 (*a*) 25·13 cm^4 12·57 cm^3 (*b*) 981·7 cm^4 196 cm^3
11 53·4 cm^4 21·36 cm^3
12 376·9 cm^4 3·16 cm 7·83 cm 369·3 cm^4.
14 207·5 cm^4 2·91 cm
15 7·92 cm from bottom flange 1285 cm^4
16 1·175 cm 7 cm^4
17 On line bisecting quadrant 2·4 cm from centre of curvature.
14·03 cm^4

Exercise 15

1 700 N m 56 cm^4 1664 m
2 166·7 N/mm^2
3 0·219 m 0·438 m
4 715 m 3350 N m
5 When laid on its smaller edge, resistance to bending is 4 times that when laid flat.
15·4 kN/m
6 180 N/mm^2
7 84·4 kN 45 N/mm^2
8 18·6 kN
9 147 mm
10 15·4 kN
11 160 m
12 20·5 N/mm^2
13 35·7 kN
14 100 N/mm^2 182 m
15 10 mm from underside of flange 3·79 cm^4 190 N/m
16 180 N/mm^2 in web 90 N/mm^2 in flange
17 11·25 kN
18 53 N/mm^2 compression 28·5 N/mm^2 tension
19 62 N/mm^2 compression 118 N/mm^2 tension
20 1·6 m
21 1840 N m
22 288 mm
23 10·4 kN/m
24 28·8 mm 57·6 mm 76·8 mm
25 2·08 N/mm^2
26 (*a*) 7·4 mm (*b*) 9·85 m
27 3·1 mm 0·675 N m
28 198 mm 50200 cm^4 56 kN m 73 kN m
29 11·5 N/mm^2
30 48·6 N/mm^2 575·5 m

Exercise 16

1 49·3kW
2 86mm
3 197rev/min
4 85·5mm
5 428mm 257mm
6 (*a*) 70N/mm² (*b*) 5·8kNm (*c*) 160kW
7 1·1°
8 230mm
9 23·6N/mm²
10 Solid shaft will transmit 0·42 × torque transmitted by hollow shaft.
11 $d = 0{\cdot}731\,D$
12 53·5 × 10³N/mm²
13 20 × 10³N/mm²
14 223mm
15 88mm 67mm
16 98·5mm 115N/mm²
17 5·8kNm 70N/mm² 91kW
18 159mm 2°
19 80 × 10³N/mm²
20 112mm 57N/mm²
21 Weight of solid shaft equals twice that of hollow shaft.
22 81·3 × 10³N/mm²
23 18·27kNm 93N/mm² 382kW
24 44·5N/mm² 140kW
25 81mm 2·9°
26 1·75m
27 0·00523Nm/rad 81·5 × 10³N/mm²
28 269mm 1·05°
29 420mm
30 45N/mm² 206mm 103mm

Exercise 17

1 75mm
2 97m³ 2·910tonnes
3 1295m² 124mm
4 (*a*) 8cm
(*b*) (i) 200g (ii) 311g
5 28N 0·71
6 (*a*) 4710kN 4·5m from base of vertical side
(*b*) 5190kN 6·9m from base of vertical side inclined at 65° 24′ to the horizontal
7 706kN
8 323MN 13·75m
9 (*a*) $\frac{3}{2}\rho g a^3$ (*b*) $\frac{5}{6}\rho g a^4$ (*c*) $\frac{5}{9}a$ below hinge (*d*) $\frac{5}{6}\rho g a^3$
10 Reduction in top beam load 20·2MN; reduction in bottom beam load 9·1MN
11 (*a*) 2·19m (*b*) 114kN
12 19·35kN on each higher bolt; 7·73 on lower bolt.

Exercise 18

1 1·17bar 1·74m
2 306mm 0·59bar
3 (*a*) 0·43bar (*b*) 4·75l/s
4 $C_v = 0{\cdot}97$ $C_d = 0{\cdot}61$ $C_c = 0{\cdot}63$
5 23·5m/s 2·87kg/s
117N at 30° to original direction of jet
6 16·4m
7 33l/s
8 $C_v = 0{\cdot}90$ $C_d = 0{\cdot}64$ $C_c = 0{\cdot}71$
9 160mm Pressure rises to 7·6kN/m² below atmospheric
10 26·5l/s 37kW 0·32 bar below atmospheric at inlet. 7·36 bar above atmospheric at outlet
11 8·5l/s 100watts
12 0·96
13 0·36J/kg 1·33bar
14 2·69m/s 1270kg/min
15 18550kg/h

Exercise 19

1 444N
2 133N
3 58N 116N
4 462N
5 17·6N 1·23N
6 142N
7 (*a*) 10·4kg/s (*b*) 221N

Index